Andrew Warren, Managing Di

Welcome to the 21ˢᵗ edition of our Guide to Recommended Hotels Great Britain & Ireland.

I am pleased to announce that Johansens is now part of The Condé Nast Publications Ltd., publishers of Vogue, House & Garden, Condé Nast Traveller and other prestigious monthly magazines.

New ownership has resulted in some exciting changes that, we hope you agree, make the Guide easier to use and our recommendations easier to locate in alphabetical order by country and then by county.

By opening both cover flaps you can now refer to the contents of the Guide and the amenity symbol definitions whilst the Guide is laid open at the hotel of your choice.

We feel sure that you will enjoy visiting our recommendations for 2003; these can also be found, some offering special rates and featuring their chef's favourite recipes, on our website www.johansens.com

Please remember to mention Condé Nast Johansens when you make a reservation and again when you check in. You will be made to feel very welcome.

THE CONDÉ NAST JOHANSENS PROMISE

Condé Nast Johansens is the most comprehensive illustrated reference to annually inspected, independently owned hotels throughout Great Britain, Europe and North America.

It is our objective to maintain the trust of Guide users by recommending through annual inspection a careful choice of accommodation offering quality, excellence and value for money.

Our team of over 60 dedicated Regional Inspectors visited almost 3000 hotels, country houses, inns and resorts throughout 30 countries to select only the very best for recommendation in the 2003 editions of our Guides.

No hotel can appear in our guides unless they meet our exacting standards.

Scotland & Ireland

Turn to the page shown for the start of each county

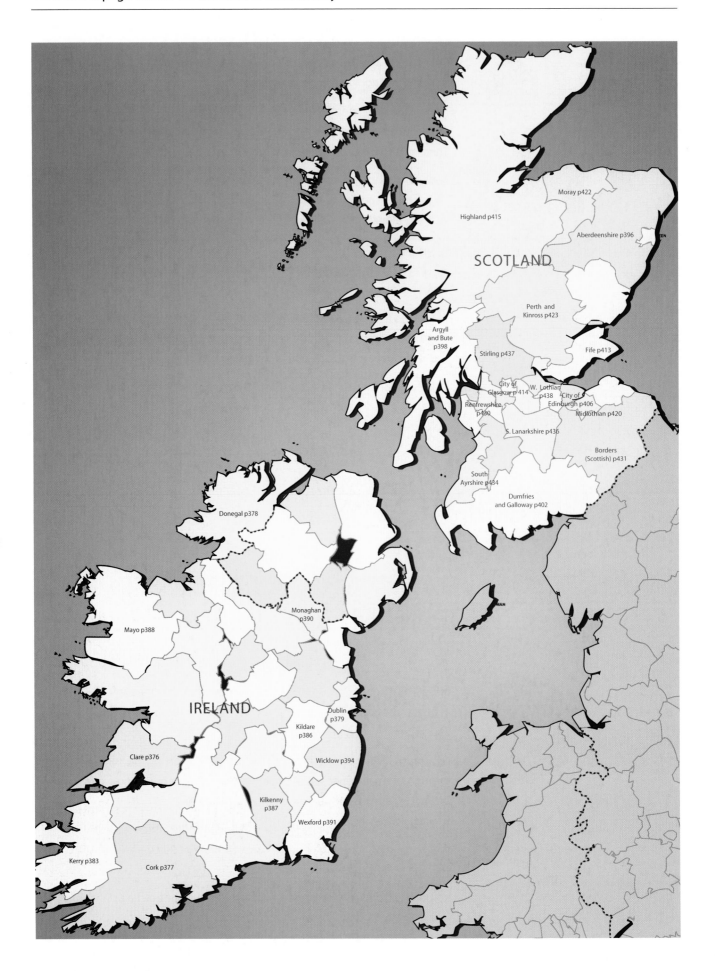

ENGLAND, WALES & CHANNEL ISLANDS

Turn to the page shown for the start of each county

Northumberland p243

Tyne & Wear p315

Durham p129

Cumbria p68

North Yorkshire p341

East Riding of Yorkshire p340

Lancashire p184

W. Yorkshire p363

Greater Manchester p235

S. Yorkshire p360

Isle of Anglesey p449

Conwy p444

Cheshire p44

Derby-shire p88

Lincolnshire p189

Nottingham-shire p247

Gwynedd p446

ENGLAND

Staffordshire p274

Shropshire p264

Leicestershire p187

Rutland p261

Norfolk p237

Birmingham p33

Powys p454

Ceredigion p443

Worcester-shire p333

Warwickshire p316

Northampton-shire p241

Cambridgeshire p42

Suffolk p276

Herefordshire p170

Bedford-shire p20

Pembrokeshire p451

WALES

Rhondda p459 Cynon Taff

Monmouth-shire p450

Gloucestershire p135

Buckingham-shire p37

Hertfordshire p172

Essex p131

Cardiff p442

S Gloucestershire p154

Bristol p36

Oxfordshire p249

London p192

Bath & NE Somerset p12

Wiltshire p326

Berkshire p22

Surrey p288

Kent p179

Somerset p268

Hampshire p155

W. Sussex p305

E. Sussex p297

Devon p100

Dorset p120

Isle of Wight p177

Cornwall p53

Channel Islands

Jersey p370

3

CONDÉ NAST JOHANSENS GUIDES

Recommending only the finest hotels in the world

As well as this guide Condé Nast Johansens also publishes the following titles:

RECOMMENDED COUNTRY HOUSES, SMALL HOTELS & INNS, GREAT BRITAIN & IRELAND

280 smaller more rural properties, ideal for short breaks or more intimate stays

RECOMMENDED HOTELS, EUROPE & THE MEDITERRANEAN

320 continental gems featuring châteaux, resorts and

Charming countryside hotels

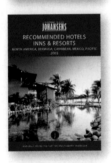

RECOMMENDED HOTELS, INNS & RESORTS, NORTH AMERICA, BERMUDA, CARIBBEAN, MEXICO, PACIFIC

200 properties including many hidden properties from across the region

RECOMMENDED VENUES FOR BUSINESS MEETINGS, CONFERENCES AND EVENTS, GREAT BRITAIN & EUROPE

230 venues that cater specifically for a business audience

WORLDWIDE LISTINGS POCKET GUIDE

Features all recommended hotels and serves as the perfect companion when travelling light

When you purchase two guides or more we will be pleased to offer you a reduction in the cost.

The complete set of Condé Nast Johansens guides may be purchased as 'The Chairman's Collection'.

**To order guides please complete the order form on page 519
or call FREEPHONE 0800 269 397**

Hildon Ltd., Broughton, Hampshire SO20 8DQ, ☎ 01794 - 301 747, Fax 01794 - 301 718
e-mail: hildon@hildon.com – www.hildon.com

CONDÉ NAST JOHANSENS

Condé Nast Johansens Ltd., 6-8 Old Bond Street, London W1S 4PH

Tel: +44 (0)20 7499 9080 Fax: +44 (0)20 7152 3565

Find Johansens on the Internet at: **www.johansens.com**

E-Mail: info@johansens.com

Publishing Director:	Stuart Johnson
P.A. to Publishing Director:	Fiona Galley
Hotel Inspectors:	Jean Branham
	Geraldine Bromley
	Robert Bromley
	Julie Dunkley
	Pat Gillson
	Martin Greaves
	Joan Henderson
	Marie Iversen
	Pauline Mason
	John O'Neill
	Mary O'Neill
	Fiona Patrick
	John Sloggie
	David Wilkinson
Production Director:	Daniel Barnett
Production Manager:	Kevin Bradbrook
Production Controller:	Laura Kerry
Senior Designer:	Michael Tompsett
Copywriters:	Norman Flack
	Debra Giles
	Rozanne Paragon
	Leonora Sandwell
Sales and Marketing Director:	Tim Sinclair
Promotions & Events Manager:	Adam Crabtree
Client Services Director:	Fiona Patrick
P.A. to Managing Director :	Siobhan Smith
Managing Director:	Andrew Warren

Whilst every care has been taken in the compilation of this Guide, the publishers cannot accept responsibility for any inaccuracies or for changes since going to press, or for consequential loss arising from such changes or other inaccuracies, or for any other loss direct or consequential arising in connection with information describing establishments in this publication.

Recommended establishments, if accepted for inclusion by our inspectors, pay an annual subscription to cover the costs of inspection, the distribution and production of copies placed in hotel bedrooms and other services.

No part of this publication may be copied or reproduced, stored in a retrieval system or transmitted, in any form or by any means, electronic, mechanical, photocopy, recording or otherwise, without the prior permission of the publishers.

The publishers request readers not to cut, tear or otherwise mark this Guide except Guest Reports, Brochure Requests and Order Coupons. No other cuttings may be taken without the written permission of the publishers.

WWW.JOHANSENS.COM

Visit the Condé Nast Johansens web site to:

- Print out detailed **road maps**

- See up to date accommodation **Special Offers**

- Access each **recommended hotel's own website**

- Find details of places to visit nearby -
  **historic houses, castles, gardens, museums
  and galleries**

Condé Nast Johansens Home Page

Search for hotels and business venues

Access local places to visit

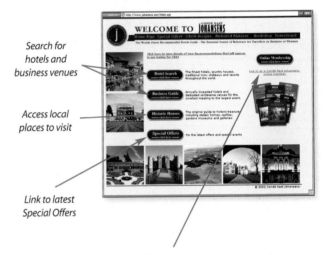

Link to latest Special Offers

Users can log in as an Online Member to receive regular e-mail updates, complete guest survey reports and create their own Personal Portfolio of favourite recommended hotels

Example of Recommended Hotel's Web Entry

Access the hotel's contact details, website and e-mail

See the latest Special Offers for this hotel

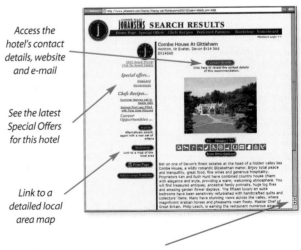

Link to a detailed local area map

Scroll down to find details of places to visit nearby

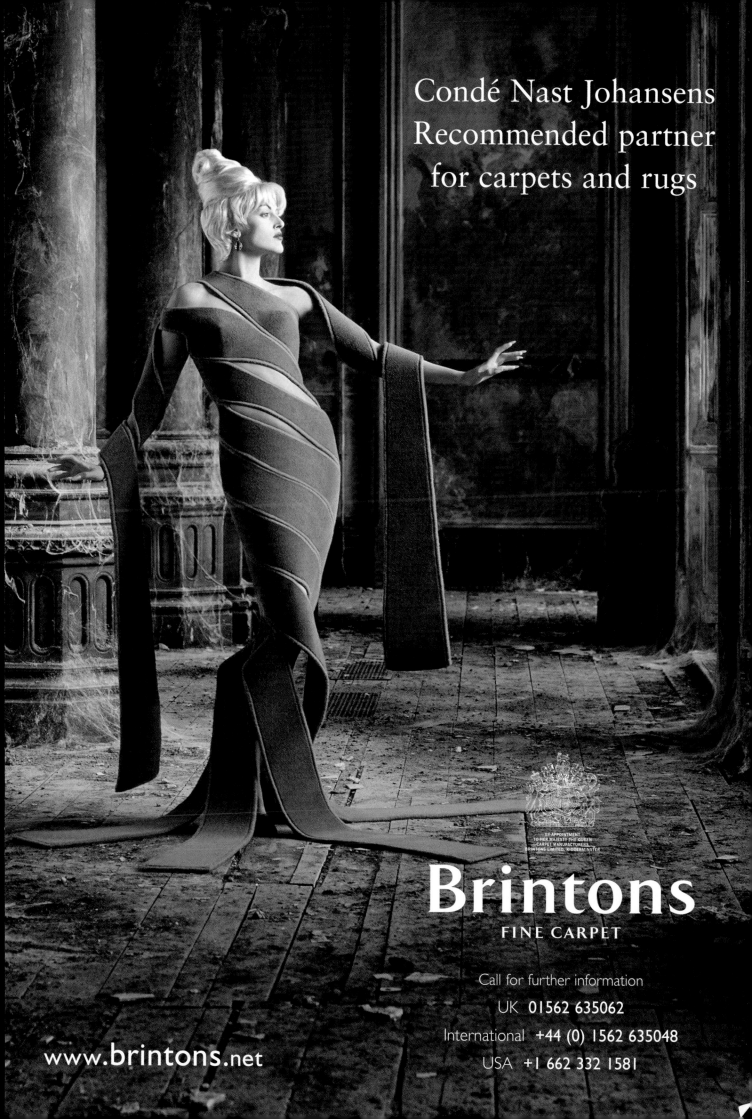

2002 Awards For Excellence

The winners of the Condé Nast Johansens 2002 Awards for Excellence

The Condé Nast Johansens 2002 Awards for Excellence were presented at the Awards Dinner held at The Dorchester hotel, London on November 12th, 2001. Awards were made to those properties worldwide that represented the finest standards and best value for money in luxury independent travel. An important source of information for these awards was the feedback provided by guests who completed Johansens Guest Survey reports. Guest Survey forms can be found on page 520.

Most Excellent Country Hotel Award

NORTHCOTE MANOR COUNTRY HOTEL – Devon, England, p100

"Great location, excellent food, attention to detail throughout this little gem of a hotel."

Most Excellent City Hotel Award

HOTEL ON THE PARK – Gloucestershire, England, p137

"Wonderful hosts, superb breakfast, a heavan of comfort."

Most Excellent London Hotel Award

THE COLONNADE, THE LITTLE VENICE TOWN HOUSE – London, England, p216

"A town house with great style, welcome and warmth in a pretty area of London close to the West End."

Most Excellent Value for Money Award

THE GIBBON BRIDGE HOTEL – Lancashire, England, p186

"A most enjoyable and relaxing hotel with good food and friendly service."

2002 AWARDS FOR EXCELLENCE

The winners of the Condé Nast Johansens 2002 Awards for Excellence

Most Excellent Service Award

COMBE HOUSE HOTEL – Devon, England, p105

"Superb service all with a genuine smile. Nothing is too much trouble."

Most Excellent Restaurant Award

MAISON TALBOOTH – Essex, England, p132

"Innovative dishes, romantic location, never fails to delight"

Most Excellent Coastal Hotel Award

THE GRAND HOTEL – East Sussex, England p300

"Eastbourne's finest - food, rooms and good old fashioned service, a truly grand hotel by the sea"

The following award winners are featured within Condé Nast Johansens 2003 guides to Country Houses – Great Britain & Ireland, Hotels – Europe & The Mediterranean, Hotels – North America. See page 519 for details of these guides.

Most Excellent Country House Award
Glenapp Castle – Ballantrae, Scotland

Most Excellent Traditional Inn Award
The Crown Hotel – Lincolnshire, England

Europe: The Most Excellent City Hotel
Hotel Rector – Salamanca, Spain

Europe: The Most Excellent Country Hotel
Château de Vault de Lugny– Avallon, France

Europe: The Most Excellent Waterside Resort
Domaine de Rochevilaine – Billiers, France

North America: Most Outstanding Hotel
Wheatleigh – Massachusetts, USA

North America: Most Outstanding Inn
The Willows – California, USA

North America: Most Outstanding Resort
Turtle Island –Yasawa Islands, Fiji

Condé Nast Johansens Special Award for Excellence
Henderson Village – Georgia, USA

Knight Frank Award for Excellence and Innovation
Nicholas Dickenson & Nigel Chapman

For further information on England, please contact:

Cumbria Tourist Board
Ashleigh, Holly Road, Windermere, Cumbria LA23 2AQ
Tel: +44 (0)15394 44444
Web: www.gocumbria.co.uk

East of England Tourist Board
Toppesfield Hall , Hadleigh, Suffolk IP7 5DN
Tel: +44 (0)1473 822922
Web: www.eastofenglandtouristboard.com

Heart of England Tourist Board
Larkhill Road, Worcester, Worcestershire WR5 2EZ
Tel: +44 (0)1905 761100
Web: www.visitheartofengland.com

Northumbria Tourist Board
Aykley Heads, Durham DH1 5UX
Tel: +44 (0)191 375 3028
Web: www.visitnorthumbria.com

North West Tourist Board
Swan House, Swan Meadow Road, Wigan, Lancashire WN3 5BB
Tel: +44 (0)1942 821 222
Web: www.visitnorthwest.com

South East England Tourist Board
The Old Brew House, Warwick Park, Tunbridge Wells, Kent TN2 5TU
Tel: +44 (0)1892 540766
Web: www.seetb.org.uk

Southern Tourist Board
40 Chamberlayne Road, Eastleigh, Hampshire SO50 5JH
Tel: +44 (0) 23 8062 5400
Web: www.visitsouthernengland.com

South West Tourist Board
Woodwater Park, Exeter, Devon EX2 5WT
Tel: +44 (0)870 442 0830
Web: www.westcountrynow.com

Yorkshire Tourist Board
312 Tadcaster Road, York, Yorkshire YO24 1GS
Tel: +44 (0)1904 707961
Web: www.ytb.org.uk
Yorkshire and North & North East Lincolnshire.

English Heritage
Customer Services Department , PO Box 569, Swindon SN2 2YP
Tel: +44 (0) 870 333 1181
Web: www.english-heritage.org.uk

Historic Houses Association
2 Chester Street, London SW1X 7BB
Tel: +44 (0)20 7259 5688
Web: www.hha.org.uk

The National Trust
36 Queen Anne's Gate, London SW1H 9AS
Tel: +44 (0)20 7222 9251
Web: www.nationaltrust.org.uk

Images from www.britainonview.com

or see **pages 466-469** for details of local attractions to visit during your stay.

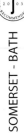

THE BATH PRIORY HOTEL AND RESTAURANT

WESTON ROAD, BATH, SOMERSET BA1 2XT

Directions: 1 mile west of the centre of Bath. Please contact the Hotel for precise directions.

Web: www.johansens.com/bathpriory
E-mail: bathprioryhotel@compuserve.com
Tel: 01225 331922
Fax: 01225 448276

Price Guide: (incl. full English breakfast)
double/twin from £230

Standing in 4 acres of gardens, The Bath Priory Hotel is close to some of England's most famous and finest architecture. Within walking distance of Bath city centre, this Gothic style, mellow stone building dates from 1835, when it formed part of a row of fashionable residences on the west side of the city. Visitors will sense the luxury as they enter the Hotel; antique furniture, many superb oil paintings and objets d'art add interest to the 2 spacious reception rooms and the elegant drawing room. Well-defined colour schemes lend an uplifting brightness throughout, particularly in the tastefully appointed bedrooms. The classical style of Michelin starred Head Chef, Robert Clayton, is the primary inspiration for the cuisine, served in 3 interconnecting dining rooms which overlook the gardens. An especially good selection of wines can be recommended to accompany meals. Private functions can be accommodated both in the terrace, pavilion and the Orangery. The Roman Baths, Theatre Royal, Museum of Costume and a host of bijou shops offer plenty for visitors to see. The Garden Spa consists of a fitness suite, swimming pool, sauna, steam room and health and beauty spa.

Our inspector loved: The intimate restaurant with views of the gardens.

THE BATH SPA HOTEL

SYDNEY ROAD, BATH, SOMERSET BA2 6JF

Nestling in seven acres of mature grounds dotted with ancient cedars, formal gardens, ponds and fountains, The Bath Spa Hotel's elegant Georgian façade can only hint at the warmth, style, comfort and attentive personal service. It is a handsome building in a handsome setting with antique furniture, richly coloured carpeting and well defined colour schemes lending an uplifting brightness throughout. The bedrooms are elegantly decorated; the bathrooms are luxuriously appointed in mahogany and marble. The Bath Spa offers all amenities that guests would expect of a Five Star Hotel while retaining the character of a homely country house. Chef Andrew Hamer's imaginative, contemporary style is the primary inspiration for the award-winning cuisine served in the two restaurants. For relaxation there is a fully equipped health and leisure spa which includes an indoor swimming pool, gymnasium, sauna, Jacuzzi, three treatment rooms, hair salon, tennis court and croquet lawn. Apart from the delights of Bath, there is motor racing at Castle Combe and hot air ballooning nearby.

Our inspector loved: The modern facilities in a traditional five star hotel.

Directions: Exit M4 at jct18 onto the A46, follow signs to Bath for 8 miles until the major roundabout. Turn right onto A4 follow City Centre signs for a mile, at the first major set of traffic lights turn left toward the A36. At mini roundabout turn right then next left after Holburne Museum into Sydney Place. The hotel is 200 yards up the hill on the right.

Web: www.johansens.com/bathspa
E-mail: fivestar@bathspa.u-net.com
Tel: 0870 400 8222
Fax: 01225 444006

Price Guide:
double/twin £210
4-poster £310
suite £360

COMBE GROVE MANOR HOTEL & COUNTRY CLUB

BRASSKNOCKER HILL, MONKTON COMBE, BATH, SOMERSET BA2 7HS

This exclusive 18th century Country House Hotel is conveniently located just 2 miles from the beautiful city of Bath. Built on the hillside site of an ancient Roman settlement, Combe Grove Manor is set in 69 acres of beautiful private gardens and woodlands, with awe-inspiring panoramic views over the magnificent Limpley Stoke Valley and surrounding areas. The Manor House features luxurious four poster rooms and suites with jacuzzi baths, whilst the rooms in the Garden Lodge have spectacular views some with private balconies. All 40 bedrooms are lavishly appointed and individual in design with superb en suite facilities. Within the Hotel's grounds are some of the finest leisure facilities in the south west, including indoor and outdoor heated pools, hydrospa beds and steam room, 4 all-weather tennis courts, a 5 hole par 3 golf course and a 16 bay driving range. Guests may use the fully-equipped gym, aerobics studio, sauna and solaria or simply indulge in the full range of treatments offered by professionally trained staff in the Clarins beauty rooms. There is also a choice of two superb restaurants; the elegant main restaurant features delicious traditional style cuisine and fine wines, whereas the informal Eden Bistro offers an exciting contemporary International menu.

Directions: Set south east of Bath, off the A36 near the University. A map can be supplied on request.

Web: www.johansens.com/combegrovemanor
E-mail: reservations@combegrovemanor.com
Tel: 01225 834644
Fax: 01225 834961

Price Guide:
single from £110
double/twin from £110;
suite from £225

Our inspector loved: The wonderful view over the Limpley Stoke Valley.

THE QUEENSBERRY

RUSSEL STREET, BATH, SOMERSET BA1 2QF

When the Marquis of Queensberry commissioned John Wood to build this house in Russel Street in 1772, little did he know that 200 years hence guests would still be being entertained in these elegant surroundings. An intimate town house hotel, The Queensberry is in a quiet residential street just a few minutes' walk from Wood's other splendours – the Royal Crescent, Circus and Assembly Rooms. Bath is one of England's most beautiful cities. Regency stucco ceilings, ornate cornices and panelling combined with enchanting interior décor complement the strong architectural style. However, the standards of hotel-keeping have far outpaced the traditional surroundings, with high quality en suite bedrooms, room service and up-to-date office support for executives. The Olive Tree Restaurant is one of the leading restaurants in the Bath area. Proprietors Stephen and Penny Ross are thoroughly versed in offering hospitality and a warm welcome. Represented in America by Josephine Barr. The hotel is closed for one week at Christmas.

Our inspector loved: *The central location in Bath with fine restaurant.*

Directions: From junction 18 of M4, enter Bath along A4 London Road. Turn sharp right up Lansdown Road, left into Bennett Street, then right into Russel Street opposite the Assembly Rooms.

Web: www.johansens.com/queensberry
E-mail: enquiries@bathqueensberry.com
Tel: 01225 447928
Fax: 01225 446065

Price Guide:
single £90–£160
double/twin £120–£210
four poster £225

THE ROYAL CRESCENT HOTEL

16 ROYAL CRESCENT, BATH, SOMERSET BA1 2LS

Directions: Detailed directions are available from the hotel on booking.

Web: www.johansens.com/royalcrescent
E-mail: reservations@royalcrescent.co.uk
Tel: 01225 823333
Fax: 01225 339401

Price Guide: (room only)
double/twin from £230
suites from £420

The Royal Crescent Hotel is a Grade I listed building of the greatest historical and architectural importance, situated in the centre of one of Europe's finest masterpieces. A sweep of 30 houses with identical façades stretch in a 500ft curve, built in 1775. The Royal Crescent Hotel was completely refurbished in 1998 and the work undertaken has restored many of the classical Georgian features with all the additional modern comforts. Each of the 45 bedrooms is equipped with air conditioning, the Cliveden bed, video/compact disc player and personal facsimile machine. Pimpernel's restaurant offers a relaxed and informal dining atmosphere, presenting a contemporary menu. Comprehensively equipped, the secure private boardroom provides self-contained business meeting facilities. Exclusive use of the hotel can be arranged for a special occasion or corporate event. Magnificent views of Bath and the surrounding countryside may be enjoyed from the hotel's vintage river launch and hot air balloon. The Bath House is a unique spa, in which to enjoy both complementary therapies and holistic massage. Adjacent to this tranquil setting is the gym & studio comprising seventeen pieces of cardio-vascular and resistance equipment.

Our inspector loved: *A beautiful building in a central location and a stunning Bath House.*

THE WINDSOR HOTEL

69 GREAT PULTENEY STREET, BATH BA2 4DL

Elegant wrought-iron railings front this attractive town house situated in the heart of the best-preserved Georgian city in Britain. Grade I listed and refurbished to the highest standards, The Windsor Hotel stands on one of the finest boulevards in Europe just a short stroll from the Royal Crescent, Circus, Assembly Rooms and Roman Baths. The hotel's tall front windows look across Georgian façades inspired by Palladio, whilst rooms at the back have views of the rolling hills beyond. Enchanting interior décor complements the strong and pleasing architectural style, and fine furniture and fabrics abound. Each individually designed en suite bedroom and suite is the essence of high quality and comfort. Afternoon tea or after dinner drinks can be enjoyed in an exquisite drawing room while memorable menus are served in a small Japanese restaurant which overlooks its own special garden. Great Pulteney Street leads onto Pulteney Bridge and the city's tempting boutiques, antique shops and award-winning restaurants. Within easy reach are Longleat Estate, Ilford Manor, the American Museum and Limpley Stoke Valley. Limited car parking is available and can be arranged upon reservation.

Our inspector loved: *The Japanese restaurant offering traditional dishes.*

Directions: From Jct18 off M4, enter Bath along A4 London Road. Turn left into Bathwick Street, then right into Sydney Place and right again into Great Pulteney Street.

Web: www.johansens.com/windsorhotel
E-mail: sales@bathwindsorhotel.com
Tel: 01225 422100
Fax: 01225 422550

Price Guide:
single £85-£115
double/twin £135-£195
suite £275

HOMEWOOD PARK

HINTON CHARTERHOUSE, BATH, SOMERSET BA2 7TB

Directions: On the A36 six miles from Bath towards Warminster.

Web: www.johansens.com/homewoodpark
E-mail: res@homewoodpark.com
Tel: 01225 723731
Fax: 01225 723820

Price Guide:
single from £114
double/twin from £144
suites from £255

Standing amid 10 acres of beautiful grounds and woodland on the edge of Limpley Stoke Valley, a designated area of natural beauty is Homewood Park, one of Britain's finest privately-owned smaller country house hotels. This lovely 19th century building has an elegant interior, adorned with beautiful fabrics, antiques, oriental rugs and original oil paintings. Lavishly furnished bedrooms offer the best in comfort, style and privacy. Each of them has a charm and character of its own and most have good views over the Victorian garden. The outstanding cuisine overseen by chef Nigel Godwin has won the hotel an excellent reputation. The à la carte menu uses wherever possible produce from local suppliers. A range of carefully selected wines, stored in the hotel's original medieval cellars, lies patiently waiting to augment lunch and dinner. Before or after a meal guests can enjoy a drink in the comfortable bar or drawing rooms, both of which have a log fire during the cooler months. The hotel is well placed for guests to enjoy the varied attractions of the wonderful city of Bath with its unique hot springs, Roman remains, superb Georgian architecture and American Museum. Further afield but within reach are Stonehenge and Cheddar caves.

Our inspector loved: *This pretty country house in pleasant grounds with easy access to Bath.*

HUNSTRETE HOUSE

HUNSTRETE, NR BATH, SOMERSET BS39 4NS

In a classical English landscape on the edge of the Mendip Hills stands Hunstrete House. This unique hotel, surrounded by lovely gardens, is largely 18th century, although the history of the estate goes back to 963AD. Each of the bedrooms is individually decorated and furnished to a high standard, combining the benefits of a hotel room with the atmosphere of a charming private country house. Many offer uninterrupted views over undulating fields and woodlands. The reception areas exhibit warmth and elegance and are liberally furnished with beautiful antiques. Log fires burn in the hall, library and drawing room through the winter and on cooler summer evenings. The Terrace dining room looks out on to an Italianate, flower filled courtyard. A highly skilled head chef offers light, elegant dishes using produce from the extensive garden, including substantial use of organic meat and vegetables. The menu changes regularly and the hotel has an excellent reputation for the quality and interest of its wine list. In a sheltered corner of the walled garden there is a heated swimming pool for guests to enjoy. For the energetic, the all weather tennis court provides another diversion and there are riding stables in Hunstrete village, a five minute walk away.

Our inspector loved: *This 18th century house set in lovely countryside surrounded by deer and horses.*

Directions: From Bath take the A4 towards Bristol and then the A368 to Wells.

Web: www.johansens.com/hunstretehouse
E-mail: reservations@hunstretehouse.co.uk
Tel: 01761 490490
Fax: 01761 490732

Price Guide:
single from £145
double/twin from £165
suite from £265

MOORE PLACE HOTEL

THE SQUARE, ASPLEY GUISE, MILTON KEYNES, BEDFORDSHIRE MK17 8DW

Directions: Only two minutes' drive from the M1 junction 13.

Web: www.johansens.com/mooreplace
E-mail: manager@mooreplace.com
Tel: 01908 282000
Fax: 01908 281888

Price Guide:
single from £65
double/twin £85
suite £150–£200

Bedford

Luton

This elegant Georgian manor house was built by Francis Moore in the peaceful Bedfordshire village of Aspley Guise in 1786. The original house, which is set on the village square, has been sympathetically extended to create extra rooms. The additional wing has been built around an attractive courtyard with a rock garden, lily pool and waterfall. The pretty Victorian-style award winning conservatory restaurant, serves food that rates among the best in the area. Vegetarian options and special diets can always be found on the menus, which offer dishes prepared in the modern English style and balanced with a selection of fine wines. The 52 bedrooms are well-appointed with many amenities, including a trouser press, hairdryer, welcome drinks and large towelling bathrobes. Banquets, conferences and dinner parties can be accommodated in five private function rooms: all are decorated in traditional style and can be equipped with the latest audiovisual facilities. The hotel is close to Woburn Abbey, Safari Park, Bletchley Park, Station X, Silverstone, Whipsnade Zoo, Milton Keynes. The convenient location and accessibility to the motorway network makes Moore Place Hotel an attractive choice, whether travelling for business or pleasure.

Our inspector loved: *The courtyard garden with its waterfall and lilypool, a year round atttraction.*

FLITWICK MANOR

CHURCH ROAD, FLITWICK, BEDFORDSHIRE MK45 1AE

Flitwick Manor is a Georgian gem, classical in style, elegant in décor, comfortable in appointment, a country house hotel that remains true to the traditions of country house hospitality. Nestling in acres of glorious rolling parkland complete with lake, grotto and church, the manor has the intimacy and warmth that make it the ideal retreat for both pleasure and business. The seventeen bedrooms, with their distinctive characters and idiosyncrasies, add to the charm of the reception rooms: a soothing drawing room, a cosy library and pine panelled morning room, the latter two doubling up as both meeting and private dining rooms. Fine antiques and period pieces, easy chairs and inviting sofas, winter fires and summer flowers, they all blend effortlessly together to make a perfect combination. The restaurant is highly acclaimed by all the major food guides and indeed the AA, with its bestowal of two Rosettes, rated Flitwick Manor as the county's best. Outside pleasures are afforded by the all-weather tennis court, croquet lawns and putting green as well as a range of local attractions such as Woburn Abbey and Safari Park. Special weekend rates available.

Our inspector loved: This elegant country house with its romantic appeal.

Directions: Flitwick is on the A5120 just north of the M1 junction 12.

Web: www.johansens.com/flitwickmanor
E-mail: flitwick@menzies–hotels.co.uk
Tel: 01525 712242
Fax: 01525 718753

Price Guide: (room only)
single from £140
double/twin/suite £165–£315

THE BERYSTEDE

BAGSHOT ROAD, SUNNINGHILL, ASCOT, BERKSHIRE SL5 9JH

Standing regally in 9 acres of landscaped gardens and woodlands this former country house is a unique and attractive blend of Gothic, Tudor and modern styles. It is a peaceful and comfortable holiday retreat and particularly convenient for golf, horseracing or polo enthusiasts. Close by is the famed Wentworth Golf Course, much favoured by showbusiness and golfing celebrities, Ascot Racecourse and the Guards Polo Ground at Windsor. The hotel's range of leisure facilities include an outdoor swimming pool, croquet lawn, putting lawn and nearby there is an ice rink, 10-pin bowling and a dry ski slope. The Berystede's spacious interiors are delightfully decorated in keeping with its country house character; the Diadem Bar is fashioned after a traditional gentleman's club smoking room – a comfortable haven of relaxation, as is the quiet Library Lounge with its open fire in winter. All bedrooms, which include six family rooms, three four-posters and four suites, are individually furnished and equipped with every modern facility. Many enjoy splendid views over the grounds. The handsome Hyperion Restaurant has a diverse menu of award-winning cuisine prepared with meticulous attention to presentation. Excellent business and conference facilities are available.

Directions: Exit M3 at junction 3, take Bagshot Road for 3 miles. Or join B3020 from A329.

Web: www.johansens.com/berystede
E-mail: berystede@macdonald-hotels.co.uk
Tel: 0870 400 8111
Fax: 01344 872301

Price Guide:
single £175
double/twin £195–£225
suite £225

Our inspector loved: The amusing bar.

MONKEY ISLAND HOTEL

BRAY-ON-THAMES, MAIDENHEAD, BERKSHIRE SL6 2EE

The name Monkey Island derives from the medieval Monk's Eyot. Circa 1723 the island was purchased by Charles Spencer, the third Duke of Marlborough, who built the fishing lodge now known as the Pavilion and the fishing temple, both of which are Grade I listed buildings. The Pavilion's Terrace Bar, overlooking acres of riverside lawn, is an ideal spot for a relaxing cocktail and the award winning Pavilion Restaurant, perched on the island's narrowest tip with fine views upstream, boasts fine English cuisine, an award-winning cellar and friendly service. The River Room is suitable for weddings or other large functions, while the Regency-style boardroom is perfect for smaller parties. It is even possible to arrange exclusive use of the whole island for a truly memorable occasion. The Temple houses 26 comfortable bedrooms and suites, the Wedgwood Room, with its splendid ceiling in high-relief plaster and octagonal Temple Room. Monkey Island is one mile downstream from Maidenhead, within easy reach of Royal Windsor, Eton, Henley and London. Weekend and boating breaks from £105 p.p.

Our inspector loved: *The recently landscaped garden.*

Directions: Take A308 from Maidenhead towards Windsor; turn left following signposts to Bray. Entering Bray, go right along Old Mill Lane, which goes over M4; the hotel is on the left.

Web: www.johansens.com/monkeyisland
E-mail: monkeyisland@btconnect.com
Tel: 01628 623400
Fax: 01628 784732

Price Guide:
single from £130
double/twin £190–£235
suite £295

FREDRICK'S HOTEL & RESTAURANT

SHOPPENHANGERS ROAD, MAIDENHEAD, BERKSHIRE SL6 2PZ

Directions: Leave M4 at exit 8/9, take A404(M) and leave at first turning signed Cox Green/White Waltham. Turn into Shoppenhangers Road; Fredrick's is on the right.

Web: www.johansens.com/fredricks
E-mail: reservations@fredricks–hotel.co.uk
Tel: 01628 581000
Fax: 01628 771054

Price Guide:
single from £195
double/twin from £240
suite from £370

Reading
Windsor
Newbury

'Putting people first' is the guiding philosophy behind the running of this sumptuously equipped hotel and indeed, is indicative of the uncompromising service guests can expect to receive. Set in two acres of grounds, Fredrick's overlooks the fairways and greens of Maidenhead Golf Club beyond. The immaculate reception rooms are distinctively styled to create something out of the ordinary. Minute attention to detail is evident in the 37 bedrooms, all immaculate with gleaming, marble-tiled bathrooms, while the suites have their own patio garden or balcony. A quiet drink can be enjoyed in the light, airy Wintergarden lounge, or in warmer weather on the patio, before entering the air-conditioned restaurant. Amid the elegant décor of crystal chandeliers and crisp white linen, fine gourmet cuisine is served which has received recognition from leading guides for many years. Particularly suited to conferences, four private function rooms with full secretarial facilities are available. Helicopter landing can be arranged. Easily accessible from Windsor, Henley, Ascot, Heathrow and London. Closed 24 Dec to 3 Jan.

Our inspector loved: The new interior design of the restaurant and bar.

CLIVEDEN

TAPLOW, BERKSHIRE SL6 0JF

Cliveden, Britain's only 5 Red AA star hotel that is also a stately home, is set in 376 acres of gardens and parkland, overlooking the Thames. The former home of Frederick, Prince of Wales, 3 Dukes and the Astor family, Cliveden has been at the centre of Britain's social and political life for over 300 years. It is exquisitely furnished in a classical English style; oil paintings, antiques and objets d'art abound. The guest rooms and suites are spacious and luxurious and the choice of dining rooms and the scope of the menus are superb. The French Dining Room, with its original Madame de Pompadour rococo decoration, is the finest 18th century boiserie outside France. Relish the award winning cuisine of Waldo's Restaurant. Spring Cottage, secluded in its own gardens on the edge of the River Thames, provides unrivalled peace and privacy. Guests can enjoy a range of treatments in the Pavilion Spa, roam the magnificent gardens or enjoy a river cruise. A choice of sports, including indoor and outdoor swimming, tennis, squash, gymnasium, golf, clay pigeon shooting, horse riding and polo lessons are also available. Well-equipped, the 2 secure private boardrooms provide self-contained business meeting facilities. Exclusive use of the house can be arranged. Cliveden's style may also be enjoyed at the Cliveden Town House in London and the Royal Crescent in Bath.

Directions: Situated on the B476, Cliveden is 2 miles north of Taplow.

Web: www.johansens.com/cliveden
E-mail: Reservations@clivedenhouse.co.uk
Tel: 01628 668561
Fax: 01628 661837

Price Guide:
(full English breakfast incl. VAT)
double/twin from £250
suites from £465

Our inspector loved: The views from the balcony down to the Thames.

Donnington Valley Hotel & Golf Club

OLD OXFORD ROAD, DONNINGTON, NEWBURY, BERKSHIRE RG14 3AG

Directions: Leave the M4 at junction 13, go south towards Newbury on A34, then follow signs for Donnington Castle.

Web: www.johansens.com/donningtonvalley
E-mail: general@donningtonvalley.co.uk
Tel: 01635 551199
Fax: 01635 551123

Price Guide:
single from £155
double/twin £155–£180
suite from £220

Uncompromising quality is the hallmark of this hotel built in contrasting styles in 1991 with its own golf course. The grandeur of the Edwardian era has been captured by the interior of the hotel's reception area with its splendid wood-panelled ceilings and impressive overhanging gallery. Each individually designed bedroom has been thoughtfully equipped to guarantee comfort and peace of mind. In addition to the standard guest rooms Donnington Valley offers a number of non-smoking rooms, family rooms, superior executive rooms and luxury suites. With its open log fire and elegant surroundings, the Piano Bar is an ideal place to meet friends or enjoy the relaxed ambience. Guests lunch and dine in the The Winepress Restaurant which offers fine international cuisine is complemented by an extensive choice of wines and liqueurs. The 18-hole, par 71, golf course is a stern test for golfers of all abilities, through a magnificent parkland setting. Special corporate golfing packages are offered and tournaments can be arranged. 11 purpose-built function suites provide the flexibility to meet the demands of corporate and special events. Donnington Castle, despite a siege during the Civil War, still survives for sight-seeing.

Our inspector loved: *The golf course.*

THE VINEYARD AT STOCKCROSS

NEWBURY, BERKSHIRE RG20 8JU

The Vineyard at Stockcross, Sir Peter Michael's 'restaurant-with-suites' is a European showcase for the finest Californian wines including those from the Peter Michael Winery. Head Sommelier, Edoardo Amadi, has selected the best from the most highly-prized, family owned Californian wineries, creating one of the widest, most innovative, international wine lists. Awarded 5 Stars and 3 Rosettes by the AA, the modern British cuisine with classical French elements matches the calibre of the wines. Pure flavours, fresh ingredients and subtle design blend harmoniously with the fine wines. A stimulating collection of paintings and sculpture includes the keynote piece, Fire and Water by William Pye FRBS and 'Deconstructing the Grape', a sculpture commissioned for the The Vineyard Spa. A vine-inspired, steel balustrade elegantly dominates the restaurant and the luxurious interior is complemented by subtle attention to detail throughout with stunning china and glass designs. The 31 well-appointed bedrooms include 15 suites offering stylish comfort with distinctive character. The Vineyard Spa features an indoor pool, spa bath, sauna, steam room, gym and treatment rooms.

Our inspector loved: *The wonderful artwork throughout the hotel.*

Directions: From M4, exit Jct13, A34 towards Newbury, then Hungerford exit. 1st roundabout Hungerford exit, 2nd roundabout Stockcross exit. Hotel on right.

Web: www.johansens.com/vineyardstockcross
E-mail: general@the-vineyard.co.uk
Tel: 01635 528770
Fax: 01635 528398

Price Guide: (excluding VAT)
single/double/twin £160–£229
suite £295–£599

THE REGENCY PARK HOTEL

BOWLING GREEN ROAD, THATCHAM, BERKSHIRE RG18 3RP

Ideally situated for access to both London and the South West, the Regency Park is a modern hotel that takes great pride in providing not only the most sophisticated facilities but combining them with the most attentive service and care. The style is neat and crisp with an understated elegance throughout, from the airy and spacious bedrooms to the array of meeting venues housed in the Business Centre. The Parkland Suite is a beautiful setting for any occasion, and with its own entrance and facilities for up to 200 guests it is the ideal place for wedding receptions and parties, as well as conferences and launches. "Escape" is the name of the leisure complex, and true to its name it really is a place where state-of-the-art technology and sheer luxury meet to form a special retreat. The serenity of the 17m swimming pool and the large health and beauty salon create an instantly relaxing atmosphere where fully qualified staff offer holistic health and beauty treatments. The Watermark Restaurant again has a contemporary elegance and stunning views over the Waterfall gardens, that is reflected in its excellent menu of modern flavours and fusions. There is even a children's menu to ensure all guests are catered for.

Directions: Between Newbury and Reading. Leave M4 at Jct12 or 13; the hotel is signposted on A4, on the western outskirts of Thatcham.

Web: www.johansens.com/regencypark
E-mail: info@regencyparkhotel.co.uk
Tel: 01635 871555
Fax: 01635 871571

Price Guide:
single £84–£195
double/twin £95–£215
suite £230–£355

Our inspector loved: The leisure facility. It is a great asset.

THE FRENCH HORN

SONNING-ON-THAMES, BERKSHIRE RG4 OTN

For over 150 years The French Horn has provided a charming riverside retreat from the busy outside world. Today, although busier on this stretch of the river, it continues that fine tradition of comfortable accommodation and outstanding cuisine in a beautiful setting. The hotel nestles beside the Thames near the historic village of Sonning. The well-appointed bedrooms and suites are fully-equipped with modern amenities and many have river views. The old panelled bar provides an intimate scene for pre-dinner drinks and the restaurant speciality, locally reared duck, is spit roasted here over an open fire. By day the sunny restaurant is a lovely setting for lunch, while by night diners can enjoy the floodlit view of the graceful weeping willows which fringe the river. Dinner is served by candlelight and the cuisine is a mixture of French and English cooking using the freshest ingredients. The French Horn's wine list is reputed to be amongst the finest in Europe. Places of interest include Henley, Stratfield Saye, Oxford, Blenheim Palace and Mapledurham. There are numerous golf courses and equestrian centres in the area.

Our inspector loved: *The roast English duck, its a must.*

Directions: Leave the M4 at J8/9. Follow A404/M then at Thickets Roundabout turn left on A4 towards Reading for 8 miles. Turn right for Sonning. Cross Thames on B478. Hotel is on right.

Web: www.johansens.com/frenchhorn
E-mail: TheFrenchHorn@Compuserve.com
Tel: 01189 692204
Fax: 01189 442210

Price Guide:
single £100–£160
double/twin £120–£195

THE SWAN AT STREATLEY

STREATLEY-ON-THAMES, BERKSHIRE RG8 9HR

In a beautiful setting on the banks of the River Thames, this hotel offers visitors comfortable accommodation. All of the 46 bedrooms, many of which have balconies overlooking the river, are appointed to high standards with individual décor and furnishings. The hotel's innovative cooking ensures it maintains its two AA Rosettes. Guests can dine in the Cygnetures restaurant, which, with the Cygnet Bar and outdoor terrace, offers superb riverside views. Business guests are well catered for with six conference suites – all with natural daylight. Moored alongside the hotel is the Magdalen College Barge – a unique venue for small meetings and cocktail parties. Special themed programmes can be arranged such as Bridge weekends. Reflexions leisure club is equipped with a heated 'fitness' pool, sauna, sunbeds, spa bath, steam room and a wide range of exercise equipment. Cruising on the river may be arranged by the hotel and golf, horse riding, and clay pigeon shooting are available locally. Events in the locality include Henley Regatta, Ascot and Newbury Races, while Windsor Castle, Blenheim Palace, Oxford and London's airports are easily accessible.

Directions: The hotel lies just off the A329 in Streatley village.

Web: www.johansens.com/swanatstreatley
E-mail: sales@swan-at-streatley.co.uk
Tel: 01491 878800
Fax: 01491 872554

Price Guide:
single £89–£137.50
double/twin £119–£177
suites £179-£258

Our inspector loved: *The newly arrived four poster beds.*

THE CASTLE HOTEL

HIGH STREET, WINDSOR, BERKSHIRE SL4 1LJ

Steeped in history, this splendid Georgian hotel stands in the High Street beneath the solid rampards and towers of Windsor's magnificent Norman castle. With a quiet charm and dignity, the hotel combines fine furnishings from the past with every comfort associated with life today. The stylish interior décor of the hotel creates a prestigious venue for visitors, who receive a bonus when discovering it provides one of the finest views of the Changing of the Guard procession. The ancient ceremony can be enjoyed by guests while taking morning coffee with teacakes in the elegant lounge at 11am. Sympathetic additions and refurbishment over the years have enhanced the appeal of this attractive town hotel which now offers 111 opulent bedrooms and superb suites, each providing the highest standards of facilities and amenities. The grand and beautifully decorated Castle Restaurant provides award-winning British and International cuisine, whilst the Fresh Fields Restaurant, Pennington Lounge and Windsor Bar offer a superb choice for relaxed informal dining. As well as the Castle and Windsor Great Park, among the many attractions within easy reach are Eton College, Ascot, Henley, Maidenhead, Thorpe Park and Legoland.

Our inspector loved: being so close to Windsor Castle.

Directions: Exit M4 at junction 6, follow signs for Windsor Castle.

Web: www.johansens.com/castlewindsor
E-mail: castle@macdonald-hotels.co.uk
Tel: 0870 400 8300
Fax: 01753 830244

Price Guide:
single £181
double/twin £223
suite £266

Reading
Windsor
Newbury

Sir Christopher Wren's House Hotel

THAMES STREET, WINDSOR, BERKSHIRE SL4 1PX

A friendly and homely atmosphere makes Sir Christopher Wren's House a perfect location for guests seeking a break from the hectic pace of modern life. Built by the famous architect in 1676, it nestles beneath the ramparts and towers of Windsor Castle, beside the River Thames and Eton Bridge. With a quiet charm and dignity of its own, the hotel combines fine furnishings from the past with every comfort and convenience associated with life today. Additions to the original house, including a beautiful conservatory overlooking the Thames, and there are now 92 bedrooms available for guests. These have all recently been refurbished to the highest standards and while some feature a balcony and river views, others overlook the famous castle. All offer a full range of amenities, including direct dial telephone, cable TV, trouser press, tea and coffee-making facilities, mineral water and an air cooling system. Stroks Riverside Restaurant offers a good selection of beautifully cooked and well-presented meals by master chef Philip Wild. The hotel has recently added a state of the art gym. The Windsor area has a great deal to offer, for those with time to explore. Among the many attractions within easy reach are Windsor Castle, Eton College, Royal Ascot, Thorpe park, Henley, Saville Gardens and Legoland.

Directions: Windsor is just 2 miles from junction 6 of the M4.

Web: www.johansens.com/sirchristopher
E-mail: reservations@wrensgroup.com
Tel: 01753 861354
Fax: 01753 860172

Price Guide:
single from £170
double/twin from £225
suite from £325

Reading
Windsor
Newbury

Our inspector loved: The new rooms and gym.

THE BURLINGTON HOTEL

BURLINGTON ARCADE, 126 NEW STREET, BIRMINGHAM, WEST MIDLANDS B2 4JQ

The Burlington is a hotel embodying the legendary old Midland Hotel which had played such an important role since its opening in 1871. The original handsome Victorian façade has not been destroyed, only embellished, while skilful restoration has retained much of the historic charm within. The hotel is in Birmingham's pedestrianised City Centre, approached through an attractive arcade. It is focused on the commercial arena, with a strong emphasis on facilities for conferences and corporate activities. All bedrooms are pleasantly furnished, spacious, well-equipped and comfortable, with the extras expected by today's traveller, including fax and modem links, electronic voice mail box and satellite television. The bathrooms are well designed. On the first floor, guests will find the delightful lounge – a peaceful retreat – the traditional bar and the splendid Victorian restaurant with its swathed windows, chandeliers and moulded ceilings. The fifth floor houses the leisure centre. The main function area is self-contained, with its own entrance and foyer. Other rooms are ideal for seminars or board meetings. The Burlington is well placed for shopping, the Symphony Hall and just 15 minutes drive from the NEC.

Our inspector loved: *The superb banqueting facilities.*

Directions: Close to New Street Station, 10 minutes from the airport, accessible from the M5, M6, M42. NCP parking.

Web: www.johansens.com/burlington
E-mail: mail@burlingtonhotel.com
Tel: 0121 643 9191
Fax: 0121 643 5075

Price Guide: (room only)
single £152
double/twin £167
suite £220

HOTEL DU VIN & BISTRO

CHURCH STREET, BIRMINGHAM B3 2NR

Direction: From the M6, junction 6 take the A38 to the city centre, take flyover and exit at St. Chad's circus signposted "Jewellery Quarter". Take the 2nd left into Great Charles Street, then the first left into Livery Street. Take the 3rd turning right into Barwick Street then right into Church Street.

Web: www.johansens.com/hotelduvinbirmingham
E-mail: info@birmingham.hotelduvin.com
Tel: 0121 200 0600
Fax: 0121 236 0889

Price Guide:
double/twin from £110
superior from £145

Hotel du Vin & Bistro, originally the Birmingham Eye Hospital, is a unique venue in the heart of cosmopolitan Birmingham. Its stunning early Victorian architecture enhances the luxury of the tasteful, modern interior design. 66 tranquil bedrooms emphasize simplicity and quality with superb beds, luxurious Egyptian linens and attention to detail. The Hotel has 20 bars: The Bubble Lounge is based on a Venetian café and serves over 50 different types of champagne; The Cellar Bar features an eye-catching oil painting of a lobster, the colourful backdrop for its vast selection of wines; big, comfortable sofas, low-lighting and relaxation are essential to the Cigar Divan. The Hotel's excellent chef chooses only the freshest of local ingredients to create a sumptuous feast, which is served in the elegant surrounds of the Bistro. Unwind and pamper your body in the Hotel's private health and beauty spa, which features state-of-the-art equipment, sauna, steam room, massage, aromatherapy and a range of wonderful beauty treatments using natural ingredients. Only minutes away from Birmingham's old city centre, there is fantastic shopping, waterways, art galleries, theatres and the Symphony Hall nearby.

Our inspector loved: *The superb selection of wines including a choice of over 60 Champagnes by the glass- of course these were not all tried.*

NEW HALL

WALMLEY ROAD, ROYAL SUTTON COLDFIELD, WEST MIDLANDS B76 1QX

Cocooned by a lily filled moat and surrounded by 26 acres of beautiful gardens and parkland, New Hall dates from the 12th century and is reputedly the oldest fully moated manor house in England. This prestigious hotel is full of warmth and luxury and exudes a friendly, welcoming atmosphere. New Hall proudly holds the coveted RAC Gold Ribbon Award, and AA Inspectors' Hotel of the Year for England 1994. The cocktail bar and adjoining drawing room overlook the terrace from which a bridge leads to the yew topiary, orchards and sunlit glades. The superbly appointed bedrooms and individually designed suites offer every modern comfort and amenity and have glorious views over the gardens and moat. A 9-hole par 3 golf course and floodlit tennis court are available for guests' use, as are a heated indoor pool, Jacuzzi, sauna, steam room and gymnasium. For those wishing to revitalise mind, body and soul, New Hall offers a superb range of beauty treatments. Surrounded by a rich cultural heritage, New Hall is convenient for Lichfield Cathedral, Warwick Castle, Stratford-upon-Avon, the NEC and the ICC in Birmingham. The Belfry Golf Centre is also nearby.

Our inspector loved: The relaxing atmosphere of the Drawing Room before dinner.

Directions: From exit 9 of the M42, follow A4097 (ignoring signs to A38 Sutton Coldfield). At B4148 turn right at the traffic lights. New Hall is 1 mile on the left.

Web: www.johansens.com/newhall
E-mail: new-hall@thistle.co.uk
Tel: 0121 378 2442
Fax: 0121 378 4637

Price Guide:
single from £166
double/twin from £200
suite from £230

HOTEL DU VIN & BISTRO

THE SUGAR HOUSE, NARROW LEWINS MEAD, BRISTOL BS1 2NU

Set around a courtyard dating from the 1700's, this hotel comprises six listed warehouses that have been used for a number of industrial purposes over the centuries. The imposing 100ft chimney is a lasting testimony to the buildings' impressive past and other distinctive vestiges relating to this period feature inside. The individually named bedrooms are decorated with fine fabrics such as Egyptian linen and offer a good range of facilities including oversized baths and power showers. Guests may relax in the convivial Cocktail bar with its walk-in Cigar humidor or enjoy a glass of wine from the well-stocked cellar before dining in the Bistro. The traditional menu has been created using the freshest local ingredients and is complemented by an excellent wine list. Throughout the property the cool, understated elegance is evident as is the owners attention to even the smallest detail. The hotel has a selection of specially designed rooms for private meetings or dinner parties. Do not expect stuffy formality at the Hotel du Vin!

Our inspector loved: The amazing bathrooms with freestanding baths and huge showers.

Directions: Follow the M32 to the end and then follow signs for the City Centre. Go past Broadmead Shopping Centre on your left, and approximately 500 yards further on you will approach the War Memorial in the centre. Turn right and get onto the opposite side of the carriageway. The hotel is located about 400 yards further down on your left, offset from the main road.

Web: www.johansens.com/hotelduvinbristol
E-mail: info@bristol.hotelduvin.com
Tel: 0117 925 5577
Fax: 0117 925 1199

Price Guide:
double/twin from £120
studio suite from £175
loft suite from £190

HARTWELL HOUSE

OXFORD ROAD, NR AYLESBURY, BUCKINGHAMSHIRE HP17 8NL

Standing in 90 acres of gardens and parkland landscaped by a contemporary of 'Capability' Brown, Hartwell House has both Jacobean and Georgian façades. This beautiful house, brilliantly restored by Historic House Hotels, was the residence in exile of King Louis XVIII of France from 1809 to 1814. The large ground floor reception rooms, with oak panelling and decorated ceilings, have antique furniture and fine paintings which evoke the elegance of the 18th century. There are 46 individually designed bedrooms and suites, some in the house and some in Hartwell Court, the restored 18th-century stables. The dining room at Hartwell is the setting for excellent food awarded 3 AA Rosettes. (Gentlemen are requested to wear a jacket for dinner). The Old Rectory, Hartwell with its two acres of gardens, tennis court and swimming pool, provides beautiful accommodation and offers great comfort and privacy. The Hartwell Spa adjacent to the hotel includes an indoor pool, whirlpool spa bath, steam room, saunas, gymnasium and beauty salons. Situated in the Vale of Aylesbury, the hotel, which is a member of Relais & Châteaux, is only an hour from London and 20 miles from Oxford. Blenheim Palace, Waddesdon Manor and Woburn Abbey are nearby. Dogs are permitted only in Hartwell Court bedrooms.

Directions: On the A418 Oxford Road, 2 miles from Aylesbury.

Web: www.johansens.com/hartwellhouse
E-mail: info@hartwell-house.com
Tel: 01296 747444
Fax: 01296 747450
From USA fax Free: 1 800 260 8338

Milton Keynes

Aylesbury

High Wycombe

Price Guide: (room only)
single £145–£185
double/twin £225–£395
suites £325–£700

Our inspector loved: This grand house that has a welcome all of its own.

THE PRIORY HOTEL

HIGH STREET, WHITCHURCH, AYLESBURY, BUCKINGHAMSHIRE HP22 4JS

The Priory Hotel is a beautifully preserved, timber-framed house dating back to 1360. It is set in the picturesque conservation village of Whitchurch, which is about 5 miles north of Aylesbury. With its exposed timbers, leaded windows and open fires, it retains all its traditional character and charm – a refreshing alternative to the all-too-familiar chain hotels of today. All ten bedrooms are individually furnished and many of them have four-poster beds. At the heart of the hotel is La Boiserie Restaurant, where classical French cuisine is served in intimate surroundings. An imaginative à la carte fixed-price menu is offered, including a range of seasonal dishes. Start, for example, with a rich terrine of partridge, wild mushrooms and pistachios, then perhaps choose marinated saddle of venison in Cognac butter sauce and garnished with truffles. Specialities include fresh lobster and flambé dishes. The self-contained conference suite can be used for private lunches, dinners and receptions. Among the places to visit locally are Waddesdon Manor, Claydon House, Stowe, Silverstone motor circuit and Oxford. Closed between Christmas and New Year's Eve; the restaurant, not the hotel, also closes on Sunday evenings.

Directions: Situated on the A413 4 miles north of Aylesbury.

Web: www.johansens.com/prioryaylesbury
E-mail:
Tel: 01296 641239
Fax: 01296 641793

Price Guide:
single £80–£95
double £130–£150
suite from £130

Milton Keynes

Aylesbury

High Wycombe

Our inspector loved: *This lovely little hotel with its wonderful antique beds.*

STOKE PARK CLUB

PARK ROAD, STOKE POGES, BUCKINGHAMSHIRE SL2 4PG

Amidst 350 acres of sweeping parkland and gardens, Stoke Park Club is the epitome of elegance and style. For more than 900 years the estate has been at the heart of English heritage, playing host to lords, noblemen, kings and queens. History has left an indelible mark of prestige on the Hotel and today it effortlessly combines peerless service with luxury. The magnificence of the palladian mansion is echoed by the lavishly decorated interior where intricate attention to detail has been paid to the décor with antiques, exquisite fabrics and original paintings and prints ensuring that each room is a masterpiece of indulgence. All 21 individually furnished bedrooms and suites are complemented by marble en suite bathrooms and some open onto terraces where an early evening drink can be enjoyed as the sun descends over the lakes and gardens. 8 beautiful function rooms, perfect for private dining and entertaining, also continue the theme of tasteful elegance. Since 1908 the Hotel has been home to one of the finest 27 hole championship parkland golf courses in the world, Stoke Poges and the recent opening of a spa, health and racquet pavilion re-affirms the Hotel's position as one of the country's leading sporting venues. Luxury facilities include 11 beauty treatment rooms, indoor swimming pool, state-of-the art gymnasium and studio and 12 tennis courts.

Our inspector loved: *The wonderful balcony views over the golf course.*

Directions: From the M4 take junction 6 or from the M40 take junction 2 then the A344. At the double roundabout at Farnham Royal take the B416. The entrance is just over 1 mile on the right.

Web: www.johansens.com/stokepark
E-mail: info@stokeparkclub.com
Tel: 01753 717171
Fax: 01753 717181

Price Guide:
single £270
suite £390

TAPLOW HOUSE HOTEL

BERRY HILL, TAPLOW, NR MAIDENHEAD, BUCKINGHAMSHIRE SL6 0DA

Directions: From the M40, exit at junction 4.

Web: www.johansens.com/taplowhouse
E-mail: taplow@wrensgroup.com
Tel: 01628 670056
Fax: 01628 773625

Price Guide: (room only)
single £65–£170
double/twin £130–£225
suite £220–£340

Elegance and splendour are the hallmarks of this majestic hotel which stands in six acres of land adorned by a historic and protected landscape. Taplow House dates back to 1598 and was given by James I to the first Governor of Virginia in 1628. Most of the house was destroyed by fire in the early 1700s but was rebuilt and purchased by the Grenfell family, famed for their equestrian activities, who commissioned the renowned gardener, Springhall, to landscape the grounds. The results can be seen today in the great trees, one of which is reputed to have been planted by Queen Elizabeth I. When the Marquess of Thomond took over the house in 1838 he had architect George Basevi redesign it to introduce the magnificent Doric columns to the reception hall and the elaborate chiselled brass banisters to the staircase which greet today's guests. It was last a private residence in 1958. Taplow House is splendid inside and out. It has recently had a £1.5 million refurbishment which has further enhanced its traditional charm and luxurious comfort. All 34 en suite bedrooms have every comfort. Chef Amanda Pay produces creative cuisine to please every palate. Her outstanding menus are complemented by an excellent and extensive wine list. Windsor, Henley, Ascot and Cliveden are close by.

Our inspector loved: The views over the oldest tulip tree in England.

DANESFIELD HOUSE HOTEL AND SPA

HENLEY ROAD, MARLOW-ON-THAMES, BUCKINGHAMSHIRE SL7 2EY

Danesfield House is set within 65 acres of gardens and parkland overlooking the River Thames and offering panoramic views across the Chiltern Hills. It is the third house since 1664 to occupy this lovely setting and it was designed and built in sumptuous style at the end of the 19th century. After years of neglect the house has been fully restored, combining its Victorian splendour with the very best modern hotel facilities. Among the many attractions of its luxury bedrooms, all beautifully decorated and furnished, are the extensive facilities they offer. These include two telephone lines (one may be used for personal fax), satellite TV, in-room movies, mini bar, trouser press, hair dryers, bath robes and toiletries. Guests can relax in the magnificent drawing room with its galleried library or in the sunlit atrium. There is a choice of two restaurants the Oak Room and Orangery Brasserie both of which offer a choice of international cuisine. The hotel also has six private banqueting and conference rooms. Leisure facilities include luxurious Spa with 20-metre pool, fitness studio and treatment rooms. Windsor Castle, Disraeli's home at Hughenden Manor, Milton's cottage and the caves of West Wycombe are nearby.

Our inspector loved: *The superb health spa with its state of the art facilities.*

Directions: Between M4 and M40 on A4155 between Marlow and Henley-on-Thames.

Web: www.johansens.com/danesfieldhouse
E-mail: sales@danesfieldhouse.co.uk
Tel: 01628 891010
Fax: 01628 890408

Price Guide:
£185
double/twin £225
suites £265

HOTEL FELIX

WHITEHOUSE LANE, HUNTINGDON ROAD, CAMBRIDGE CB3 0LX

Directions: One mile north of Cambridge city centre.

Web: www.johansens.com/felix
E-mail: info@hotelfelix.co.uk
Tel: 01223 277977
Fax: 01223 277973

Price Guide:
single £125
double/twin £155–£210

To open Autumn 2002 the sister to the excellent Grange Hotel in York, the Felix will combine Victorian and modern architecture. It sits in 4 acres of landscaped gardens and offers peaceful surroundings, yet is within minutes reach of Cambridge with its famous contrast of high-tech science parks and beautiful medieval university buildings. The furniture in the Hotel's public areas will be hand-made and the décor softly neutral with splashes of colour and carefully selected sculptures and artwork. All of the 52 en suite bedrooms will comprise of king-sized beds and state-of-the-art communication facilities. Rooms have elegant proportions and are light and airy with high ceilings and views over the gardens. A restaurant and adjacent Café Bar will act as a focal point and guests will be able to experience modern cuisine with a strong Mediterranean influence or Continental coffees and pastries, fine teas, wine and champagne by the glass. The Felix will specialise in private corporate and celebration dining and its 2 meeting rooms with natural daylight and ISDN connections will accommodate 34 boardroom and 60 theatre style. Other activities to be enjoyed in Cambridge are visits to Kings College (pictured), the Botanical Gardens, Fitzwilliam Museum and punting on the River Cam. Nearby places of interest include Ely, Bury St Edmunds and the races at Newmarket.

St Tudnos Hotel
 01492 874411

Fayrer Garden
 015394 88195

Gold Rill
 015394 35486

£64 P.A
£55 P.P.
3 Rooms
[Lodge]

Any availability next week 3 nights?

Mon Tues Wed
or
Tues Wed Thurs

Double Bed
D£105 P.P
or
£101 P.P. P.P.

1 double
How much.

Mullion Cottages   <ins>23 A's</ins>

Cornish Cottage Holidays 01326 573808 (NO)

Dartmouth Cottages 01803 839499   1 see over

Dinas Dinlle Caravan Park 01286 830492 (NO)

Caerfai Bay Caravan Park St. Davids 01437 720274 (NO)

Timber Hill (Lodges) Broadhaven 01437 781239 message
_____

Broomhill Manor Bude (cottages) 01288 352940 (NO)

Classy Cottages (Looe/Polperro) 07000 423000 (NO)

Kennacott Court (Bude) 01288 361766 (NO)

Trewargy Cottages (Looe) 01503 262730 (NO)

Bealy Court (Chumleigh) 01769 580312 left message

Corffe (Barnstaple) 01271 342588 (No)

Knowle Farm 01364 73914 (No)

Ham Farm 01805 624000 left message   clockwork

Oxenways Estate 01404 881785 (Cottage 7 1 Bedroom

Wheel Farm (Coombe Martin) 01271 882100 Phone back (NO)

Little Norton Mill (Somerset) 01935 881337

                                                  ₤ 2 ₲ 6

01288   ↳ Sat – Wed.
354240 Devon Tourist Board.
                                             4 nights. 1 Bedroom.

01271 870333   Watermeet

Any vacancies next week

Mon Tues Wed   £96 P.P.
        or
Tues Wed Thurs 1 evening room.
Standard Double   Premier   Mandy.

Price   double   2 adults
                 3 nights ?

Tues   Wed   Thurs   £120
26   27   28

THE HAYCOCK

WANSFORD, PETERBOROUGH, CAMBRIDGESHIRE PE8 6JA

The Haycock, part of the Arcadian Hotel Group is a handsome old coaching inn of great charm, character and historic interest. It was host to Mary Queen of Scots in 1586 and Princess Alexandra Victoria, later Queen Victoria, in 1835. Overlooking the historic bridge that spans the River Nene, the Hotel is set in a delightful village of unspoilt cottages. All bedrooms are individually designed and equipped to the highest standards with beautiful soft furnishings. The restaurant is renowned for the quality of its contemporary style menu complemented by a selection of interesting and outstanding wines with dishes utilising the freshest possible ingredients. A purpose built ballroom, with lovely oak beams and its own private garden, is a popular venue for a wide range of events, including balls, wedding receptions and Christmas parties. The Business Centre has also made its mark; it is well-equipped with every facility required and offers the flexibility to cater for meetings, product launches, seminars and conferences. Places of interest nearby include Rockingham Motor Speedway, Stamford, Burghley House, Nene Valley Railway, Elton Hall, Rutland Water, Peterborough Cathedral and East of England Showground.

Our inspector loved: Coming off the busy A1 straight into this quiet, historic and pretty riverside village.

Directions: Clearly signposted on the A1, a few miles south of Stamford, on the A1/A47 intersection west of Peterborough.

Web: www.johansens.com/haycock
E-mail: haycock@arcadianhotels.co.uk
Tel: 01780 782223 or 0800 9 177 877
Fax: 01780 783031

Price Guide:
single from £80
double/twin room from £95
Four posters from £120

THE ALDERLEY EDGE HOTEL

MACCLESFIELD ROAD, ALDERLEY EDGE, CHESHIRE SK9 7BJ

This privately owned award-winning hotel has 37 executive bedrooms, 11 superior rooms and 4 suites including the Presidential and Bridal Suites offering a high standard of decor. The restaurant is in the sumptuous conservatory with exceptional views and attention is given to the highest standards of cooking; fresh produce, including fish delivered daily, is provided by local suppliers. Specialities include hot and cold seafood dishes, puddings served piping hot from the oven and a daily selection of unusual and delicious breads, baked each morning in the hotel bakery. The wine list features 100 champagnes and 600 wines. Special wine and champagne dinners are held quarterly. In addition to the main conference room there is a suite of meeting and private dining rooms. The famous Edge walks are nearby, as are Tatton and Lyme Parks, Quarry Bank Mill and Dunham Massey. Manchester's thriving city centre is 15 miles away and the airport is a 20-minute drive.

Directions: Follow M6 to M56 Stockport. Exit junction 6, take A538 to Wilmslow. Follow signs 1½ miles to Alderley Edge. Turn left at end of the main shopping area on to Macclesfield Rd (B5087) and the hotel is 200 yards on the right. From M6 take junction 18 and follow signs for Holmes Chapel and Alderley Edge.

Web: www.johansens.com/alderleyedge
E-mail: sales@alderley-edge-hotel.co.uk
Tel: 01625 583033
Fax: 01625 586343

Price Guide:
single £45–£160
double £90–£190
suites from £250

Our inspector loved: The extensive list of champagnes.

Warrington
Chester
Crewe

THE CHESTER CRABWALL MANOR

PARKGATE ROAD, MOLLINGTON, CHESTER, CHESHIRE CH1 6NE

Crabwall Manor can be traced back to Saxon England, prior to the Norman Conquest. Set in 11 acres of mature woodland on the outskirts of Chester, this Grade II listed manor house has a relaxed ambience, which is enhanced by staff who combine attentive service with friendliness and care. The interior boasts elegant drapes complemented by pastel shades which lend a freshness to the décor of the spacious lounge and reception areas, while the log fires in the inglenook fireplaces add warmth. The hotel has won several awards for their renowned cuisine, complemented by an excellent selection of fine wines and outstanding levels of accommodation. Four meeting suites and a further ten syndicate rooms are available. The Reflections leisure club features a 17 metre pool, gymnasium, dance studio, sauna, spa pool, juice bar. Those wishing to be pampered will enjoy the three beauty treatment rooms. 100 yards from the hotel guests have reduced green fees at Mollington Grange 18 hole championship golf course. The ancient city of Chester with its many attractions is only 1½ miles away. Weekend breaks available.

Our inspector loved: The excellent leisure club and swimming pool.

Directions: Go to end of M56, ignoring signs to Chester. Follow signs to Queensferry and North Wales, taking A5117 to next roundabout. Left onto A540, towards Chester for 2 miles. Crabwall Manor is on the right.

Web: www.johansens.com/crabwallmanor
E-mail: crabwallmanor@marstonhotels.com
Tel: 01244 851666
Fax: 01244 851400

Price Guide:
single from £136
double/twin from £167–£187
suite from £207–£250

45

GREEN BOUGH HOTEL

60 HOOLE ROAD, CHESTER, CHESHIRE CH2 3NL

Directions: Leave M53 at Jct12. Take A56 into Chester for 1 mile. The Green Bough Hotel is on the right.

Web: www.johansens.com/greenbough
E-mail: luxury@greenbough.co.uk
Tel: 01244 326241
Fax: 01244 326265

Price Guide:
single £80–£105
double/twin £105–£150
suites £175–£225

A late Victorian town house, the Green Bough Hotel is conveniently situated in the ancient city of Chester. Bought by Philip and Janice Martin in 1997, the hotel has been completely refurbished and redecorated; a Roman theme is evident throughout. This totally non-smoking hotel perfectly combines the convenience of modern facilities with the charm of period features and furnishings. Most bedrooms have antique beds, whilst many of the original architectural features of the building and the adjoining Victorian Lodge bedroom wing remain intact. The Olive Tree restaurant is presided over by Philip Martin who trained at the Savoy Hotel, working with the renowned Maître Chef de Cuisine Silvino S Trompetto. The menu, is complemented by a wine list of a range and quality that belies the relatively small size of the hotel. The Green Bough provides an excellent base for exploring the city of Chester and hires bicycles for this purpose. It is also ideal for those venturing further afield into the beautiful Cheshire countryside and Snowdonia. Places of interest in Chester include the cathedral, river, race course, and the Blue Planet Aquarium and Chester Zoo.

Our inspector loved: *The Roman theme which is prevalent throughout the hotel.*

NUNSMERE HALL

TARPORLEY ROAD, OAKMERE, NORTHWICH, CHESHIRE CW8 2ES

Set in peaceful Cheshire countryside and surrounded on three sides by a lake, Nunsmere Hall epitomises the elegant country manor where superior standards of hospitality still exist. Wood panelling, antique furniture, exclusive fabrics, Chinese lamps and magnificent chandeliers evoke an air of luxury. The 30 bedrooms and 6 suites most with spectacular views of the lake and gardens, are beautifully appointed with king-size beds, comfortable breakfast seating and marbled bathrooms containing soft bathrobes and toiletries. The Brocklebank, Delamere and Oakmere business suites are air-conditioned, soundproofed and offer excellent facilities for boardroom meetings, private dining and seminars. The Restaurant has a reputation for fine food and uses only fresh seasonal produce. Twice County Restaurant of the Year in the Good Food Guide. A snooker room is available and there are several championship golf courses nearby. Oulton Park racing circuit and the Cheshire Polo Club are next door. Golf pitch and putt is available in the grounds. Archery and air rifle shooting by arrangement. Although secluded, Nunsmere is convenient for major towns and routes. AA 3 Red Star and Two Rosettes.

Our inspector loved: The magnificent setting surrounded by lake.

Directions: Leave M6 at junction 19, take A556 to Chester (approximately 12 miles). Turn left onto A49. Hotel is 1 mile on left

Web: www.johansens.com/nunsmerehall
E-mail: reservations@nunsmere.co.uk
Tel: 01606 889100
Fax: 01606 889055

Price Guide:
single £105–£150
double/twin £185–£250
suites from £250

ROWTON HALL HOTEL

WHITCHURCH ROAD, ROWTON, CHESTER, CHESHIRE CH3 6AD

Directions: From the centre of Chester, take A41 towards Whitchurch. After 3 miles, turn right to Rowton village. The hotel is in the centre of the village.

Web: www.johansens.com/rowtonhall
E-mail: rowtonhall@rowtonhall.co.uk
Tel: 01244 335262
Fax: 01244 335464

Price Guide:
single £102–£145
double/twin £114–£185
suites £224

Set in over 8 acres of award-winning gardens, Rowton Hall is located at the end of a leafy lane, only 3 miles from Chester city centre. Built as a private residence in 1779, it retains many of its original features, including extensive oak panelling, a self-supporting hand-carved staircase, an original Inglenook fireplace and an elegant Robert Adam fireplace. Each luxury bedroom is individually and tastefully decorated with attention to detail, and is equipped with every modern amenity, including private bathroom, satellite television, direct dial telephone with modem points, personal safe, luxury bathrobes, trouser press and hostess tray. Dining in the oak-panelled Langdale Restaurant is a delight; every dish is carefully created by Executive Chef, Anthony O'Hare, who uses the finest ingredients from local markets and the Hall's gardens to produce exquisite cuisine. Guests can enjoy the indoor Health Club and relax in the Jacuzzi, steam room or sauna. For the more energetic, a workout in the well-equipped gymnasium and dance studio is available and 2 floodlit all-weather tennis courts are within the grounds. Four main conference and banqueting suites make the Hall an ideal venue for meetings, weddings, private dining or conferences and corporate events for up to 200 guests. Marquee events can be arranged in the gardens.

Our inspector loved: The lovingly tended gardens.

CREWE HALL

WESTON ROAD, CREWE, CHESHIRE CW1 6UZ

Set in vast, impressive grounds, the magnificent Crewe Hall is the jewel of Cheshire. Once the seat of the Earls of Crewe and owned by the Queen as part of the estate of the Duchy of Lancaster, this Stately Home transports guests back to an age of splendour and luxury where quality and service were imperative. An exquisite Jacobean carving, which adorns the lavish main entrance, is reflected over the whole exterior from the balustraded terraces to the tip of the tall West Wing Tower. Crewe Hall's beautiful interior boats a confident juxtaposition between the traditional and modern. The newly refurbished and air-conditioned west wing, with its stylish, contemporary décor, is contrasted with the traditional home rooms, which have magnificent panelling and marble, huge stone fireplaces, intricate carvings, stained glass and antique furniture. Regarded as one of the finest specimens of Elizabethan architecture, the staircase in the East Hall climbs majestically upwards. Guests can dine in the quiet, elegant dining room or the informal Brasserie, which has an unique revolving bar (whose smooth motion means you will not notice you are moving until the view has suddenly changed) and offers imaginative, delicious meals complemented by international beers and wines.

Our inspector loved: The ecletic mix of tradition and modern.

Directions: From the M6, exit at junction 16 and follow the A500 towards Crewe. At the first roundabout take the last exit. At the next roundabout take the first exit. After ¼ mile turn right into the drive.

Warrington

Chester

Crewe

Web: www.johansens.com/crewehall
E-mail: info@crewehall.com
Tel: 01270 253333
Fax: 01270 253322

Price Guide:
single £135–£185
double/twin £160–£215
suite £260–£380

MERE COURT HOTEL

WARRINGTON ROAD, MERE, KNUTSFORD, CHESHIRE WA16 0RW

Directions: From M6, exit at junction 19. Take A556 towards Manchester. After 1 mile turn left at traffic lights onto A50 towards Warrington. Mere Court is on the right.

Web: www.johansens.com/merecourt
E-mail: sales@merecourt.co.uk
Tel: 01565 831000
Fax: 01565 831001

Price Guide:
single £80–£140
double/twin £98–£185

This attractive Edwardian house stands in seven acres of mature gardens and parkland in one of the loveliest parts of Cheshire. Maintained as a family home since being built in 1903, Mere Court has been skilfully restored into a fine country house hotel offering visitors a peaceful ambience in luxury surroundings. Comforts and conveniences of the present mix excellently with the ambience and many original features of the past. The bedrooms have views over the grounds and ornamental lake. All are individually designed and a number of them have a four-poster beds, Jacuzzi spa bath, mini bar and separate lounge. Facilities include safes, personalised voice mail telephones and modem points. Heavy ceiling beams, polished oak panelling and restful waterside views are features of the elegant Aboreum Restaurant which serves the best of traditional English and Mediterranean cuisine. Lighter meals can be enjoyed in the Lounge Bar. The original coach house has been converted into a designated conference centre with state of the art conference suites and syndicate rooms accommodating up to 120 delegates. Warrington, Chester, Manchester Airport and many National Trust properties are within easy reach.

Our inspector loved: The oak-panelled restaurant overlooking the Lake.

THE STANNEYLANDS HOTEL

STANNEYLANDS ROAD, WILMSLOW, CHESHIRE SK9 4EY

Owned and managed by a dedicated family, Stanneylands is a handsome country house set in several acres of impressive, tranquil gardens with a collection of unusual trees and shrubs. Guests experience a truly warm welcome in a unique and special atmosphere, where luxurious comfort provides the perfect setting for business or pleasure. Some of the bedrooms offer lovely views over the gardens whilst others overlook the undulating Cheshire countryside. A sense of quiet luxury prevails in the reception rooms, where classical décor and comfortable furnishings create a relaxing ambience. In the award-winning restaurant guests can choose from an enticing blend of innovative and traditional English and international cuisine. Stanneylands is an excellent venue for both private and business events. The Oak Room accommodates up to 60 people, whilst the Stanley Suite is available for conferences and larger celebrations. The hotel is conveniently located for tours of the Cheshire plain or the more rugged Peak District, as well as the bustling market towns and industrial heritage of the area. Special corporate and weekend rates are available.

Our inspector loved: Strolling through the gardens.

Directions: Three miles from Manchester International Airport. Come off at Junction 5 on the M56 (airport turn off). Follow signs to Cheadle/Wilmslow, turn left into station road, bear right onto Stanneylands Road.

Warrington
Chester
Crewe

Web: www.johansens.com/stanneylands
E-mail: sales@stanneylandshotel.co.uk
Tel: 01625 525225
Fax: 01625 537282

Price Guide:
single £70–£135
double/twin £102–£145
suite £145

ROOKERY HALL

WORLESTON, NANTWICH, NR CHESTER, CHESHIRE CW5 6DQ

Rookery Hall, part of the Arcadian Hotel Group, enjoys a peaceful setting where guests can relax, yet is convenient for road, rail and air networks. Within the original house are elegant reception rooms and the mahogany and walnut panelled restaurant, which is renowned for its cuisine. Dine by candlelight in the intimate dining room overlooking the lawns. Over 300 wines are in the cellar. Private dining facilities are available for meetings and weddings – summer lunches can be taken alfresco on the terrace. Companies can hire the hotel as their own "Country House", with leisure pursuits such as archery, clay pigeon shooting and off road driving available within the grounds. Tennis or croquet, fishing, golf and riding can be arranged. All of the bedrooms are individually designed and luxuriously furnished with spacious marbled bathrooms. Many afford views over fields and woodlands. Suites are available including the self-contained stable block. Special breaks and celebrations packages are offered with gourmet evenings in the restaurant. The hotel is perfectly situated for historic Chester and North Wales and is an ideal location for weddings and conferences.

Directions: From M6 junction 16 take A500 to Nantwich, then B5074 to Worleston.

Web: www.johansens.com/rookeryhall
E-mail: rookery@arcadianhotels.co.uk
Tel: 01270 610016 or 0800 9 177 877
Fax: 01270 626027

Price Guide:
single £95–£150
double/twin £95–£175
suite £185

Our inspector loved: *This elegant Victorian Hotel set in the Cheshire countryside.*

THE NARE HOTEL

CARNE BEACH, VERYAN-IN-ROSELAND, TRURO, CORNWALL TR2 5PF

Peace, tranquillity and stunning sea views make The Nare a real find. Superbly positioned, the Hotel overlooks the fine sandy beach of Gerrans Bay, facing south and sheltered by The Nare and St Mawes headlands. In recent years extensive refurbishments have ensured comfort and elegance without detracting from the country house charm of this friendly family run Hotel. All bedrooms are close to the sea, many with patios and balconies taking advantage of the spectacular outlook. In the main dining room guests can enjoy the sea views from 3 sides of the room where local seafood, such as lobster and delicious home-made puddings, are served with Cornish cream, complemented by an interesting range of wines. The new Quarterdeck Restaurant is open all day serving morning coffee, light luncheons, cream teas and offers relaxed dining in the evening. The Nare remains the highest rated AA 4 star hotel in the south west with 2 Rosettes for its food. Surrounded by subtropical gardens and National Trust land the Hotel's seclusion is ideal for exploring the coastline and villages of the glorious Roseland Peninsula. It is also central for many of Cornwall's beautiful houses and gardens including the famous Heligan. Guests arriving by train or air are met, by prior arrangement, at Truro Station or Newquay Airport. The Hotel is open throughout the year, including Christmas and New Year.

Our inspector loved: This serene country house by the sea.

Directions: Follow the road to St Mawes. 2 miles after Tregony Bridge turn left for Veryan. The Hotel is 1 mile beyond Veryan.

Web: www.johansens.com/nare
E-mail: office@narehotel.co.uk
Tel: 01872 501111
Fax: 01872 501856

Price Guide:
single £87-£170
double/twin £174-£310
suite £310-£490

THE GREENBANK HOTEL

HARBOURSIDE, FALMOUTH, CORNWALL TR11 2SR

Directions: Take the A39 from Truro and on approaching Falmouth join the Old Road going through Penryn. Turn left at the second roundabout where the hotel is signposted.

Web: www.johansens.com/greenbank
E-mail: sales@greenbank-hotel.com
Tel: 01326 312440
Fax: 01326 211362

Price Guide:
single £60–£75
double/twin £95–£165
suite £185–£225

Surrounded by the vibrant atmosphere of Falmouth, the Greenbank is the only hotel on the banks of one of the world's largest and deepest natural harbours. Because of its position as a ferry point to Flushing its history stretches back to the 17th century, and visitors have included Florence Nightingale and Kenneth Grahame, whose letters from the hotel to his son formed the basis for his book 'The Wind in the Willows'. Seaward views from the hotel are stunning, and reaching out from each side are lovely clifftop paths leading to secluded coves where walkers can relax while enjoying a paddle in clear blue waters and breathing in fresh, clean sea air. Most of the charming, delightfully furnished and well equipped en suite bedrooms enjoy panoramic views across the harbour to Flushing and St Mawes. Keen appetites will be well satisfied by the variety of dishes offered in the Harbourside Restaurant with seafood and local lamb specialities on the menu. There are opportunities locally for golf, sailing, riding and fishing. Interesting places nearby include Cornwall's National Maritime Museum, several heritage sites and many National Trust properties and gardens.

Our inspector loved: The harbourside location.

PENMERE MANOR

MONGLEATH ROAD, FALMOUTH, CORNWALL TR11 4PN

Set in five acres of subtropical gardens and woodlands, this elegant Georgian country house is an oasis of gracious living and fine food. From arrival to departure the Manor's attentive staff ensure that guests have everything they need to enjoy their stay. Bedrooms offer every comfort and are furnished to maintain the country house ambience. The spacious Garden rooms (as illustrated) are delightful. Each is named after a famous Cornish garden and has either king or queen size beds and a lounge area. The restaurant serves excellent international cuisine that includes an extensive lobster speciality menu which must be ordered 24 hours in advance. Light snacks and substantial lunchtime dishes are also provided in the bar which overlooks the garden and terrace. There is a heated outdoor swimming pool in the old walled garden and a splendid indoor pool, together with Jacuzzi spa, sauna, solarium and gym. Golfers can benefit from reduced green fees at Falmouth Golf Course. Cornish gardens, National Trust and English Heritage properties are within reach. Flambards Theme Park, Poldark Mine and Gweek Seal Sanctuary are less than ten miles away.

Our inspector loved: *The garden suites which are spacious and first class.*

Directions: From Truro follow the A39 towards Falmouth. Turn right at Hillhead roundabout and after 1 mile turn left into Mongleath Road.

Web: www.johansens.com/penmeremanor
E-mail: reservations@penmere.co.uk
Tel: 01326 211411
Fax: 01326 317588

Price Guide:
single £58–£97
double/twin £90–£126

BUDOCK VEAN - THE HOTEL ON THE RIVER

NEAR HELFORD PASSAGE, MAWNAN SMITH, FALMOUTH, CORNWALL TR11 5LG

Directions: From the A39 Truro to Falmouth road, follow the brown tourist signs for Trebah Garden. Budock Vean appears ½ mile after passing Trebah on the left-hand side.

Web: www.johansens.com/budockvean
E-mail: relax@budockvean.co.uk
Tel: reservations 01326 252100
Fax: 01326 250892

Price Guide:
single £56–£85
double/twin £112–£170
suites £217–£275

Newquay   Bodmin

Penzance

Isles of Scilly

This friendly 4 star hotel is nestled in 65 acres of award-winning gardens and parkland with a private foreshore on the tranquil Helford River. Set in a designated area of breathtaking natural beauty, the hotel is a destination in itself with outstanding leisure facilities and space to relax and be pampered. The AA rosette restaurant offers excellent cuisine using the finest local produce to create exciting and imaginative five-course dinners, with fresh seafood being a speciality. On site are a golf course, large indoor swimming pool, tennis courts, a billiard room, boating, fishing, and the Natural Health Spa. The local ferry will take guests from the hotel's jetty to waterside pubs, to Frenchman's Creek or to hire a boat. The hotel also takes out guests on its own 32 foot 'Sunseeker'. A myriad of magnificent country and coastal walks from the wild grandeur of Kynance and the Lizard to the peace and tranquillity of the Helford itself, as well as several of the Great Gardens of Cornwall, are in the close vicinity. For those guests staying at the hotel and wishing to dine on the 5-course dinner add £10 per person per night.

Our inspector loved: *The beatiful grounds and wonderful feel of relaxation.*

MEUDON HOTEL

MAWNAN SMITH, NR FALMOUTH, CORNWALL TR11 5HT

Set against a delightfully romantic backdrop of densely wooded countryside between the Fal and Helford Rivers, Meudon Hotel is a unique, family-run, superior retreat with sub-tropical gardens leading to its own private sea beach. The French name originates from a nearby farmhouse built by Napoleonic prisoners of war and called after their eponymous home village in the environs of Paris. 9 acres of sub-tropical gardens are coaxed into early bloom by the Gulf Stream and mild Cornish climate; Meudon is safely surrounded by 200 acres of beautiful National Trust land and the sea. All bedrooms are in a modern wing, have en suite bathrooms and each enjoy spectacular garden views. Many a guest is enticed by the cuisine to return; in the restaurant fresh seafood, caught by local fishermen, is served with wines from a judiciously compiled list. Rich in natural beauty with a myriad of watersports and country pursuits to indulge in, you can play golf free at nearby Falmouth Golf Club and 5 others in Cornwall, sail aboard the Hotel's skipperd 34-foot yacht or just laze on the beach.

Our inspector loved: Its location between the Fal & Helford Rivers and beautiful sub-tropical gardens.

Directions: From Truro A39 torwards Falmouth at Hillhead roundabout take 2nd exit. The hotel is four miles on the left.

Web: www.johansens.com/meudon
E-mail: wecare@meudon.co.uk
Tel: 01326 250541
Fax: 01326 250543

Price Guide: (including dinner)
single £105
double/twin £210
suite £270

FOWEY HALL HOTEL & RESTAURANT

HANSON DRIVE, FOWEY, CORNWALL PL23 1ET

Directions: On reaching Fowey, go straight over the mini roundabout and turn right into Hanson Drive. Fowey Hall Drive is on the right.

Web: www.johansens.com/foweyhall
E-mail: info@foweyhall.com
Tel: 01726 833866
Fax: 01726 834100

Price Guide:
double/twin from £145
superior double from £180
suite from £200

Situated in five acres of beautiful grounds overlooking the Estuary, Fowey Hall Hotel is a magnificent Victorian mansion renowned for its excellent service and comfortable accommodation. The fine panelling and superb plasterwork ceilings add character to the spacious public rooms. Located in either the main house or the Court, the 24 bedrooms include suites and interconnecting rooms. All are well-proportioned with a full range of modern comforts. The panelled dining rooms provide an intimate atmosphere where guests may savour the local delicacies. Using the best of regional produce, the menu comprises tempting seafood and fish specialities. The hotel offers a full crèche service. Guests may swim in the indoor swimming pool or play croquet in the gardens. Older children have not been forgotten and the cellars of the mansion are well-equipped with table tennis, table football and many other games. Outdoor pursuits include sea fishing, boat trips and a variety of water sports such as sailing, scuba-diving and windsurfing. There are several coastal walks for those who wish to explore Cornwall and its beautiful landscape.

Our inspector loved: *A wonderful first class haven for families.*

St Martin's On The Isle

ST. MARTIN'S, ISLES OF SCILLY, CORNWALL TR25 0QW

This unique hotel offers guests the chance to 'step back in time' and appreciate the serenity and unspoilt beauty of one of the most remote offshore islands in the UK. Upon arrival at St Martin's a warm and personal welcome is extended by the General Manager, Keith Bradford, whose staff are always on hand to advise, guide, or simply assist in the art of relaxation. Unwinding in the laidback atmosphere of the Round Island Bar or garden is easy, and many people choose to chat and share experiences with fellow visitors. Surrounded by clear blue seas, white sandy beaches and spectacular views, the island offers endless opportunities for walking, picnics, watersports and boat trips. On foot, it takes a leisurely four hours to explore the coastal paths' ever changing scenery, while launches leave the hotel quay regulary for visits to the Eastern Isles where colonies of Atlantic grey seals bask on the rocks. Nature lovers can also enjoy a dusk walk with local 'bird man' Viv Jackson, and the more adventurous will be satisfied with snorkelling at the Dive Centre or a day out shark fishing with one of the island's boatmen. After a hard day, dinner of Scillonian crab or Lobster in the hotel's excellent restaurant is a must.

Our inspector loved: *The total peace, seclusion and first class overall cuisine and service.*

Directions: A twenty minute launch transfer from St Mary's.

Web: www.johansens.com/stmartins
E-mail: stay@stmartinshotel.co.uk
Tel: 01720 422090
Fax: 01720 422298

Price Guide: (including dinner)
single £95–£130
double/twin £190–£300
suite £300–£390

NEW

TREGLOS HOTEL

CONSTANTINE BAY, NR PADSTOW, CORNWALL PL28 8JH

Directions: From St Merryn take the B3276 for ¼ mile. Constantine Bay and Treglos are well signposted.

Web: www.johansens.com/treglos
E-mail: enquiries@treglos-hotel.co.uk
Tel: 01841 520727
Fax: 01841 521163

Price Guide: (incl dinner)
single £66–£89
double/twin £132–£178

Newquay   Bodmin

Penzance

Isles of Scilly

'Betjeman country' with its dramatic headlands and sweeping Atlantic views is the lovely setting for Treglos Hotel. Here, guests can relax in the warm, friendly and relaxing atmosphere of this old Country House, enjoying every modern comfort. The Hotel has remained in the ownership of the same family for over 30 years and has maintained the highest standards, providing first-class service and tasteful décor demonstrated by the extensive refurbishments to the bedrooms and bathrooms. Many overlook the stunning Constantine Bay but the best place to relax during the day are the elegant and comfortable lounges. The Cornish sea-air is guaranteed to sharpen any appetite and the Hotel's restaurant offers tempting menus for all tastes, including fresh local seafood and the finest traditional cuisine, complemented by superb wines. Manager Wally Vellacott is among the best sommeliers in the country, being a runner-up in the Premier Crew Awards! For sheer relaxation, there is a heated indoor pool and Jacuzzi, as well as snooker and pool tables. The Hotel's landscaped gardens offer a quiet retreat, while further afield there are numerous country and cliff top walks. 5 self-catering apartments are available in the Hotel grounds. Newquay Airport is 8 miles away.

Our inspector loved: *A lovely country house hotel by the sea - a golfers paradise.*

TALLAND BAY HOTEL

TALLAND-BY-LOOE, CORNWALL PL13 2JB

This lovely old Cornish manor house, parts of which date back to the 16th century, enjoys a completely rural and unspoilt setting. Surrounded by over 2 acres of beautiful gardens, it offers glorious views over the dramatic headlands of Talland Bay itself. Bedrooms are individually furnished to a high standard, some having lovely sea views. Sitting rooms open to the south-facing terrace by a heated outdoor swimming pool. In keeping with the period of the house, the newly refurbished restaurant, bar and lounges are tastefully decorated. The restaurant has been awarded 2 AA Rosettes, the dinner menus are imaginative and incorporate seafood from Looe, Cornish lamb and West Country cheeses. A choice of à la carte supplementary dishes changes with the seasons. Meals are complemented by a list of about 100 carefully selected wines. Leisure pursuits at the hotel include putting, croquet, painting courses and other special interest holidays. Talland Bay is a magically peaceful spot from which to explore this part of Cornwall: there are breathtaking coastal walks at the hotel's doorstep and many National Trust houses and gardens to visit locally. This hotel provides old-fashioned comfort in beautiful surroundings at exceptionally moderate prices. Resident owners: George and Mary Granville. Closed Jan–late Feb.

Directions: The hotel is signposted from the A387 Looe–Polperro road.

Web: www.johansens.com/tallandbay
E-mail: tallandbay@aol.com
Tel: 01503 272667
Fax: 01503 272940

Price Guide: (including dinner)
single £72–£106.50
double/twin £144–£212

Newquay   Bodmin

Penzance

Isles of Scilly

Our inspector loved: *The charm and friendly atmosphere.*

61

THE LUGGER HOTEL

PORTLOE, NR TRURO, CORNWALL TR2 5RD

Directions: Turn off A390 St Austell to Truro onto B3287 Tregony. Then take A3048 signed St Mawes, after 2 miles take left fork following signs for Portloe.

Web: www.johansens.com/lugger
E-mail: office@luggerhotel.com
Tel: 01872 501322
Fax: 01872 501691

Price Guide: (including dinner)
double/twin from £250

Newquay   Bodmin

Penzance

Isles of Scilly

Set on the water's edge and sheltered on three sides by green rolling hills tumbling into the sea, this lovely little former inn is as picturesque as any you will come across. Reputedly the haunt of 17th-century smugglers The Lugger Hotel overlooks a tiny working harbour in the scenic village of Portloe on the unspoilt Roseland Peninsula. It is a conservation area of outstanding beauty and an idyllic location in which to escape the stresses of today's hectic world. Seaward views from the hotel are stunning and reaching out from each side are lovely coastal paths leading to secluded coves. Welcoming owners Sheryl and Richard Young have created an atmosphere of total comfort and relaxation whilst retaining a historic ambience. The 20 bedrooms have every amenity; each is en suite, tastefully decorated and furnished, whilst some are situated across an attractive courtyard. A great variety of dishes and innovative dinner menus are offered in the restaurant overlooking the harbour. Local seafood is a specialty with crab and lobster being particular favourites. For beach lovers, the sandy stretches of Pendower and Carne are within easy reach, as are many National Trust properties and gardens, including the Lost Gardens of Heligan and the Eden project.

Our inspector loved: *The new owners loving and professional presentation of this idyllically located little gem.*

ROSE-IN-VALE COUNTRY HOUSE HOTEL

MITHIAN, ST AGNES, CORNWALL TR5 0QD

This 18th-century Cornish manor house, lies hidden away in 11 acres of glorious gardens, woodland and pasture in a wooded valley of great natural beauty. There is a sense of timelessness: a world apart from the bustle of modern living. Tasteful décor contrasts with dark mahogany throughout the elegant public rooms and pretty bedrooms, many of which have outstanding views across the valley gardens. Three ground floor rooms have level access. The Rose Suite and Master Rooms feature four-poster/half-tester beds, other rooms have coronet king-sized beds. Chef Phillip Sims serves imaginative, international cuisine and speciality Cornish crab/lobster/flambé dishes in the "Opie's Room" where sweeping, softly-draped bay windows overlook lawns and flower-beds. The gardens feature ponds, a gliding stream, a secluded, heated swimming pool, croquet, badminton, dovecote and summer house. There is a solarium, sauna and games room, and massage, aromatherapy and reflexology can be arranged. National Trust properties abound and special walks are available. Six golf courses, The Eden Project, The Glorious Gardens of Cornwall, riding, fishing, gliding, swimming and water sports are all close by. Self-catering is available in a nearby converted chapel.

Our inspector loved: This beautifully hidden away hotel offering total comfort.

Directions: A30 through Cornwall. Two miles beyond Zelah turn right onto B3284. Cross A3075 and take third left turn signposted Rose-in-Vale.

Web: www.johansens.com/roseinvalecountryhouse
E-mail: reception@rose-in-vale-hotel.co.uk
Tel: 01872 552202
Fax: 01872 552700

Price Guide:
single £50–£66
double/twin £110–£132
suite £155

NEW

HUSTYNS HOTEL & LEISURE CLUB

ST. BREOCK DOWNS, WADEBRIDGE, CORNWALL PL27 7LG

Directions: Take the A30 from the M5 Exeter to Bodmin. Take the A389 from Bodmin to Wadebridge. From Wadebridge Town Centre follow brown tourist signs to Hustyns.

Web: www.johansens.com/hustyns
E-mail: reception@hustyns.com
Tel: 01208 893700
Fax: 01208 893701

Price Guide:
single £90
double/twin £120
suite £175

This is a contemporary oasis nestled within the beautiful and peaceful Cornish countryside. Set in 180 acres, with unniterrupted views across Bodmin Moor and just a short distance from Padstow, Rock and the Eden Project, Hustyns is the perfect getaway for those seeking a relaxing break. The aim of the Hotel is to ensure that all expectations are surpassed and offers luxurious modern living with the highest levels of good old fashioned service and commitment. Hustyns Hotel and lodges offer luxury accommodation with stylish bedrooms and spacious bathrooms, many having jacuzzi baths and private saunas. Leisure facilities include 2 family swimming pools, a tennis court and state-of-the-art fitness equipment. Fitness enthusiasts may take advantage of the landscaped running track, alternatively, for the more leisurely, the grounds are an idyllic setting to meander through for a relaxing walk. Through the affiliation with golf professional Gary Alliss and Trevose Golf Club, guests can take private lessons and access can be arranged to the best golf courses in the country including the famous St. Enodoc Golf links. Domestic and corporate needs are equally well catered for; the conference facilities are modern and progressive, whilst a number of outdoor lodges provide multi-bedroomed accommodation away from the mainstay of the Hotel; an ideal base for a family holiday.

Our inspector loved: The location and sense of peace and seclusion.

THE GARRACK HOTEL & RESTAURANT

BURTHALLAN LANE, ST IVES, CORNWALL TR26 3AA

This family-run hotel, secluded and full of character, ideal for a family holiday, is set in two acres of gardens with fabulous sea views over Porthmeor Beach, the St Ives Tate Gallery and the old town of St Ives. The bedrooms in the original house are in keeping with the style of the building. The additional rooms are modern in design. All rooms have private bathrooms and baby-listening facilities. Superior rooms have either four-poster beds or whirlpool baths. A ground-floor room has been fitted for guests with disabilities. Visitors return year after year to enjoy informal yet professional service, good food and hospitality. The restaurant specialises in seafood especially fresh lobsters. The wine list includes over 70 labels from ten regions. The lounges have books, magazines and board games for all and open fires. The small attractive leisure centre contains a small swimming pool with integral spa, sauna, solarium and fitness area. The hotel has its own car park. Porthmeor Beach, just below the hotel, is renowned for surfing. Riding, golf, bowls, sea-fishing and other activities can be enjoyed locally. St Ives, with its harbour, is famous for artists and for the new St Ives Tate Gallery. Dogs by prior arrangement.

Our inspector loved: The location and family owned feel of welcome.

Directions: A30–A3074–B3311–B3306. Go ½ mile, turn left at mini-roundabout, hotel signs are on the left as the road starts down hill.

Web: www.johansens.com/garrack
E-mail: garrack@accuk.co.uk
Tel: 01736 796199
Fax: 01736 798955

Price Guide:
single £64–£67
double/twin £108–£168

Newquay   Bodmin

Penzance

Isles of Scilly

THE WELL HOUSE

ST KEYNE, LISKEARD, CORNWALL PL14 4RN

Directions: Leave A38 at Liskeard, take A390 to town centre, then take B3254 south to St Keyne Well and hotel.

Web: www.johansens.com/wellhouse
E-mail: enquiries@wellhouse.co.uk
Tel: 01579 342001
Fax: 01579 343891

Price Guide:
single from £75
double/twin £115–£170
family suite from £180

The West Country is one corner of England where hospitality and friendliness are at their most spontaneous and nowhere more so than at The Well House, just beyond the River Tamar. New arrivals are entranced by their first view of this lovely Victorian country manor. Its façade wrapped in rambling wisteria and jasmine trailers is just one of a continuous series of delights including top-quality service, modern luxury and impeccable standards of comfort and cooking. The hotel is professionally managed by proprietor Nick Wainford and General Manager Guy Down, whose attention to every smallest detail has earned his hotel numerous awards, among them the AA 2 Red Stars. From the tastefully appointed bedrooms there are fine rural views and each private bathroom offers luxurious bath linen, soaps and gels. Continental breakfast can be served in bed – or a traditional English breakfast may be taken in the dining room. Chef Matthew Corner selects fresh, seasonal produce to create his superbly balanced and presented cuisine. Tennis and swimming are on site and the Cornish coastline offers matchless scenery for walks. The Eden Project is a short drive away.

Our inspector loved: *The most friendly welcome, superb cuisine and total peace and tranquility.*

THE ROSEVINE HOTEL

PORTHCURNICK BEACH, PORTSCATHO, ST MAWES, TRURO, CORNWALL TR2 5EW

At the heart of Cornwall's breathtaking Roseland Peninsula, the Rosevine is an elegant and gracious late Georgian hotel that offers visitors complete comfort and peace. The Rosevine stands in its own landscaped grounds overlooking Portscatho Harbour, a traditional Cornish fishing village. The superbly equipped bedrooms are delightfully designed, with some benefiting from direct access into the gardens and from their own private patio. This is the only hotel in Cornwall to hold the awards of 3 AA Red Stars and the RAC Blue Ribbon and Triple Dining Rosettes. The restaurant serves exceptional food, utilising the freshest seafood and locally grown produce. After dining, guests can relax in any of the three tasteful and comfortably presented lounges, bathe in the spacious heated swimming pool, or read in the hotel's well stocked library. Drinks are served in the convivial bar which offers a dizzy array of top quality wines and spirits. Visitors to the region do not forget the walks to the charming villages dotted along the Roseland Peninsula, and the golden sand of the National Trust maintained beach. Visitors can also take river trips on small ferries, once the only means of travel around the peninsula. The region is awash with National Trust gardens and the beautiful town of Truro is easily reached.

Our inspector loved: *This elegant and gracious hotel offering total peace, seclusion and first class cuisine.*

Directions: From Exeter take A30 towards Truro. Take the St. Mawes turn and the hotel is on the left.

Web: www.johansens.com/rosevinehotel
E-mail: info@rosevine.co.uk
Tel: 01872 580206
Fax: 01872 580230

Price Guide:
single £80–£160
double/twin £160–£220
suite £210–£340

LOVELADY SHIELD COUNTRY HOUSE HOTEL

NENTHEAD ROAD, ALSTON, CUMBRIA CA9 3LF

Directions: The hotel's driveway is by the junction of the B6294 and the A689, 21/4 miles east of Alston.

Web: www.johansens.com/loveladyshield
E-mail: enquiries@lovelady.co.uk
Tel: 01434 381203
Fax: 01434 381515

Price Guide:
single £70–£90
double/twin £140–£180

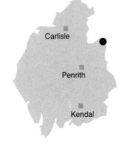

Carlisle

Penrith

Kendal

Reached by the A646, one of the worlds ten best drives and two-and-a-half miles from Alston, England's highest market town, Lovelady Shield, nestles in three acres of secluded riverside gardens. Bright log fires in the library and drawing room enhance the hotel's welcoming atmosphere. Owners Peter and Marie Haynes take great care to create a peaceful and tranquil haven where guests can relax and unwind. The five-course dinners created by master chef Barrie Garton, rounded off by home-made puddings and a selection of English farmhouse cheeses, have consistently been awarded AA Rosettes for the past 10 years for food. Many guests first discover Lovelady Shield en route to Scotland. They then return to explore this beautiful and unspoiled part of England and experience the comforts of the hotel. Golf, fishing, shooting, pony-trekking and riding can be arranged locally. The Pennine Way, Hadrian's Wall and the Lake District are within easy reach. Facilities for small conferences and boardroom meetings are available. Open all year, Special Christmas, New Year, and short breaks are offered with special rates for 2 and 3 day stays.

Our inspector loved: *This informal relaxing hotel set in a picturesque valley.*

HOLBECK GHYLL COUNTRY HOUSE HOTEL

HOLBECK LANE, WINDERMERE, CUMBRIA LA23 1LU

The saying goes that all the best sites for building a house in England were taken long before the days of the motor car. Holbeck Ghyll has one such prime position. It was built in the early days of the 19th century and is superbly located overlooking Lake Windermere and the Langdale Fells. Today this luxury hotel has an outstanding reputation and is managed personally and expertly by its proprietors, David and Patricia Nicholson. As well as being awarded the RAC Gold Ribbon and 3 AA Red Stars they are among an élite who have won an AA Courtesy and Care Award, Holbeck Ghyll was 2000 Cumbria Tourist Board Hotel of the Year. The majority of bedrooms are large and have spectacular and breathtaking views. All are recently refurbished to a very high standard and include decanters of sherry, fresh flowers, fluffy bathrobes and much more. There are six suites in the lodge. The oak-panelled restaurant, awarded a coveted Michelin star and 3 AA Rosettes, is a delightful setting for memorable dining and the meals are classically prepared, with the focus on flavours and presentation, while an extensive wine list reflects quality and variety. The hotel has an all-weather tennis court and a health spa with gym, sauna and treatment facilities.

Our inspector loved: The 3 deer that crossed the drive as she arrived.

Directions: From Windermere, pass Brockhole Visitors Centre, then after ½ mile turn right into Holbeck Lane. Hotel is ½ mile on left

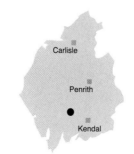

Web: www.johansens.com/holbeckghyll
E-mail: stay@holbeckghyll.com
Tel: 015394 32375
Fax: 015394 34743

Price Guide: (including dinner)
single from £95
double/twin £150–£320
suite £200–£320

ROTHAY MANOR

ROTHAY BRIDGE, AMBLESIDE, CUMBRIA LA22 0EH

Directions: ¼ mile from Ambleside on the A593 to Coniston.

Web: www.johansens.com/rothaymanor
E-mail: hotel@rothaymanor.co.uk
Tel: 015394 33605
Fax: 015394 33607

Price Guide:
single £74–£80
double/twin £120–£148
suite £160–£180

Situated just a ¼ mile from Lake Windermere and a short walk from Ambleside, this elegant Regency country house stands in its own landscaped gardens. The individually designed bedrooms include 3 beautifully furnished suites close to the manor which afford space and privacy. Two can easily accommodate up to 5 people, while one suite and a ground floor bedroom have been designed with particular attention to the comfort of guests with disabilities. Care and consideration are evident throughout. The menu is varied and meals are prepared with flair and imagination to high standards, complemented by a comprehensive wine list. For health and fitness, residents have free use of the nearby Low Wood Leisure Club, with swimming pool, sauna, steam room and Jacuzzi. Squash courts, sunbeds and a health and beauty salon are also available. Cycling, sailing, horseriding, fishing (permits available) and golf can be arranged locally, or guests can take a cruise on Lake Windermere or a trip on a steam railway. Small functions and conferences can be catered for. A full programme of specialised holidays is offered, including antiques, painting, bridge, walking, gardening, photography, music and Lake District heritage. Closed 3 January to 7 February. Represented in the USA by Josephine Barr: 800 323 5463.

Our inspector loved: *The delicious cakes for afternoon tea.*

THE SAMLING

AMBLESIDE ROAD, WINDERMERE, CUMBRIA LA23 1LR

Tucked away in 67 acres of woodlands and gardens on the northeastern shore of Lake Windermere, the Samling is a real gem and wonderfully relaxing. Secluded and private, with stunning views of the lake, guests will enjoy a unique getaway where attention to detail and excellent service provides a luxurious home from home experience. Beautifully decorated bedrooms retain their authentic rustic features, which are combined with stylish modern comforts, Turkish rugs and huge baths. Breakfast is in bed! Irresistibly delicious cuisine and splendid wines are served in the gracious dining room, which is light and airy. The cosy drawing room has comfortable sofas and a warm ambience, the perfect place for a drink by the fireside. Guests can admire a magnificent sunset from the outdoor hottub. Horse riding, water skiing, hiking, sailing, paragliding, diving and canoeing is available for the adventurous whilst picnics on the hillside or ten course banquets can be provided. There are first class business facilities available. The Dutch Barn is available for wedding celebrations or conferences for up to 60 delegates.

Our inspector loved: Sitting in the outdoor spa bath overlooking Lake Windermere.

Directions: Leave M6 at Jct36 and take A590/A591 past Windermere towards Ambleside. The Samling is up a long drive, 100 yards past the Low Wood Hotel.

Web: www.johansens.com/samling
E-mail: info@thesamling.com
Tel: 015394 31922
Fax: 015394 30400

Price Guide:
single £145–£295
double/twin £145–£340

Carlisle

Penrith

Kendal

APPLEBY MANOR COUNTRY HOUSE HOTEL

ROMAN ROAD, APPLEBY-IN-WESTMORLAND, CUMBRIA CA16 6JB

Directions: From the South take junction 38 of the M6 and then the B6260 to Appleby (13 miles). Drive through the town to a T-junction, turn left, first right and follow road for two-thirds of a mile.

Web: www.johansens.com/applebymanor
E-mail: reception@applebymanor.co.uk
Tel: 017683 51571
Fax: 017683 52888

Price Guide:
single £72–£91
double/twin £104–£146

Carlisle

Penrith

Kendal

Surrounded by half a million acres of some of the most beautiful landscapes in England, sheltered by the mountains and fells of the Lake District, by the North Pennine Hills and Yorkshire Dales, in an area aptly known as Eden stands Appleby Manor, a friendly and relaxing hotel owned and run by the Dunbobbin family. The high quality, spotlessly clean, bedrooms induce peaceful, undisturbed sleep. (Dogs are welcome in The Coach House accommodation). The public areas are also restfully comfortable – the inviting lounges nicely warmed by log fires on cooler days, the cocktail bar and sunny conservatory luring guests with a choice of more than 70 malt whiskies and the restaurant offering an imaginative selection of tasty dishes and fine wines. The hotel pool, sauna, steam room, Jacuzzi, solarium and games room keep indoor athletes happy. Locally there are outdoor sports: fishing, golf, riding, squash and for the more venturesome, rambling on the fells. Appleby is an ideal base from which to visit the Lake District and an attractive stopover on journeys north-south.

Our inspector loved: Relaxing in the conservatory looking at the views of the Eden Valley.

TUFTON ARMS HOTEL

MARKET SQUARE, APPLEBY-IN-WESTMORLAND, CUMBRIA CA16 6XA

This distinguished Victorian coaching inn, owned and run by the Milsom family, has been refurbished to provide a high standard of comfort. The bedrooms evoke the style of the 19th century, when the Tufton Arms became one of the premier hotels in Victorian England. The kitchen is run under the auspices of David Milsom and Shaun Atkinson, who spoil guests for choice with a gourmet dinner menu as well as a grill menu, the restaurant being renowned for its fish dishes. Complementing the cuisine is an extensive wine list. There are conference and meeting rooms including the air conditioned Hothfield Suite which can accommodate up to 100 people. Appleby, the historic county town of Westmorland, stands in splendid countryside and is ideal for touring the Lakes, Yorkshire Dales and Pennines. It is also a convenient stop-over en route to Scotland. Members of the Milsom family also run The Royal Hotel in Comrie. Superb fishing for wild brown trout on a 24-mile stretch of the main River Eden, salmon fishing can be arranged on the lower reaches of the river. Shooting parties for grouse, duck and pheasant are a speciality. Appleby has an 18-hole moorland golf course.

Our inspector loved: *Being taken fishing by Nigel Milsom on the River Eden.*

Directions: In centre of Appleby (bypassed by the A66), 38 miles west of Scotch Corner, 13 miles east of Penrith (M6 junction 40), 12 miles from M6 junction 38.

Web: www.johansens.com/tuftonarms
E-mail: info@tuftonarmshotel.co.uk
Tel: 017683 51593
Fax: 017683 52761

Price Guide:
single £55–£100
double/twin £90–£135
suite £150

FARLAM HALL HOTEL

BRAMPTON, CUMBRIA CA8 2NG

Directions: Farlam Hall is 2½ miles east of Brampton on the A689, not in Farlam village.

Web: www.johansens.com/farlamhall
E-mail: farlamhall@dial.pipex.com
Tel: 016977 46234
Fax: 016977 46683

Price Guide: (including dinner)
single £130–£145
double/twin £240–£270

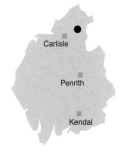

Farlam Hall was opened in 1975 by the Quinion and Stevenson families who over the years have managed to achieve and maintain consistently high standards of food, service and comfort. These standards have been recognised and rewarded by all the major guides and membership of Relais et Châteaux. This old border house, dating in parts from the 17th century, is set in mature gardens which can be seen from the elegant lounges and dining room, creating a relaxing and pleasing environment. The fine silver and crystal in the dining room complement the quality of the English country house cooking produced by Barry Quinion and his team of chefs. There are 12 individually decorated bedrooms varying in size and shape, some having Jacuzzi baths, one an antique four-poster bed and there are two ground floor bedrooms. This area offers many different attractions: miles of unspoiled countryside for walking, eight golf courses within 30 minutes of the hotel, Hadrian's Wall, Lanercost Priory and Carlisle with its castle, cathedral and museum. The Lake District, Scottish Borders and Yorkshire Dales each make an ideal day's touring. Winter and spring breaks are offered. Closed Christmas.

Our inspector loved: *Luxurious elegance of this borders hotel.*

GRAYTHWAITE MANOR

FERNHILL ROAD, GRANGE-OVER-SANDS, CUMBRIA LA11 7JE

This beautifully furnished, traditionally run country house, owned by The Auchlochan Trust, extends a warm welcome to its guests. It enjoys a superb setting in eight acres of private landscaped gardens and woodland on the hillside overlooking Morecambe Bay. Each bedroom is decorated and furnished in the best of taste and many offer superb views across the gardens and bay to the Pennines beyond. Elegant, spacious lounges with fresh flowers and antiques provide an exclusive setting and log fires are lit to add extra cheer on cooler nights. The Manor enjoys an excellent reputation for its cuisine and guests can look forward to a 5-course dinner comprising carefully prepared dishes complemented by the right wine from the extensive cellar. A few miles inland from Grange-over-Sands are Lake Windermere and Coniston Water and some of the most majestic scenery in the country. Nearby are the village of Cartmel, Holker Hall, Levens Hall and Sizergh Castle. The area abounds with historic buildings, gardens and museums.

Our inspector loved: The carefully tended landscaped gardens.

Directions: Take M6 to junction 36 and then the A590 towards Kendal, followed by the A590 towards Barrow. At roundabout take B5277 to Grange-over-Sands and go through town turning right opposite the fire station into Fernhill Road. The hotel is on the left.

Carlisle

Penrith

Kendal

Web: www.johansens.com/graythwaitemanor
E-mail: sales@graythwaitemanor.co.uk
Tel: 015395 32001
Fax: 015395 35549

Price Guide:
single £55–£78
double/twin £110–£150

THE WORDSWORTH HOTEL

GRASMERE, CUMBRIA LA22 9SW

Directions: The hotel is located next to Grasmere village church.

Web: www.johansens.com/wordsworth
E-mail: enquiry@wordsworth–grasmere.co.uk
Tel: 015394 35592
Fax: 015394 35765

Price Guide: (including dinner)
single £80–£135
double/twin £130–£190
suite £220–£270

In the very heart of the English Lakeland, The Wordsworth Hotel combines AA 4 Star standards with the magnificence of the surrounding fells. Set in its own grounds in the village of Grasmere, the hotel provides first-class, year-round facilities for both business and leisure travellers. It has a reputation for the high quality of its food, accommodation and hospitality. The comfortable bedrooms have well-equipped bathrooms and there are two suites with whirlpool baths. 24-hour room service is available for drinks and light refreshments. Peaceful lounges overlook landscaped gardens and the heated indoor pool opens on to a sun-trap terrace. There is a Jacuzzi, mini-gym, sauna and solarium. As well as a Cocktail Bar, the hotel has its own pub, "The Dove and Olive Branch", which has received many accolades. In "The Prelude Restaurant", which has 2 AA Rosettes, menus offer a good choice of dishes, prepared with skill and imagination from the freshest produce. The Wordsworth Hotel is a perfect venue for conferences, incentive weekends corporate entertaining and weddings. Three function rooms are available with highly professional back-up. Lakeland's principal places of interest are all within easy reach.

Our inspector loved: *Having a morning swim in the pool.*

THE DERWENTWATER HOTEL

PORTINSCALE, KESWICK, CUMBRIA CA12 5RE

Built as a doctor's summer residence in 1837, this handsome lakeside hotel lies amidst 16 acres of gardens and watermeadow, dedicated to the preservation of local wildlife. For a number of years the Hotel's owners have worked alongside English Nature to create a safe and natural haven for hundreds of creatures. Guests can sit in the comfortable conservatory and watch red squirrels, mallards, hedgehogs and pheasants, while a wander down to the lake may reveal sightings of water fowl, frogs, and even a family of timid roe deer. The Derwentwater has a unique style, each bedroom is individually furnished, and most enjoy views over the lake or the mountains beyond. Local produce is used in the wide variety of dishes served in The Deer's Leap restaurant. The Hotel is immensely proud of its excellent reputation for quality of staff and high standards of hospitality. The surrounding area lends itself to numerous activities, from walking and cycling, to fishing, trips on the lake and golf. Adult guests have complimentary use of nearby health spa.

Our inspector loved: *The gardens and wildlife wetlands leading down to the lake.*

Directions: Take the M6, exit at junction 40. Take the A66 westwards, bypass Keswick, after about a mile turn left into Portinscale, then follow signs to hotel.

Web: www.johansens.com/derwentwater
E-mail: info@derwentwater–hotel.co.uk
Tel: 017687 72538
Fax: 017687 71002

Carlisle

● Penrith

Kendal

Price Guide:
single £80–£120
double/twin £130–£190
suite £160

THE BORROWDALE GATES COUNTRY HOUSE HOTEL

GRANGE-IN-BORROWDALE, KESWICK, CUMBRIA CA12 5UQ

Directions: M6 junction 40 A66 into Keswick. B5289 to Borrowdale. After four miles right into Grange over double hump back bridge.

Web: www.johansens.com/borrowdalegates
E-mail: hotel@borrowdale-gates.com
Tel: 017687 77204
Fax: 017687 77254

Price Guide: (Including dinner)
single £70–£98
double/twin £120–£180

Built in 1860, Borrowdale Gates is surrounded on all sides by the rugged charm of the Lake District National Park. It affords a panoramic vista of the Borrowdale Valley and glorious fells and nestles in two acres of wooded gardens on the edge of the ancient hamlet of Grange, close to the shores of Derwentwater. Tastefully decorated bedrooms offer every modern comfort and most command picturesque views of the surrounding scenery. The comfortable lounges and bar, decorated with fine antiques and warmed by glowing log fires in cooler months, create the perfect setting in which to enjoy a drink and forget the bustle of everyday life. Fine food is served in the restaurant, with menus offering a wide and imaginative selection of dishes. The cuisine is complemented by a thoughtfully chosen wine list and excellent service. This Lakeland home is a haven of peace and tranquillity and is ideally located for walking, climbing and touring. There are also many places of literary and historical interest within easy reach, for example Wordsworth's birthplace in Cockermouth. The hotel is closed throughout January. Special breaks available.

Our inspector loved: *The beautiful setting in the Borrowdale Valley.*

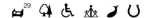

SHARROW BAY COUNTRY HOUSE HOTEL

HOWTOWN, LAKE ULLSWATER, PENRITH, CUMBRIA CA10 2LZ

Now in its 55th year, Sharrow Bay is known to discerning travellers the world over, who return again and again to this magnificent lakeside hotel. It wasn't always so. The late Francis Coulson arrived in 1948, he was joined by the late Brian Sack in 1952 and the partnership flourished, to make Sharrow Bay what it is today. Nigel Lightburn and his staff are carrying on the tradition of Sharrow. All the bedrooms are elegantly furnished and guests are guaranteed the utmost comfort. In addition to the main hotel, there are four cottages nearby which offer similarly luxurious accommodation. All the reception rooms are delightfully decorated. Sharrow Bay is universally renowned for its wonderful cuisine. The team of chefs led by Johnnie Martin and Colin Akrigg ensure that each meal is a special occasion, a mouth-watering adventure! With its private jetty and 12 acres of lakeside gardens Sharrow Bay offers guests boating, swimming and fishing. Fell-walking is a challenge for the upwardly mobile. Sharrow Bay is the oldest British member of Relais et Châteaux. Closed in December, January and February.

Our inspector loved: Having afternoon tea in the new Garden overlooking the fountain.

Directions: M6 junction 40, A592 to Lake Ullswater, into Pooley Bridge, then take Howtown road for 2 miles.

Web: www.johansens.com/sharrowbaycountryhouse
E-mail: enquiries@sharrow–bay.com
Tel: 017684 86301/86483
Fax: 017684 86349

Price Guide:(incl. 6-course dinner and full English breakfast)
single £145–£250
double/twin £300–£400
suites from £420

Carlisle

Penrith

Kendal

THE INN ON THE LAKE

LAKE ULLSWATER, GLENRIDDING, CUMBRIA CA11 0PE

With its 15 acres of grounds and lawns sweeping down to the shore of Lake Ullswater, The Inn on the Lake truly boasts one of the most spectacular settings in the Lake District. Recently bought and refurbished by the Graves family, it now offers a wide range of excellent facilities as well as stunning views of the surrounding scenery. Downstairs, comfortable lounges provide a calm environment in which to relax with a drink, whilst dinner can be enjoyed in the Lake View restaurant. Most of the 46 en suite bedrooms look across to the Lake or the fells and 5 lake view four poster rooms add an extra touch of luxury. The Hotel welcomes wedding ceremonies and receptions and is happy to provide a full private function service as well as conference facilities for up to 120 business delegates. The list of nearby leisure activities for children and adults alike is endless; rock climbing, pony trekking, canoeing, windsurfing, sailing and fishing are all available. Trips around the Lake can be taken aboard the Ullswater steamers and many of the most stunning Lake District walks begin in this area.

Our inspector loved: *Strolling across the garden down to Lake Ullswater.*

Directions: Leave the M6 at junction 40, then take the A66 west. At the first roundabout, by Rheged Discovery Centre, head towards Pooley Bridge then follow the shoreline of Lake Ullswater to Glenridding.

Web: www.johansens.com/innonthelake
E-mail: info@innonthelakeullswater.co.uk
Tel: 017684 82444
Fax: 017684 82303

Price Guide:
single £55–£130
double/twin £88–£180

RAMPSBECK COUNTRY HOUSE HOTEL

WATERMILLOCK, LAKE ULLSWATER, NR PENRITH, CUMBRIA CA11 0LP

A beautifully situated hotel, Rampsbeck Country House stands in 18 acres of landscaped gardens and meadows leading to the shores of Lake Ullswater. Built in 1714, it first became a hotel in 1947, before the present owners acquired it in 1983. Thomas and Marion Gibb, with the help of Marion's mother, Marguerite MacDowall, completely refurbished Rampsbeck with the aim of maintaining its character and adding only to its comfort. Most of the well-appointed bedrooms have lake and garden views. Three have a private balcony and the suite overlooks the lake. In the elegant drawing room, a log fire burns and French windows lead to the garden. Guests and non-residents are welcome to dine in the intimate candle-lit restaurant. Imaginative menus offer a choice of delicious dishes, carefully prepared by Master Chef Andrew McGeorge and his team. A good bar lunch menu offers light snacks as well as hot food. Guests can stroll through the gardens, play croquet or fish from the lake shore, around which there are designated walks. Lake steamer trips, riding, golf, sailing, wind-surfing and fell-walking are available nearby. Closed from end of January to mid-February. Dogs by arrangement only.

Our inspector loved: *The wonderful views of Lake Ullswater.*

Directions: Leave M6 at junction 40, take A592 to Ullswater. At T-junction at lake turn right; hotel is 1½ miles on left.

Web: www.johansens.com/rampsbeckcountryhouse
E-mail: enquiries@rampbeck.fsnet.co.uk
Tel: 017684 86442
Fax: 017684 86688

Carlisle

Penrith

Kendal

Price Guide:
single £60–£120
double/twin £100–£200
suite £200

GILPIN LODGE

CROOK ROAD, NEAR WINDERMERE, CUMBRIA LA23 3NE

Directions: M6 exit 36. A591 Kendal bypass then B5284 to Crook.

Web: www.johansens.com/gilpinlodge
E-mail: hotel@gilpin-lodge.co.uk
Tel: 015394 88818
Fax: 015394 88058

Price Guide: (including 6 course dinner)
single £105–£125
double/twin £130–£250

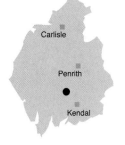

Carlisle

Penrith

Kendal

Gilpin Lodge is a friendly, elegant, relaxing country house hotel set in 20 acres of woodlands, moors and country gardens 2 miles from Lake Windermere, yet just 12 miles from the M6. The original building, tastefully extended and modernised, dates from 1901. A profusion of flower arrangements, picture-lined walls, antique furniture and log fires in winter are all part of John and Christine Cunliffe's perception of hospitality. The 14 sumptuous bedrooms all have en suite bathrooms and every comfort. Some have four-poster beds, split levels and whirlpool baths. The exquisite food, created by a team of 7 chefs, earns 3 rosettes from the AA. The award winning wine list contains 175 labels from 13 different countries. The beautiful gardens are the perfect place in which to muse while savouring the lovely lake-land scenery. Windermere golf course is $\frac{1}{2}$ a mile away. There is almost every kind of outdoor activity imaginable. Guests have free use of a nearby private leisure club. This is Wordsworth and Beatrix Potter country and nearby there are several stately homes, gardens and castles. England for Excellence Silver award 1997 Hotel of the year, English Tourist Board Gold award, AA 3 Red Stars and RAC Gold Ribbon award. A Pride of Britain Hotel.

Our inspector loved: The relaxing ambience and superb service.

LANGDALE CHASE

WINDERMERE, CUMBRIA LA23 1LW

Langdale Chase stands in five acres of landscaped gardens on the shores of Lake Windermere, with panoramic views over England's largest lake to the Langdale Pikes beyond. Visitors will receive warm-hearted hospitality in this well-run country home, which is splendidly decorated with oak panelling, fine oil paintings and ornate, carved fireplaces. A magnificent staircase leads to the well-appointed bedrooms, many overlooking the lake. One unique bedroom is sited over the lakeside boathouse, where the traveller may be lulled to sleep by the gently lapping waters below. The facilities also include a private boat mooring which is available on request. For the energetic, there is a choice of water-skiing, swimming or sailing from the hotel jetty. Guests can stroll through the gardens along the lake shore, in May the gardens are spectacular when the rhododendrons and azaleas are in bloom. Being pampered by attentive staff will be one of the many highlights of your stay at Langdale Chase. The variety of food and wine is sure to delight the most discerning diner. Combine this with a panoramic tableau across England's largest and loveliest of lakes and you have a truly unforgettable dining experience.

Our inspector loved: The views over Lake Windermere.

Directions: Situated on the A591, three miles north of Windermere, two miles south of Ambleside.

Web: www.johansens.com/langdalechase
E-mail: sales@langdalechase.co.uk
Tel: 015394 32201
Fax: 015394 32604

Price Guide:
single £80–£150
double/twin £100–£175
suite £200

MILLER HOWE

RAYRIGG ROAD, WINDERMERE, CUMBRIA LA23 1EY

Directions: From the M6 junction 36 follow the A591 through Windermere, then turn left onto the A592 towards Bowness. Miller Howe is ½ mile on the right.

Web: www.johansens.com/millerhowe
E-mail: lakeview@millerhowe.com
Tel: 015394 42536
Fax: 015394 45664

Price Guide: (including 5-course dinner)
single £95–£185
double/twin £140–£310
cottage suites £240–£360

One of the finest views in the entire Lake District is from the restaurant, conservatory and terrace of this lovely hotel which stands high on the shores of Lake Windermere. Lawned gardens bedded with mature shrubs, trees and borders of colour sweep down to the water's edge. It is a spectacular scene. Visitors receive warm hospitality from this well-run and splendidly decorated hotel now owned by Charles Garside, the former Editor-in-Chief of the international newspaper 'The European'. Previous owner John Tovey, the celebrated chef and author, remains as a consultant. All the bedrooms are furnished in a luxurious style, the majority of which have views over the lake to the mountains beyond. There are 3 luxury cottage suites They feature every modern amenity amongst the antiques. Chef Paul Webster's imaginative menus will delight the most discerning guest, while the panoramic tableau across England's largest lake as the sun sets, presents an unforgettable dining experience. Guests can enjoy a range of water sports or boat trips on Lake Windermere and there are many interesting fell walks close by.

Our inspector loved: *The luxurious new suites in the cottage.*

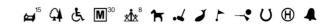

STORRS HALL

WINDERMERE, CUMBRIA LA23 3LG

From this magnificent listed Georgian manor house not another building can be seen. Just a spectacular, seemingly endless view over beautiful Lake Windermere. Built in the 18th century for a Lancashire shipping magnate, Storrs Hall stands majestically in an unrivalled peninsular position surrounded by 17 acres of landscaped, wooded grounds which slope down to half a mile of lakeside frontage. Apart from Wordsworth, who first recited 'Daffodils' in the Drawing Room at Storrs, the hotel was frequented by all the great Lakeland poets and Beatrix Potter. It is owned by Mr Les Hindle who rescued the manor from decay and restored it to its former glory, furnishing the rooms with antiques and objets d'art including a private collection of ship models, reflecting the maritime fortunes which built the hall. Opened as a hotel in 1998, the Hall has 25 beautifully furnished bedrooms, each en suite, spacious and with every comfort. Most have views over the lake, which was once the property of the Hall. Equally splendid views are enjoyed from an exquisite lounge, library, writing room and cosy bar. The Terrace Restaurant is renowned for the superb cuisine prepared by Head Chef Michael Dodd. Special breaks available.

Our inspector loved: Strolling in the gardens on the shore of Lake Windermere.

Directions: On A592 2 miles south of Bowness and 5 miles north of Newby Bridge.

Web: www.johansens.com/storrshall
E-mail: reception@storrshall.com
Tel: 015394 47111
Fax: 015394 47555

Price Guide:
single £125
double/twin £160–£300

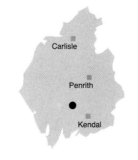

LINTHWAITE HOUSE HOTEL

CROOK ROAD, BOWNESS-ON-WINDERMERE, CUMBRIA LA23 3JA

Situated in 14 acres of gardens and woods in the heart of the Lake District, Linthwaite House overlooks Lake Windermere and Belle Isle, with Claife Heights and Coniston Old Man beyond. Here, guests will find themselves amid spectacular scenery, yet only a short drive from the motorway network. The hotel combines stylish originality with the best of traditional English hospitality. Superbly decorated en suite bedrooms, most of which have lake or garden views. The comfortable lounge is the perfect place to unwind and there is a fire on winter evenings. In the restaurant, excellent cuisine features the best of fresh, local produce, accompanied by a fine selection of wines. Within the hotel grounds, there is a 9-hole putting green and a par 3 practice hole. Fly fishermen can fish for brown trout in the hotel tarn. Guests have complimentary use of a private swimming pool and leisure club nearby, while fell walks begin at the hotel's front door. The area around Linthwaite abounds with places of interest: this is Beatrix Potter and Wordsworth country, and there is much to interest the visitor.

Our inspector loved: *Walking through the landscaped gardens down to the tarn.*

Directions: From the M6 junction 36 follow Kendal by-pass (A590) for 8 miles. Take B5284 Crook Road for 6 miles. 1 mile beyond Windermere Golf Club, Linthwaite House is signposted on left.

Web: www.johansens.com/linthwaitehouse
E-mail: admin@linthwaite.com
Tel: 015394 88600
Fax: 015394 88601

Price Guide:
single £90–£120
double/twin £90–£220
suite £240–£270

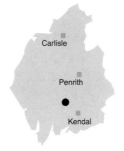

LAKESIDE HOTEL ON LAKE WINDERMERE

LAKESIDE, NEWBY BRIDGE, CUMBRIA LA12 8AT

Lakeside Hotel offers you a unique location on the water's edge of Lake Windermere. It is a classic, traditional Lakeland hotel offering four star facilities and service. All the bedrooms are en suite and enjoy individually designed fabrics and colours, many of the rooms offer breathtaking views of the lake. Guests may dine in either the award-winning Lakeview Restaurant or Ruskin's Brasserie, where extensive menus offer a wide selection of dishes including Cumbrian specialities. The Lakeside Conservatory serves drinks and light meals throughout the day – once there you are sure to fall under the spell of this peaceful location. Berthed next to the hotel there are cruisers which will enable you to explore the lake from the water. To enhance your stay, there is a leisure club including a 17m indoor pool, gymnasium, sauna, steam room and health & beauty suites. The hotel offers a fully equipped conference centre and many syndicate suites allowing plenty of scope and flexibility. Most of all you are assured of a stay in an unrivalled setting of genuine character. The original panelling and beams of the old coaching inn create an excellent ambience, whilst you are certain to enjoy the quality and friendly service. Special breaks available.

Our inspector loved: Sitting in the conservatory watching the boats sail by.

Directions: From M6 junction 36 join A590 to Newby Bridge, turn right over bridge towards Hawkshead; hotel is one mile on right.

Web: www.johansens.com/lakeside
E-mail: sales@lakesidehotel.co.uk
Tel: 08701 541586
Fax: 015395 31699

Price Guide:
single from £110
double/twin £150–£220
suites from £230

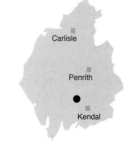

CALLOW HALL

MAPPLETON ROAD, ASHBOURNE, DERBYSHIRE DE6 2AA

Directions: Take the A515 through Ashbourne towards Buxton. At the Bowling Green Inn on the brow of a steep hill, turn left, then take the first right, signposted Mappleton and the hotel is over the bridge on the right.

Web: www.johansens.com/callowhall
E-mail: stay@callowhall.co.uk
Tel: 01335 300900
Fax: 01335 300512

Price Guide:
single £85–£110
double/twin £130–£165
suite £190

The approach to Callow Hall is up a tree-lined drive through the 44-acre grounds. On arrival visitors can take in the splendid views from the hotel's elevated position, overlooking the valleys of Bentley Brook and the River Dove. The majestic building and Victorian gardens have been restored by resident proprietors, David, Dorothy, son Anthony and daughter, Emma Spencer, who represent the fifth and sixth generations of hoteliers in the Spencer family. The famous local Ashbourne mineral water and home-made biscuits greet guests in the spacious period bedrooms. Fresh local produce is selected daily for use in the kitchen, where the term 'home-made' comes into its own. Home-cured bacon, sausages, fresh bread, traditional English puddings and melt-in-the-mouth pastries are among the items prepared on the premises which can be enjoyed by non-residents. Visiting anglers can enjoy a rare opportunity to fish for trout and grayling along a mile-long private stretch of the Bentley Brook, which is mentioned in Izaak Walton's The Compleat Angler. Callow Hall is ideally located for some of England's finest stately homes. Closed at Christmas. East Midlands Airport is 35 minutes away.

Our inspector loved: *The great pleasure in reading and absorbing a superb wine list.*

THE IZAAK WALTON HOTEL

DOVEDALE, NEAR ASHBOURNE, DERBYSHIRE DE6 2AY

This converted 17th-century farmhouse hotel, named after the renowned author of 'The Compleat Angler', enjoys glorious views of the surrounding Derbyshire Peaks. The River Dove runs in the valley below. The Izaak Walton is ideal for guests wishing to indulge in a warm welcome and a relaxing ambience. The 30 en suite bedrooms are diverse in their designs; some have four-poster beds whilst others are located in the old farmhouse building and still retain their old oak beams and décor. All the bedrooms are beautifully furnished and offer television, radio, hairdryer, direct dial telephone and several other amenities. The Haddon Restaurant, with an AA rosette, has a diverse menu of creative yet traditional cuisine. Informal meals and light snacks can be enjoyed in the Dovedale Bar. Leisure pursuits include rambling, fishing (the hotel has 4 rods on the River Dove and private tuition is available), mountain biking and hand-gliding. Places of interest nearby include the Peak District, Alton Towers, the Staffordshire Potteries and fine country properties such as Chatsworth House and Haddon Hall.

Our inspector loved: *The wonderful views and situation.*

Directions: Dovedale is 2 miles north-west of Ashbourne between A515 and A52.

Web: www.johansens.com/izaakwalton
E-mail: reception@izaakwaltonhotel.com
Tel: 01335 350555
Fax: 01335 350539

Price Guide:
single £89-£105
double/twin £115–£155

RIVERSIDE HOUSE

ASHFORD-IN-THE-WATER, NR BAKEWELL, DERBYSHIRE DE45 1QF

Directions: Exit M1 at junction 29. Take A617 to Chesterfield, then A619 to Bakewell, then take A6 to Ashford-in-the-Water. Riverside House is at the end of the villge main street next to the Sheepwash Bridge.

Web: www.johansens.com/riversidehouse
E-mail: riversidehouse@enta.net
Tel: 01629 814275
Fax: 01629 812873

Price Guide:
single £85–£125
double/twin £115–£150

This graceful Georgian Mansion nestles peacefully on the banks of the river Wye in one of the Peak District's most picturesque villages. It is an intimate gem of a country hotel, a tranquil rural retreat in the finest traditions of classic hospitality and friendliness. Small and ivy-clad, Riverside House sits majestically in the heart of secluded grounds that feature exquisite landscaped gardens and lawns. Elegance, style, intimacy and informality abound within its interior. Individually designed en suite bedrooms have their own distinctive character and are comfortably and delightfully furnished with rich fabrics and antique pieces. An atmosphere of complete relaxation is the hallmark of the welcoming public rooms whose large windows offer superb views. Guests can enjoy a distinctive fusion of modern English, International and local cuisine in the excellent and charming 2 AA Rosetted restaurant where service is of the highest quality. As well as being conveniently situated to explore the glories of the Peak District, Chatsworth House and Haddon Hall, the Hotel is also an ideal base for guests wishing to visit the Derbyshire Dales, Lathkill and Dovedale.

Our inspector loved: The lengths they will go to, to help, even your car will be pampered, if you ask.

HASSOP HALL

HASSOP, NR BAKEWELL, DERBYSHIRE DE45 1NS

The recorded history of Hassop Hall reaches back 900 years to the Domesday Book, to a time when the political scene in England was still dominated by the power struggle between the barons and the King, when the only sure access to that power was through possession of land. By 1643, when the Civil War was raging, the Hall was under the ownership of Rowland Eyre, who turned it into a Royalist garrison. It was the scene of several skirmishes before it was recaptured after the Parliamentary victory. Since purchasing Hassop Hall in 1975, Thomas Chapman has determinedly pursued the preservation of its outstanding heritage. Guests can enjoy the beautifully maintained gardens as well as the splendid countryside of the surrounding area. The bedrooms, some of which are particularly spacious, are well furnished and comfortable. A four-poster bedroom is available for romantic occasions. A comprehensive dinner menu offers a wide and varied selection of dishes, with catering for most tastes. As well as the glories of the Peak District, places to visit include Chatsworth House, Haddon Hall and Buxton Opera House. Christmas opening – details on application. Inclusive rates available on request.

Our inspector loved: The attention to detail given to the breakfast served in the bedroom. True theatre.

Directions: From M1 exit 29 (Chesterfield), take A619 to Baslow, then A623 to Calver; left at lights to B6001 Hassop Hall is 2 miles on right.

Web: www.johansens.com/hassophall
E-mail: hassophallhotel@btinternet.com
Tel: 01629 640488
Fax: 01629 640577

Price Guide: (excluding breakfast)
double/twin £79–£149

EAST LODGE COUNTRY HOUSE HOTEL

ROWSLEY, NR MATLOCK, DERBYSHIRE DE4 2EF

Directions: Set back from the A6 in Rowsley village, 3 miles from Bakewell. The hotel entrance is adjacent to the B6012 junction to Sheffield/Chatsworth.

Web: www.johansens.com/eastlodgecountryhouse
E-mail: info@eastlodge.com
Tel: 01629 734474
Fax: 01629 733949

Price Guide:
single £75
double/twin from £95

This graceful 17th century lodge on the edge of the Peak District was originally built as the East Lodge to Haddon Hall, the Derbyshire seat of the Duke of Rutland. Converted to a hotel in the 1980's, East Lodge is now owned and run by Joan and David Hardman and their attentive staff. The lodge has won many accolades including AA 3 star 74%. The attractive conservatory, charming restaurant and spacious hall offers high levels of comfort combined with a warm and relaxed atmosphere. The 15 en suite bedrooms are tastefully furnished, each having its own distinctive character. Imaginative lunches and dinners are served daily in the excellent AA Rosetted restaurant with lighter meals available in the conservatory. A wide selection of fine wines is on offer. Set in 10 acres of attractive gardens and surrounded by rolling Derbyshire countryside, East Lodge provides a tranquil setting for relaxing breaks, conferences and corporate activity/team building events. The nearby Peak District National Park, boasts some of the country's most spectacular walks. The famous stately homes, Chatsworth House and Haddon Hall, are within 2 miles. Bakewell, Buxton, Matlock and Crich are a short drive away.

Our inspector loved: *Its homely and relaxing atmosphere situated in a superb setting.*

CAVENDISH HOTEL

BASLOW, DERBYSHIRE DE45 1SP

This enchanting hotel offers travellers an opportunity to stay on the famous Chatsworth Estate, close to one of England's greatest stately houses, the home of the Duke and Duchess of Devonshire. The hotel has a long history of its own – once known as the Peacock Inn on the turnpike road to Buxton Spa. When it became The Cavendish in 1975, the Duchess personally supervised the transformation, providing some of the furnishings from Chatsworth and her design talents are evident throughout. Guests have a warm welcome before they are conducted to the luxurious bedrooms, all of which overlook the Estate. Harmonious colours, gorgeous fabrics and immense comfort prevail. Every imaginable extra is provided, from library books to bathrobes. Breakfast is served until lunchtime – no rising at cockcrow – and informal meals are served from morning until bed-time in The Garden Room. Sit at the kitchen table and watch super food being prepared as you dine. At dusk you can sample cocktails and fine wines in the bar before dining in the handsome restaurant with its imaginative menu and extensive list of carefully selected wines. Climbing The Peak, exploring The Dales, fishing, golf and Sheffield's Crucible Theatre are among the many leisure pursuits nearby.

Our inspector loved: *The atmosperic light effects in the new Gallery Restaurant.*

Directions: M1/J29, A617 to Chesterfield then A619 west to Baslow.

Web: www.johansens.com/cavendish
E-mail: info@cavendish–hotel.net
Tel: 01246 582311
Fax: 01246 582312

Price Guide: (excluding breakfast)
single from £95
double/twin from £125

FISCHER'S

BASLOW HALL, CALVER ROAD, BASLOW, DERBYSHIRE DE45 1RR

Directions: Baslow is within 12 miles of the M1 motorway, Chesterfield and Sheffield. Fischer's is on the A623 in Baslow.

Web: www.johansens.com/fischers
E-mail: m.s@fischers–baslowhall.co.uk
Tel: 01246 583259
Fax: 01246 583818

Price Guide:
single £80–£100
double/twin £150–£180
suite £150

Glossop

Bakewell

Derby

Situated on the edge of the magnificent Chatsworth Estate, Baslow Hall enjoys an enviable location surrounded by some of the country's finest stately homes and within easy reach of the Peak District's many cultural and historical attractions. Standing at the end of a winding chestnut tree-lined driveway, this fine Derbyshire manor house was tastefully converted by Max and Susan Fischer into an award-winning country house hotel in 1989. Since opening, Fischer's has consistently maintained its position as one of the finest establishments in the Derbyshire/ South Yorkshire regions earning the prestigious Johansens 'Most Excellent UK Restaurant' award in 2001. Whether you are staying in the area for private or business reasons, it is a welcome change to find a place that feels less like a hotel and more like a home, combining comfort and character with an eating experience which is a delight to the palate. Max presides in the kitchen. Guests can choose from the more formal Michelin–starred gourmet menu or the Café-Max menu, where the emphasis is on more informal eating and modern tastes. Baslow Hall offers facilities for small conferences or private functions.

Our inspector loved: *The contrast in style of the new rooms. A perfect balance.*

THE LEE WOOD HOTEL & RESTAURANT

THE PARK, BUXTON, DERBYSHIRE SK17 6TQ

In the heart of the Peak District, in the 18th century market town of Buxton, famous for its spa water and impressive architecture, the Lee Wood Hotel has been held in high regard since being built in 1838. The elegant and harmonious décor is emphasised in this traditional family owned Hotel where the personal approach by friendly staff ensures a welcoming atmosphere and an extremely comfortable stay. The peaceful setting creates a feeling of quiet tranquillity amidst the beautifully landscaped gardens. Spacious and tastefully decorated bedrooms offer all modern conveniences. Delicious English and International dishes are lovingly created and served in the award winning Garden Restaurant, a remarkable conservatory for dining under the stars. Guests can enjoy a drink or simply relax whilst reading a newspaper in the Devonshire Lounge Bar. In the summer, snacks are served throughout the day on the Garden Terrace, the perfect place to enjoy tea or coffee. Civil wedding receptions are a speciality whilst conferences, banquets and other special occasions up to 200 can easily be organised. The beautifully restored Buxton Opera House and nearby Chatsworth House delight visitors and there are a plethora of interesting buildings in Buxton. For outdoor enthusiasts, the stunning Peak National Park offers a variety of awe-inspiring landscapes to explore.

Our inspector loved: *A delightful lunch, following a walk through the garden to Buxton.*

Directions: From the north: M1 Jct29 Chesterfield–Baslow–Buxton. M6 Jct19 A537 Knutsford– Macclesfield–Buxton. M56/M60 and M62 Stockport A6 to Buxton. From the south: M1 Jct23A/24; take A50 for approx. 19 miles then Ashbourne A515 to Buxton. M6 Jct14 Stone A53 to Leek/Buxton.

Glossop

Bakewell

Derby

Web: www.johansens.com/leewood
E-mail: leewoodhotel@btinternet.com
Tel: 01298 23002
Fax: 01298 23228

Price Guide: (room only)
single £85
double/twin £100

RINGWOOD HALL HOTEL

RINGWOOD ROAD, BRIMINGTON, CHESTERFIELD, DERBYSHIRE S43 1DQ

Directions: From Jct 30 M1 take the A619 towards Chesterfield, passing through Mastin Moor and Staveley. Continue on A619 and rising out of the valley the hotel is set back on the left.

Web: www.johansens.com/ringwood
E-mail:
Tel: 01246 280077
Fax: 01246 472241

Price Guide:
single from £65
double/twin from £75
suite from £98

Since its purchase by Lyric Hotels in November 1999, the Ringwood Hall Hotel has undergone major refurbishment. Sensitive and tasteful, the transformation has created one of the finest country house hotels in North East Derbyshire. The charm and character of the Grade II exterior is continued inside with an impressive reception area featuring intricate plaster frieze work, a galleried landing and glazed dome ceiling. 29 acres of gardens and parkland provide a magnificent backdrop, and even the original Victorian gardens are being carefully restored and replanted to provide vegetables and herbs for the hotel kitchen. Finest local produce is used for the extensive menus in the "Expressions" Restaurant. The hotel offers numerous conference packages and provides a wonderful setting for wedding receptions and civil ceremonies. Staff are on hand to assist in planning events. Ringwood Hall sits on the brink of the Peak District, and offers plenty of opportunities to explore the surrounding area. Families can enjoy trips to theme parks such as Alton Towers and The Wind in the Willows Exhibition, while those with an interest in history can soak up the past at the Chesterfield Museum, Hardwick Hall and Bolsover Castle. An impressive array of local events such as the Chatsworth Country Fair take place through the year. An exclusive health-fitness club relax-for body and soul opens in November 2002.

Our inspector loved: *The fact that nothing is too much trouble.*

RISLEY HALL COUNTRY HOUSE HOTEL

DERBY ROAD, RISLEY, DERBYSHIRE DE72 3SS

Situated equal distance between Derby and Nottingham in a quiet location and close to East Midlands airport, the former glory of Risley Hall is evident once more as this Country House Hotel has recently undergone a careful and extensive restoration. A Grade II listed building, Risley Hall is an ideal retreat for those seeking a peaceful atmosphere. The beautiful gardens were laid out in Elizabethan times and are quite spectacular with colourful floral arrangements and an old moat. Inside, the décor is rather charming with comfortable furnishings, oak beams and ornate fireplaces. The bedrooms, individually designed and all tastefully decorated in period style, offer every modern amenity including a television, hairdryer and tea/coffee making facilities. 20 new suites boast separate lounge areas with wide-screen televisions and D.V.D. players, mini-bars and ISDN lines. Guests recline in the cosy Drawing Room with their afternoon tea or enjoy an after dinner coffee, whilst the Cocktail Bar serves lunchtime drinks or pre-dinner apéritifs. Risley Hall has the perfect surroundings for corporate meetings or any special occasion. The area is surrounded by historic buildings such as Chatsworth House, Nottingham Castle and Kedleston Hall and is also known for its literary connections with Lord Byron and D.H. Lawrence.

Our inspector loved: The quiet environment and attention to detail offered. So near to excellent air, rail and road links. "A little oasis."

Directions: The nearest motorway is the M1. Exit at junction 25 towards Sandiacre.

Web: www.johansens.com/risleyhall
E-mail: johansens@risleyhallhotel.co.uk
Tel: 0115 939 9000
Fax: 0115 939 7766

Price Guide:
single £85–£105
double/twin £105–£125
suites £140–£200

THE GEORGE AT HATHERSAGE

MAIN ROAD, HATHERSAGE, DERBYSHIRE S32 1BB

The George dates back to the end of the Middle Ages when it was an alehouse serving the packhorse road. Later it was well-known to Charlotte Brontë and it features anonymously in Jane Eyre. The present owner, an experienced hotelier, is ably backed by a team of professional senior personnel who guarantee guests a warm welcome and excellent personal service. In its latest hands the building has undergone extensive renovation. However, great care has been taken to preserve the character of the old inn and the stone walls, oak beams, open fires and antique furniture all remain as reminders of a distant age. The simple and pleasant bedrooms offer every modern amenity, including power showers and luxuriously enveloping bath sheets. There is a well-equipped bar in which to relax and enjoy a drink before moving on to the brasserie-style restaurant with its regularly changed menu. Places of interest nearby include Chatsworth and Haddon Halls, Buxton and Bakewell. The area provides some of the most picturesque countryside for walking including renowned Stanage Ridge (with stunning views overlooking the Derwent Reservoirs) and Hope Valley. "Great for the energetic, relaxing for the not-so-energetic".

Directions: From the M1 Jct29 take the A617 to Baslow, then the A623 and B6001 to Hathersage. The George is in the main street of the village.

Web: www.johansens.com/georgehathersage
E-mail: info@george-hotel.net
Tel: 01433 650436
Fax: 01433 650099

Price Guide:
single £65–£75
double/twin £95–£125

Our inspector loved: The cheerful restaurant with its bright floral art.

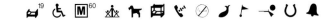

RIBER HALL

MATLOCK, DERBYSHIRE DE4 5JU

There could be few more picturesque settings than this stately Elizabethan manor house standing in its own walled garden at the foothills of the Pennine range. Views over the Peak National Park are outstanding and the atmosphere is one of total tranquillity, interrupted only by birdsong. Riber Hall has been privately owned and managed by the same family for 30 years and the latest round of awards stands testament to their skill and high standards of service. There are just 14 spacious bedrooms which are each furnished with period antiques and elegant beds; the majority of which are four poster. The log fires and oak beams of the lounge convey an instant sense of intimacy and the restaurant is renowned for its attentive service, game (when in season) and excellent wine list, which has recently been nominated for an AA award. The enchanting walled garden and oak-beamed rooms make Riber Hall the perfect setting for both weddings and conferences and there is much to see in the surrounding area for both conference delegate or wedding guest with time to spare. Chatsworth House, Haddon Hall, Hardwick Hall and Calke Abbey are within easy reach, whilst the spectacular Peak District scenery is a delight for walkers. East Midlands, Sheffield and Birmingham Airports are all nearby.

Directions: 20 minutes from Jct28 of M1, off A615 at Tansley; 1 mile further to Riber.

Web: www.johansens.com/riberhall
E-mail: info@riber-hall.co.uk
Tel: 01629 582795
Fax: 01629 580475

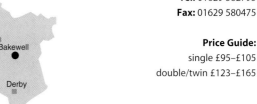

Price Guide:
single £95–£105
double/twin £123–£165

Our inspector loved: This wonderful building and continuity of 30 years.

99

NORTHCOTE MANOR COUNTRY HOUSE HOTEL

BURRINGTON, UMBERLEIGH, DEVON EX37 9LZ

Directions: 25 miles from Exeter on A377 to Barnstaple. Private drive opposite the Portsmouth Arms pub/railway station.

Web: www.johansens.com/northcotemanor
E-mail: rest@northcotemanor.co.uk
Tel: 01769 560501
Fax: 01769 560770

Price Guide: (including dinner)
single from £99
double/twin from £135
suite from £225

This 18th-century manor and the grounds high above the Taw River Valley combine to offer an ambience of timeless tranquillity. Situated in the peaceful Devonshire countryside, Northcote Manor offers complete relaxation and refreshment. Extensive refurbishment has created 11 luxury bedrooms and suites, resulting in a total redesign of the décor of the spacious sitting rooms, hall and restaurant. This has brought a series of accolades, including Condé Nast Johansens Country Hotel of the Year 2002, AA Three Red Stars in 2002, and, in 2001, the RAC Gold Ribbon Award, The Which? Hotel Guide, Tourist Board Silver Award, Michelin 2 Red Turrets Award, RAC Cooking Award level 3, and AA 2 Rosettes. The proprietors are planning to undertake extensive work in the 20-acre grounds to complete their vision of creating the West Country's leading country house hotel. North Devon is a delight to explore; Exmoor and Dartmoor are within easy reach, and guests may visit RHS Rosemoor and the many National Trust properties nearby. A challenging 18-hole golf course is next door, whilst outstanding fishing from the Taw at the bottom of the drive can be arranged with the Gillie. The area also hosts some of the best shoots in the country. A tennis court and croquet lawn are on site. Special breaks available.

Our inspector loved: *The peace and seclusion, warmth and comfort.*

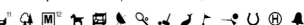

GIDLEIGH PARK

CHAGFORD, DEVON TQ13 8HH

Gidleigh Park enjoys an outstanding international reputation among connoisseurs for its comfort and gastronomy. It has collected a clutch of top culinary awards including 2 Michelin stars for its imaginative cuisine and the Gidleigh Park wine list is one of the best in Britain. Service throughout the hotel is faultless. The en suite bedrooms – two of them in a converted chapel – are luxuriously furnished with antiques. The public rooms are elegantly appointed and during the cooler months, a fire burns merrily in the lounge's impressive fireplace. Set amid 45 secluded acres in the Teign Valley, Gidleigh Park is 1½ miles from the nearest public road. Two croquet lawns, an all-weather tennis court, a bowling lawn and a splendid water garden can be found in the grounds. A 360 yard long, par 52 putting course designed by Peter Alliss was opened in 1995. Guests can swim in the river or explore Dartmoor on foot or in the saddle. There are 14 miles of trout, sea trout and salmon fishing, as well as golf facilities nearby. Gidleigh Park is a Relais et Châteaux member.

Our inspector loved: *The peaceful location, fine cuisine and total luxurious comfort.*

Directions: Approach from Chagford: go along Mill Street from Chagford Square. Fork right after 150 yards, cross into Holy Street at factory crossroads and follow lane for two miles

Web: www.johansens.com/gidleighpark
E-mail: gidleighpark@gidleigh.co.uk
Tel: 01647 432367
Fax: 01647 432574

Price Guide: (including dinner)
single £360–£460
double/twin £420–£520

Barnstaple
Exeter
Plymouth

MILL END

DARTMOOR NATIONAL PARK, CHAGFORD, DEVON TQ13 8JN

Directions: From the M5 exit at junction 31 towards Okehampton. Take the A382 at Merrymount roundabout towards Moretonhampstead. Mill End is one the right.

Web: www.johansens.com/millend
E-mail: millendhotel@talk21.com
Tel: 01647 432282
Fax: 01647 433106

Price Guide:
single £56–£89
double/twin £75–£120

Gleaming white under slate grey roof tiles and with windows and doors opening onto a beautiful English country garden, Mill End is an idyllic hideaway in Dartmoor's National Park. The lawned garden with its wide, deeply shrubbed and colourful borders runs down to the languid waters of the River Teign, a water wheel slowly turns in the courtyard to the enjoyment of guests and diners. Built in the mid 1700s the hotel was a former flour mill, and inside there are numerous little corner nooks, paintings and old photographs that imbue a feeling of seclusion, enhanced by the smell of wood smoke and polished wood. The delightful en suite bedrooms have undergone major refurbishment incorporating excellent décor, lovely fabrics and attractive local hand-crafted furniture. Plus, of course, every facility one would expect. The elegance of the dining room is matched by the delicious award-winning cuisine of Master Chef of Great Britain–Wayne Pearson. His menus are full and varied; one shouldn't miss, for example, lobster ravioli with seared scallops and lemon grass broth followed by grilled turbot with aubergine caviar and a dark chocolate tort with burnt orange sauce and rosewater ice creame. An 18-hole golf course is nearby and pony trekking and shooting can be arranged.

Our inspector loved: *This idyllic hideaway in Dartmoors National Park.*

NEW

PLANTATION HOUSE HOTEL & MATISSE RESTAURANT

TOTNES ROAD, ERMINGTON, DEVON PL21 9NS

Nestling between Dartmoor and the estuaries and beaches of the South Devon coast, Plantation House is set amidst rolling hills and trees brimming with rural charm. In a delightful setting, away from the hustle and bustle of every day life but with Plymouth only 15 minutes away, this is the perfect place to relax and unwind, whether visiting for business or leisure, with friendly, attentive staff tending to every need. Originally an 18th century rectory, it has been tastefully refurbished and is adorned with the owner's collection of carvings and delightful works of art. Bright, modern artworks adorn the walls of the chic Matisse Restaurant, which since opening in Easter 2002, has won 2 AA Rosettes for its exciting innovative cuisine. The food is complemented by the wine list with its new world connoisseur collection featuring the absolute best from the new world alongside the old world classics. The Hotel has 10 beautifully decorated bedrooms and suits many with original works of art. All 10 bedrooms reflect the standard expected from the discerning traveller, including room service, minibar and telephones with P.C. connectivity for internet access. The terrace and courtyard offer a wonderful environment for enjoying the extensive views of the Devon countryside.

Our inspector loved: *The elegant and casual feel of a town house in the country. The crab cakes are to die for!*

Directions: Plantation House Hotel is situated on Totnes Road, Ermington 5 miles off the A38 to Plymouth,
Web: www.johansens.com/plantation
E-mail: enquiries@plantationhousehotel.com
Tel: 01548 831100
Fax: 01548 831248

Price Guide:
single from £95
double from £115

HOTEL BARCELONA

MAGDALEN ROAD, EXETER, DEVON EX2 4HY

This glamorous Hotel has recently won the prestigious césar award for 2002 as 'Design Hotel of the Year.' The former West of England Victorian Eye Infirmary has been transformed into a glorious fusion of vibrant colours, original artwork and post-war furnishings. Designed as a refreshing alternative for both business and leisure guests, it blends sophistication, comfort and enjoyment with excellent food and attentive service. Each of the 46 bedrooms feature teak and ebony furnishings, aqua blue en suite bathrooms and all modern facilities. Café Paradiso is the lively Mediterranean restaurant overlooking the terrace area and hotel gardens where guests can enjoy a variety of dishes such as authentic Italian pizza, antipasti, fresh fish and seafood. There is also the exclusive nightclub 'Kino' where guests can enjoy entertainment, cocktails and dancing most weekend nights. Guests can explore the historic buildings of Exeter, including the Norman Cathedral and many National Trust gardens such as Killerton, Exmouth and Dartmoor National Park.

Our inspector loved: *The unique presentation.*

Directions: Exit M5 at junction 30 and take A379 towards Exeter city centre. Follow Topsham Road for approximately 2 miles and turn right into Magdalen Road. The Hotel is on the right.

Web: www.johansens.com/barcelona
E-mail: info@hotelbarcelona–uk.com
Tel: 01392 281000
Fax: 01392 281001

Price Guide: (room only)
single £75
double/twin £85
King £95–£105

COMBE HOUSE HOTEL & RESTAURANT

GITTISHAM, HONITON, NR EXETER, DEVON EX14 3AD

Combe House is a wildly romantic Grade 1 Elizabethan manor hidden in 3,500 acres of Devon's finest estates where magnificent Arabian horses and pheasants roam freely. Total peace and tranquillity together with generous hospitality can be enjoyed here in this warm and welcoming atmosphere created by the comfy sofas, flamboyant flowers and roaring log-fires. 15 intimate bedrooms and suites, many with panoramic views, are decorated with style and individuality. The candlit restaurant serves innovative, contemporary British cuisine prepared by Master Chef of Great Britain, Philip Leach, perfectly complemented by a well-chosen wine list, including a specialist Chablis collection. The recently restored Georgian Kitchen is the ideal setting for a highly individual private lunch or dinner, dining by lamps and candlelight. Down Combe's mile-long drive is Gittisham, once described by H.R.H. Prince Charles as, 'the ideal English Village,' with its thatched cottages, Norman church and village green. The World Heritage Jurassic coast, from Lyme Regis to Sidmouth, Honiton antique shops, numerous historic houses and gardens, the cathedral of Exeter and the wide open spaces of Dartmoor can all be explored.

Our inspector loved: From when she drove through the gates along the driveway catching the first glimpse of the house - that was it.

Directions: From M5 take exit 28 to Honiton and Sidmouth, or exit 29 to Honiton. Follow signs to Fenny Bridges and Gittisham. A303/A30 exit Honiton to Sidmouth.

Web: www.johansens.com/combehousegittisham
E-mail: stay@thishotel.com
Tel: 01404 540400
Fax: 01404 46004

Barnstaple

●Exeter

Plymouth

Price Guide:
single £99–£125
double/twin £138–£190
suites £265

FAIRWATER HEAD COUNTRY HOUSE HOTEL

HAWKCHURCH, AXMINSTER, DEVON EX13 5TX

Directions: Exit M5 at junction 25 onto A358. Then left onto A35 towards Bridport; left onto B3165 to Lyme Regis, Crewkerne road. Follow signs for Hawkchurch and hotel on left.

Web: www.johansens.com/fairwaterhead
E-mail: jclowe@btinternet.com
Tel: 01297 678349
Fax: 01297 678459

Price Guide:
single £91–£95
double/twin £157–£167

In an idyllic setting on the Devon, Dorset and Somerset borders, Fairwater Head – also the name of the stream's source – not only has its own magnificent landscaped gardens but is situated at the highest point of the land and boasts the most spectacular views over the Axe valley. Built from local stone and with a rich local history, this is a perfect retreat for guests seeking peace and tranquillity from which to explore the Devon and Dorset environs. The bedrooms are charming, both in the main house and the "garden rooms", and most overlook the beautiful grounds and open countryside. The spacious dining room is light and airy, and again has wonderful views, and it is here that a superb menu of traditional and contemporary cuisine is served – recently awarded 1 AA Rosette and 2 RAC dining awards. This is an area rich in countryside walks and historic houses and gardens, and there is also Forde Abbey, picturesque Lyme Regis, and a donkey sanctuary nearby. AA rosette. Escorted tours and special breaks are available.

Our inspector loved: *The warm traditional welcome and the wonderfully arranged trips to enable one to forget the car.*

ILSINGTON COUNTRY HOUSE HOTEL

ILSINGTON VILLAGE, NEAR NEWTON ABBOT, DEVON TQ13 9RR

The Ilsington Country House Hotel stands in ten acres of beautiful private grounds within the Dartmoor National Park. Run by friendly proprietors, Tim and Maura Hassell, the delightful furnishings and ambience offer a most comfortable environment in which to relax. Stylish bedrooms all boast outstanding views across the rolling pastoral countryside and every comfort and convenience to make guests feel at home. The distinctive candle-lit dining room is perfect for savouring the superb cuisine, awarded an AA Rosette, created by talented chefs from fresh local produce. The library is ideal for an intimate dining party or celebration whilst the conservatory or lounge is the place for morning coffee or a Devon cream tea. There is a fully equipped purpose built gymnasium, heated indoor pool, sauna, steam room and spa. Some of England's most idyllic and unspoilt scenery surrounds Ilsington, with the picturesque villages of Lustleigh and Widecombe-in-the-Moor close by. Footpaths lead from the hotel on to Dartmoor. Riding, fishing and many other country pursuits can be arranged. Special breaks available.

Our inspector loved: The beautiful location within the Dartmoor National Park.

Directions: From M5 join A38 at Exeter following Plymouth signs. After approximately 12 miles exit for Moretonhampstead and Newton Abbot. At roundabout follow signs for Ilsington.

Web: www.johansens.com/ilsington
E-mail: hotel@ilsington.co.uk
Tel: 01364 661452
Fax: 01364 661307

Price Guide:
single from £71
double/twin from £110

THE ARUNDELL ARMS

LIFTON, DEVON PL16 0AA

Directions: Lifton is approximately ¼ mile off A30 2 miles east of Launceston and the Cornish Border.

Web: www.johansens.com/arundellarms
E-mail: reservations@arundellarms.com
Tel: 01566 784666
Fax: 01566 784494

Price Guide:
single £65–£85
double/twin £130
suite £160

In a lovely valley close to the uplands of Dartmoor, the Arundell Arms is a former coaching inn which dates back to Saxon times. Its flagstone floors, cosy fires, paintings and antiques combine to create a haven of warmth and comfort in an atmosphere of old world charm. One of England's best-known sporting hotels for more than half a century, it boasts 20 miles of exclusive salmon and trout fishing on the Tamar and five of its tributaries and a famous school of Fly Fishing. Guests also enjoy a host of other country activities, including hill walking, shooting, riding and golf. The hotel takes great pride in its elegant 3 AA Rosette restaurant, presided over by Master Chefs Philip Burgess and Nick Shopland. Their gourmet cuisine has won the restaurant an international reputation. A splendid base from which to enjoy the wonderful surfing beaches nearby, the Arundell Arms is also well placed for visits to Tintagel and the historic houses and gardens of Devon and Cornwall and the Eden Project. Only 45 minutes from Exeter and Plymouth, it is also ideal for the business executive, reached by fast roads from all directions. A spacious conference suite is available.

Our inspector loved: *A haven for fishing, outdoor sports and finest cuisine.*

KITLEY HOUSE HOTEL & RESTAURANT

THE KITLEY ESTATE, YEALMPTON, NR PLYMOUTH, DEVON PL8 2NW

This imposing Grade I listed country house hotel, built of silver grey Devonshire "marble", is situated in 300 acres of richly timbered parkland at the head of one of Yealm estuary's wooded creeks, only ten minutes from the city of Plymouth. It is one of the earliest Tudor revival houses in England and has been splendidly restored to its former glory. Approached by a mile long drive through a magnificent private estate, Kitley is an oasis of quiet luxury, providing the highest standards in comfort, cuisine and personal service. A sweeping staircase leads to 18 spacious bedrooms and suites. Each has panoramic views over the estate and is richly appointed with furnishings designed to reflect the traditional elegance of the house whilst incorporating all modern facilities. The lounge area, with its huge open fireplace, and bar are stylish and relaxing. The restaurant is sumptuously decorated in burgundy and gold and provides the perfect atmosphere in which to enjoy the finest of cuisine – whatever the occasion. Guests can enjoy fishing in the private lake and golf, shooting and riding are nearby. Murder mystery dinners and mid week breaks available.

Our inspector loved: *The standards, comfort and peace yet only 10 minutes from the city of Plymouth.*

Directions: A38 towards Plymouth (A3121). Then turn right onto the A379. The hotel entrance is on the left after Yealmpton village.

Web: www.johansens.com/kitleyhouse
E-mail: sales@kitleyhousehotel.com
Tel: 01752 881555
Fax: 01752 881667

Price Guide:
single £95–£115
double/twin £110–£130
suite from £120

Soar Mill Cove Hotel

SOAR MILL COVE, SALCOMBE, SOUTH DEVON TQ7 3DS

Directions: A384 to Totnes, then A381 to Soar Mill Cove.

Web: www.johansens.com/soarmillcove
E-mail: info@makepeacehotels.co.uk
Tel: 01548 561566
Fax: 01548 561223

Price Guide:
single £89–£150
double/twin £154–£190
suite from £216

Owned and loved by the Makepeace family who, for over 21 years, have provided a special blend of friendly yet professional service. The hotel's spectacular setting is a flower-filled combe, facing its own sheltered sandy bay and entirely surrounded by 2000 acres of dramatic National Trust coastline. While it is perhaps one of the last truly unspoiled corners of South Devon, Soar Mill Cove is only 15 miles from the motorway system (A38). The hotel has been awarded the prestigious RAC Blue Ribbon and 3 AA Red Stars. All the bedrooms are at ground level, each with a private patio opening onto the gardens, which in spring or summer provides wonderful alfresco opportunities. In winter, crackling log fires and efficient double glazing keeps cooler weather at bay. A strict "no conference policy" guarantees that the peace of guests shall not be compromised. Both the indoor and outdoor pools are spring-water fed, the former being maintained all year at a constant 88°F. Here is Keith Stephen Makepeace's award winning cuisine, imaginative and innovative, reflecting the very best of the West of England; fresh crabs and lobster caught in the bay are a speciality. Soar Mill Cove is situated midway between the old ports of Plymouth and Dartmouth.

Our inspector loved: *The most wonderful location offering all one could wish for.*

THE TIDES REACH HOTEL

SOUTH SANDS, SALCOMBE, DEVON TQ8 8LJ

This luxuriously appointed hotel is situated in an ideal position for those wishing to enjoy a relaxing or fun-filled break. Facing south in a tree-fringed sandy cove just inside the mouth of the Salcombe Estuary it has an extensive garden on one side, the sea and a safe bathing sandy beach a few steps opposite and, to the rear, a sheltering hill topped by the subtropical gardens of Overbecks. The Tides Reach has been under the supervision of owners, Mr and Mrs Roy Edwards, for more than 30 years and they have built up a reputation for hospitality and courteous service. The atmosphere is warm and friendly, the décor and furnishings tasteful and comfortable. All 35 spacious bedrooms are en suite, well equipped and decorated with flair and originality. The lawned garden centres around an ornamental lake with waterfall and fountain which is surrounded by landscaped tiers of colourful plants, shrubs and palms. Overlooking it is the restaurant where chef Finn Ibsen's excellent gourmet cuisine has earned AA Rosettes. A superb indoor heated swimming pool is the nucleus of the hotel's leisure complex which includes a sauna, solarium, spa bath, gymnasium, squash court and snooker room. The hotel has facilities for windsurfing, water skiing, sailing and canoeing.

Our inspector loved: The location, presentation and overall feeling of total welcome.

Directions: From the M5, exit at junction 30 and join the A38 towards Plymouth. Exit for Totnes and then take the A381.

Web: www.johansens.com/tidesreach
E-mail: enquire@tidesreach.com
Tel: 01548 843466
Fax: 01548 843954

Price Guide: (incl dinner)
single £75–£110
double/twin £130–£250

BUCKLAND-TOUT-SAINTS

GOVETON, KINGSBRIDGE, DEVON TQ7 2DS

Directions: Signed from A381 between Totnes and Kingsbridge.

Web: www.johansens.com/bucklandtoutsaints
E-mail: buckland@tout–saints.co.uk
Tel: 01548 853055
Fax: 01548 856261

Price Guide:
single from £75
double/twin from £130
suite from £270

Buckland-Tout-Saints is an impressive Grade II listed manor house, built in 1690 during the reign of William and Mary. Recently refurbished to a superb standard, the wonderful hospitality and cuisine that guests enjoy at this hotel today would certainly have impressed its royal visitors of the past. Idyllic amongst its own woodlands and beautiful gardens, it is invitingly close to the spectacular beaches and dramatic cliffs of the Devonshire coastline. A warm and welcoming atmosphere prevails throughout, from the leather-clad couches of the convivial bar to the family of bears – Teddy Tout-Saints – whose individual members welcome guests to their deluxe rooms and suites. Many of these delightful period style rooms enjoy stunning views across the beautiful South Hams area with its moorland and river estuaries. The food served in the Queen Anne restaurant is delectable and deserving of the many accolades it has won. The combination of fresh local produce and exotic foreign cuisine is selected and prepared by a renowned chef and is accompanied by an equally tantalising selection of fine wines and vintage ports. Conferences, weddings and seminars are effortlessly accommodated in the Kestrel Rooms, where helpful staff and elegant surroundings ensure a successful occasion. Several well-known golf courses and sailing centres are nearby.

Our inspector loved: The location and feel of tranquillity.

HOTEL RIVIERA

THE ESPLANADE, SIDMOUTH, DEVON EX10 8AY

A warm welcome awaits guests arriving at this prestigious award-winning hotel. With accolades such as the AA Courtesy and Care Award and more recently, the Which? Hotel Guide's Hotel of the Year 1999, it comes as no surprise that Peter Wharton's Hotel Riviera is arguably one of the most comfortable and most hospitable in the region. The exterior, with its fine Regency façade and bow fronted windows complements the elegance of the interior comprising handsome public rooms and beautifully appointed bedrooms, many with sea views. Perfectly located at the centre of Sidmouth's historic Georgian esplanade and awarded four stars by both the AA and the RAC, the Riviera is committed to providing the very highest standard of excellence which makes each stay at the property a totally pleasurable experience. Guests may dine in the attractive salon, which affords glorious views across Lyme Bay, and indulge in the superb cuisine, prepared by Swiss and French trained chefs. The exceptional cellar will please the most discerning wine connoisseur. Activities include coastal walks, golf, bowling, croquet, putting, tennis, fishing, sailing, riding and exploring the breathtaking surroundings with its gardens, lush countryside and stunning coastline.

Our inspector loved: The wonderful location overlooking Lyme bay and the feeling of warmth and welcome.

Directions: The hotel is situated at the centre of the esplanade.

Web: www.johansens.com/riviera
E-mail: enquiries@hotelriviera.co.uk
Tel: 01395 515201
Fax: 01395 577775

Barnstaple

Exeter

Plymouth

Price Guide: (including seven-course dinner):
single £95–£125
double/twin £170–£230
suite £230–£250

THE PALACE HOTEL

BABBACOMBE ROAD, TORQUAY, DEVON TQ1 3TG

Directions: From seafront follow signs for Babbacombe. Hotel entrance is on the right.

Web: www.johansens.com/palacetorquay
E-mail: info@palacetorquay.co.uk
Tel: 01803 200200
Fax: 01803 299899

Price Guide:
single £75–£85
double/twin £150–£170
executive £199
suite £240–£280

Once the residence of the Bishop of Exeter, the privately owned Palace Hotel is a gracious Victorian building set in 25 acres of beautifully landscaped gardens and woodlands. The comfortable bedrooms are equipped with every modern amenity and there are also elegant, spacious suites available. Most rooms overlook the hotel's magnificent grounds. The main restaurant provides a high standard of traditional English cooking, making full use of fresh, local produce, as well as offering a good variety of international dishes. The cuisine is complemented by a wide selection of popular and fine wines. Light meals are also available from the lounge and during the summer months, a mediterranean style menu is served on the terrace. A host of sporting facilities has made this hotel famous. These include a short par 3 9-hole championship golf course, indoor and outdoor swimming pools, two indoor and four outdoor tennis courts, two squash courts, saunas, snooker room and a well equipped fitness suite. Places of interest nearby include Dartmoor, South Hams and Exeter. Paignton Zoo, Bygone's Museum and Kent's Cavern are among the local attractions.

Our inspector loved: *This gracious hotel - beautiful grounds and the fact one can stay onsite and forget the car.*

ORESTONE MANOR HOTEL & RESTAURANT

ROCKHOUSE LANE, MAIDENCOMBE, TORQUAY, DEVON TQ1 4SX

This delightful Georgian manor house has recently been the subject of a complete and loving restoration programme by its new owners, and now offers guests the epitome of elegance and luxury in this delightful location on the rural fringe of Torbay. Standing in two acres of its own grounds, the hotel has beautiful views out to the sea beyond and has a refreshing sense of peace and calm. This serenity is continued inside the hotel, where elegant high ceilings and an abundance of space lead guests from the stylish new drawing room into the fresh leafy conservatory and out to the pretty sun terrace with its lovely gardens and views. The 12 bedrooms are delightfully presented and many have their own terrace or balcony; attention to detail is obvious with fresh orange juice, flowers and fluffy bathrobes. The 2 AA Rosette restaurant is stunning with a tempting range of dishes – choose from chargrilled scallops with sautéed samphire cress & lemon butter sauce or seared escalope of veal with a stilton and aubergine puree. A wide range of watersports is available, and there is a number of coastal walks from the hotel, while Dartmoor itself is nearby as are many National Trust properties and a Food & Wine Trail.

Our inspector loved: *The charm and ambience.*

Directions: About 3 miles north of Torquay on the A379 (Formerly B3199). Take the coast road towards Teignmouth.

Web: www.johansens.com/orestonemanor
E-mail: enquiries@orestone.co.uk
Tel: 01803 328098
Fax: 01803 328336

Price Guide:
single £50–£120
double/twin £100–£160

DEVON - TORQUAY (MEADFOOT)

THE OSBORNE HOTEL & LANGTRY'S RESTAURANT

MEADFOOT BEACH, TORQUAY, DEVON TQ1 2LL

Directions: The hotel is in Meadfoot, to the east of Torquay.

Web: www.johansens.com/osborne
E-mail: enq@osborne-torquay.co.uk
Tel: 01803 213311
Fax: 01803 296788

Price Guide:
single £55–£80
double/twin £95–£150
suite £120–£200

The combination of Mediterranean chic and the much-loved Devon landscape has a special appeal which is reflected at The Osborne. The hotel is the centrepiece of an elegant recently refurbished Regency crescent in Meadfoot, a quiet location within easy reach of the centre of Torquay. Known as a 'country house by the sea', the hotel offers the friendly ambience of a country home complemented by the superior standards of service and comfort expected of a hotel on the English Riviera. Most of the 29 bedrooms have magnificent views and are decorated in pastel shades. Overlooking the sea, Langtry's acclaimed award-winning restaurant provides fine English cooking and tempting regional specialities, while the Brasserie has a menu available throughout the day. Guests may relax in the attractive 5-acre gardens and make use of indoor and outdoor swimming pools, gymnasium, sauna, solarium, tennis court and putting green – all without leaving the grounds. Sailing, archery, clay pigeon shooting and golf can be arranged. Devon is a county of infinite variety, with its fine coastline, bustling harbours, tranquil lanes, sleepy villages and the wilds of Dartmoor. The Osborne is ideally placed to enjoy all these attractions.

Our inspector loved: *The grandeur of the building and spectacular location.*

PERCY'S COUNTRY HOTEL & RESTAURANT

COOMBESHEAD ESTATE, VIRGINSTOW, DEVON EX21 5EA

The Hotel's motto, "Relax...Taste...Enjoy..." is evident in this charming Devon hideaway. Set amongst 130 acres of unspoilt countryside, Percy's is ideal for those wishing to relax and unwind in a smoke and child-free environment and boasts breathtaking views over both Dartmoor and Bodmin Moor. Combining modern architectural intelligence with traditional country house comfort, guests are tempted from their own personal jacuzzi by the short, seasonal menu served in the highly accolaoded restaurant. Here, Tina Bricknell-Webb, the only chef in Devon to have been awarded 4 Dining Awards by the RAC, creates contemporary country cuisine using only the finest local organic produce. Her unique style recently gained an unprecendented 9/10 from Giles Coren of The Saturday Times, who described Percy's as "a very rare place indeed." Wellington boots are at hand to explore the Estate's beauty spots and with the company of the resident labradors Bonnie, Tommy and Bonzo, guests can observe and enjoy the diverse and stunning wildlife in its natural habitat. Percy's is ideally situated to explore the Eden Project, RHS Gardens at Rosemoor and the region's many National Trust properties. Only minutes way, Roadford Reservoir offers excellent watersports and fishing with many interesting walks and superb tearooms overlooking the lake.

Our inspector loved: *The peaceful, 'away from it all' location.*

Directions: From Okehampton take the A3079 to Metherell Cross. After 8.3 miles turn left. The Hotel is 6.5 miles on the left.

Web: www.johansens.com/percys
E-mail: info@percys.co.uk
Tel: 01409 211236
Fax: 01409 211275

Price Guide:
single £90–£125
double £140–£195

WOOLACOMBE BAY HOTEL

SOUTH STREET, WOOLACOMBE, DEVON EX34 7BN

Woolacombe Bay Hotel stands in 6 acres of grounds, leading to three miles of golden sand. Built by the Victorians, the hotel has an air of luxury, style and comfort. All rooms are en suite with satellite TV, baby listening, ironing centre, some with a balcony. Traditional English and French dishes are offered in the dining room. Superb recreational amenities on site include unlimited free access to tennis, squash, indoor and outdoor pools, billiards, bowls, croquet, dancing and films, a health suite with steam room, sauna, spa bath with high impulse shower. Power-boating, fishing, shooting and riding can be arranged and preferential rates are offered for golf at the Saunton Golf Club. The "Hot House" aerobics studio, beauty salon, cardio vascular weights room, solariums, masseur and beautician. However, being energetic is not a requirement for enjoying the qualities of Woolacombe Bay. Many of its regulars choose simply to relax in the grand public rooms and in the grounds, which extend to the rolling surf of the magnificent bay. A drive along the coastal route in either direction will guarantee splendid views. Exmoor's beautiful Doone Valley is an hour away by car. Closed January.

Our inspector loved: The most wonderful atmosphere for families offering every amenity.

Directions: At the centre of the village, off main Barnstaple–Ilfracombe road.

Web: www.johansens.com/woolacombebay
E-mail: woolacombe.bayhotel@btinternet.com
Tel: 01271 870388
Fax: 01271 870613

Price Guide: (including dinner)
single £50–£110
double/twin £160–£220

Barnstaple

Exeter

Plymouth

WATERSMEET HOTEL

MORTEHOE, WOOLACOMBE, DEVON EX34 7EB

Watersmeet personifies the comfortable luxury of a country house hotel. Majestically situated on the rugged North Atlantic coastline, the hotel commands dramatic views across the waters of Woolacombe Bay past Hartland Point to Lundy Island. The gardens reach down to the sea and private steps lead directly to the beach. Attractive décor, combined with striking coloured fabrics, creates a warm impression all year round. All the bedrooms look out to sea and guests can drift off to sleep to the sound of lapping waves or rolling surf. Morning coffee, lunch and afternoon tea can be served in the relaxing comfort of the lounge, on the terrace or by the heated outdoor pool. The new indoor pool and spa is a favourite with everyone. English and international dishes are served in the award-winning Watersmeet Restaurant where each evening candles flicker as diners absorb a view of the sun slipping below the horizon. The hotel has been awarded an AA Rosette for cuisine, the AA Courtesy and Care Award and a Silver Award by the English Tourism Council. There is a grass tennis court and local surfing, riding, clay pigeon shooting and bracing walks along coastal paths. Open February to January.

Our inspector loved: The elevated location over the North Devon coast and warm welcome.

Directions: From M5, Jct27, follow A361 towards Ilfracombe, turn left at roundabout and follow signs to Mortehoe.

Web: www.johansens.com/watersmeet
E-mail: info @watersmeethotel.co.uk
Tel: 01271 870333
Fax: 01271 870890

Price Guide: (including dinner)
single £93–£145
double/twin £136–£280

BRIDGE HOUSE HOTEL

PROUT BRIDGE, BEAMINSTER, DORSET DT8 3AY

Directions: From M3 take A303 Crewkerne exit then A356 through Crewkerne, then A3066 to Beaminster. Hotel is 100 yds from town centre car park, on the left.

Web: www.johansens.com/bridgehousebeam
E-mail: enquiries@bridge–house.co.uk
Tel: 01308 862200
Fax: 01308 863700

Price Guide:
single £72–£95
twin/double £101–£134

Country house relaxed informality, together with excellent wine and food, are the hallmarks of Peter Pinkster's lovely old mellow stone house. dating back to the 13th century, this former priest's house is at the heart of the market town of Beaminster, and is set in a restful and beautiful walled garden. Staff and owner alike strive to create a welcome for guests and to provide them with the highest standards of home comforts. The warm stone, ancient beams and large fireplaces combine with a refreshingly uncomplicated approach to hotelkeeping, to provide a pleasing and unpretentious enviroment which guests will recall with pleasure. Attractively decorated and furnished bedrooms include a colour television and tea and coffee making facilities. Four of them are on the ground floor and offer easy access. The pride of the house is its food, where attention to detail is evident. In the candlelit Georgian dining room an imaginative menu offers dishes that make use of fresh produce from the local farms and fishing ports. Beaminster is convenient for touring, walking and exploring the magnificent Dorset countryside. Places of interest nearby include many fine houses and gardens. Several golf courses, fresh and salt water fishing, riding, sailing and swimming in the sea are all within reach.

Our inspector loved: *Its old fashioned atmosphere and charming bedrooms.*

NEW

MENZIES EAST CLIFF COURT

EAST OVERCLIFF DRIVE, BOURNEMOUTH, DORSET BH1 3DN

In a spectacular setting directly on the sea front, the Menzies East Cliff Court offers panoramic views across the bay and has recently been the subject of an extensive refurbishment programme. Now with 67 luxury bedrooms and suites, the Hotel is keen to establish itself as the premier luxury town house destination for Bournemouth and no stone has been left unturned to ensure guests' every comfort. The majority of the bedrooms and suites enjoy unparalleled coastal views, whilst the south-facing terrace has a sheltered and heated swimming pool that is a charming spot in which to relax and enjoy the warm sun of the west country summer. The new restaurant is elegantly appointed and offers a wide-ranging menu of traditional and lighter continental dishes. Conference facilities are state-of-the-art, with two principle meeting rooms and four smaller syndicate rooms, whilst the Garden Suite can host a dinner for up to 100 delegates. There is a vast amount of interest on the Hotel's doorstep with Beaulieu Motor Museum, walking in the New Forest, Corfe Castle and Poole Harbour or even boat trips to Brownsea Island and the Isle of Wight.

Our inspector loved: The unrivalled panorama of sea and sky.

Directions: From M3/M27 take A338 towards Bournemouth, which leads onto Wessex Way. Follow the signs to East Cliff and the Hotel is located on the sea front.

Web: www.johansens.com/eastcliff
E-mail: eastcliffcourt@menzies-hotel.co.uk
Tel: 01202 554545
Fax: 01202 557456

Price Guide: (room only)
single £110
double/twin £130-£160
suite £175

LANGTRY MANOR - LOVENEST OF A KING

DERBY ROAD, EAST CLIFF, BOURNEMOUTH, DORSET BH1 3QB

Directions: Take A338 Wessex Way to the station. First exit at roundabout, over next roundabout, first left into Knyveton Road, second right into Derby Road.

Web: www.johansens.com/langtrymanor
E-mail: lillie@langtrymanor.com
Tel: 01202 553887
Fax: 01202 290115

Price Guide: (minimum stay 2 nights)
double/twin £139.50–£219.50

Known originally as The Red House, this fine house was built in 1877 by Edward VII (then Prince of Wales) as a love nest for his mistress. The concept of a themed small hotel was created by the present owners around the famous Lillie Langtry story exactly a hundred years later. The Edward VII suite is a fine spacious room which retains two original floral wall paintings and features a grand Jacobean four-poster bed. Other feature rooms have four-posters, corner spa baths and are all designed to engender a romantic ambience. This was the first hotel in Dorset to be licensed for civil marriages; it is a popular wedding venue – and a natural for honeymoons, anniversaries and birthdays. Saturday night guests are invited to take part in a delicious 6 course Edwardian Banquet – which features an interlude of words and music based on the life of the 'Jersey Lily' – served in the quite splendid Dining Hall with its minstrels gallery and stained glass windows. Some of the bedrooms offered are close by in The Lodge – once the home of Lord Derby. Guests can enjoy complementary use of a state of the art leisure club just 2 minutes away. Sandy beaches, Hardy Country, the New Forest, art galleries, theatres and gardens.

Our inspector loved: The Edward and Lillie fantasy.

NORFOLK ROYALE HOTEL

RICHMOND HILL, BOURNEMOUTH, DORSET BH2 6EN

Bournemouth has long been a popular seaside resort and has not lost its unique character – The Norfolk Royale is a fine example of the elegant buildings that grace the town. It is a splendid Edwardian house, once the holiday home of the Duke of Norfolk, after whom it is named. Extensive restoration work throughout the hotel, while enhancing its comfort, has not eliminated the echoes of the past and new arrivals are impressed by the elegant furnishings and courtesy of the staff. The designs of the spacious bedrooms reflect consideration for lady travellers, busy business executives, non-smokers and the disabled. The rich fabrics of the delightful colour schemes contribute to their luxurious ambience. Guests relax in the lounge or attractive club bar, in summer enjoying the gardens or patio – all with waiter service – and delicious breakfasts, lunches and candle-lit dinners are served in the Orangery Restaurant, which has an excellent wine list. The good life includes the pleasures of a pool and spa while Bournemouth offers golf courses, tennis, water sports, a casino and theatre. It has a large conference and exhibition centre. Poole Harbour, The New Forest, Thomas Hardy country and long sandy beaches are nearby.

Our inspector loved: Its wonderful cast-iron balconies.

Directions: From the M27, A31 & A338 find the hotel on the right, halfway down Richmond Hill approaching the town centre.

Web: www.johansens.com/norfolkroyale
E-mail: norfolkroyale@englishrosehotels.co.uk
Tel: 01202 551521
Fax: 01202 299729

Price Guide:
single from £105
double/twin £145–£175
suite £185–£350

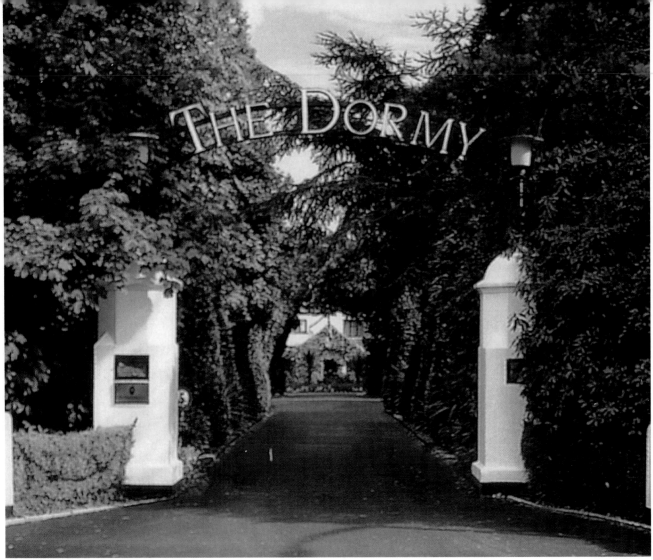

THE DORMY

NEW ROAD, FERNDOWN, NEAR BOURNEMOUTH, DORSET BH22 8ES

Situated close to the picturesque New Forest, this country style hotel, with its log fires and oak-panelled lounges, is the essence of comfort. All bedrooms are furnished in either a traditional or a more modern fashion and include all the latest amenities such as satellite television, radio, telephone and hospitality tray. Guests can relax in the Dormy Bar and the golf themed Alliss Bar. Recently awarded two AA Rosettes, the elegant Hennessys Restaurant, situated in the hotel grounds, offers the finest contemporary cuisine. The Garden Restaurant continues to build upon its reputation and a third, more relaxed, option is the Pavillion Brasserie. The newly upgraded Leisure Club comprises of a large indoor pool and various other facilities such as sauna, spa bath and solaria. Fitness fanatics may exercise in the well-equipped gymnasium, toning suite and aerobics studio or make use of the squash and tennis courts. The Dormy lies centre to some of Dorset's finest golf courses. Activities nearby include quad biking, clay pigeon shooting and riding in the New Forest.

Directions: Nearest motorway is M27 to Ringwood, then A31 to Ferndown, then left at the traffic lights onto A347. The hotel is just one mile on the left hand side.

Web: www.johansens.com/dormybournemouth
E-mail: dormy@devere-hotels.com
Tel: 01202 872121
Fax: 01202 895388

Price Guide:
single £95–£115
double/twin £125–£200
suite £200–£260

Shaftsbury

Bridport

Bournemouth

Weymouth

Our inspector loved: The refurbished Spa.

SUMMER LODGE

SUMMER LANE, EVERSHOT, DORSET DT2 0JR

A charming Georgian building, idyllically located in Hardy country, Summer Lodge was formerly the dower house of the Earls of Ilchester. Now it is a luxurious hotel where owners Nigel and Margaret Corbett offer their guests a genuinely friendly welcome, encouraging them to relax as if in their own home. Summer Lodge was Johansens Country Hotel of the year in 1999. The bedrooms have views over the 4-acre sheltered gardens or overlook the village rooftops across the meadowland. In the dining room, with its French windows that open on to the garden, the cuisine is highly regarded. Fresh local produce is combined with the culinary expertise to create a distinctive brand of English cooking. The unspoiled Dorset countryside and its coastline, 12 miles south, make for limitless exploration and bring to life the setting of Tess of the d'Urbervilles, The Mayor of Casterbridge, Far from the Madding Crowd and the other Hardy novels. Many National Trust properties and gardens in the locality are open to the public. There are stables, golf courses and trout lakes nearby.

Our inspector loved: Its village setting and exceptional standards. Be prepared to go home and re-plan your garden.

Directions: The turning to Evershot leaves the A37 halfway between Dorchester and Yeovil. Once in the village, turn left into Summer Lane and the hotel entrance is 150 yards on the right.

Web: www.johansens.com/summerlodge
E-mail: reception@summerlodgehotel.com
Tel: 01935 83424
Fax: 01935 83005

Price Guide:
single from £95
double/twin £145–£385
suite £225–£305

PLUMBER MANOR

STURMINSTER NEWTON, DORSET DT10 2AF

An imposing Jacobean building of local stone, occupying extensive gardens in the heart of Hardy's Dorset, Plumber Manor has been the home of the Prideaux-Brune family since the early 17th century. Leading off a charming gallery, hung with family portraits, are six very comfortable bedrooms. The conversion of a natural stone barn lying within the grounds, as well as the courtyard building, has added a further ten spacious bedrooms, some of which have window seats overlooking the garden and the Develish stream. Three interconnecting dining rooms comprise the restaurant, where a good choice of imaginative, well-prepared dishes is presented, supported by a wide-ranging wine list. Chef Brian Prideaux-Brune's culinary prowess has been recognised by all the major food guides. Open for dinner every evening and Sunday lunch. The Dorset landscape, with its picture-postcard villages such as Milton Abbas and Cerne Abbas, is close at hand, while Corfe Castle, Lulworth Cove, Kingston Lacy and Poole Harbour are not far away. Riding can be arranged locally: however, if guests wish to bring their own horse to hack or hunt with local packs, the hotel provides free stabling on a do-it-yourself basis. Closed during February.

Directions: Plumber Manor is two miles south west of Sturminster Newton on the Hazelbury Bryan road, off the A357.

Web: www.johansens.com/plumbermanor
E-mail: book@plumbermanor.com
Tel: 01258 472507
Fax: 01258 473370

Price Guide:
single from £85
double/twin from £100

Our inspector loved: The epitome of a true country house in an exquisite setting.

THE PRIORY HOTEL

CHURCH GREEN, WAREHAM, DORSET BH20 4ND

Dating from the early 16th century, the one-time Lady St Mary Priory has, for hundreds of years, offered sanctuary to travellers. In Hardy's Dorset, 'far from the madding crowd', it placidly stands on the bank of the River Frome in four acres of immaculate gardens. Steeped in history, The Priory has undergone a sympathetic conversion to a hotel which is charming yet unpretentious. Each bedroom is distinctively styled, with family antiques lending character and many rooms have views of the Purbeck Hills. A 16th century clay barn has been transformed into the Boathouse, consisting of four spacious luxury suites at the river's edge. Tastefully furnished, the drawing room, residents' lounge and intimate bar together create a convivial atmosphere. The Garden Room Restaurant is open for breakfast and lunch, while splendid dinners are served in the vaulted stone cellars. There are moorings for guests arriving by boat. Dating back to the 9th century, the market town of Wareham has more than 200 listed buildings. Corfe Castle, Lulworth Cove, Poole and Swanage are all close by with superb walks and beaches .

Our inspector loved: The true country house atmosphere and its delightful riverside setting at the heart of historic Wareham.

Directions: Wareham is on the A351 to the west of Bournemouth and Poole. The hotel is beside the River Frome at the southern end of the town near the parish church.

Web: www.johansens.com/priorywareham
E-mail: reservations@theprioryhotel.co.uk
Tel: 01929 551666
Fax: 01929 554519

Price Guide:
single £105
double/twin £135–£245
suite £285

MOONFLEET MANOR

FLEET, WEYMOUTH, DORSET DT3 4ED

Directions: Take B3157 Weymouth to Bridport Road, then turn off towards the sea at sign for Fleet.

Web: www.johansens.com/moonfleetmanor
E-mail: info@moonfleetmanor.com
Tel: 01305 786948
Fax: 01305 774395

Price Guide:
single from £80
double/twin £100–£215
suite £255–£300

Overlooking Chesil Beach, a unique feature of the Dorset coast, Moonfleet Manor is both a luxury hotel and a family resort. The owners have applied the same flair for design evident in their other family friendly properties, Woolley Grange and Fowey Hall in Cornwall. The use of a variety of unusual antiques and objects from around the world lends a refreshing and individual style to this comfortable and attractive hotel. Bedrooms are beautifully decorated and furnished and a range of amenities ensures that guests enjoy standards of maximum comfort and convenience. An enthusiastic and attentive staff works hard to ensure that guests feel at home, whatever their age. Moonfleet's dining room, whose décor and style would do credit to a fashionable London restaurant, offers an excellent and varied menu based on fresh local produce but bringing culinary styles from around the world. Facilities at the hotel include an indoor swimming pool with squash and tennis courts for the more energetic. Key places of interest nearby include Abbotsbury, Dorchester, Corfe Castle and Lulworth Cove, while in Weymouth itself the Sea Life Park, The Deep Sea Adventure and The Titanic Story are worth a visit.

Our inspector loved: *Its unique stylish provision for families with children.*

HEADLAM HALL

HEADLAM, NR GAINFORD, DARLINGTON, COUNTY DURHAM DL2 3HA

This magnificent 17th century Jacobean mansion stands in four acres of formal walled gardens. The grand main lawn, ancient beach hedges and flowing waters evoke an air of tranquillity. Located in the picturesque hamlet of Headlam and surrounded by over 200 acres of its own rolling farmland, Headlam Hall offers guests a special ambience of seclusion and opulence. The traditional bedrooms are all en suite and furnished to a high standard, many with period furniture. The restaurant offers the very best of classic English and Continental cuisine with the kitchen team enjoying a fine reputation for their dishes. An extensive well-chosen wine list highlights the dining experience. Guests may dine in the tasteful surroundings of either the Panelled room, the Victorian room, the Patio room or Conservatory. The main hall features huge stone pillars and the superb original carved oak fireplace, which has dominated the room for over 300 years. The elegant Georgian drawing room opens on to a stepped terrace overlooking the main lawn. The hotel also offers extensive conference facilities and a fine ballroom, the Edwardian Suite with its oak floor and glass ceiling, suitable for up to 150 people. The vast range of leisure facilities include an indoor pool, sauna, gym, tennis court, croquet lawn, course fishery and a snooker room. There are also eight golf courses within a 20 minute drive.

Directions: Headlam is 2 miles N of Gainford off A67 Darlington–Barnard Castle road.

Web: www.johansens.com/headlamhall
E-mail: admin@headlamhall.co.uk
Tel: 01325 730238
Fax: 01325 730790

Durham

Hartlepool

Darlington

Price Guide:
single £75–£93
double/twin £90–£110
suite £120

Our inspector loved: The four poster and antique beds.

SEAHAM HALL HOTEL & ORIENTAL SPA

LORD BYRON'S WALK, SEAHAM, CO DURHAM SR7 7AG

Directions: From A1 (north) take exit A19 for Tyne Tunnel. From A1 (south) take exit at Jct 62 for A690, then travel north through Houghton le Spring. Take exit for A19 southbound. Come off A19 at exit marked B1404 Seaham.

Web: www.johansens.com/seahamhall
E-mail: reservations@seaham-hall.com
Tel: 0191 516 1400
Fax: 0191 516 1410

Price Guide:
single £185–£315
double/twin £195–£325
suites £385–£500

Durham
Hartlepool
Darlington

Surrounded by wild, beautiful countryside and with views of the North Sea, the Cheviots and the Yorkshire Dales, Seaham Hall is an unforgettably charming hotel set amongst 30 acres of landscaped clifftop grounds. Lord Byron married here and regal court was held within its solid stone walls. Within the elegant interior, quality and attention to detail are immediately palpable and guests are welcomed by extremely hospitable staff. Spacious bedrooms have sea views and exude an air of opulent decadence with huge beds, a pillow menu, stunning limestone fireplaces and original works of art, all with CD, surround sound, intelligent lighting and internet access. Outstanding bathrooms have baths for two and ground floor suites have private gardens. Eclectic modern cuisine that is both imaginative and delicious is created using only the finest fresh ingredients. Guests may enjoy a wonderful breakfast in bed every morning. The Oriental spa, is based on Feng Shui principles and promises to be the best of its kind in Europe. It offers a variety of holistic and exotic body treatments for complete relaxation. Seaham Hall is a stones throw from the historic Hadrians Wall and Durham, with its renowned Norman cathedral whilst the stunning Lake District is a short drive away.

Our inspector loved: *The fascinating vortex water sculpture outside the front door.*

FIVE LAKES HOTEL, GOLF, COUNTRY CLUB & SPA

COLCHESTER ROAD, TOLLESHUNT KNIGHTS, MALDON, ESSEX CM9 8HX

Set in 320 acres, Five Lakes is a superb hotel which combines the latest in sporting, leisure and health activities with a range of conference, meeting and banqueting facilities. The 114 bedrooms are furnished to a high standard and offer every comfort and convenience. With its two 18-hole golf courses – one of them, the Lakes Course, designed by Neil Coles MBE and used annually by the PGA European Tour – the hotel is already recognised as one of East Anglia's leading golf venues. Guests are also invited to take advantage of the championship standard indoor tennis courts; outdoor tennis; squash and badminton, indoor pool with Jacuzzi, steam and sauna; gymnasium; jogging trail; snooker and Viverano's Health and Beauty Spa. There is a choice of restaurants, where good food is complemented by excellent service. Lounges and two bars provide a comfortable environment in which to relax and enjoy a drink. Extensive facilities for conferences, meetings, exhibitions and functions include 21 meeting rooms, a 2,500 sqm exhibition hall, suitable for over 2,000 people and a dedicated activity field.

Our inspector loved: This venue, be it for sport, beauty or business.

Directions: From M25 jct 28 to A12, look for brown signs at Gt Braxted/Silver End or A12 from north, look for brown signs at Kelvedon all the way.

Web: www.johansens.com/fivelakes
E-mail: enquiries@fivelakes.co.uk
Tel: 01621 868888
Fax: 01621 869696

Price Guide: (room only)
single £105
double/twin £148
suites £198

MAISON TALBOOTH

STRATFORD ROAD, DEDHAM, COLCHESTER, ESSEX CO7 6HN

Directions: Dedham is about a mile from the A12 between Colchester and Ipswich.

Web: www.johansens.com/maisontalbooth
E-mail: maison@talbooth.co.uk
Tel: 01206 322367
Fax: 01206 322752

Price Guide:
single £120–£150
double/twin £155–£210

In the north-east corner of Essex, where the River Stour borders with Suffolk, is the Vale of Dedham, an idyllic riverside setting immortalised in the early 19th century by the paintings of John Constable. One summer's day in 1952, the young Gerald Milsom enjoyed a 'cuppa' in the Talbooth tearoom and soon afterwards took the helm at what would develop into Le Talbooth Restaurant. Business was soon booming and the restaurant built itself a reputation as one of the best in the country. In 1969 Maison Talbooth was created in a nearby Victorian rectory, to become, as it still is, a standard bearer for Britain's premier country house hotels. Indeed, in 1982 Gerald Milsom became the founder of the Pride of Britain group. With its atmosphere of opulence, Maison Talbooth has ten spacious guest suites which all have an air of quiet luxury. Every comfort has been provided. Breakfast is served in the suites. The original Le Talbooth Restaurant is about half a mile upstream on a riverside terrace reached by leisurely foot or courtesy car. The hotel arranges special Constable tours. Exclusive use available. Telephone for details of special short breaks.

Our inspector loved: Being greeted on the front steps.

The Pier At Harwich

THE QUAY, HARWICH, ESSEX CO12 3HH

Housed in two historic, listed buildings, The Pier Hotel stands on the quayside of old Harwich, overlooking the bustling east coast harbour where the rivers Orwell and Stour meet. The main blue and white building is topped by a stubby tower and was built in the 1850s to serve travellers bound for the continent. Inside are two celebrated seafood restaurants, the blue and white nautically themed Ha'Penny Bistro on the ground floor opposite the bar and the first floor Harbourside with its splendid views. Chef patron Chris Oakley provides frequently changing menus to take maximum advantage of the fresh fish and shellfish. The hotel's salt-water tanks make lobster the house speciality and ensure they are always in prime condition. Most of the comfortably furnished second floor en suite bedrooms overlook the estuary which is alive with a preponderance of bobbing boats, high-speed craft and cruise liners heading for sunny climes. The next door building, a former public house dating from the 18th century, was acquired last year. It has been handsomely refurbished and converted into seven further guestrooms, including the Mayflower Suite with panoramic sea views. The building's sitting room is simply delightful. This is Constable country, and there are many charming old towns and villages to visit.

Directions: From the A12 at Colchester, take the A120 directly to The Quay.

Web: www.johansens.com/pieratharwich
E-mail: info@pieratharwich.co.uk
Tel: 01255 241212
Fax: 01255 551922

Price Guide:
single £62.50–£75
double/twin £80–£100
suite £150

Our inspector loved: *The Mayflower Suite and views across the harbour.*

GREENWOODS ESTATE

STOCK ROAD, STOCK, ESSEX CM4 9BE

Directions: From the A12 take the B1007.

Web: www.johansens.com/greenwoods
E-mail: info@greenwoodsestate.com
Tel: 01277 829990
Fax: 01277 829899

Price Guide:
single from £100
double/twin from £120
suite from £180

For rest, relaxation and rebuilding energy few places can better this new luxury health spa and peaceful retreat situated deep in glorious Essex countryside, just 40 minutes from London. Greenwoods stands on a high point at the edge of the historic village of Stock, famed for its church belfry whose beams originate from Spanish galleons. A beautifully restored and extended Grade II listed manor house, its architecture is a combination of Georgian and Victorian. Amidst the 42 acres of parkland there are 4 acres of formal gardens, a sunken garden and herb, fruit and vegetable gardens supplying the kitchens with the freshest produce. The Yoga-loving chef offers an imaginative and creative combination of fine dining and a naturally balanced 'act of well-being' menu. The emphasis is on nutritional balance and the style contemporary with a twist! Guests are offered opulence without intimidation, character, charm and welcoming hospitality. Public areas are lavishly decorated with sumptuous panelling, superb original fireplaces and comfortable sofas. Bedrooms are individually designed and furnished, fitted to the highest standards. Some have antique beds, many have panoramic views. The spa facilities include a full range of health, beauty and holistic treatments, 25 qualified therapists, sauna, steam and ice rooms, gymnasium and a 20 metre swimming pool.

Our inspector loved: *The delightful carved details in the panelling.*

The Swan Hotel At Bibury

BIBURY, GLOUCESTERSHIRE GL7 5NW

The Swan Hotel at Bibury in the South Cotswolds, a 17th century coaching inn, is a perfect base for both leisurely and active holidays which will appeal especially to motorists, fishermen and walkers. The hotel has its own fishing rights and a moated ornamental garden encircled by its own crystalline stream. Bibury itself is a delightful village, with its honey-coloured stonework, picturesque ponds, the trout filled River Coln and its utter lack of modern eyesores. The beautiful Arlington Row and its cottages are a vision of old England. When Liz Rose acquired The Swan, she had the clear intention of creating a distinctive hotel in the English countryside which would acknowledge the needs of the modern day sophisticated traveller. A programme of refurbishment and upgrading of the hotel and its services began with the accent on unpretentious comfort. Oak-panelling, plush carpets and sumptuous fabrics create the background for the fine paintings and antiques that grace the interiors. The 18 bedrooms are superbly appointed with luxury bathrooms and comfortable furnishings. Guests may dine in either the restaurant or the brasserie which serves meals all day during the summer months. Midweek saver rates available.

Our inspector loved: *This beautiful village location, her bedroom overlooked the river Coln and the clear water where trout basked in the sunshine.*

Directions: Bibury is signposted off A40 Oxford–Cheltenham road, on the left-hand side. Secure free parking now available next to the hotel.

Web: www.johansens.com/swanhotelatbibury
E-mail: swanhotl@swanhotel-cotswold.co.uk
Tel: 01285 740695
Fax: 01285 740473

Price Guide:
single £99–£155
double/twin £124–£260

HOTEL KANDINSKY

BAYSHILL ROAD, MONTPELLIER, CHELTENHAM, GLOUCESTERSHIRE GL50 3AS

This smart Regency building houses the latest addition to Montpellier's hotel stock. With a contemporary approach to hotelkeeping, the Kandinsky provides a young feel to appeal to the young at heart. Aimed at both business and leisure guests it is a fun, stylish and comfortable place to stay. With slight tongue in cheek, the public areas are both buzzy and clubby with log fires providing that welcoming touch for those who simply wish to watch the world go by. A feature of the informal Cafe Paradiso is the brushwood oven in which Neapolitan pizzas are cooked to order, while salads from freshest organic produce are prepared at the table. The U-Bahn Club offering 50s style, music and exclusive membership free to hotel guests, is a perfect night venue. The bedrooms, unusual in their contemporary design, are comfortable and stylish with internationally inspired furnishings; many have six-foot beds. Bathrooms are sparkling and modern. Telephones with dataport facilities include a magic eye facility linked to the nightclub. Cheltenham, with its fine shopping and celebrated Racecourse stands at the gateway to the Cotswolds with excellent rail links from London and the West Country.

Directions: From M5 J11 take A40 into town centre. From Lansdown Road, past Lansdown Crescent, follow left for Parabola Road: the hotel is on the corner.

Web: www.johansens.com/kandinsky
E-mail: info@hotelkandinsky.com
Tel: 01242 527788
Fax: 01242 226412

Price Guide:
single £75
double/twin £89
suite £99– £120

Our inspector loved: The simplistic style of the bedrooms.

HOTEL ON THE PARK

EVESHAM ROAD, CHELTENHAM, GLOUCESTERSHIRE GL52 2AH

Set in the Regency town of Cheltenham, Hotel on the Park is an attractive town house hotel which combines the attentive service of bygone times with an excellent standard of accommodation. The impressive façade, dominated by the grand pillared doorway, hints at the splendour that lies inside. Each of the 12 bedrooms are individually styled and decorated with interesting antiques and exquisite fabrics. Every possible comfort has been provided. Throughout the property the theme of understated elegance prevails and this is truly evident in The Bacchanalian Restaurant, with its high ceilings and beautiful hand-detailed cornice work. Guests may enjoy the glorious views of Pittville Park whilst sampling the inspired creations from the extensive menu along with a selection from the detailed wine list. The well-appointed Library is an ideal venue for board meetings or seminars. Special occasions including private banquets or wedding receptions can be arranged. Synonymous with National Hunt Racing, the spa town of Cheltenham is particularly popular during the racing season and hosts the Gold Cup. The town is also renowned for its Regency architecture, attractive promenade and exclusive boutiques. Historic properties, museums and theatres abound whilst other activities include golf, horse-riding, rambling and exploring the Cotswolds.

Our inspector loved: *This stunning town house with its immaculate bedrooms - A little gem!*

Directions: Opposite Pittville Park, 5 mins walk from town centre.

Web: www.johansens.com/hotelonthepark
E-mail: stay@hotelonthepark.co.uk
Tel: 01242 518898
Fax: 01242 511526

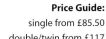

Price Guide:
single from £85.50
double/twin from £117

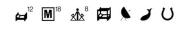

THE GREENWAY

SHURDINGTON, CHELTENHAM, GLOUCESTERSHIRE GL51 4UG

Directions: On the outskirts of Cheltenham off the A46 Cheltenham–Stroud road, 2½ miles from the town centre.

Web: www.johansens.com/greenway
E-mail: greenway@btconnect.com
Tel: 01242 862352
Fax: 01242 862780

Price Guide:
single from £99
double/twin £150–£240

Set amidst gentle parkland with the rolling Cotswold hills beyond, The Greenway is an Elizabethan country house with a style that is uniquely its own – very individual and very special. Renowned for the warmth of its welcome, its friendly atmosphere and its immaculate personal service, The Greenway is the ideal place for total relaxation. The public rooms with their antique furniture and fresh flowers are elegant and spacious yet comfortable, with roaring log fires in winter and access to the formal gardens in summer. The 21 bedrooms all have private bathrooms and are individually decorated with co-ordinated colour schemes. Eleven of the rooms are located in the main house with a further ten rooms in the converted Georgian coach house immediately adjacent to the main building. The award-winning conservatory dining room overlooks the sunken garden, providing the perfect backdrop to superb cuisine of international appeal complemented by an outstanding selection of wines. Situated in one of Britain's most charming areas, The Greenway is well placed for visiting the spa town of Cheltenham, the Cotswold villages and Shakespeare country.

Our inspector loved: *The attractive dining room overlooking the sunken garden and hillside beyond.*

CHARINGWORTH MANOR

NR CHIPPING CAMPDEN, GLOUCESTERSHIRE GL55 6NS

The ancient manor of Charingworth lies amid the gently rolling Cotswold countryside, just a few miles from the historic towns of Chipping Campden and Broadway. Beautiful old stone buildings everywhere recall the flourishing wool trade that gave the area its wealth. The 14th century manor house overlooks its own 50 acre grounds and offers peace and enthralling views. Inside, Charingworth is a historic patchwork of intimate public rooms with log fires burning during the colder months. There are 26 individually designed bedrooms, including a limited number of non smoking rooms, all furnished with antiques and fine fabrics. Outstanding cuisine is regarded as being of great importance and guests at Charingworth are assured of imaginative dishes. Great emphasis is placed on using only the finest produce and the AA has awarded the cuisine 2 rosettes. There is an all-weather tennis court within the grounds, while inside, a beautiful swimming pool, sauna, steam room, solarium and gym are available, allowing guests to relax and unwind. Warwick Castle, Hidcote Manor Gardens, Batsford Arboretum, Stratford-upon-Avon, Oxford and Cheltenham are all within easy reach. Short break rates are available on request.

Our inspector loved: The intimate style of the dining rooms.

Directions: Charingworth Manor is on the B4035 between Chipping Campden and Shipston-on-Stour.

Web: www.johansens.com/charingworthmanor
E-mail: charingworthmanor@englishrosehotels.co.uk
Tel: 01386 593555
Fax: 01386 593353

Price Guide: (including full breakfast)
limited double sole occupancy from £115
double/twin from £180

COTSWOLD HOUSE

HIGH STREET, CHIPPING CAMPDEN, GLOUCESTERSHIRE GL55 6AN

Directions: Chipping Campden is 2 miles north-east of A44, on the B4081. The hotel has parking facilities.

Web: www.johansens.com/cotswoldhouse
E-mail: reception@cotswoldhouse.com
Tel: 01386 840330
Fax: 01386 840310

Price Guide:
single from £115
double/twin from £165
four poster from £250
cottage rooms from £275

Chipping Campden is a nostalgic Cotswold town, unspoilt by the twentieth century, and Cotswold House is a splendid 17th century mansion facing the town square, impressive with colonnades flanking the front door and built in the lovely soft local stone. The interior has been sensitively decorated and modernised so there is no distraction from the graceful pillared archway and staircase. Lovely antiques, fine paintings and fabrics reminiscent of the Regency era blend easily with comfortable sofas in the elegant drawing room. The bedrooms are very individual, but all are peaceful, decorated in harmonious colours and have 'country house' style furnishings. Cotswold House is deservedly proud of its kitchen, which has won many accolades. The attractive Garden Room Restaurant has a splendid menu and a cellar book of 150 wines. Informal meals are in Hicks' Brasserie. Private functions and small conferences can be held in the secluded Courtyard Room. Guests enjoy exploring Chipping Campden's intriguing shops and alleyways. The hotel is a superb base for Stratford-on-Avon, Oxford.

Our inspector loved: *The wonderful transformation of the newly refurbished rooms.*

THE NOEL ARMS HOTEL

HIGH STREET, CHIPPING CAMPDEN, GLOUCESTERSHIRE GL55 6AT

A long tradition of hospitality awaits you at the Noel Arms Hotel. In 1651 the future Charles II rested here after his Scottish army was defeated by Cromwell at the battle of Worcester and for centuries the hotel has entertained visitors to the ancient and unspoilt, picturesque Cotswold Village of Chipping Campden. Many reminders of the past; fine antique furniture, swords, shields and other mementoes can be found around the hotel. There are 26 en suite bedrooms in either the main house or in the tastefully constructed new wing, some of which boast luxurious antique four-poster beds and all offering the standards you expect from a country hotel. The impressive oak panelled, restaurant, awarded 2 AA Rosettes, offers an excellent menu including a seasonal selection of fresh local produce. You may be tempted to choose from the extensive range of bar snacks available in the conservatory or Dovers Bar. The fine selection of wines from around the world are delicious accompaniments to any meal. Try some of the traditional cask ales and keg beers. Browse around the delightful array of shops in Chipping Campden or many of the enchanting honey-coloured Cotswold Villages, Hidcote Manor Gardens, Cheltenham Spa, Worcester, Oxford and Stratford-upon-Avon which are all close by.

Our inspector loved: The cosy atmospere of this traditional hotel with its array of fresh flowers and plants.

Directions: The Noel Arms is in the centre of Chipping Campden, which is on the B4081, 2 miles east of the A44

Web: www.johansens.com/noelarms
E-mail: bookings@cotswold-inns-hotels.co.uk
Tel: 01386 840317
Fax: 01386 841136

Price Guide:
single £80
double £115–£135

 ²⁶ ⁴⁵

THE BEAR OF RODBOROUGH

RODBOROUGH COMMON, STROUD, NR CIRENCESTER, GLOUCESTERSHIRE GL5 5DE

This 17th century former Ale House offers comfortable accommodation in an area of outstanding beauty. Nestling on the top of a steep hill, The Bear of Rodborough is situated in the verdant landscape of the western Cotswolds, described by the author, Laurie Lee, as "vegetative virginity". The inn has recently undergone a careful and precise restoration, at the request of the new owners, yet many of its past features such as the original archway entrance have been retained. The refurbished bedrooms are exquisite, adorned with plush carpets and beautiful fabrics. All have en suite facilities and several thoughtful extras. The superb bar, popular with the locals, is renowned for its large selection of traditional beers. Elegantly furnished, the restaurant is enhanced by the ceiling beams with a 'running bear' design. Specialities include the full English breakfast, made with fresh local produce, whilst the light luncheons and sumptuous dinners must also be savoured.

Directions: The nearest motorway is the M5, junction 13.

Web: www.johansens.com/bearofrodborough
E-mail: bookings@cotswold-inns-hotels.co.uk
Tel: 01453 878522
Fax: 01453 872523

Price Guide:
single £75–£95
double/twin £120–£130
suite £160

Our inspector loved: The traditional bar, with its cosy atmosphere and log fires.

Gloucester
Cheltenham
Cirencester

LOWER SLAUGHTER MANOR

LOWER SLAUGHTER, GLOUCESTERSHIRE GL54 2HP

With a history that spans nearly a thousand years, this Grade II listed Manor stands in complete tranquillity within private grounds on the edge of one of the Cotswold's prettiest villages. Lower Slaughter Manor is now owned by Daphne and Roy Vaughan, who have lovingly overseen its transformation. Visitors are warmly welcomed by a team of dedicated staff, and enjoy elegant, spacious surroundings. All rooms are beautifully furnished, with carefully chosen antiques, fine china and original paintings. The Manor has a stunning indoor heated swimming pool, while outside the wonderful grounds reveal a croquet lawn and tennis court, and, within the delightful walled garden, a unique two-storey dovecote dating back to the 15th century when the Manor was a convent. The award-winning cuisine is prepared using the best local and continental ingredients, and an outstanding wine list offers a range of 800 specially selected wines from the Old and New Worlds. An excellent setting for business meetings, The Sir George Whitmore Suite accommodates up to 16 people, and offers phone line, full secretarial services and audio visual equipment. For more leisurely pursuits, visitors can explore the Cotswolds, Cheltenham, Stratford, and Warwick and Sudeley Castles. Lower Slaughter Manor is a member of The Leading Small Hotels of the World.

Our inspector loved: The drawing room with its open fire and grand piano which guests can listen to before dinner.

Directions: The Manor is on the right as you enter Lower Slaughter from A429.

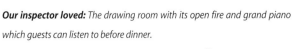

Web: www.johansens.com/lowerslaughtermanor
E-mail: lowsmanor@aol.com
Tel: 01451 820456
Fax: 01451 822150

Price Guide:
single £175–£375
double/twin £200–£400
suite £350–£400

WASHBOURNE COURT HOTEL

LOWER SLAUGHTER, GLOUCESTERSHIRE GL54 2HS

Directions: The hotel is situated ½ a mile from the main A429 Fosseway between Stow-on-the-Wold and Bourton-on-the-Water (signed To the Slaughters).

Web: www.johansens.com/washbournecourt
E-mail:
Tel: 01451 822143
Fax: 01451 821045

Price Guide: (including dinner)
single from £155
double/twin £210–£270

Gloucester
Cheltenham
Cirencester

Under the private ownership of Roy and Daphne Vaughan, Washbourne Court Hotel is in the heart of the tranquil and beautiful Cotswold village of Lower Slaughter, set on the bank of the River Eye. The four acres of private gardens have been lovingly re-landscaped with lawns and many delightful features. With just twenty eight bedrooms, it has parts dating back to the 17th century. The recent additions to the hotel, a spacious new dining room and a further six guest rooms with comfortable and elegant furnishings, blend in perfectly with the original building. Always full of freshly picked flowers and planted bowls, the hotel has the feel of a private house with the many personal touches. The modern English cuisine offers an abundance of fresh local produce, concentrating on good textures and intense flavours combined with outstanding presentation. Head Chef Sean Ballington now oversees the running of the kitchen. Drinks, light lunches and traditional afternoon tea are also served on the garden terrace during the summer months.

Our inspector loved: *The beautiful setting of this Cotswold village hotel next to the river.*

THE MANOR HOUSE HOTEL

MORETON-IN-MARSH, GLOUCESTERSHIRE GL56 0LJ

This former 16th century manor house is set in beautiful gardens in the Cotswold village of Moreton-in-Marsh. The Manor House Hotel has been tastefully extended and restored, yet retains many of its historic features, among them a priest's hole and secret passages. The 38 well-appointed bedrooms have been individually decorated and furnished. The restaurant offers imaginative and traditional English dishes using only the freshest ingredients, accompanied by an expertly selected wine list. For the guest seeking relaxation, leisure facilities include an indoor heated swimming pool and spa bath. Sports enthusiasts will also find that tennis, golf and riding can be arranged locally. Spacious modern business facilities, combined with the peaceful location, make this an excellent venue for executive meetings. It is also an ideal base for touring, with many attractions nearby, including Stratford-upon-Avon, Warwick and the fashionable centres of Cheltenham, Oxford and Bath.

Our inspector loved: The cottage style of the newly refurbished rooms.

Directions: The Manor House Hotel is on the A429 Fosse Way near the junction of the A44 and A429 north of Stow, on the Broadway side of the intersection.

Web: www.johansens.com/manorhousemoreton
E-mail: bookings@cotswold-inns-hotels.co.uk
Tel: 01608 650501
Fax: 01608 651481

Gloucester
Cheltenham
Cirencester

Price Guide:
single £99
double/twin £125–£160
suite £160

145

THE PAINSWICK HOTEL

KEMPS LANE, PAINSWICK, GLOUCESTERSHIRE GL6 6YB

The village of Painswick stands high on a hill overlooking the beautiful rolling valleys of the Cotswolds. Dating back to the 14th century, the village was an old wool community, medieval cottages mingle gracefully with elegant Georgian merchants' houses. A feature of the village is the church, with its ancient churchyard graced by 99 Yew trees planted in 1792 and 17th century table tombs in memory of the wealthy clothiers. Situated majestically within these architectural gems is the Palladian-style Painswick Hotel, built in 1790 and formerly the home of affluent village rectors. Each of the luxury en suite bedrooms have modern amenities, beautiful fabrics, antique furniture and objets d'art; creating a restful atmosphere and the impression of staying in a comfortable private house. The stylish restaurant, with its pine panelling, offers delicious cuisine with an emphasis upon regional produce such as locally reared Cotswold meat, game, wild Severn salmon and Gloucestershire cheeses. The private Dining Room accommodates quiet dinner parties, wedding occasions and business meetings.

Directions: M5 Jct13. Painswick is on A46 between Stroud and Cheltenham, turn into road by the church and continue round the corner, taking the first right. The hotel is at the bottom of the road on the right hand side.

Web: www.johansens.com/painswick
E-mail: Reservations@Painswickhotel.com
Tel: 01452 812160
Fax: 01452 814059

Price Guide:
single from £90
double/twin from £120–£195

Gloucester
Cheltenham
Cirencester

Our inspector loved: The private terrace of her bedroom overlooking the garden with stunning views.

THE GRAPEVINE HOTEL

SHEEP STREET, STOW-ON-THE-WOLD, GLOUCESTERSHIRE GL54 1AU

Set in the pretty town of Stow-on-the-Wold, regarded by many as the jewel of the Cotswolds, The Grapevine Hotel has an atmosphere which makes visitors feel welcome and at ease. The outstanding personal service provided by a loyal team of staff is perhaps the secret of the hotel's success. This, along with the exceptionally high standard of overall comfort and hospitality, earned The Grapevine the 1991 Johansens Hotel Award for Excellence – a well-deserved accolade. Beautifully furnished bedrooms, including six superb garden rooms across the courtyard, offer every facility. Visitors can linger over imaginative cuisine in the relaxed and informal atmosphere of the conservatory restaurant. Awarded one AA Rosettes for food. The restaurant, like all of the bedrooms, is non-smoking. The hotel has its own tennis court, 1.5 miles away. Whether travelling on business or pleasure, guests will wish to return to The Grapevine again and again. The local landscape offers unlimited scope for exploration, whether to the numerous picturesque villages in the Cotswolds or to the towns of Oxford, Cirencester and Stratford-upon-Avon. Nature enthusiasts must visit the beautiful gardens of Hidcote, Kifsgate and Barnsley House nearby. Open over Christmas.

Our inspector loved: *The lovely dining room with its seating under the grapevines.*

Directions: Sheep Street is part of A436 in the centre of Stow-on-the-Wold.

Web: www.johansens.com/grapevine
E-mail: johansens@vines.co.uk
Tel: 01451 830344
Fax: 01451 832278

Price Guide:
single from £90
double/twin from £130

THE UNICORN HOTEL

SHEEP STREET, STOW-ON-THE-WOLD, GLOUCESTERSHIRE GL54 1HQ

Directions: The nearest motorway is the M40 junction 10. Then take the A44 or the A436 in the direction of Stow-on-the-Wold. The hotel is located on the A429.

Web: www.johansens.com/unicorn
E-mail: bookings@cotswold-inns-hotels.co.uk
Tel: 01451 830257
Fax: 01451 831090

Price Guide:
single £65–£75
double/twin £120–£145

Low oak-beamed ceilings and large stone fireplaces pay tribute to The Unicorn's lengthy past. Over the last 300 years, the inn has changed its standards of accommodation, incorporating the latest modern facilities, yet many vestiges of the former centuries remain. The recently refurbished interior is decorated in a stylish manner featuring Jacobean furniture and antique artefacts whilst log fires abound. Enhanced by floral quilts and comfortable armchairs, the 20 en suite bedrooms are simple yet charming. Fine paintings adorn the walls of the public rooms and the cosy bar offers hand-carved wooden chairs and rich carpets. Modern British cooking is served in the elegant surroundings of the Georgian restaurant from an imaginative à la carte menu. The hotel is well-frequented on Sundays by guests wishing to indulge in the delicious lunchtime roast. Local leisure facilities include horse-riding and the golf course. Shooting and fishing are popular outdoor pursuits. Many historic buildings and castles are within easy reach including the magnificent Blenheim Palace and Warwick Castle. Nature enthusiasts will be delighted with the splendid gardens at Sudeley Castle.

Our inspector loved: This lovely little Cotswold hotel with its open fire and cosy armchairs in which to curl up and read a book.

WYCK HILL HOUSE

WYCK HILL, STOW-ON-THE WOLD, GLOUCESTERSHIRE GL54 1HY

Wyck Hill House is a magnificent Cotswold mansion built in the early 1700s, reputedly on the site of an early Roman settlement. It is set in 100 acres of gardens and wooded grounds, overlooking the beautiful Windrush Valley. The hotel has been elegantly restored and the bedrooms, some of which are located in the Coach House and Orangery, are individually furnished to combine superb antiques with modern comforts. There is a suite with a large, antique four-poster bed, which is perfect for a honeymoon or for other special occasions. The cedar-panelled library is an ideal room in which to read, if you wish, and to relax with morning coffee or afternoon tea. The award-winning restaurant provides the highest standards of modern British cuisine from the freshest seasonally available local produce. The menus are complemented by a superb wine list. Wyck Hill House hosts several special events, including opera, travel talks, cultural weekends and a variety of theme activities. The hotel is an ideal base from which to tour the university city of Oxford and the Georgian city of Bath. Cheltenham, Blenheim Palace and Stratford-upon-Avon are just a short drive away. Special price 2-night breaks are available.

Our inspector loved: Taking drinks on the patio in the peace and quiet overlooking the gardens.

Directions: 1½ miles south of Stow-on-the-Wold on A424 Stow–Burford road.

Web: www.johansens.com/wyckhillhouse
E-mail: wyckhill@wrensgroup.com
Tel: 01451 831936
Fax: 01451 832243

Price Guide:
single £110
double/twin £160
suite £260

149

LORDS OF THE MANOR HOTEL

UPPER SLAUGHTER, NR BOURTON-ON-THE-WATER, GLOUCESTERSHIRE GL54 2JD

Directions: Upper Slaughter is 2 miles west of the A429 between Stow-on-the-Wold and Bourton-on-the-Water.

Web: www.johansens.com/lordsofthemanor
E-mail: lordsofthemanor@btinternet.com
Tel: 01451 820243
Fax: 01451 820696

Price Guide:
single from £99
double/twin £155–£305

Situated in the heart of the Cotswolds, on the outskirts of one of England's most unspoiled and picturesque villages, stands the Lords of the Manor Hotel. Built in the 17th century of honeyed Cotswold stone, the house enjoys splendid views over the surrounding meadows, stream and parkland. For generations the house was the home of the Witts family, who historically had been rectors of the parish. It is from these origins that the hotel derives its distinctive name. Charming, walled gardens provide a secluded retreat at the rear of the house. Each bedroom bears the maiden name of one of the ladies who married into the Witts family; each room is individually and imaginatively decorated with period furniture. The reception rooms are magnificently furnished with fine antiques, paintings, traditional fabrics and masses of fresh flowers. Log fires blaze in cold weather. The heart of this English country house is its dining room, where truly memorable dishes are created from the best local ingredients. Nearby are Blenheim Palace, Warwick Castle, the Roman antiquities at Bath and Shakespeare country.

Our inspector loved: The wonderful drawing room overlooking the garden.

CALCOT MANOR

NR TETBURY, GLOUCESTERSHIRE GL8 8YJ

This delightful old Manor House, built of Cotswold stone, offers guests tranquillity amidst acres of rolling countryside. Situated in the southern Cotswolds close to the historic town of Tetbury the building dates back to the 15th century and was a farmhouse until 1983. Its beautiful stone barns and stables include one of the oldest tithe barns in England, built in 1300 by the Cistercian monks from Kingswood Abbey. These buildings form a quadrangle and the stone glistening in the dawn or glowing in the dusk is quite a spectacle. Professional service is complemented by cheerful hospitality without any hint of over-formality. Excellent facilities for families include a number of family suites complete with bunk beds and baby listening devices. A new play facility to keep older children entertained will open in April 2003 with Playstation, X boxes and a small cinema. A full-day care crèche for younger children will also be available. Parents can escape to the state-of-the-art spa with 16 metre pool, steam and sauna, gym and outdoor hot tub. The spa, which opens in April 2003, will also offer a full range of beauty treatments. In the elegant conservatory restaurant dinner is very much the focus of a memorable stay and the congenial Gumstool Bistro and Bar offers a range of simpler traditional food and local ales. A discreet conference facility is available.

Directions: From Tetbury, take the A4135 signposted Dursley; Calcot is on the right after 3½ miles.

Web: www.johansens.com/calcotmanor
E-mail: reception@calcotmanor.co.uk
Tel: 01666 890391
Fax: 01666 890394

Price Guide:
double/twin £145–£185
family rooms £185
family suites £200

Our inspector loved: The cosy drawing room with its homely atmosphere.

THE CLOSE HOTEL

LONG STREET, TETBURY, GLOUCESTERSHIRE GL8 8AQ

Directions: The Close is on Long Street, the main street of Tetbury which can be found on the A433, minutes from the M4 and M5. Private parking is at the rear of the hotel in Close Gardens.

Web: www.johansens.com/closehotel
E-mail: reception@theclosehotel.co.uk
Tel: 01666 502272
Fax: 01666 504401

Price Guide:
single £90
double/twin £160

Built in 1585, the Close Hotel and Restaurant is an idyllic Elizabethan manor house with 15 charming, individually styled bedrooms, set in the heart of the delightful market town of Tetbury. Since becoming a hotel in 1974, its reputation has developed, and today it holds the prestigious accolade of 3 AA rosettes for food over three consecutive years. The dinner menu offers a delightful composition of modern and contemporary tastes, each enhanced by thoughtful companions such as star anise ice cream or balsamic jelly and pear chutney, whilst the Tastings menu offers guests a gastronomic journey through 7 courses of the chef's latest creations. An appetite for such a culinary experience can easily be worked up by scouring the many antique shops within walking distance of the hotel, as this area really is a collector's paradise. The historic towns of Cirencester, Cheltenham and Bath are all within easy access, as are the Royal Estates of Highgrove and Gatcombe. Horticulturalists will love the arboretum at Westonbirt, and sporting enthusiasts can enjoy Cheltenham races and motor racing at Castle Combe. The Close is an ideal venue for weddings and small conferences, offering a range of beautifully styled meeting rooms and private use. (N.B. min. age in the restaurant: 12 years).

Our inspector loved: *The warm welcome at this lovely town house hotel.*

CORSE LAWN HOUSE HOTEL

CORSE LAWN, NR TEWKESBURY, GLOUCESTERSHIRE GL19 4LZ

Although only 6 miles from the M5 and M50, Corse Lawn is a completely unspoiled, typically English hamlet in a peaceful Gloucestershire backwater. The hotel, an elegant Queen Anne listed building set back from the village green, stands in 12 acres of gardens and grounds and still displays the charm of its historic pedigree. Visitors can be assured of the highest standards of service and cooking: Baba Hine is famous for the dishes she produces, while Denis Hine, of the Hine Cognac family, is in charge of the wine cellar. The service here, now in the hands of son Giles, is faultlessly efficient, friendly and personal. As well as the renowned restaurant, there are three comfortable drawing rooms, a large lounge bar, a private dining-cum-conference room for up to 45 persons and a similar, smaller room for up to 20. A tennis court, heated indoor swimming pool and croquet lawn adjoin the hotel and most sports and leisure activities can be arranged. Corse Lawn is ideal for exploring the Cotswolds, Malverns and Forest of Dean.

Our inspector loved: *The informal atmosphere of this once coaching inn.*

Directions: Corse Lawn House is situated on the B4211 between the A417 (Gloucester–Ledbury road) and the A438 (Tewkesbury–Ledbury road).

Web: www.johansens.com/corselawn
E-mail: hotel@corselawnhouse.u-net.com
Tel: 01452 780479/771
Fax: 01452 780840

Price Guide:
single £80
double/twin £125
four-poster £145

THORNBURY CASTLE

THORNBURY, SOUTH GLOUCESTERSHIRE BS35 1HH

Built in 1511 by Edward Stafford, third Duke of Buckingham, Thornbury Castle was later owned by Henry VIII, who stayed here in 1535 with Anne Boleyn. Today it stands in 15 acres of regal splendour with its vineyard, high walls and the oldest Tudor garden in England. Rich furnishings are displayed against the handsome interior features, including ornate oriel windows, panelled walls and large open fireplaces. The 25 carefully restored bedchambers retain many period details. Thornbury Castle has received many accolades for its luxurious accommodation and excellent cuisine, which includes delights such as summer salad of English lobster, fillet of seabass with herb risotto or pan fried fillet of beef with crushed Jersey potatoes. The Castle also provides peaceful and secluded meeting facilities. Thornbury is an ideal base from which to explore Bath, Wales and the Cotswolds. Personally guided tours are available to introduce guests to the little-known as well as the famous places which are unique to the area. In addition, clay pigeon shooting, archery and golf may be enjoyed locally.

Directions: The entrance to the Castle is left of the Parish Church at the lower end of Castle Street.

Web: www.johansens.com/thornburycastle
E-mail: thornburycastle@compuserve.com
Tel: 01454 281182
Fax: 01454 416188

Price Guide:
single from £110
double/twin from £140
suite from £280

Our inspector loved: *A Tudor castle surrounded by history.*

ESSEBORNE MANOR

HURSTBOURNE TARRANT, ANDOVER, HAMPSHIRE SP11 0ER

Esseborne Manor is small and unpretentious, yet stylish. The present house was built at the end of the 19th century and carries the name used to record details of the local village in the Domesday Book. It is set in a pleasing garden amid the rich farmland of the North Wessex Downs in a designated area of outstanding natural beauty. Ian and Lucilla Hamilton, who own the house, have established the restful atmosphere of a private country home where guests can unwind and relax. There are just 15 comfortable bedrooms, some reached via a courtyard. Two doubles and a delightful suite are in converted cottages with their own patio overlooking the main gardens. The pretty sitting room and cosy library are comfortable areas in which to relax. Dave Morris's fine 2 Rosette cooking is set off to advantage in the new dining room and adjoining bar. There is now a spacious meeting and function facility. In the grounds there is a herb garden, an all-weather tennis court, a croquet lawn and plenty of good walking beyond. Nearby Newbury racecourse has a busy programme of steeple-chasing and flat racing. Places to visit include Highclere Castle, Stonehenge, Salisbury, Winchester and Oxford.

Our inspector loved: The towering century old lime tree in the drive.

Directions: Midway between Newbury and Andover on the A343, 1½ miles north of Hurstbourne Tarrant.

Web: www.johansens.com/essebornemanor
E-mail: esseborne@aol.com
Tel: 01264 736444
Fax: 01264 736725

Price Guide:
single £95–£130
double/twin £100–£180

FIFEHEAD MANOR

MIDDLE WALLOP, STOCKBRIDGE. HAMPSHIRE SO20 8EG

Directions: From M3, exit at junction 8 onto A303 to Andover. Then take A343 south for 6 miles to Middle Wallop.

Web: www.johansens.com/fifeheadmanor
E-mail: fifeheadmanor@ukonline.co.uk
Tel: 01264 781565
Fax: 01264 781400

Price Guide:
single £70–£90
double/twin £110–£150

The foundations of this lovely Manor House date from the 11th century when it was owned by the wife of the Saxon Earl of Godwin whose son, King Harold, was killed at the Battle of Hastings. Today, Fifehead Manor offers all the comfort of a country house hotel but, with its barns and stables surrounded by acres of gardens, the historic atmosphere lingers. The beamed dining room with its lead-paned windows and huge open fireplace has a unique atmosphere illuminated by the light of flickering candles and a warmth generated by centuries of hospitality. Substantial changes have brought about vast improvements to this fine hotel. The award-winning cuisine is outstanding and the restaurant is featured in major guides throughout Europe. All 17 en suite bedrooms are individually furnished and have every amenity, 9 are located in the garden wing. Fifehead Manor is ideally situated for visiting Salisbury, Winchester, Stonehenge, Romsey Abbey, Broadlands and Wilton House. Golf, fishing, riding and motor racing at Thruxton are nearby.

Our inspector loved: *The turf covered Tudor steps and stone mullioned windows.*

TYLNEY HALL

ROTHERWICK, HOOK, HAMPSHIRE RG27 9AZ

Arriving at this hotel in the evening with its floodlit exterior and forecourt fountain, you can imagine arriving for a party in a private stately home. Grade II listed and set in 66 acres of ornamental gardens and parkland, Tylney Hall typifies the great houses of the past. Apéritifs are taken in the wood-panelled library bar; haute cuisine is served in the glass-domed Oak Room restaurant. The hotel holds RAC and AA food awards also AA 4 Red Stars and RAC Gold Ribbon. New health and leisure facilities include heated pool and whirlpool, solarium, fitness studio, beauty and hairdressing, sauna, tennis, croquet and snooker, while hot-air ballooning, archery, clay pigeon shooting, golf and riding can be arranged. Surrounding the hotel are wooded trails ideal for jogging. Functions for up to 100 people are catered for in the Tylney Suite or Chestnut Suite; more intimate gatherings are available in one of the other ten private banqueting rooms. Tylney Hall is licensed to hold wedding ceremonies on site. The cathedral city of Winchester and Stratfield Saye House are nearby. Legoland and Windsor Castle are a 40-minute drive away.

Our inspector loved: *The Edwardian chequerboard floor and the abundance of flowers everywhere, inside and out.*

Directions: M4, Jct11, towards Hook and Rotherwick, follow signs to hotel. M3, Jct5, A287 towards Newnham, over A30 into Old School Road. Left for Newnham and right onto Ridge Lane. Hotel is on the left after 1 mile.

Web: www.johansens.com/tylneyhall
E-mail: reservations@tylneyhall.com
Tel: 01256 764881
Fax: 01256 768141

Price Guide:
single £125–£385
double/twin £159–£210
suite £270–£410

157

THE MONTAGU ARMS HOTEL

BEAULIEU, NEW FOREST, HAMPSHIRE SO42 7ZL

Situated at the head of the River Beaulieu in the heart of the New Forest, The Montagu Arms Hotel carries on a tradition of hospitality started 700 years ago. As well as being a good place for a holiday, the hotel is an ideal venue for small conferences. Each of the 24 bedrooms has been individually styled and many are furnished with four-poster beds. Dine in the oak-panelled restaurant overlooking the garden, where you can enjoy cuisine prepared by award-winning chef Haydn Laidlow. The menu is supported by an outstanding wine list. Alternatively dine less formally in Monty's Bar Brasserie now delightfully presented in keeping with the building. It offers homemade fare together with real ales and an extensive choice of wine. The hotel offers complimentary membership of an exclusive health club 6 miles away. Facilities there include a supervised gymnasium, large indoor ozone pool, Jacuzzi, steam room, sauna and beauty therapist. With much to see and do around Beaulieu why not hire a mountain bike? Visit the National Motor Museum, Exbury Gardens or Bucklers Hard, or walk for miles through the beautiful New Forest. Special tariffs are available throughout the year.

Directions: The village of Beaulieu is well-signposted and the hotel commands an impressive position at the foot of the main street.

Web: www.johansens.com/montaguarms
E-mail: enquiries@montagu–arms.co.uk
Tel: 01590 612324
Fax: 01590 612188

Price Guide: (inclusive terms available)
single £85
double/twin £130–£140
suites £155–£200

Our inspector loved: The polished floors and resident donkeys.

THE MASTER BUILDER'S HOUSE

BUCKLER'S HARD, BEAULIEU, NEW FOREST, HAMPSHIRE SO42 7XB

A careful and extensive refurbishment of the hotel has transformed The Master Builder's House into a top quality 3 star property, set in a magnificent location with beautiful views across the Beaulieu river. The heart of the estate was originally home to the Master shipbuilder Henry Adams who built Nelson's favourite, the Agamemnon. The 25 en suite bedrooms are beautifully appointed, offering every modern facility and a range of thoughtful extras. The public rooms are charming with Inglenook fireplaces and comfortable furnishings. A hearty full English breakfast is served in the morning whilst the restaurant, awarded 2 AA Rosettes, specialises in traditional cuisine comprising classic recipes and local produce. The beaches at Barton-on-Sea and Milford-on-Sea, the National Motor Museum and the Georgian town of Lymington are all worth a visit. The more adventurous may wish to explore the New Forest with its wildlife and picturesque villages. Sports such as golfing, sailing, fishing, salt-water angling, riding, trekking and wagon-riding may be practised close by.

Our inspector loved: *The clean lines and uncluttered dining room, wonderful river views from the terrace.*

Directions: Leave the M27 at junction 1, then take the A337 to Lyndhurst and then the B3056 to Beaulieu. Follow signs to Buckler's Hard.

Web: www.johansens.com/masterbuildershouse
E-mail: res@themasterbuilders.co.uk
Tel: 01590 616253
Fax: 01590 616297

Price Guide:
single from £125
double/twin from £170
superior from £225

CAREYS MANOR HOTEL

BROCKENHURST, NEW FOREST, HAMPSHIRE SO42 7RH

Directions: From M27 junction 1, follow A337 signed to Lymington. Careys Manor is on the left after 30 mph sign at Brockenhurst

Web: www.johansens.com/careysmanor
E-mail: info@careysmanor.com
Tel: 01590 623551
Fax: 01590 622799

Price Guide:
double/twin £129–£179
suite £199

Careys Manor, dates from 1888 and is built on the site of a royal hunting lodge used by Charles II. Situated close to the glorious New Forest countryside, the hotel is proud of the personal welcome and care it extends to its visitors. The bedrooms are comfortably appointed and furnished in a range of styles. In the modern Garden Wing some rooms have balconies and others open directly onto lawns and borders. The restaurant offers a hearty breakfast and a English and French influenced cuisine at dinner. The Carat Club is a prestigious health and leisure complex comprising a large indoor swimming pool withJacuzzi ,sauna and a Turkish steam room. In addition, guests can work out in the professionally supervised fitness suite, where there are also rooms for massage, sports injury and beauty treatments. Windsurfing, riding and sailing can all be enjoyed locally, while Stonehenge, Beaulieu, Broadlands, Salisbury and Winchester are a short distance away. Business interests can be catered for – there are comprehensive self-contained conference facilities.

Our inspector loved: *The attentive staff, and the central New Forest location.*

NEW PARK MANOR

LYNDHURST ROAD, BROCKENHURST, NEW FOREST, HAMPSHIRE SO42 7QH

Escape from the pressures of a hectic lifestyle in this grade II listed former hunting lodge of Charles II which dates from the 16th century. The house stands within its own clearing in the heart of the New Forest, yet is easily accessed from the main Lyndhurst/Lymington road. All bedrooms boast fine views of the surrounding parklands and forest and are individually decorated, in keeping with the historic nature of the house. The New Forest rooms are contemporary in style and even have LCD TV screens in the bathrooms! Wondering ponies and wild deer can be viewed from the Hotel and on the many walks and paths that run through the forest. The Hotel has its own Equestrian Centre, with BHS trained stable crew, heated outdoor pool and tennis courts. It affords a perfect starting point from which to explore the surrounding countryside and to visit the nearby coast and sailing of the Solent. The new, lively Polo Bar (the Hotel has its own polo field!) offers a light menu throughout the day whilst the romantic restaurant provides a more extensive menu serving traditional British cuisine with a continental twist. The views from the New Forest room, with its picture windows, provides a wonderful setting for parties and functions, which are tailor-made to suit personal requirements.

Our inspector loved: *Its own riding stables and the opportunity to see deer from the windows.*

Directions: New Park Manor is ½ mile off the A337 between Lyndhurst and Brockenhurst, easily reached from the M27 junction 1.

Web: www.johansens.com/newparkmanor
E-mail: enquiries@newparkmanorhotel.co.uk
Tel: 01590 623467
Fax: 01590 622268

Price Guide:
single from £85
double/twin £110–£190
four poster £190

RHINEFIELD HOUSE HOTEL

RHINEFIELD ROAD, BROCKENHURST, NEW FOREST, HAMPSHIRE SO42 7QB

Directions: A35 West from Lyndhurst the hotel is signed in about 3 mile.

Web: www.johansens.com/rhinefield
E-mail: info@rhinefieldhousehotel.co.uk
Tel: 01590 622922
Fax: 01590 622800

Price Guide:
single from £100
double/twin from £150
suite from £195

Known locally as the 'jewel in the forest', at first sight the sheer grandeur of Rhinefield House surpasses all expectations. A hint of Italian Renaissance sweeps across ornamental gardens, with canals reflecting the mellow stonework. Lovingly restored to their original 1890s design, over 5,000 yew trees form the maze and formal parterres where a grass amphitheatre has been carved out of the western slopes for summer evening concerts. The interiors are equally impressive, the journey through the rooms is a voyage of discovery. Authentically created in the style of a Moorish Palace, the Alhambra Room has Islamic inscriptions, onyx pillars and mosaic flooring. Fine cuisine is served in the elegant Armada Restaurant – so called after its splendid carving depicting the Spanish Armada. An airy sunlit conservatory and attractive bedrooms appointed in accordance with the style of the house all add to Rhinefield's appeal. The Grand Hall is a model replica of Westminster Hall – an ideal setting for balls, society weddings and stylish banquets. A wide range of conference rooms and equipment is available for business events.

Our inspector loved: *The Moorish Alhambra Room complete with mosaic tiles.*

OLD THORNS HOTEL, GOLF & COUNTRY CLUB

LONGMOOR ROAD, GRIGGS GREEN, LIPHOOK, HAMPSHIRE GU30 7PE

Originally a 17th century farmhouse, Old Thorns is situated within 400 acres of some of the finest Hampshire countryside. The stunning 18 hole championship golf course was designed by well-known golf course architect, Commander John Harris and completed by Peter Alliss and Dave Thomas. The elevated positions of many of the holes offer spectacular views and the rolling fairways bring the numerous natural springs, lakes and trees into play. The design of the course ensures a challenge for the top player, whilst affording satisfaction for the amateur. There are 33 four star deluxe en suite bedrooms, and the Country Club offers an indoor pool, sauna, steam room, fitness centre, outdoor tennis courts as well as a range of facials, wraps and spa treatments. Guests are able to enjoy the very traditional Nippon Kan authentic Japanese restaurant where the Teppan Yaki is a speciality, alternatively guests may eat in the informal Sands Brasserie. Old Thorns is also a popular conference venue, easily accessible from London and M25 and the Garden Room is available as part of a conference or for private dining. The Executive Boardroom has its own balcony overlooking the 1st tee and 18th green of the golf course. Places of interest include Jane Austen's house, the Gilbert White Museum and the Hollycombe Steam Collection.

Directions: From the M25 jct 10 turn south on the A3 and exit at Griggs Green. The Hotel is signed after ½ mile.

Web: www.johansens.com/oldthorns
E-mail: info@oldthorns.com
Tel: 01428 724555
Fax: 01428 725036

Price Guide:
single from £130
double/twin from £150
suite from £195

Our inspector loved: Dining in the authentic Japanese restaurant.

PASSFORD HOUSE HOTEL

MOUNT PLEASANT LANE, LYMINGTON, HAMPSHIRE SO41 8LS

Set in nine acres of picturesque gardens and rolling parkland, the Passford House Hotel lies midway between the charming New Forest village of Sway and the Georgian splendour of Lymington. Once the home of Lord Arthur Cecil, it is steeped in history and the traditions of leisurely country life. Pleasantly decorated bedrooms include a number of superior rooms, while comfort is the keynote in the four public lounges. The hotel prides itself on the standard and variety of cuisine served in its delightful restaurant and the extensive menu aims to give pleasure to the most discerning of palates. Meals are complemented by a speciality wine list. The hotel boasts a compact leisure centre, catering for all ages and activities. In addition to two heated swimming pools, there is a multi-gym, sauna, pool table, croquet lawn, pétanque and tennis court. Just a short drive away are Beaulieu, the cathedral cities of Winchester and Salisbury and ferry ports to the Isle of Wight and France. The New Forest has numerous golf courses, riding and trekking centres, cycling paths, beautiful walks, and of course sailing on the Solent. Milford-on-Sea, four miles away, is the nearest beach.

Directions: Exit 1/M27, A337 to Brockenhurst. After railway bridge & mini roundabout, right at Tollhouse Pub & bear right into Mount Pleasant Lane. Hotel is 1 mile past garden centre.

Web: www.johansens.com/passfordhouse
E-mail: sales@passfordhousehotel.co.uk
Tel: 01590 682398
Fax: 01590 683494

Price Guide:
single from £80
double/twin from £130

Our inspector loved: *The dedication to guests' comfort and the two swimming pools.*

STANWELL HOUSE

HIGH STREET, LYMINGTON, NEW FOREST, HAMPSHIRE SO41 9AA

Stanwell House Hotel combines a highly individual style with informal and unobtrusive personal service. This Georgian town house is set on Lymington's fine wide high street, which still hosts a bustling Saturday market, serving the local community and antiques hunters alike. The owner's vibrant personality and theatrical background are reflected in her choice of colours and furnishings which set the mood for some surprises in the 23 bedrooms and five fantasy suites. The restaurant has been awarded two rosettes, and there is an intimate bar and bistro. A delightful conservatory leads onto a flower-filled patio and charming walled garden. Adjacent to the hotel, in a quiet courtyard off the high street, is Elgars Cottage. This pretty period cottage is furnished to a very high standard and offers a full range of amenities. Lymington is a charming Regency town, close to the New Forest and the magnificent Solent with all its yacht facilities. There are opportunities for walking, riding and golf and river or sea fishing. Crossings by car ferry from Lymington to Yarmouth bring the Isle of Wight within a 30 minute journey.

Our inspector loved: *The very stylish shabby chic.*

Directions: From the M27 junction 1 through Lyndhurst and Brockenhurst.

Web: www.johansens.com/stanwellhouse
E-mail: sales@stanwellhousehotel.co.uk
Tel: 01590 677123
Fax: 01590 677756

Price Guide:
single £85
double/twin £110–£130
suites £150–£160

165

LE POUSSIN AT PARKHILL

BEAULIEU ROAD, LYNDHURST, NEW FOREST, HAMPSHIRE SO43 7FZ

Directions: From Lyndhurst take B3056 towards Beaulieu. Parkhill is approximately a mile from Lyndhurst on the right.

Web: www.johansens.com/lepoussinatparkhill
E-mail: sales@lepoussinatparkhill.co.uk
Tel: 023 8028 2944
Fax: 023 8028 3268

Price Guide:
single from £70
double/twin from £80
suites from £140

A winding drive through glorious parkland and lawned grounds leads to this gracious 18th century country house which is now a renowned and popular restaurant with accommodation. Built on the site of a 13th century hunting lodge, Le Poussin stands in an elevated position with superb views across its 13-acre surrounds and open forest. It offers remoteness and period comfort coupled with an outstanding excellence of standards, service and cuisine. Dining in the elegant restaurant is a delight to be sampled leisurely while viewing deer grazing just a few steps away. Internationally acclaimed Chef patron Alex Aiken holds a Michelin Star and three AA Rosettes. His innovative, imaginative cuisine is a joy not to be missed. The bedrooms are being refurbished to high standards compatible with the delightful restaurant and public rooms. There is also a small cottage with its own walled garden for those wishing to bring a dog. It is ideal for visiting the many places of interest, all within easy driving distance. These include Exbury Gardens, home to one of the world's finest collections of rhododendrons and azaleas, Broadlands, the old home of Lord Mountbatten, and the cathedral cities of Salisbury and Winchester.

Our inspector loved: *The tiles in the gentlemens' loo; and the stunning food - be prepared to eat.*

CHEWTON GLEN

NEW MILTON, HAMPSHIRE BH25 6QS

Voted 'Best Country House Hotel in the World' by Gourmet magazine and the only privately owned hotel in the UK to hold five AA Red Stars, Chewton Glen is set in 130 acres of gardens, woodland and parkland on the edge of the New Forest, close to the sea. Owners Martin and Brigitte Skan have created a haven of tranquillity, luxury and comfort. The wonderful setting of the restaurant, which overlooks the landscaped gardens, adds to the sublime culinary experience created by Head Chef Pierre Chevillard, who uses fresh local produce to create surprising and delicious dishes, complemented by an impressive wine list. The 59 sumptuous bedrooms, all individually designed with carefully chosen fabrics, are the ultimate in luxury with fantastic marble bathrooms, cosy bathrobes, crystal sherry decanters and views over the surrounding parkland. The stunning new Health Club opened in Spring 2002. In addition to the magnificent 17.5m pool, there are now improved changing rooms with their own steam room and sauna, more treatment rooms, larger gym, hydrotherapy pool and a totally new lounge, buffet and bar with a conservatory and sun terrace There are indoor and outdoor tennis courts, a 9-hole golf course and an outdoor swimming pool. Fishing, shooting and riding can be arranged locally.

Our inspector loved: Its impeccable standards and dedication to quality.

Directions: Take A35 from Lyndhurst towards Bournemouth. Turn left at Walkford, then left before roundabout. The hotel is on the right.

Web: www.johansens.com/chewtonglen
E-mail: reservations@chewtonglen.com
Tel: 01425 275341
Fax: 01425 272310

Price Guide: (Room only)
double £250–£405
suites £480–£720

167

HOTEL DU VIN & BISTRO

SOUTHGATE STREET, WINCHESTER, HAMPSHIRE SO23 9EF

Directions: M3 to Winchester. Southgate Street leads from the City centre to St. Cross.

Web: www.johansens.com/hotelduvinwinchester
E-mail: info@tunbridgewells.hotelduvin.com
Tel: 01962 841414
Fax: 01962 842458

Price Guide:
single/double/twin from £105
suite from £185

Relaxed, charming and unpretentious are words which aptly describe the stylish and intimate Hotel du Vin & Bistro. This elegant hotel is housed in one of Winchester's most important Georgian buildings, dating back to 1715. It was the first of this successful groups properties and established an entirely new approach to what hotels are all about. The 23 individually decorated bedrooms feature superb beds made up with crisp, Egyptian cotton and offer every modern amenity, including trouser press, mini bar and CD players. Each bedroom is sponsored by a wine house whose vineyard features in its decorations. Bathrooms boasting power showers, oversized baths and fluffy towels and robes add to guests' sense of luxury and comfort. Quality food cooked simply with fresh ingredients is the philosophy behind the Bistro, where as you would expect an outstanding and reasonably priced wine list is available. There are also 2 function rooms for special occasions. A welcoming and enthusiastic staff cater for every need. The hotel is a perfect base for exploring England's ancient capital, famous for its cathedral, its school and antique shops. The New Forest is a short drive away.

Our inspector loved: *The relaxed informality of service and rooms.*

LAINSTON HOUSE HOTEL

SPARSHOLT, WINCHESTER, HAMPSHIRE SO21 2LT

The fascinating history of Lainston House is well documented, some of its land having been recorded in the Domesday Book of 1087. Set in 63 acres of superb downland countryside, this graceful William and Mary country house has been sympathetically restored to create a beautiful hotel with a stately home atmosphere. From the individually designed bedrooms to the main reception rooms, elegant and comfortable furnishings are the hallmark of Lainston House. Freshly prepared food, attentive service and views over the lawn make the restaurant one of the most popular in Hampshire. Facilities are available for small meetings in the Mountbatten Room or larger functions in the 17th century Dawley Barn. Latest facillities include a fully equipped gymnasium. The charming grounds hold many surprises – an ancient chapel, reputedly haunted by the legendary Elizabeth Chudleigh, an 18th century herb garden and a dovecote. Historic Winchester is only 2½ miles south, while Romsey Abbey, Salisbury and the New Forest are a short drive away. Other local activities include riding, country walking and good trout fishing on the River Test at nearby Stockbridge.

Our inspector loved: Supremely spacious and elegant, new rooms with bathrooms to match.

Directions: Lainston House is well signposted off the B3049 Winchester–Stockbridge road, at Sparsholt 2½ miles from Winchester.

Web: www.johansens.com/lainston
E-mail: enquiries@lainstonhouse.com
Tel: 01962 863588
Fax: 01962 776672

Price Guide:
single from £100
double/twin from £150
suite from £285

ALLT-YR-YNYS HOTEL

WALTERSTONE, NR ABERGAVENNY HEREFORDSHIRE HR2 0DU

Nestling in the foothills of the Black Mountains, on the fringes of the Brecon Beacons National park, Allt-yr-Ynys is an impressive Grade II 16th century manor house hotel. The Manor was the home of the Cecil family whose ancestry dates back to Rhodri Mawr, King of Wales in the 8th century. A more recent Cecil was Lord Burleigh, Chief Minister to Queen Elizabeth I, portrayed by Sir Richard Attenborough in the recent film, 'Elizabeth'. Features of this interesting past still remain and include moulded ceilings, oak panelling and beams and a 16th century four-poster bed in the Jacobean suite. However, whilst the charm and the character of the period remains, the house has been sympathetically adapted to provide all the comforts expected of a modern hotel. The former outbuildings have been transformed into spacious and well-appointed guest bedrooms. Fine dining is offered in the award-winning restaurant and the conference/function suite accommodates up to 200 guests. Facilities include a heated pool, Jacuzzi, clay pigeon shooting range and private river fishing. Pastimes include exploring the scenery, historic properties and plethora of tourist attractions.

Directions: 5 miles north of Abergavenny on A465 Abergavenny/ Hereford trunk road, turn west at Old Pandy Inn in Pandy. After 400 metres turn right down lane at grey/green barn. The hotel is on the right after 400 metres.

Web: www.johansens.com/alltyrynys
E-mail: allthotel@compuserve.com
Tel: 01873 890307
Fax: 01873 890539

Price Guide:
single from £65
double/twin from £95
suite £130

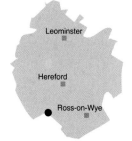

Leominster

Hereford

● Ross-on-Wye

Our inspector loved: A beautiful quiet location and features of a 16th Century Manor House.

THE CHASE HOTEL

GLOUCESTER ROAD, ROSS-ON-WYE, HEREFORDSHIRE HR9 5LH

The Chase Hotel, just a few minutes' walk from the historic market town of Ross-on-Wye, is a handsome Georgian Country House Hotel situated in 11 acres of beautiful grounds and landscape gardens. The 36 en suite bedrooms contain all the latest amenities, including satellite television. The bedrooms and lounge areas, preserve the original Georgian style of the Hotel. Guests wishing to relax will enjoy the convivial ambience and comfortable décor in the Chase Lounge and Bar. Overlooking Chase Hill, the tall elegant windows of the Lounge expose the splendour of the surrounding landscape. The delightful Chase Restaurant, with its delicate peach furnishings, is renowned for its superb traditional cuisine and excellent service and has won several accolades and awards including an AA Rosette. The hotel is an ideal venue for conferences, exhibitions, training activities, weddings including civil ceremonies and events for up to 300 guests. Activities within the locality include water sports, theatre, countryside rambles, fascinating antique centres or perusing the shops in either the historic city of Hereford or Regency Cheltenham.

Our inspector loved: *The extensive conference and banqueting facilities in the heart of the beautiful town of Ross-On-Wye.*

Directions: From the M50 (Jct4) turn left for Ross-on-Wye, take A40 Gloucester at the second roundabout and turn right for town centre at third roundabout. The Hotel is ½ mile on the left.

Web: www.johansens.com/chasehotel
E-mail: info@chasehotel.co.uk
Tel: 01989 763161
Fax: 01989 768330

Price Guide:
single £70–£110
double/twin £85–£130
suite £150

SOPWELL HOUSE HOTEL, COUNTRY CLUB & SPA

COTTONMILL LANE, SOPWELL, ST ALBANS, HERTFORDSHIRE AL1 2HQ

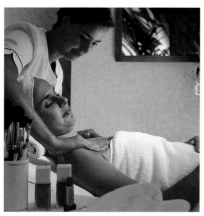

Directions: Close to M25, M1, M10, A1(M). 28m from Heathrow Airport. From motorways or A414 take A1081 to St Albans. Turn left at Grillbar. Cross mini-roundabout. Hotel is ¼ mile on left.

Web: www.johansens.com/sopwellhouse
E-mail: enquiries@sopwellhouse.co.uk
Tel: 01727 864477
Fax: 01727 844741/845636

Price Guide: (room only)
single £85–£125
double/twin £120–£165
suites from £175

Once the country home of Lord Mountbatten, surrounded by a peaceful and verdant 12-acre estate, Sopwell House is an oasis just minutes away from the motorways. The classical reception rooms reflect its illustrious past and the grand panelled ballroom opens out onto the terraces and gardens. The bedrooms, some with four-posters, are spacious and well-equipped. Beautifully designed Mews Suites are ideal for long-stay executives and bridal parties. Superb English and international cuisine and fine wines are served in the enchanting Magnolia Restaurant amidst the trees after which it is named, whilst Bejerano's Brasserie offers an informal ambience. The conference and banqueting suites, overlooking the splendid gardens and terrace, are popular venues for weddings and special events. A Business Centre provides guests with facilities such as photocopier, fax and e-mail. The Country Club & Spa, dedicated to health and relaxation, has a full range of fitness facilities and highly qualified beauty therapists.

Our inspector loved: *The huge new entrance lobby with sofas & open fire set in a French Chateâu fireplace.*

ST MICHAEL'S MANOR

ST MICHAEL'S VILLAGE, FISHPOOL STREET, ST ALBANS, HERTFORDSHIRE AL3 4RY

Owned and run by the Newling Ward family for the past thirty-five years, St Michael's Manor is a rare gem – peaceful, intimate, and set in delightful landscaped grounds. It is also within the historic village of St Michael's and a stone's throw from the magnificent St Albans Abbey. Each of the 22 bedrooms has been individually designed – some have four-poster beds and some are sitting-room suites – and all have an elegance and charm. Many of the bedrooms overlook the award-winning grounds, set in five acres, with wide sweeping lawns and a beautiful lake that hosts a variety of wildlife. The Georgian lounge and the award-winning conservatory dining room also overlook the gardens and make a wonderful setting for a tantalising dinner. There is also an excellent variety of vegetarian dishes. Coffee may be served in the Oak Lounge, which dates from 1586, with its fine panelled walls and original Elizabethan ceiling. Hatfield House and the Roman remains of Verulamium are within easy reach, as is London, which is only twenty minutes away by train. Weekend rates from £60 per person.

Our inspector loved: *The gardens and the lake, they are wonderful.*

Directions: Easy access to M1 Junction 6/7, M25 Junction 21a 10 minutes, M4/M40 25 minutes, Luton airport 20 minutes.

Web: www.johansens.com/stmichaelsmanor
E-mail: smmanor@globalnet.co.uk
Tel: 01727 864444
Fax: 01727 848909

Price Guide:
single £125–£195
double/twin £160–£260
suites £245–£320

DOWN HALL COUNTRY HOUSE HOTEL

HATFIELD HEATH, NR BISHOP'S STORTFORD, HERTFORDSHIRE CM22 7AS

Directions: The hotel is 14 miles from the M25, 7 miles from the M11 and Bishop's Stortford Station. Heathrow airport is 60 miles away; Stansted is 9 miles. There is ample free parking.

Web: www.johansens.com/downhall
E-mail: reservations@downhall.co.uk
Tel: 01279 731441
Fax: 01279 730416

Price Guide:
single £128–£168
double/twin £148–£188
suite £240

Set in 110 acres of parkland, this Italianate mansion is the perfect choice for those wishing to escape the pressures of everyday life. A peaceful ambience pervades this tastefully restored country house hotel. The well-appointed bedrooms all feature period furnishings and in-room safes and afford picturesque views across the grounds. Gastronomes will be pleased with the excellent cuisine served in the Downham and the new Ibbetsons 2-Rosette restaurant. Here, English and French dishes are prepared with only the finest fresh ingredients. The superb on site sporting facilities include two all-weather tennis courts, a putting green, croquet lawn, swimming pool, sauna and whirlpool. Clay pigeon shooting, horse-riding and golf can be arranged nearby. Day excursions include visits to Cambridge, horse racing at Newmarket, Constable Country and the old timbered village of Thaxted. This is an ideal venue for board meetings, conferences and corporate hospitality as it offers elegant, airy meeting rooms, a range of good facilities and a secluded environment. The rooms accommodate 10 delegates boardroom-style and up to 240 theatre-style. Weekend rates available.

Our inspector loved: *The chandelliers and beautiful flower arrangements in the high ceilinged elegant lounge.*

PENDLEY MANOR HOTEL & CONFERENCE CENTRE

COW LANE, TRING, HERTFORDSHIRE HP23 5QY

The Pendley Manor was commissioned by Joseph Grout Williams in 1872. His instructions to architect John Lion were to build it in the Tudor style, reflecting the owner's interest in flora and fauna on the carved woodwork and stained-glass panels. The bedrooms are attractively furnished and well-equipped and the restaurant boasts AA and RAC awards. Pendley Manor offers flexible conference facilities for up to 250 people. 9 purpose-built conference suites and 8 syndicate rooms, all with natural daylight, are available. Team-building and multi-activity days within the grounds can be arranged as well as marquee events. On the estate, which lies at the foot of the Chiltern Hills, sporting facilities include tennis courts, gymnasium, a snooker room with full-size table, games rooms, buggy riding, laser shooting, archery and hot-air balloon rides. The Hotel's new health and leisure facilities including an indoor heated swimming pool, jacuzzi, sauna and solarium. Places of interest nearby include Woburn, Winslow Hall, Chenies Manor, Tring Zoological Museum and Dunstable Downs.

Our inspector loved: *The clever new swimming pool which adapts for functions.*

Directions: Leave the M25 at junction 20 and take the new A41. Take the exit marked 'Tring'. At the roundabout take the A4251, then the first right turn into Cow Lane.

Web: www.johansens.com/pendleymanor
E-mail: sales@pendley–manor.co.uk
Tel: 01442 891891
Fax: 01442 890687

Price Guide:
single £110
double/twin £130–£150
suites £160

HANBURY MANOR

WARE, HERTFORDSHIRE SG12 0SD

Directions: On the A10 25 miles north of London and 32 miles south of Cambridge

Web: www.johansens.com/hanburymanor
E-mail: conferenceandevents.hanburymanor@marriotthotels.co.uk
Tel: 01920 487722
Fax: 01920 487692

Price Guide:
single/double/twin from £149
suites £249–£349

An outstanding 5-star hotel, Marriott Hanbury Manor, London's favourite Hotel and Country Club combines palatial grandeur with the most up-to-date amenities. Designed in 1890 in a Jacobean style, the many impressive features include elaborately moulded ceilings, carved wood panelling, leaded windows, chandeliers, portraits and huge tapestries. These create an elegant and comfortable environment. The two dining rooms vary in style from the more traditional and formal Zodiac Restaurant to the contemporary Oakes Grill. All the cuisine is under the inspired guidance of Executive Chef Glen Watson. The health club includes a 17m indoor swimming pool, spa bath, resistance gymnasium, cardiovascular suite, dance studio, crèche, sauna and steam rooms. Professional treatments include herbal wraps, aromatherapy, mineral baths and massage, while specialists can advise on a personal fitness programme. There is an 18-hole golf course par excellence designed by Jack Nicklaus II, previous host to the PGA European Tour English Open. Outdoor pursuits including shooting, archery, horse-riding and hot-air ballooning can be arranged. Ideal for conferences, twelve rooms offer versatile business meetings facilities, with fax, photocopying, secretarial services and full professional support available. Stansted Airport is 16 miles away.

Our inspector loved: *The decorative plastered ceiling in the Zodiac Restaurant.*

ISLE OF WIGHT - SEAVIEW

THE PRIORY BAY HOTEL

PRIORY DRIVE, SEAVIEW, ISLE OF WIGHT PO34 5BU

From decades gone by this beautiful site has been built upon by Medieval monks, Tudor farmers and Georgian gentry. Now its medley of buildings has been sympathetically restored and brought to life as a splendid hotel. Situated in gorgeous open countryside to the south of Seaview, the Priory Bay overlooks its own private beach. Everything about it is stylish and elegant, from the massive arched stone entrance with magnificent carved figures to the delightful, flower-filled gardens with their shady corners and thatched roofed tithe barns. The public rooms are a delight, exquisitely and comfortably furnished, with tall windows framed by rich curtains and liberally filled with vases of flowers. Log fires blaze in open fireplaces during colder months. Each of the 18 comfortable bedrooms is individually decorated and has picturesque views over the gardens. The dining room is establishing a reputation for first-class gastronomy, complemented by a fine wine list. Guests can relax under shady umbrellas in the garden or on the surrounding terraces. For the more energetic guest, there is an outdoor pool and the hotel's adjoining 9-hole golf course. Butterfly World, a tiger sanctuary, Carisbrook Castle and Osborne House are all nearby.

Our inspector loved: The painted dining room.

Directions: Ferry from Portsmouth, Lymington or Southampton to Fishbourne, Yarmouth. Ryde, East or West Cowes. The hotel is on the B3330.

Web: www.johansens.com/priorybayiow
E-mail: reception@priorybay.co.uk
Tel: 01983 613146
Fax: 01983 616539

Price Guide:
single £70–£195
double/twin £140–£258

THE GEORGE HOTEL

QUAY STREET, YARMOUTH, ISLE OF WIGHT PO41 0PE

Directions: From the M3/M27, exit at junction 1 and take the A377 to Lymington and then the ferry to Yarmouth. Alternatively, ferry services run regularly to the island from Southampton and Portsmouth. The A3054 leads direct to Yarmouth.

Web: www.johansens.com/georgeyarmouth
E-mail: res@thegeorge.co.uk
Tel: 01983 760331
Fax: 01983 760425

Price Guide:
single from £125
double/twin from £170

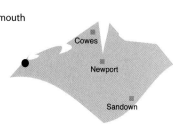

This historic 17th century town house is superbly located just a few paces from Yarmouth's ancient harbour. Built for Admiral Sir Robert Holmes, a former governor of the island, it once welcomed Charles II through its doors. With the cosy ambience of a well-loved home, The George is the perfect place for self-indulgence. Beautifully furnished and well-equipped bedrooms complement the luxurious surroundings. Enjoy either the 3 AA Rosette cuisine in the elegant restaurant or opt for a more informal à la carte meal in the lively brasserie with its lovely sea views. The excellent cellar contains particularly good claret. The hotel has its own private beach and there is no shortage of leisure opportunities in the near vicinity, including world class sailing on the Solent. Yarmouth remains the gateway to the downs and villages of the West Wight and there are countless opportunities to make the most of this area of outstanding natural beauty by walking, hiking or enjoying a host of other country pursuits, golf too. Historic places of interest include Carisbrook Castle and Osborne House.

Our inspector loved: *Watching the boats come and go.*

EASTWELL MANOR

BOUGHTON LEES, NR ASHFORD, KENT TN25 4HR

Set in the 'Garden of England', Eastwell Manor has a past steeped in history dating back to the 16th century when Richard Plantagenet, son of Richard III, lived on the estate. Surrounded by impressive grounds it encompasses a formal Italian garden, scented rose gardens and attractive lawns and parkland. The magnificent exterior is matched with the splendour of the interior. Exquisite plasterwork and carved oak panelling adorn the public rooms whilst throughout the Manor interesting antique pieces abound. The individually furnished bedrooms and suites, some with fine views across the gardens, feature every possible comfort. There are 19 courtyard apartments giving 39 more bedrooms, all with en suite facilities. The new health & fitness spa features an indoor and outdoor heated 20m pool, hydrotherapy pool, sauna, steam room, Technogym gymnasium and 14 beauty treatment rooms. Guests can enjoy a choice of dining experiences, fine British cuisine in the Manor Restaurant, and a similar standard of food at the less formal Brasserie. Nearby attractions include the cathedral city of Canterbury, Leeds Castle and several charming market towns. Situated near Ashford Eurostar station, Eastwell is perfect for trips to Paris and Brussels.

Our inspector loved: The panelled rooms and the water curtain in the Spa.

Directions: M20 Jct 9. A28 towards Canterbury, then A251 signed Faversham. Hotel is 3 miles north of Ashford in Boughton Lees

Web: www.johansens.com/eastwellmanor
E-mail: eastwell@marstonhotels.com
Tel: 01233 213000
Fax: 01233 635530

Price Guide:
single From £170
double/twin £200–£245
suites £265–£355

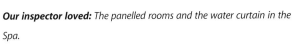

ROWHILL GRANGE HOTEL AND SPA

WILMINGTON, DARTFORD, KENT DA2 7QH

Directions: M20 junction 1/M25 junction 3. Take the B2173 into Swanley and B258 north at Superstore roundabout. After Hextable Green the entrance is almost immediately on the left.

Web: www.johansens.com/rowhillgrange
E-mail: admin@rowhillgrange.com
Tel: 01322 615136
Fax: 01322 615137

Price Guide: (room only)
single £140–£245
double/twin £165–£205
suite £215–£305

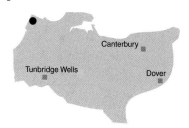

An unexpected find on the outer edge of London bordering on the Kent countryside, Rowhill Grange nestles in nine acres of woodlands and mature gardens descending to a picturesque lake. A combination of top service and friendliness makes Rowhill Grange the perfect venue for everything from weekend breaks to special occasions such as weddings and anniversaries. All the luxurious named bedrooms boast individual character and decoration, with a full range of facilities available to ensure maximum comfort and convenience for guests. The à la carte Restaurant is supplemented with the delightful Brasserie. From late spring and through the summer months guests may take dinner on the terrace, sharing a scenic view with the swans and ducks. For special occasions, business meetings or dinners, private dining rooms are available. The Clockhouse Suite is a self contained functions annexe with a dining/dancing area, comfortable lounge and a bar. The Utopia Health and Leisure Spa is outstanding with all the latest equipment for women and for men including the UK's first therapy pool of its kind.

Our inspector loved: *This surprising green oasis and the trend setting pool and pamper facilities.*

CHILSTON PARK

SANDWAY, LENHAM, NR MAIDSTONE, KENT ME17 2BE

This magnificent Grade I listed mansion, one of England's most richly decorated hotels, was built in the 13th century and remodelled in the 18th century. Now sensitively refurbished, the hotel's ambience is enhanced by the lighting, at dusk each day, of over 200 candles. The drawing room and reading room offer guests an opportunity to relax and to admire the outstanding collection of antiques. The entire hotel is a treasure trove full of many interesting objets d'art. The opulently furnished bedrooms are fitted to a high standard and many have four-poster beds. Good, fresh English cooking features on outstanding menus supported by an excellent wine list. Several intimate and delightful rooms afford wonderful opportunities for private dining parties. In keeping with the traditions of a country house, a wide variety of sporting activities are available, golf and riding nearby, fishing in the natural spring lake and punting.

Our inspector loved: The astonishing collections of object d'art.

Directions: Take junction 8 off the M20, then A20 to Lenham Station. Turn left into Boughton Road. Go over the crossroads and M20; Chilston Park is on the left.

Web: www.johansens.com/chilstonpark
E-mail: chilstonpark@arcadianhotels.co.uk
Tel: 01622 859803
Fax: 01622 858588

Price Guide:
single from £85
double/twin from £98
suite from £250

HOTEL DU VIN & BISTRO

CRESCENT ROAD, ROYAL TUNBRIDGE WELLS, KENT TN1 2LY

Directions: From M25 take A21 south in the direction of Hastings. to Tunbridge Wells. The hotel has parking facilities.

Web: www.johansens.com/hotelduvintunbridge
E-mail: reception@tunbridgewells.hotelduvin.com
Tel: 01892 526455
Fax: 01892 512044

Price Guide: (room only)
double/twin from £85

Set in the historic town of Tunbridge Wells, this Grade II sandstone mansion dates back to 1762 and although in the centre, it enjoys spectacular views over Calverley Park. An inviting ambience is present throughout the property, from the convivial bar to the sunny terrace. The 36 en suite bedrooms have been individually decorated and are enhanced by the superb Egyptian linen, CD players and satellite television. The spacious bathrooms feature power showers, large baths and fluffy robes and towels. The hotel takes great pride in its excellent bistro cuisine and the outstanding wine list. The imaginative dishes are prepared using the freshest local ingredients and are exceptionally good value. Fine wine dinners are often held at the hotel, whilst private tastings may be organised given prior notice. There are many castles, gardens and stately homes within the vicinity, such as Chartwell, Groombridge Place and Hever Castle. Guests can work up their appetites by rambling through the orchards and hop fields, perusing the shops and boutiques in the Pantiles or playing golf nearby.

Our inspector loved: *The informality, and its own tiny vineyard.*

THE SPA HOTEL

MOUNT EPHRAIM, ROYAL TUNBRIDGE WELLS, KENT TN4 8XJ

The Spa was originally built in 1766 as a country mansion with its own landscaped gardens and three beautiful lakes. A hotel for over a century now, it retains standards of service reminiscent of life in Georgian and Regency England. All the bedrooms are individually furnished and many offer spectacular views. Above all else, The Spa Hotel prides itself on the excellence of its cuisine. The grand, award winning Chandelier restaurant features the freshest produce from Kentish farms and London markets, complemented by a carefully selected wine list. Within the hotel is Sparkling Health, a magnificent health and leisure centre which is equipped to the highest standards. Leisure facilities include an indoor heated swimming pool, a fully equipped state-of-the-art gymnasium, cardiovascular gymnasium, steam room, sauna, beauty and hairdressing salons, flood-lit hard tennis court and 1/2 mile jogging track. The newly established stables include gentle trails and safe paddocks for children to enjoy pony riding under expert guidance. Special half board weekend breaks are offered, for a minimum 2 nights stay, with rates from £85 per person per night – full details available on request.

Our inspector loved: *Its traditional grand dining room.*

Directions: Facing the common on the A264 in Tunbridge Wells.

Web: www.johansens.com/spahotel
E-mail: reservations@spahotel.co.uk
Tel: 01892 520331
Fax: 01892 510575

Price Guide: (room only)
single £88–£98
double/twin £110–£165

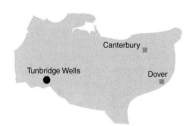

Canterbury

Tunbridge Wells

Dover

ASTLEY BANK HOTEL & CONFERENCE CENTRE

BOLTON ROAD, DARWEN, LANCASHIRE BB3 2QB

Directions: From Blackburn take the M65 east. Exit at junction 4 and take the A666 south towards Bolton. After approximately two miles pass through Darwen. The hotel is on the right.

Web: www.johansens.com/astleybank
E-mail: sales@astleybank.co.uk
Tel: 01254 777700
Fax: 01254 777707

Price Guide:
single £80–£105
double/twin £100–£130

Morecambe

Blackpool

Blackburn

Astley Bank stands high and impressive overlooking six acres of magnificent grounds and flower-filled gardens adjacent to the peaceful West Pennine Moors midway between Blackburn and Bolton. Built in the early 19th century it was, over the years, home to some of Lancashire's leading dignitaries. Today it is a stylish, comfortable country retreat with a character and ambience reflecting its mansion house era combined with all modern facilities demanded by today's discerning visitor. The public rooms are spacious and elegant and the en suite bedrooms are decorated and furnished to the highest standard. Most of them enjoy superb views over the garden and the four-poster and executive bedrooms provide additional luxury. In the attractive garden restaurant chef James Andrew produces tasty à la carte and table d'hôte menus which are complemented by an extensive selection of wines. Being within easy reach of the motorway network and Manchester Airport, Astley Bank is a popular venue with meetings organisers. There are three conference rooms supported by six purpose built syndicate rooms. All have natural daylight and are fitted with a variety of audiovisual equipment.

Our inspector loved: The stained glass windows on the upstairs landing.

NEW

NORTHCOTE MANOR

NORTHCOTE ROAD, LANGHO, BLACKBURN BB6 8BE

Large, redbrick and typically Victorian, this attractive and externally decorative Hotel stands in the foothills of the RibbleValley amidst some of Lancashire's most spectacular countryside. Excellently run by joint proprietors Craig Bancroft, a wine connoisseur, and Nigel Haworth, an award-winning chef, Northcote Manor has been an esteemed restaurant with rooms since 1983. Its high standards of hospitality, comfort, décor and food has earned it the prestigious award of 'The Independent Hotel of the Year' by the Caterer and Hotelkeeper. Nigel, proud member of the Academy of Culinary Arts, trained in Switzerland and London and his gourmet cuisine has received innumerable accolades, including a Michelin Star and Egon Ronay's 1995 Chef of the Year distinction. His superb local and creative International dishes are presented with professionalism and aplomb in a delightful restaurant. Each meal is complemented by a superb wine list that is 400 bin strong. The Hotel has 14 beautifully furnished, en suite bedrooms that offer every comfort. Nearby are the Trough of Bowland and the Roman town of Ribchester and 4 golf courses are within a 10 mile radius. The Yorkshire Dales and Lake District are within easy reach.

Our inspector loved: *Nigel Haworth's herb and organic vegetable garden.*

Directions: From M6 junction 31 take A59 towards Glitheroe. After 8 miles turn left into Northcote Road, immediately before the Langho roundabout.

Web: www.johansens.com/northcotelancs
E-mail: sales@northcotemanor.com
Tel: 01254 240555
Fax: 01254 246568

Price Guide:
single £100–£130
double/twin £130–£160

THE GIBBON BRIDGE HOTEL

NR CHIPPING, FOREST OF BOWLAND, LANCASHIRE PR3 2TQ

Directions: From the south: M6 Exit 31A, follow signs for Longridge. From the north: M6 Exit 32, follow A6 to Broughton and B5269 to Longridge; approx 3 miles from Longridge follow Gibbon Bridge brown tourism signs.

Web: www.johansens.com/gibbonbridge
E-mail: reception@gibbon–bridge.co.uk
Tel: 01995 61456
Fax: 01995 61277

Price Guide:
single £70–£120
double/twin £100–£120
suites £130–£250

This award-winning hotel in the heart of Lancashire in the Forest of Bowland is a welcoming and peaceful retreat. The area, a favourite of the Queen, is now officially recognised as the centre of the Kingdom! Created in 1982 by resident proprietor Janet Simpson and her late Mother Margaret, the buildings combine traditional architecture with interesting Gothic masonry. Individually designed and equipped to the highest standard, the seven bedrooms and 22 suites include four-posters, half-testers, Gothic brass beds and whirlpool baths. The restaurant overlooks the garden and is renowned for traditional and imaginative dishes incorporating home-grown vegetables and herbs. The garden bandstand is perfect for musical repertoires or civil wedding ceremonies. Elegant rooms, lounges and a unique 'Al Fresco' dining area are available for private dinner parties and wedding receptions. For executive meetings and conference facilities the hotel will offer that 'something a bit different'. Leisure facilities include beauty salon, gymnasium, solarium, steam room, all-weather tennis court and outdoor activities.

Our inspector loved: The spectacular landscaped gardens surrounding the bandstand.

QUORN COUNTRY HOTEL

66 LEICESTER ROAD, QUORN, LEICESTERSHIRE LE12 8BB

Originally Leicestershire's most exclusive private club, created around the original 17th century listed building, this award winning 4 star hotel is set in 4 acres of landscaped gardens. For the tenth consecutive year the hotel has received all 3 RAC merit awards for excellence in cuisine, hospitality and comfort and was also a recipient of a second AA Rosette Award in 1997. The bedrooms are equipped to the very highest standard with attention given to every detail. Suitable for both the business traveller or for weekend guests seeking those extra 'touches' which help create the ideal peaceful retreat. Ladies travelling alone can feel reassured that their special needs are met and indeed exceeded. Particular emphasis is given to the enjoyment of food with a declared policy of using, whenever possible, the freshest local produce. Guests' stay will be enhanced by the choice of two different dining experiences. They can choose between the Shires Restaurant with its classical cuisine with a modern style or the Orangery Brasserie with its changing selection of contemporary dishes.

Our inspector loved: *The new bedrooms overlooking the lovely gardens leading up to the waters edge.*

Directions: Situated just off the A6 Leicester to Derby main road, in the bypassed village of Quorn (Quorndon), five miles from junction 23 of the M1 from North, junction 21A from South, East and West.

Web: www.johansens.com/quorncountry
E-mail: reservations@quorncountryhotel.co.uk
Tel: 01509 415050
Fax: 01509 415557

Price Guide: (room only)
single £105
double/twin £120
executive double/twin £145
suite £155

STAPLEFORD PARK HOTEL, SPA, GOLF & SPORTING ESTATE

NR MELTON MOWBRAY, LEICESTERSHIRE LE14 2EF

Directions: By train Kings Cross/Grantham in 1 hour. A1 north to Colsterworth then B676 via Saxby.

Web: www.johansens.com/staplefordpark
E-mail: reservations@stapleford.co.uk
Tel: 01572 787 522
Fax: 01572 787 651

Price Guide:
double/twin £205–£345
suites from £425

Melton Mowbray

Leicester

Hinckley

A stately home and sporting estate where casual luxury is the byword. This 16th-century house was once coveted by Edward, Prince of Wales, but his mother Queen Victoria forbade him to buy it for fear that his morals would be corrupted by the Leicestershire hunting society! Today, Stapleford Park offers guests and club members a "lifestyle experience" to transcend all others in supreme surroundings with views over 500 acres of parkland. Stapleford was voted 'Top UK Hotel for Leisure Facilities' Conde Nast Traveller, Johansens' most 'Excellent Business Meeting Venue 2000' and holds innumerable awards for its style and hospitality. Individually designed bedrooms and a four-bedroom cottage have been created by famous names such as Mulberry, Wedgwood, Liberty and Crabtree & Evelyn. British cuisine lightened up with Asian-Caribbean flavours is carefully prepared to the highest standards and complemented by an adventurous wine list. Sports include fishing, shooting, falconry, riding, tennis and an 18-hole championship golf course designed by Donald Steel. The luxurious Carnegie Clarins Spa with indoor pool, Jacuzzi, sauna and fitness room offers an array of health therapies. 11 elegant function and dining rooms are suited to private dinners, special occasions and corporate hospitality.

Our inspector loved: *The stunning views of the Leicestershire countryside from the window seat in the bedroom.*

THE OLDE BARN HOTEL

TOLL BAR ROAD, MARSTON, LINCOLNSHIRE NG32 2HT

Once a farmstead, this recently refurbished hotel is set in peaceful and picturesque countryside and provides every modern facility whilst retaining its rustic charm. The Olde Barn Hotel is a stylish hideaway ideal for exploring the area's cultural sites, which are steeped in history. Each of the 60 bedrooms are spacious, well equipped and tastefully decorated for a comfortable stay. There are also specially designed disabled rooms on the ground floor. Three luxurious suites are available for families, long-term guests or for an extra-special stay. Visitors can enjoy the romantic ambience of the newly refurbished Barn Restaurant which serves delicious traditional English and continental cuisine, complemented by an extensive list of fine wines. Less formal meals may be taken in the welcoming atmosphere of the hotel's traditional country bar. A state-of-the-art fitness centre and heated indoor swimming pool are available as well as spa, steam and sauna facilities, and eight golf courses are nearby. Excellent business services for conferences and meetings are provided, and wedding ceremonies and receptions for up to 120 guests can be arranged. The charming market town of Newark is nearby, and visitors can explore its bustling antiques and agricultural fairs.

Our inspector loved: *The peaceful rural location yet with the convenience of the nearby A1.*

Directions: 4 miles north of Grantham off the southbound carriageway. The Hotel is signposted from Marston.

Web: www.johansens.com/oldebarnhotel
E-mail: sales@oldebarnhotel.co.uk
Tel: 01400 250909
Fax: 01400 250130

Scunthorpe

Lincoln

Spalding

Price Guide:
single £65-£100
double/twin £75-£120

THE GEORGE OF STAMFORD

ST MARTINS, STAMFORD, LINCOLNSHIRE PE9 2LB

Directions: Stamford is one mile from the A1 on the B1081. The George is in the town centre opposite the gallows sign. Car parking is behind the hotel.

Web: www.johansens.com/georgeofstamford
E-mail: reservations@georgehotelofstamford.com
Tel: 01780 750750
Fax: 01780 750701

Price Guide:
single from £80–£110
double/twin from £105–£145
suite £145–£220

The George, a beautiful, 16th century coaching inn, retains the charm of its long history, as guests will sense on entering the reception hall with its oak travelling chests and famous oil portrait of Daniel Lambert. Over the years, The George has welcomed a diverse clientèle, ranging from highwaymen to kings – Charles I and William III were both visitors. At the heart of the hotel is the lounge, its natural stone walls, deep easy chairs and softly lit alcoves imparting a cosy, relaxed atmosphere, while the blazing log fire is sometimes used to toast muffins for tea! The flair of Julia Vannocci's interior design is evident in all the expertly styled, fully appointed bedrooms. Exotic plants, orchids, orange trees and coconut palms feature in the Garden Lounge, where a choice of hot dishes and an extensive cold buffet are offered. Guests may also dine alfresco in the courtyard garden. The more formal, oak-panelled restaurant serves imaginative but traditional English dishes and an award-winning list of wines. Superb facilities are incorporated in the Business Centre, converted from the former livery stables. Special weekend breaks available.

Our inspector loved: *The Stamford Room which has been decorated with fabulous murals by Jenny Bell.*

LONDON

Recommendations in London appear on pages 191-234

For further information on London, please contact:

London Tourist Board
Glen House, Stag Place
London SW1E 5LT
Internet: www.londontouristboard.com

or see **pages 466-469** for details of
local attractions to visit during your stay.

Images from www.britainonview.com

THE HALKIN

5 HALKIN STREET, BELGRAVIA, LONDON SW1X 7DJ

Directions: The nearest tube station is Hyde Park Corner.

Web: www.johansens.com/halkin
E-mail: res@halkin.co.uk
Tel: 020 7333 1000
Fax: 020 7333 1100

Price Guide:
Room £305
suite from £460

Quality of service, luxury, opulence and style are the very essence of The Halkin, an elegant and tranquil haven in the very heart of fashionable Belgravia just minutes from Knightsbridge's exclusive shopping and dining. Room design, décor, furniture, furnishings and facilities are magnificently modernistic, clear and refreshing, giving the hotel a very special feel that has guests returning time and again. Each of 41 spacious and luxurious air-conditioned rooms and suites have individual harmonious colour themes and combine the comforts of home with personal, 24-hour service. Facilities include superb all-marble bathroom, direct number fax, dual line telephone with voice mail, cable and CNN television, VCR and CD player and a high security key system. Valet and butler services are also available together with a concierge who handle entertainment, travel and sightseeing. The Halkin is renowned for its innovative restaurant Nahm. Serving stunning Thai cuisine, the restaurant has one Michelin star and open for both lunch and dinner - Pre and post dinner drinks can be enjoyed in the comfortable lounge bar.

Our inspector loved: *The spacious reception and welcoming bar.*

THE ACADEMY, THE BLOOMSBURY TOWN HOUSE

21 GOWER STREET, LONDON WC1E 6HG

Set in a superb location within London's leafy Bloomsbury district with its many garden squares, The Academy is just a few minutes' walk from the West End, Oxford Street and Covent Garden and very convenient for The British Museum. This charming collection of 5 Georgian Town Houses which hides away 2 private patio gardens, offers an oasis of style and tranquility that belies its prime location amongst the city hustle and bustle. Having undergone a complete refurbishment programme, the result of which is a unique blend of contemporary style and period charm creating a wonderfully comfortable ambience. Each of the 49 guestrooms is beautifully designed, retaining many of the original Georgian features, with elegant drapes, Regency striped wallpaper and free standing baths. The Garden Suite even has its own private courtyard garden – a real luxury in the heart of London. The Boardroom leads directly to the Conservatory Lounge and Garden, and with facilities for up to 16 delegates makes it an ideal small meeting venue, and perfect for intimate cocktail or wedding parties. The Alchemy breakfast room and Bar also lend themselves to functions.

Our inspector loved: The pretty, quiet garden and fresh attractive bedrooms.

Directions: Nearest tube Goodge Street or Tottenham Court Road. Euston and King's Cross stations are within a mile.

Web: www.johansens.com/academytownhouse
E-mail: res_academy@etontownhouse.com
Tel: 020 7631 4115
Fax: 020 7636 3442

Price Guide: (excluding VAT)
single £136
double/twin £156
suites £205–£225

Enfield

Central London

Richmond

Croydon

41

41 BUCKINGHAM PALACE ROAD, LONDON SW1W 0PS

Directions: Victoria Station and Underground links are within minutes' walk; Gatwick Express 30 minutes; Heathrow 40 minutes.

Web: www.johansens.com/41buckinghampalaceroad
E-mail: book41@rchmail.com
Tel: 020 7300 0041
Fax: 020 7300 0141

Price Guide:
king bedded £220
junior suite £400
master suite £500

This small and intimate Hotel is quietly situated, overlooking the Royal Mews and Buckingham Palace Gardens. Adjacent also to St James's Park it is perfectly positioned for access to the City and West End. The Hotel reflects a remarkable attention to detail, from its discreet and secluded guest entrance and magnificent architectural features to the beautiful furniture and club-like qualities of its superb day rooms. The 16 deluxe bedrooms and 4 split-level suites are furnished with traditional mahogany and black leather décor. With outstanding, affordable 5 star service, breakfast in the morning and a wide range of tasty snacks throughout the day can be enjoyed in the Executive Lounge. Flooded with natural daylight and comfortable chairs, the Lounge is the perfect place to read, meet or just take a moment to unwind. "41" has the world's most comfortable, hand-made English mattresses and pure wool carpets throughout, bathrooms are in marble with bespoke bath and beauty products. Every room features an interactive audio-visual station with D.V.D./C.D. players and full internet/e-mail facilities. A state-of-the-art boardroom offers ISDN teleconferencing, secretarial support, chauffeur driven cars, chef services and private dining. Trafalgar Square, the Houses of Parliament and West End Theatres are all nearby.

Our inspector loved: *The split-level rooms and very comfortable club-style lounge.*

THE RUBENS AT THE PALACE

39 BUCKINGHAM PALACE ROAD, LONDON SW1W 0PS

Excellently placed for the leisure visitor as well as the corporate customer, the Rubens has completed refurbishment of the highest order to meet the demands of the modern traveller including an exclusive Royal Wing. Located opposite Buckingham Palace, just a short stroll from St James's and Green Park. Providing guests with outstanding personal service, it is comfortably furnished with attention to every detail. In the Cavalry Bar, with its traditional English theme, there is discreet service and live piano music every evening, whilst the Palace Lounge overlooking the Royal Mews is an ideal venue for afternoon tea. Guests may choose to dine either in the Old Masters restaurant, popular for pre-theatre dining where succulent roasts are available, or in the 2 AA rosette Library restaurant, which provides an intimate and luxurious atmosphere for fine dining. Guest bedrooms offer ultimate luxury in traditional surroundings. Facilities include satellite TV and movie, fax/modem lines, complimentary beverages and 24-hour room service. The 13 air-conditioned signature suites and 8 Royal rooms, in addition to the above, offer CD systems, personal safes, mini-bars and fax machines. The Rubens also has five well-appointed, air-conditioned meeting and conference rooms, the largest accommodating up to 90 delegates. The Palace, Westminster Abbey and Parliament are all close by.

Our inspector loved: The welcoming attentive staff and variety of facilities.

Directions: 3 minutes' walk from Victoria Station, for Gatwick Express rail connection, and 10 minutes' taxi ride to Heathrow Express line.

Web: www.johansens.com/rubensatthepalace
E-mail: bookrb@rchmail.com
Tel: 020 7834 6600
Fax: 020 7828 5401

Price Guide: (room only, excluding VAT)
single from £140
double/twin from £150

CIRCUS APARTMENTS

39 WESTFERRY CIRCUS, CANARY WHARF, LONDON E14 8RW

Directions: Nearest underground station is Canary Wharf.

Web: www.johansens.com/circus
E-mail: res@circusapartments.co.uk
Tel: 020 7719 7000
Fax: 020 7719 7001

Price Guide: (excluding VAT)
1-bed apartments
£240 (daily) £1547 (weekly)
2-bed apartments
£290 (daily) £1827 (weekly)

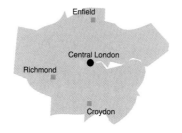

These modern and stylish serviced apartments are situated in the heart of London's latest cosmopolitan and dynamic business district and provide convenient surroundings for a private or business visit. The Square Mile lies a short distance to the West of the apartments, City Airport is a 10-minute drive away, the West End 15 minutes by underground. Around and about is a chic enclave teeming with bars and some of the best eateries in the capital, all inhabited by high-flying, design-conscious customers. Circus Apartments provide an exclusive retreat with all the comforts of a first-class hotel combined with the privacy and relaxed atmosphere of home. Each luxury one or two-bedroom apartment is spacious, individually designed to the highest standard, with every modern facility catered for. Huge floor-to-ceiling windows offer superb views; cavernous baths provide total relaxation after a busy day. Nearby Holmes Place health club with its extensive gymnasium and riverside swimming pool is available for guests' use during their stay. For the travelling executive and corporate meeting organiser, Circus has its own meetings area and fully equipped, high-tech business centre.

Our inspector loved: *The spacious, uncluttered apartments and use of the amazing health club.*

DRAYCOTT HOUSE APARTMENTS

10 DRAYCOTT AVENUE, CHELSEA, LONDON SW3 3AA

Draycott House is an attractive period town house, standing in a quiet, tree-lined avenue in the heart of Chelsea. Housed in an attractive period building, the apartments have been designed in traditional styles to provide the ideal surroundings and location for a leisure or business visit, combining comfort, privacy and security with a convenient location. All are spacious, luxury suites with a kitchen and a wonderful alternative to a hotel, with three, two or one bedrooms. Some have private balconies, a roof terrace and overlook the private courtyard garden. Each apartment is fully equipped with all home comforts; cable television, video, CD/hi-fi, private direct lines for own telephone/fax/answer machine/data, provisions/continental breakfast on arrival. A complimentary membership to an exclusive nearby health club, maid service, covered garage parking and laundry service. Additional services include airport transfers, transport, catering, travel, theatre tickets, dry cleaning/laundry, childminding and secretarial services. The West End and the City are within easy reach. Knightsbridge within walking distance. Long term reservations may attract preferential terms. Contact Jane Renton, General Manager.

Our inspector loved: The wonderful staff and homely surroundings.

Directions: Draycott House is situated on the corner of Draycott Avenue and Draycott Place, close to Sloane Square.

Web: www.johansens.com/draycotthouseapartments
E-mail: sales@draycotthouse.co.uk
Tel: 020 7584 4659
Fax: 020 7225 3694

Price Guide: (excluding VAT)
£188–£468 per night
from £1178–£2948 per week

GREAT EASTERN HOTEL

LIVERPOOL STREET, LONDON EC2M 7QN

Directions: Adjacent to Liverpool Street rail and tube station on the corner of Bishopgate.

Web: www.johansens.com/greateastern
E-mail: sales@great-eastern-hotel.co.uk
Tel: 020 7618 5000
Fax: 020 7618 5001

Price Guide:
Queen double from £240

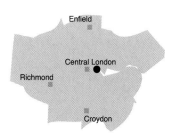

From the moment visitors enter the hotel lobby or the imposing, high-rise atrium they realise that this is an especially exciting hotel. It reopened with 246 bedrooms and 21 suites, four restaurants, 4 bars, gym, treatment rooms and 12 private dining rooms in 2000 after extensive refurbishment. Grade II listed and situated on the eastern edges of the City of London, the Great Eastern originally opened in two phases, in 1884 and 1901. The refurbishment beautifully revives the splendour of those eras, combined with 21st century modernity and facilities. No two bedrooms are alike. Those on the fifth and sixth floors have a light and airy 'loft' feel; those below have higher ceilings and period features. Rooms in the east wing are detailed with ornate late Victorian features; those in the west wing are more restrained. All have every home comfort and high-tech business facilities. Each of the hotel's restaurants and bars has its own distinctive identity. Terminus re-interprets the classic railway buffet-brasserie, Fishmarket is sea green beneath plaster cherubs, Aurora is grand and beautiful and George is Jacobean style oak-panelled. The food is equally distinctive, from classically inspired dishes to sushi and sashimi or fish and crustacea. London's major tourist attractions and theatreland are within easy reach.

Our inspector loved: The many experiences to experience - from the ultra modern bedrooms to the restaurants and bars - all great fun!

LONDON BRIDGE HOTEL & APARTMENTS

8–18 LONDON BRIDGE STREET, LONDON SE1 9SG

This elegant 4-star hotel is as ideal for the leisure visitor seeking to enjoy the cultural delights of London as it is for the business executive. It stands on the edge of the City and its heritage dates back to Roman times; archaeological finds are in the Museum of London, There is easy access to Docklands, London City Airport, Waterloo and the West End. Local attractions include Tate Modern, Shakespeare's Globe, the London Eye and Vinopolis city of wine. All 138 en suite bedrooms and suites are air-conditioned and have a blend of modern and classic furnishings with up-to-date facilities. There are also six rooms specially designed for the less mobile guest, two non-smoking floors and an executive wing. The three apartments, each with two bedrooms, are extremely spacious and comfortable and available for short and long term stays. There are five conference rooms complete with the latest audiovisual equipment. The adjacent wine bar is a convenient venue for an informal chat over drinks or a snack. London Bridge is home to one of the famed Simply Nico restaurants, which provides a popular and sophisticated setting in which to enjoy excellent and imaginative cuisine with a modern French flavour. Guests have free use of Curzons state-of-the-art gymnasium. Weekend rates available.

Our inspector loved: It's fascinating Roman history, smart rooms and city location.

Directions: Opposite London Bridge tube/rail station.

Web: www.johansens.com/londonbridge
E-mail: sales@london–bridge–hotel.co.uk
Tel: 020 7855 2200
Fax: 020 7855 2233

Price Guide: (room only)
standard rooms from £190
studio suites £265– £475

 138 M100

KINGSWAY HALL

GREAT QUEEN STREET, LONDON WC2B 5BX

Situated in the heart of London's cosmopolitan Covent Garden, Kingsway Hall is ideal for both the business and leisure visitor to London. One of the few remaining privately-owned hotels, this luxury 170-bedroom, fully air-conditioned hotel is convenient for theatreland and the City. Behind its classical façade is a spacious and dramatic foyer of modern glass and warm textured walls, leading to an elegant Lounge Bar with comfortable traditional furnishings, an ideal rendezvous for business or pleasure, especially pre- or post-theatre. Delicious modern cuisine in the restaurant is matched by an oak-timbered and marble floor set against softly-lit, painted walls under a gently undulating ceiling – dramatic in concept and colours. Facilities in all the 170 bedrooms include satellite and interactive TV, mini-bar, in-room safe and four ISDN lines. There are non-smoking floors, same-day laundry and dry cleaning, 24-hour room service and a fully equipped fitness centre. Excellent service is provided both for the individual guest and business meetings for ten up to 150 delegates. The convivial location offers a plethora of shops, bars, restaurants and theatres to explore; the Royal Opera House is close by, and easily accessible are the British Museum and Oxford Street.

Directions: Kingsway Hall is just a five minute walk from either Covent Garden or Holborn tube stations.

Web: www.johansens.com/kingswayhall
E-mail: kingswayhall@compuserve.com
Tel: 020 7309 0909
Fax: 020 7309 9696

Price Guide: (Including VAT & Service)
standard room from £230
double/twin from £240
suite from £325

Enfield

Central London

Richmond

Croydon

Our inspector loved: *The spacious lobby, the excellent welcome and trendy bar.*

ONE ALDWYCH

1 ALDWYCH, LONDON WC2B 4RH

Brilliant contemporary interiors, 2 fabulous restaurants, the happening Lobby Bar, stunning swimming pool, private screening room, thoughtful unpretentious service, cutting-edge technology, exciting private art collection, a great location in Covent Garden... just some of the reasons to stay at the privately owned, award winning One Aldwych. Its sumptuous, calm bedrooms all have individually controlled air conditioning, mini televisions in the bathrooms, CD players, high speed modem connections and private lines. Thoughtful, luxurious touches include fresh fruit and flowers delivered daily and 100% pure and natural products in the bathrooms. Some of the suites have a private gymnasium, terrace or dining room. Guests have the choice of 2 of London's busiest and most fashionable restaurants, Axis and Indigo. Both are within easy walking distance of the opera and theatres, great for before or after a show. Fitness facilities include a large, state-of-the-art gymnasium, an 18 metre lap swimming pool with underwater music, personal trainers, sauna, steam room and beauty/therapy treatments.

Our inspector loved: The clean lines of its design coupled with good old fashioned service.

Directions: Located at the point where the Strand meets the Aldwych, in the heart of Covent Garden, walking distance from 15 major theatres and the opera.

Web: www.johansens.com/onealdwych
E-mail: reservations@onealdwych.com
Tel: 020 7300 1000
Fax: 020 7300 1001

Price Guide: (excluding VAT)
single £295–£360
double/twin £315–£380
Weekend rates: (including VAT)
single/double from £195

WEST LODGE PARK COUNTRY HOUSE HOTEL

COCKFOSTERS ROAD, HADLEY WOOD, BARNET, HERTFORDSHIRE EN4 0PY

West Lodge Park is a country house hotel which stands in 34 acres of Green Belt parklands and gardens. These include a lake and an arboretum with hundreds of mature trees. Despite the advantages of this idyllic setting, the hotel is only 1 mile from the M25 and within easy reach of London. Run by the Beale family for over 50 years, West Lodge Park was originally a gentleman's country seat, rebuilt in 1838 on the site of an earlier keeper's lodge. In the public rooms, antiques, original paintings and period furnishings create a restful atmosphere. All the bright and individually furnished bedrooms, many of which enjoy country views, have a full range of modern amenities. Well presented cuisine is available in the elegant restaurant. Residents enjoy free membership and a free taxi to the nearby leisure centre, which has excellent facilities. Hatfield House and St Albans Abbey are 15 minutes drive. The hotel is credited with AA 4 stars and 2 Rosettes, RAC 4 stars plus 3 merit awards.

Directions: The hotel is on A111 one mile north of Cockfosters underground station and one mile south of junction 24 on M25.

Web: www.johansens.com/westlodgepark
E-mail: info@westlodgepark.com
Tel: 020 8216 3900
Fax: 020 8216 3937

Price Guide:
single £75–£140
double/twin from £95–£180

Our inspector loved: The countryside views and fabulous arboretum, yet only 1 mile from either London Underground or M25.

HARRINGTON HALL

5-25 HARRINGTON GARDENS, LONDON SW7 4JW

The original façade of late Victorian houses cleverly conceals a privately owned hotel of substantial proportions and contemporary comfort. Harrington Hall offers 200 air-conditioned spacious bedrooms which have all been most pleasantly furnished and equipped with an extensive array of facilities. 125 of the rooms feature king-size beds. A marble fireplace dominates the comfortable and relaxing Lounge Bar, where guests can enjoy a drink in pleasant surroundings. Serving a varied international menu, the restaurant is a delightful setting for all diners from large luncheon parties to those enjoying intimate evening meals. A choice of buffet or à la carte menu is available, both offering a tempting selection of dishes. Nine fully air-conditioned conference and banqueting suites, with walls panelled in rich lacewood and solid cherry, provide a sophisticated venue for conferences, exhibitions or corporate hospitality. Harrington Hall also has a Business Centre for the exclusive use of its guests, along with a private new equipped Fitness Centre with saunas and showers.

Our inspector loved: A comfortable conventional hotel as ideal for business needs as for weekend or mid week breaks to London.

Directions: Harrington Hall is situated in the Royal Borough of Kensington and Chelsea, in Harrington Gardens south of the Cromwell Road, close to Gloucester Road underground station, two stops from Knightsbridge and Harrods.

Web: www.johansens.com/harringtonhall
E-mail: harringtonsales@compuserve.com
Tel: 020 7396 9696
Fax: 020 7396 9090

Price Guide: (including VAT & service)
single from £185
double £195
suites £245

KENSINGTON HOUSE HOTEL

15-16 PRINCE OF WALES TERRACE, KENSINGTON, LONDON W8 5PQ

Directions: Nearest underground station is High Street Kensington.

Web: www.johansens.com/kensingtonhouse
E-mail: reservations@kenhouse.com
Tel: 020 7937 2345
Fax: 020 7368 6700

Price Guide:
single £150
double/twin £175
junior suites £215

This attractive hotel with its architecturally splendid tall, ornate windows and pillared entrance stands grandly on a 19th-century site long associated with style and elegance. Just off Kensington High Street, this charming town house is an ideal base from which to explore London's attractions. Views cover delightful mews houses, leafy streets and out across city rooftops. The emphasis is on providing informal, professional service in an atmosphere of relaxation and comfort. Each of the 41 intimate bedrooms offers en suite facilities. Rooms are bright and airy with modern furniture and fittings adding to the fresh, contemporary treatment of a classic design. Home-from-home comforts include crisp linen, duvets and bathrobe. Other features are courtesy tray, ceiling fan, voicemail, modem connection and in-room safe. The two junior suites can convert into a family room. The stylish Tiger Bar is a popular venue for coffee or cocktails prior to enjoying a delicious dinner, with a menu that draws on a range of influences offering both traditional and modern dishes. The serenity of Kensington Gardens is just a gentle stroll away, and some of the capital's most fashionable shops, restaurants and cultural attractions are within walking distance. Weekend rates available.

Our inspector loved: *The tucked away, quiet location yet a stone's throw from bustling Kensington.*

THE LEXHAM APARTMENTS

32-38 LEXHAM GARDENS, KENSINGTON, LONDON W8 5JE

The Lexham has been created from four of the elegant and gracious early Victorian houses surrounding a quiet, tree-lined garden square in the heart of one of the most fashionable areas of London. The luxury one and two bedroom apartments have been stylishly furnished to provide the ideal surroundings for a family or business visit, combining comfort, flexibility, privacy and security with a convenient location. All are spacious, light and airy and equipped with all home comforts, including cable television, safe, voice mail and private phone and fax lines. Each has a full-sized, well-appointed kitchen including a washing machine/tumble dryer and a dishwasher. Many feature extra comforts such as an additional sofa bed. There is daily maid service on weekdays and 24-hour porterage. Reservations for a restaurant, theatre, car or nearby health club/swimming pool can be arranged. The Lexham has a spacious landscaped garden at the rear in which guests can relax on warmer days and evenings. The fashionable shops and restaurants of Kensington, Knightsbridge and Chelsea as well as West End theatres and the capital's tourist attractions are within easy reach. Minimum stay at the Lexham is seven days.

Our inspector loved: *The high ceilings and large windows giving a big feel of spaciousness.*

Directions: Nearest underground stations are Gloucester Road and High Street Kensington.

Web: www.johansens.com/lexham
E-mail: reservations@lexham.com
Tel: 020 7559 4444
Fax: 020 7559 4400

Price Guide: (excluding VAT)
1-bed apartment £1,275–£1375 per week
2-bed apartment £1,575–£1675 per week
Additional days pro rata

THE MILESTONE HOTEL & APARTMENTS

1 KENSINGTON COURT, LONDON W8 5DL

Directions: At the end of Kensington High Street, at the junction with Princes Gate.

Web: www.johansens.com/milestone
E-mail: bookms@rchmail.com
Tel: 020 7917 1000
Fax: 020 7917 1010

Price Guide:
single from £250
double/twin £270
suites from £430

The beautifully appointed Condé Nast Johansens award winning Milestone Hotel is situated opposite Kensington Palace with views over Kensington Gardens and the Royal parklands. A Victorian showpiece, this unique hotel has been carefully restored to its original splendour whilst incorporating every modern facility. The 57 bedrooms include 12 suites and six apartments; all are individually designed with antiques, elegant furnishings and some have private balconies. Guests may relax in the comfortable, panelled Park Lounge which, in company with all other rooms, provides a 24-hour service. The hotel's restaurant, Cheneston's, the early spelling of Kensington, has an elaborately carved ceiling, original fireplace and ornate windows. The Windsor Suite is a versatile function room, perfect for private dining and corporate meetings. The health and fitness centre offers guests the use of a Jacuzzi, sauna and gymnasium. The traditional bar, Stables, on the ground floor as well as the bright and airy conservatory are ideal for meeting and entertaining friends. The Milestone is within walking distance of some of the finest shopping in Kensington and in Knightsbridge such as Harrods and is a short taxi ride to the West End, the heart of London's Theatreland. The Royal Albert Hall and all the museums in Exhibition Road are nearby.

Our inspector loved: *The emphasis on comfort and attention to detail for the guest at this sumptious hotel.*

TWENTY NEVERN SQUARE

LONDON SW5 9PD

A unique experience in hospitality awaits guests at this elegant 4-star town house hotel. Sumptuously restored, the emphasis is on natural materials and beautiful hand-carved beds and furniture. The hotel overlooks a tranquil garden square and has its own delightful restaurant, Café Twenty, which is also available for small dinner & cocktail parties. Each of the 20 intimate bedrooms provides white marble, compact en suite facilities, and is individually designed echoing both Asian and European influences. You can choose the delicate silks of the Chinese Room or a touch of opulence in the Rococo Room. The grandeur of the Pasha Suite, complete with four-poster bed and balcony, makes an ideal setting for a special occasion. All rooms have full modern facilities including wide-screen digital TV, CD player, private safe and a separate telephone and internet/fax connection. Gym facilities are available by arrangement. The location is ideal – close to Earl's Court and Olympia exhibition centres and the tube. The Picadilly Line brings guests arriving at Heathrow in just over 30 minutes. Guests are a mere 10 minutes from London's most fashionable shopping areas, restaurants, theatres and cultural attractions such as the V&A and Science Museums.

Our inspector loved: *It's hideaway location in a pretty square.*

Directions: Two minutes from Earls Court station.

Web: www.johansens.com/twentynevernsquare
E-mail: hotel@twentynevernsquare.co.uk
Tel: 020 7565 9555
Fax: 020 7565 9444

Price Guide:
single £110–£140
double/twin £140–£195
suite £275

   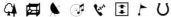

WARREN HOUSE

WARREN ROAD, COOMBE, KINGSTON-UPON-THAMES, SURREY KT2 7HY

This impressive 19th-century redbrick house with its York stone door surrounds, balustrades and tall chimneys stands in four acres of landscaped gardens. It is ideally situated for both the leisure and business visitor, just five miles from Central London, within easy reach of Heathrow and Gatwick airports and on the doorstep of Surrey's sweeping countryside and attractions. For some years Warren House has been a dedicated business venue, but under new ownership is widening its appeal. Built in 1884, the house has been sensitively restored to its original style with the addition of 21st-century facilities. The en suite bedrooms and suites are individually designed, tastefully decorated and furnished to the highest standard, including desk, television, direct dial telephone and modem connection. Chef Paul Bellingham prides himself on his international cuisine, attentively served in an elegant restaurant featuring an Oriental tiled fireplace. There is a spacious lounge, well-stocked library and excellent leisure facilities including a heated swimming pool and gymnasium. Richmond Park and two golf courses are close by with Hampton Court, Wisley Gardens, Windsor, Sandown Park, Epsom and Kempton racecourses within easy reach.

Directions: From M25 Jct 10 follow A3 north to Robin Hood roundabout. Turn left onto A308 to Kingston Hill. At the top turn left after 2nd zebra crossing into Warren Road.

Web: www.johansens.com/warren
E-mail: carolyn@warrenhouse.com
Tel: 020 8547 1777
Fax: 020 8547 1175

Price Guide:
single from £188
double/twin from £240.88

Our inspector loved: A surprising country setting in Kingston, with unexpected views.

BASIL STREET HOTEL

BASIL STREET, LONDON SW3 1AH

The Basil with its traditional and caring service feels more like an English home than a hotel. Privately owned by the same family for three generations, this traditional Edwardian hotel is situated in a quiet corner of Knightsbridge, in the midst of London's most exclusive residential and shopping area. Harrods, Harvey Nichols and other famous stores are only minutes away. It is also close to museums and theatres. The spacious public rooms are furnished with antiques, paintings, mirrors and objets d'art. All the bedrooms are individually furnished and vary in size, style and décor. The Hotel's Dining Room is an ideal venue either for unhurried, civilised lunch or dinner by candlelight with piano music whilst the Parrot Club, a lounge for the exclusive use of ladies, is a haven of rest in delightful surroundings. There are also a number of smaller intimate rooms available for private dining and meetings. The Basil ideally suits the leisure guest but with its own business centre and modem points in all bedrooms, equally meets the needs of international business travellers. There is a discount scheme for regular guests, for weekends and stays of five nights or more. Garage parking space available on request.

Our inspector loved: *The olde worlde charm and excellent location between Harvey Nicholls and Harrods.*

Directions: Close to Pavilion Road car park. Basil Street runs off Sloane Street in the direction of Harrods. Near Knightsbridge Underground and bus routes.

Web: www.johansens.com/basilstreet
E-mail: info@thebasil.com
Tel: 020 7581 3311
Fax: 020 7581 3693

Price Guide: (excluding VAT)
single from £138
double/twin from £198
family room from £275

THE BEAUFORT

33 BEAUFORT GARDENS, KNIGHTSBRIDGE, LONDON SW3 1PP

Directions: From Harrods exit at Knightsbridge underground station take third left.

Web: www.johansens.com/beaufortknights
E-mail: enquiries@thebeaufort.co.uk
Tel: 020 7584 5252
Fax: 020 7589 2834

Price Guide: (excluding VAT)
single from £155
double/twin from £185
junior suite £310

The Beaufort offers the sophisticated traveller all the style and comfort of home – combining warm, contemporary colourings with the highest possible personal attention. The Beaufort is situated in a quiet, tree-lined square only 100 yards from Harrods. On arrival, guests are greeted at the front door and given their own door key to come and go as they please. The closed front door gives added security and completes that feeling of home. All bedrooms are individually decorated, with air conditioning, twice daily maid service and many extras such as shortbread, Belgium chocolates and fruit cup. The hotel owns a video and cassette library and is home to a magnificent collection of original English floral watercolours. Breakfast comprises hot rolls and croissants, freshly squeezed orange juice and home-made preserves, tea and coffee. Complimentary offerings include champagne and all drinks from the bar, an English cream tea plus membership of a top London Health Club. A private car to or from the airport is available if staying in a Junior Suite (subject to a minimum 3 night stay). Open all year.

Our inspector loved: *The warm welcome, the bright airy drawing room and delicious home made scones available at tea-time.*

THE CADOGAN

SLOANE STREET, LONDON SW1X 9SG

The Cadogan is an imposing late-Victorian building in terracotta brick situated in a desirable location in Sloane Street, Knightsbridge. It is well-known for its association with Lillie Langtry, the 'Jersey Lily', actress and friend of King Edward VII. Her house in Pont Street now forms part of the hotel. Playwright Oscar Wilde was a regular guest here and was arrested in the hotel in 1895. The Cadogan's elegant drawing room is popular for afternoon tea, and the meals served in the air-conditioned restaurant, which has 2 AA Rosettes, combine imaginative cuisine with value for money. The hotel has 65 comfortable, air-conditioned bedrooms and suites equipped to the highest standards. The Langtry Rooms on the ground floor, once the famous actress's drawing room, make a delightful setting for small meetings, private parties and wedding receptions. The hotel also has a wedding licence. The Cadogan, close to Harrods and Harvey Nichols, is an excellent base for shopping trips. Business visitors will find its central position and easy access make it a fine place to stay when visiting London.

Our inspector loved: The peaceful and tranquil elegant drawing room.

Directions: The hotel is halfway along Sloane Street at junction with Pont Street. Close to Knightsbridge and Sloane Square tubes.

Web: www.johansens.com/cadogan
E-mail: info@cadogan.com
Tel: 020 7235 7141
Fax: 020 7245 0994

Price Guide: (incl continental breakfast & VAT)
single £235–£270
double/twin £294
studio/suite £317–£423

BEAUFORT HOUSE

45 BEAUFORT GARDENS, KNIGHTSBRIDGE, LONDON SW3 1PN

Directions: Beaufort Gardens leads off Brompton road near Knightsbridge underground station. 24hr car park nearby.

Web: www.johansens.com/beauforthouseapartments
E-mail: info@beauforthouse.co.uk
Tel: 020 7584 2600
Fax: 020 7584 6532

Price Guide: (excluding VAT)
£230–£650

Situated in Beaufort Gardens, a quiet tree-lined Regency cul-de-sac in the heart of Knightsbridge, 250 yards from Harrods, Beaufort House is an exclusive establishment comprising 21 self-contained fully serviced luxury apartments. All the comforts of a first-class hotel are combined with the privacy, discretion and relaxed atmosphere of home. Accommodation ranges in size from an intimate one bedroom to a spacious four-bedroomed apartment. Each apartment has been individually and traditionally decorated to the highest standard. All apartments have direct dial telephones with voice mail, personal safes, satellite television and DVD players. Some apartments benefit from balconies or patios. The fully equipped kitchens include washer/dryers and many have dishwashers. A daily maid service is included at no additional charge. Full laundry/dry cleaning services are available. A dedicated Guests Services team provides 24 hours coverage and will be happy to organise tours, theatre tickets, restaurant bookings, taxis or chauffeur driven limousines and other services. Complimentary membership at Champney's Health Club in Piccadilly is offered to all guests during their stay. Awarded five stars by the English Tourism Council.

Our inspector loved: *This well equipped and comfortable establishment, as ideal for weekend breaks as it is for longer stays.*

THE CAPITAL HOTEL & APARTMENTS

22-24 BASIL STREET, KNIGHTSBRIDGE, LONDON SW3 1AT

This lovely town house hotel is one of the capital's secrets, tucked away in a quiet street just a short walk from Harrods, Sloane Street, Hyde Park and the West End. Guests are welcomed in winter by an open fire and in summer by vases of flowers and cool air conditioning. The luxurious Capital was created by its Scottish proprietor, David Levin, more than 30 years ago and is still family-owned and run. Each of the comfortable bedrooms has its own specially selected fabrics, wallpapers and original paintings, and offers lavish marble bathrooms. Radio and television are controlled from bedside consoles and the beds – some super king-size – have hand-made mattresses. The Capital's fully refurbished apartments are contemporary and elegantly furnished. The hotel's small restaurant attracts a discriminating clientele who enjoy French inspired cuisine prepared by Michelin two star chef Eric Chavot. An attractive bar is a favourite pre and after dinner venue. Afternoon tea can be enjoyed in a snug sitting room. Guests have access to an exclusive private members gym and pool nearby. The concierge can arrange theatre tickets and limousines, book flights or provide a porter to accompany guests on shopping trips. Car parking facilities are on site.

Our inspector loved: *This gorgeous gem of a hotel always ready with a huge welcome for its ' guests.*

Directions: Next to Harrods, between Sloane Street and Beauchamp Place. Nearest underground station: Knightsbridge.

Web: www.johansens.com/capital
E-mail: reservations@capitalhotel.co.uk
Tel: 020 7589 5171
Fax: 020 7225 0011

Price Guide:
single £190
double/twin £245–£315
suite £375

THE CLIVEDEN TOWN HOUSE

26 CADOGAN GARDENS, LONDON SW3 2RP

Directions: Nearest underground station is Sloane Square.

Web: www.johansens.com/clivedentownhouse
E-mail: reservations@clivedentownhouse.co.uk
Tel: 020 7730 6466
Fax: 020 7730 0236

Price Guide: (excluding VAT)
single from £110
Queen double from £195
deluxe double/twin from £255
suites £390

The award-winning Cliveden Town House offers the perfect balance of luxury, service, privacy and location. Tucked away in a tranquil, tree-lined garden square between Harrods and the Kings Road, it is at the centre of fashionable London and epitomises style and elegance. Like its gracious country cousin at Cliveden, one of England's most famous stately homes, it combines the grandeur of the past with the conveniences of today, offering guests the exclusive ambience of a grand private residence. All 35 rooms are individually decorated reflecting the Edwardian period and combine 24-hour room service with all that today's discerning traveller requires. Nine of the opulent suites can be arranged to create the atmosphere of a private home with a fully-equipped kitchen and/or separate sitting room. The beautifully panelled boardroom overlooking the private residents' garden provides the perfect venue for small meetings and private parties. The shops and restaurants of Knightsbridge, Chelsea and Belgravia, West End theatres and the City are within easy reach, and a chauffeur is available for airport transfers and personalised tours. Enjoy complimentary afternoon tea or a glass of champagne in the Drawing Room.

Our inspector loved: *The complete tranquility of this country house style London town house.*

NUMBER ELEVEN CADOGAN GARDENS

11 CADOGAN GARDENS, SLOANE SQUARE, KNIGHTSBRIDGE, LONDON SW3 2RJ

In a quiet tree-lined square between Harrods and the Kings Road, Number Eleven Cadogan Gardens is an elegant town house hotel with a reputation for first class service. The hotel remains traditional yet stylish; no reception desk, no endless signing of bills, total privacy and security. The 60 bedrooms are well-appointed and furnished with antiques and oriental rugs. The Garden Suite, with its large double bedroom, has a particularly spacious drawing room overlooking the attractive gardens. Pre-dinner drinks and canapés are served every evening in the Drawing Room, whilst a varied menu is available throughout the day in the very pretty. light and airy dining room; room service operates around the clock. The Library is one of three private rooms available where small parties and business meetings can be held. Sauna and massage facilities are available or for a more strenuous work out, a personal trainer is on call in the in-house gymnasium. The fashionable shops and restaurants of Knightsbridge and Chelsea are within easy walking distance whilst the chauffeured Mercedes is available for airport and Eurostar connections. Theatre tickets, restaurant bookings and travel arrangements are all part of our unique personal service.

Our inspector loved: *The wonderful 'Englishness' of this lovely traditional hotel.*

Directions: Off Sloane Street. Nearest underground is Sloane Square.

Web: www.johansens.com/numberelevencadogangardens
E-mail: reservations@number–eleven.co.uk
Tel: 020 7730 7000
Fax: 020 7730 5217

Price Guide: (excl VAT)
single from £145
double/twin from £185
suite from £275

THE COLONNADE, THE LITTLE VENICE TOWN HOUSE

2 WARRINGTON CRESCENT, LONDON W9 1ER

Directions: Warwick Avenue underground station and taxi rank are close by. Paddington station with its direct Heathrow link is one stop away or a quick taxi ride.

Web: www.johansens.com/colonnadetownhouse
E-mail: res_colonnade@etontownhouse.com
Tel: 020 7286 1052
Fax: 020 7286 1057

Price Guide: (excluding VAT)
single £126
suites from £230

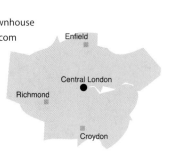

This tall, elegant Victorian town house is delightfully situated in the smart and sophisticated residential area of Little Venice which embodies the tranquil Regents Canal. It is a beautifully furnished residence offering all the comforts of a luxury hotel and is conveniently within reach of London's many sights, restaurants, theatres and business areas. The Colonnade was originally built as two private homes in 1865 and later converted into a girl's boarding school and a hospital for ladies until opening as a hotel in 1935. The House has recently been completely refurbished and has an innovative, boutique style interior. Sumptuous fabrics and lavish antiques have been carefully selected to create a unique style and ambience in each of the 43 guest rooms and suites, many of them with a terrace and four poster bed. All are individually decorated and feature every modern facility. The relaxing drawing room is ideal for guests to have pre dinner drinks or a night cap. The renowned Town House breakfast is served in the stylish breakfast room and is second to none. Car parking and airport transfers can be arranged.

Our inspector loved: Its' elegance, sophistication and warmth - all rolled into one. Please discover it for yourself!

THE LEONARD

15 SEYMOUR STREET, LONDON W1H 7JW

Four late 18th-century Georgian town houses set the character of this relaxing Johansens award-winning property. Superbly located off Portman Square, and celebrating its 7th anniversary in 2003, The Leonard has become popular very quickly with discerning travellers and celebrities alike. Imaginative reconstruction has created 11 rooms and 21 suites decorated individually to a very high standard, with a further 12 rooms and a small roof garden completed in 2002. All rooms are fully air-conditioned and include private safe, mini-bar, hi-fi system and provision for fax/modem. Bathrooms are finished in marble, and some of the larger suites have a butler's pantry or fully-fitted kitchen. The first-floor Grand suites are particularly impressive, and the Café Bar offers breakfast and light meals throughout the day. For physical fitness and stress reduction there is a compact exercise room. With professional, friendly 'Can-do' staff, The Leonard is the epitome of casual luxury in the heart of London's West End. Available opposite, also part of the hotel, The Leonard residence offers five serviced apartments which are available for longer stays.

Our inspector loved: *The new 5th floor rooftop bedrooms, as well as the 'hide-away' Central London location.*

Directions: The Leonard is north of Marble Arch off Portman Square and just around the corner from Oxford Street and Selfridges. Parking in Bryanston Street.

Web: www.johansens.com/leonard
E-mail: the.leonard@dial.pipex.com
Tel: 020 7935 2010
Fax: 020 7935 67000

Price Guide: (excl VAT)
double from £220
suites £280– £550

DORSET SQUARE HOTEL

39 DORSET SQUARE, MARYLEBONE, LONDON NW1 6QN

This little gem of a hotel is in a prime location for all that the west end of London has to offer. Set in a leafy square that was the original site for Thomas Lord's cricket ground, the Regency townhouse has been lovingly restored and designed to offer the ultimate in comfort and charm with a chic London edge. Each of the 38 bedrooms has been perfectly appointed to offer the latest amenities such as air-conditioning, modem ports and the marble bathrooms are equipped to an extremely high standard. The Potting Shed restaurant is a delight – light and airy and exuding character with an array of terracotta pots along one wall. The cuisine is a selection of modern British, and on several weeknights there is live jazz. For those who prefer to remain in the luxury of their bedrooms there is also the wonderful "bedroom picnic" – a basket laden with cold meats, fresh fruits, cheeses and pastries and chilled champagne. Madame Tussauds, the Planetarium and Regent's Park zoo are all within two minutes walk, and the shops of Oxford Street, Baker Street and even Bond Street are not far away. Theatreland is only a few minutes away, and even the city is easily accessible by tube.

Directions: Left from Marylebone tube or right from Baker street tube – the hotel is just minutes from each.

Web: www.johansens.com/dorsetsquare
E-mail: dorset@firmdale.com
Tel: 020 7723 7874
Fax: 020 7724 3328

Price Guide: (excl VAT)
single from £98
double/twin from £140
suite from £240

Our inspector loved: Everything! but in particular the light, airy and fun Potting Shed restaurant.

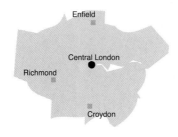

Enfield

Central London

Richmond

Croydon

THE ASCOTT MAYFAIR

49 HILL STREET, LONDON W1J 5NB

This, the latest concept in city centre accommodation, offers all the benefits of a hotel and yet also privacy and space in what the brochure describes as "residences", with one, two or three bedrooms, in a spectacular art deco building. The apartments have a 24 hour concierge for security and assistance. A maid will be assigned to you for the full duration of your stay. A complimentary Continental breakfast is served in The Terrace, overlooking the private gardens. There is an Honour Bar in The Club where guests can mingle or entertain. The Hothouse offers a gym, sauna, steam room and solarium. The Business Service includes the use of a private boardroom. A marvellous kitchen is provided in each apartment with everything necessary for entertaining in the versatile lounge. The study area has fax and computer links. The sitting room is extremely comfortable and beautifully decorated. It has satellite television, a music system and video. The luxurious bedrooms have amazing en suite bathrooms, full of soft white towels. The Ascott is in the heart of London – Mayfair being close to all the major shopping centres and best restaurants, theatre-land and sightseeing.

Our inspector loved: *At The Ascott Mayfair, you feel at home away from home.*

Directions: Hill Street is off Berkeley Square, near Green Park Underground Station.

Web: www.johansens.com/ascottmayfair
E-mail: enquiry.london@the–ascott.com
Tel: 020 7659 4321
Fax: 020 7659 4322

Price Guide: (excluding VAT)
Studio £205 daily, £1360 weekly
1 bed £260 daily, £1,725 weekly
2 beds £435 daily, £2,895 weekly

THE CHESTERFIELD MAYFAIR

35 CHARLES STREET, MAYFAIR, LONDON W1J 5EB

Directions: Nearest underground station is Green Park.

Web: www.johansens.com/chesterfieldlondon
E-mail: book@rchmail.com
Tel: 020 7491 2622
Fax: 020 7491 4793

Price Guide: (excuding VAT)
single £165-£210
double/twin £175-£265
themed rooms & suites £265-£495

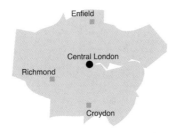

Set in the heart of Mayfair, this charming hotel with its Georgian elegance combines up-to-date facilities and an excellent, truly personal service. All rooms and public areas are air-conditioned, and the surroundings provide the perfect ambience in which to dine or relax. Guests can enjoy the tranquil 'al fresco' atmosphere of The Conservatory, catch up on reading and correspondence in the wood-panelled Library, or unwind with a drink to the sound of a gentle piano in the club-style Bar. There is a range of themed rooms including the Music Room and Theatre Room. The AA Rosette Restaurant serves the finest in British and international cuisine, complemented by superb wines which can be sampled in the wine room. Bedrooms are beautifully furnished and include many thoughtful extras such as bathrobes, complimentary bottled water, and deluxe toiletries. The business traveller has also been considered, and can take advantage of full secretarial support, voicemail, fax and modem lines and essential office supplies. All events, from meetings to conferences and banquets can be held at The Chesterfield, and the Hotel is licensed for wedding ceremonies. Bond Street with its shops is close by, as are numerous museums and theatres and the City. Themed room packages available.

Our inspector loved: *The attentiveness and warm welcome by the staff.*

THE DORCHESTER

PARK LANE, MAYFAIR, LONDON W1A 2HJ

Built in 1931, this grand Hotel successfully combines ultra-modern convenience with traditional service and atmosphere. All 250 rooms, including 55 suites, have air-conditioning, an entertainment and business system, video on demand (up to 60 films), direct Internet access and Mircrosoft Word, Excel and Powerpoint operated via an infrared keyboard on the TV. These individually decorated, cosy English Country House style bedrooms also boast a fax, scanner, copier, DVD and CD player, with a music library of 2,500 tracks available, in all the rooms, 90 of which have 42" plasma screens. All the rooms will undergo a multi million pound refurbishment programme in 2002. A variety of cuisine is on offer; from traditional British food in The Grill Room, Cantonese in The Oriental Restaurant, Italian cooking in The Dorchester Bar and traditional afternoon tea in The Promenade. The fully air-conditioned banqueting rooms can be hired independently. There is a highly regarded day spa, offering a wide range of treatments. Personalised care is a pillar of The Dorchester's fine reputation. Year round packages are available.

Our inspector loved: *The superb example of English elegance, charm and superb service.*

Directions: Towards Hyde Park Corner/Piccadilly end of Park Lane.

Web: www.johansens.com/thedorchester
E-mail: reservations@dorchesterhotel.com
Tel: 020 7629 8888
Fax: 020 7409 0114

Price Guide: (excluding VAT)
single £305–£325
double/twin £340–£370
suite £525–£2,150

NEW

THE WESTBOURNE

165 WESTBOURNE GROVE, NOTTING HILL, LONDON W11 2RS

Directions: Close to Queensway Underground , Paddington Station and Westbourne Grove.

Web: www.johansens.com/westbourne
E-mail: info@aliaswestbourne.com
Tel: 020 7243 6008
Fax: 020 7229 7201

Price Guide: (room only, including VAT)
portrait £175
landscaped £195
garden £225

Notting Hill, which is bustling with trendy restaurants, bijoux shops and charming cafés, is the perfect setting for The Westbourne; a unique venue with a wonderful Bohemian atmosphere enhanced by the most creative design. Highly polished floors, funky furniture and artistic lighting create a stunning effect and superb attention to detail. Friendly service and excellent, attentive staff combine to make a highly pleasurable stay. Individually commissioned, comfortable bedrooms feature ultra modern décor and have crisp quality linens with simple colour co-ordinated fabrics. The attractive Garden Rooms have skylights and open onto the patio; a glorious suntrap. All rooms have high-tech facilities including D.V.D. players. Exciting art by well-known contemporary artists is on display and includes work by Gavin Turk, Angus Fairhurst and Dan Macmillan. A delicious breakfast is served in the quiet surrounds of the dining area and, although dinner is not served in the Hotel, there is an extensive room service menu and an abundance of quality restaurants within walking distance. The famous Portobello Road Market is fascinating to explore and sells just about everything. Guests will enjoy the eclectic shopping, pubs and bars in the Notting Hill area. London's main tourist areas are easy to reach by train, bus or taxi and Paddington Station is convenient for the Heathrow Express.

Our inspector loved: *The modern and trendy surroundings; both in and out.*

PEMBRIDGE COURT HOTEL

34 PEMBRIDGE GARDENS, LONDON W2 4DX

This gracious Victorian town house has been lovingly restored to its former glory whilst providing all the modern facilities demanded by today's discerning traveller. The 20 rooms all of which have air conditioning and are individually decorated with pretty fabrics and the walls adorned with an unusual collection of framed fans and Victoriana. The charming and tranquil sitting room is as ideal for a quiet drink and light snacks as it is for a small informal meeting. There is also a small boardroom and sitting room on the lower ground floor. The Pembridge Court is renowned for the devotion and humour with which it is run. Its long serving staff and its two famous cats "Spencer" and "Churchill" assure you of a warm welcome and the very best in friendly, personal service. Over the years the hotel has built up a loyal following amongst its guests, many of whom regard it as their genuine 'home from home' in London. The Pembridge is situated in quiet tree-lined gardens in Londons' trendy Notting Hill Gate. The area is lively, colourful and full of life with lots of great pubs and restaurants and the biggest antiques market in the world at nearby Portobello Road.

Our inspector loved: The welcome from the staff...and cats, as well as the excellent atmosphere.

Directions: Pembridge Gardens is a small turning off Notting Hill Gate/Bayswater Road, just 2 minutes from Portobello Road Antiques Market

Web: www.johansens.com/pembridgecourt
E-mail: reservations@pemct.co.uk
Tel: 020 7229 9977
Fax: 020 7727 4982

Price Guide: (inclusive of English breakfast & VAT)
single £130–£170
double/twin £190–£200

THE ATHENAEUM HOTEL & APARTMENTS

116 PICCADILLY, LONDON W1J 7BJ

Directions: The nearest underground station is Green Park.

Web: www.johansens.com/athenaeum
E-mail: info@athenaeumhotel.com
Tel: 020 7499 3464
Fax: 020 7493 1860

Price Guide:
(excl VAT) single from £265
double/twin from £295
suite/apartment from £415

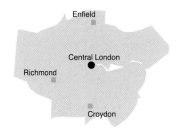

Set in a superb location, the stylish Athenaeum Hotel & Apartments is extremely welcoming with friendly staff and highly personalised service. Comfortable and luxurious décor adorns the cosy, secluded Windsor Lounge and the public areas. Lovely airy and bright bedrooms, some with views over Green Park, have fresh colour schemes, double, twin or king-size beds and all the modern conveniences to create a contemporary yet traditional ambience. Housed in Edwardian town houses adjacent to the Hotel, the spacious and elegantly furnished 1 and 2 bedroom apartments have a private entrance and kitchen facilities. Modern, British cuisine using the finest seasonal ingredients, is served in the highly acclaimed Bullochs restaurant whose warm and intimate surroundings feature a floor of imported Jerusalem stone. For the energetic or those wishing to be pampered, the Spa offers a well-equipped gym, jacuzzi, steam room, sauna, beauty therapy and massage. With its central location, the Athenaeum is ideal for business, leisure and shopping. Buckingham Palace, Hyde Park, Bond Street and the theatre district are a short walk away. Harrods, Covent Garden, Westminster, Kensington Palace and Soho are only a few minutes by taxi or underground.

Our inspector loved: Everything! From the comfortable drawing room and cosy bar to the attractive restaurant and wonderful views.

THE PETERSHAM

NIGHTINGALE LANE, RICHMOND-UPON-THAMES, SURREY TW10 6UZ

With its curves, columns and arches, tall slim windows, elaborate carvings, wrought-iron balcony railings and a majestic peaked tower this luxurious Victorian hotel impresses its visitors again and again. Beautifully situated in 'the London countryside', it is just 8 miles from the capital's centre. It stands high on Richmond Hill with views over one of the most attractive stretches of the River Thames. Built in 1865, the hotel's character emanates from its architecture which, as well as the landmark tower, features the longest unsupported Portland Stone staircase in England. Overhead are superb restored ceiling paintings. The classically styled en suite bedrooms and suites combine every modern comfort with the elegance and grandeur of the past. The Petersham Penthouse is particularly sumptuous and extremely good value. Many of the guest rooms offer panoramic Thamesside views. Exceptional and imaginative cuisine, complemented by an extensive wine list, is prepared by talented chef Andy Johns and served with aplomb in the sophisticated restaurant. Apart from large Richmond Park with its herds of deer there are many visitor attractions nearby, including Hampton Court Palace, Syon Park, Ham House and the Royal Botanic Gardens at Kew.

Our inspector loved: *Its unrivalled location, high above the Thames and Petersham Meadows.*

Directions: From the M25, exit at junctions 8, 9, 12 or 15. From London via Cromwell Road and the A316.

Web: www.johansens.com/petersham
E-mail: enq@petershamhotel.co.uk
Tel: 020 8940 7471
Fax: 020 8939 1098

Price Guide:
single £135–£160
double/twin £170–£230
suite £295

THE RICHMOND GATE HOTEL AND RESTAURANT

RICHMOND HILL, RICHMOND-UPON-THAMES, SURREY TW10 6RP

Directions: Opposite the Star & Garter Home at the top of Richmond Hill.

Web: www.johansens.com/richmondgate
E-mail: richmondgate@corushotels.com
Tel: 020 8940 0061
Fax: 020 8332 0354

Price Guide:
single from £120
double/twin from £150
suite from £225

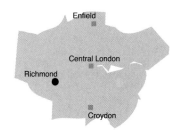

This former Georgian country house stands on the crest of Richmond Hill close to the Royal Park and Richmond Terrace with its commanding views over the River Thames. The 68 stylishly furnished en suite bedrooms combine every comfort of the present with the elegance of the past and include several luxury four-poster rooms and suites. Exceptional and imaginative cuisine, complemented by an extensive wine list offering over 100 wines from around the world is served in the sophisticated surroundings of 'Gates On The Park Restaurant'. Weddings, business meetings and private dining events can be arranged in a variety of rooms. The beautiful victorian walled garden provides for summer relaxation. Cedars Health and Leisure Club is accessed through the hotel and includes a 20 metre pool, 6 metre spa, sauna, steam room, aerobics studio, cardiovascular and resistance gymnasia and a health and beauty suite. Richmond is close to London and the West End yet in a country setting. The Borough offers a wealth of visitor attractions, including Hampton Court Palace, Syon House and Park and the Royal Botanic Gardens at Kew.

Our inspector loved: Its extensive leisure facilities.

THE CRANLEY

10-12 BINA GARDENS, SOUTH KENSINGTON, LONDON SW5 0LA

Standing in a quiet, tree-lined street in the heart of Kensington, this charming and sophisticated Victorian town house is an ideal city venue for the leisure and business visitor alike, blending traditional style and service with 21st-century technology. Furnished with beautiful antiques and hand-embroidered linen fabrics The Cranley has an understated elegance. Striking colour combinations and stone used throughout the bedrooms and reception areas are derived from the original floor in the entrance hall. Recently completely refurbished, the Cranley's bedrooms are now among some of the most comfortable in the capital. All are delightfully decorated and have king-size four-poster or half-tester canopied beds. Each room is light, air-conditioned and has facilities ranging from antique desk, two direct dial telephone lines and voicemail to interactive television with Internet access. The luxury bathrooms have traditional Victorian-style fittings combined with a lavish use of warm limestone. Guests can enjoy copious Continental breakfasts, complimentary English afternoon tea and an evening help-yourself apéritif with canapés. Many of London's attractions are within easy walking distance, including the shops and restaurants of Knightsbridge and the Kings Road.

Our inspector loved: This cosy and intimate hotel with beautiful crisp bed linen.

Directions: Nearest underground stations are Gloucester Road and South Kensington.

Web: www.johansens.com/cranley
E-mail: info@thecranley.com
Tel: 020 7373 0123
Fax: 020 7373 9497

Price Guide:
single £182.12
double/twin £211.50
suite £246.75

THE GALLERY

8-10, QUEENSBERRY PLACE, SOUTH KENSINGTON, LONDON SW7 2EA

Directions: Three minutes' walk from South Kensington underground station, just off Cromwell Road.

Web: www.johansens.com/thegallery
E-mail: reservations@eeh.co.uk
Tel: 020 7915 0000
Fax: 020 7915 4400

Price Guide: (excl. VAT)
single £120
double/twin £145
suites £220

Enfield

Central London

Richmond

Croydon

A unique experience awaits guests at this elegant Victorian house where the high standards of comfort and amenities can be enjoyed. The Gallery's atmosphere is one of quiet refinement and, true to its name, the hotel displays original art in every room. The welcoming mahogany panelled reception area and lounge features an imposing Jacobean Revival chimney piece, plump sofas and discrete bar. Old kilims adorn side tables, an Ottoman theme is repeated in the rich pile carpeting. Everything from Oriental porcelain in the lobby to the furniture and décor of the Morris Room has been expertly selected. The beautiful drawing room evokes the arts and crafts style popularised by the famed Victorian painter and designer – arbutus wallpaper, tulip and lily carpet, an oak-cased Manxman piano and an antique bar billiards table. The 34 individually decorated guest rooms offer every facility including two direct dial telephones with data port. Two master suites, Rossetti and Leighton, are furnished with the refinement befitting their names; each has its own roof terrace, Jacuzzi, CD and DVD players. Light snacks are available. The Gallery's location is ideal – close to Harrods, fashionable Knightsbridge, bohemian Chelsea and numerous museums.

Our inspector loved: *The eclectic collection of Victorian art.*

NUMBER SIXTEEN

16 SUMNER PLACE, LONDON SW7 3EG

Freshly refurbished behind an immaculate pillared façade, Number Sixteen, situated in the heart of South Kensington, is surrounded by some of London's best restaurants, bars, shops and museums. Harrods, Knightsbridge shopping, Hyde Park and the Victoria & Albert Museum are all just a short walk away. Although the area has a buzzy, cosmopolitan character, the hotel is a haven of calm and seclusion. In winter an open fire and honesty bar in the drawing room entices with its warmth, whilst in summer the conservatory opens onto an award-winning private garden. The library is ideal for greeting friends or holding an informal business meeting. The 40 bedrooms are individually designed and decorated in a traditional English style complete with crisp Frette bedlinen and white, hand-embroidered bedspreads. Each is appointed with facilities expected by the modern traveller, including mini-bar, personal safe and direct dial telephone with voice mail and modem point. A light breakfast is served in the comfort of your room. Staff are friendly and attentive ensuring that guests are looked after almost as if they were staying in a private home. South Kensington underground station is just a two-minute walk away, providing easy access to the West End and the City and a direct link to Heathrow airport.

Directions: Sumner Place is off the old Brompton Road near Onslow Square.

Web: www.johansens.com/numbersixteen
E-mail: reservations@numbersixteenhotel.co.uk
Tel: 020 7589 5232
Fax: 020 7584 8615

Price Guide: (excluding VAT)
single from £85
double/twin from £150
junior suite from £195

Our inspector loved: The complete feeling of well-being and elegance.

NEW

THE PELHAM HOTEL

15 CROMWELL PLACE, LONDON SW7 2LA

Directions: The nearest underground station is South Kensington and London Victoria train station is close by.

Web: www.johansens.com/pelham
E-mail: pelham@firmdale.com
Tel: 020 7589 8288
Fax: 020 7584 8444

Price Guide: (Excl VAT)
single from £150
double/twin from £180
suite from £275

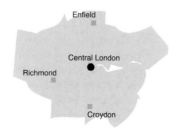

Part of the Firmdale group of hotels, The Pelham is yet another superb find in the heart of London's South Kensington. With interiors designed by Kit Kemp, the style and character of a luxury townhouse combine with a warm, welcoming ambience and impeccable service. In keeping with the grand English country tradition the wood panelled drawing room and library each boast open fireplaces and inviting sofas, while a flexible private room can be transformed for corporate meetings or intimate dining occasions. The subtly lit Kemps Bar and Restaurant is the perfect meeting place for guests and locals alike. It also provides a relaxed and popular venue for parties and receptions, serving excellent modern British food, as well as a wide selection of wines and champagnes. The Pelham's 51 bedrooms and suites are individually furnished and equipped with modern facilities including a safe, two line telephone with voice mail, modem and fax point. Beautiful fabrics and bathrooms of mahogany and granite adorn the open and spacious suites with their high ceilings and original features. With its enviable location the Hotel is just steps away from the Natural History and Victoria and Albert museums, and is within easy reach of Knightsbridge, the Earls Court Exhibition Centres and Hyde Park.

Our inspector loved: The big squashy cushions, impeccable service and Kemps Bar and Restaurant.

THE QUEENSGATE

54 QUEENS GATE, LONDON SW7 5JW

Perfectly located in desirable South Kensington opposite the magnificent Natural History Museum, the chic Queensgate opened in November 2001 and offers unpretentious, beautifully appointed surroundings in which to pamper yourself. Uncluttered spaces and pure, clean lines are combined with comfortable contemporary furniture for an elegant ambience and subtle interior design. Natural colours and light create gentle tones and a feeling of well-being. Beautiful wooden floors complement the crisp white linens and natural materials. An extremely warm and friendly welcome is given on entering this oasis of peace, creating a relaxed atmosphere. Individually designed bedrooms have private terraces and lovely views over the Natural History Museum. Egyptian percale cotton, fluffy bathrobes, D.V.D. and modem facilities reflect the quality and luxury of the Hotel. A delicious Continental breakfast is served in the Hotel's dining room and there is an excellent choice of exciting International cuisine available in the abundance of restaurants and cafés in the area. The Queensgate's bar is perfect for a relaxing drink with friends and has high ceilings, a cosy fireplace, deep sofas, occasional chairs and leather banquettes. Ideal for visiting museums, the Hotel is within walking distance of Harrods, Hyde Park, the Royal Albert Hall and Kensington High Street.

Our inspector loved: This unpretentious Hotel with uncluttered big appeal.

Directions: The Hotel is easily accessible from the M4. The nearest tube station is Gloucester Road (a 5 minute walk).

Web: www.johansens.com/queensgate
E-mail: enquiries@thequeensgate.com
Tel: 020 7761 4000
Fax: 020 7761 4040

Price Guide: (excluding VAT)
single £140
double/twin £160-£180
suites £220-£260

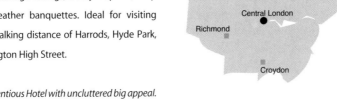

NEW

DOLPHIN SQUARE HOTEL

DOLPHIN SQUARE, CHICHESTER STREET, LONDON SW1V 3LX

Directions: The closest underground station is Pimlico.

Web: www.johansens.com/dolphinsquare
E-mail: reservations@dolphinsquarehotel.co.uk
Tel: 020 7834 3800
Fax: 020 7798 8735

Price Guide:
studio suite single £155
studio suite double/twin £180–£190
1 bedroom suite £190–£400
2 bedroom suite £320
3 bedroom suite £450

Enfield
Central London
Richmond
Croydon

Dolphin Square Hotel is centrally located in large, exquisite gardens and is bordered by the River Thames and Westminster. This quiet oasis, decorated in a wonderful contemporary style, offers discreet service and a friendly welcome. The 148 attractive suites are decorated in classical or modern décor with subtle colour co-ordinated design enhancing the warm atmosphere. Most suites have a compact, well-equipped kitchen, whilst there is 24 hour room service available and full hotel facilities, for those who prefer not to cater for themselves. Guests can relax in the informal Brasserie, which serves delicious cuisine from around the world and the Clipper Bar is a fun yet stylish venue for a drink and chat. The award winning Rhodes in the Square offers an excellent eclectic menu within an elegant setting. A variety of shops in Dolphin Square provides for your every need including a newsagent, chemist, hair salon and travel agent. The Hotel's heated swimming pool and health club are a real asset and include a fully-equipped gym, tennis courts, squash courts, croquet lawn, sauna, steam room and numerous beauty and health treatments offered by qualified professionals. Superb facilities are available for celebrations of any size and excellent business and corporate services are available.

Our inspector loved: *The mix of contemporary and classic rooms plus its marvellous health club, restaurant and gardens.*

51 BUCKINGHAM GATE

51 BUCKINGHAM GATE, WESTMINSTER, LONDON SW1E 6AF

Close to Buckingham Palace, St James's Park and the Houses of Parliament, 51 Buckingham Gate is contemporary style and luxury on a grand scale. This attractive Victorian town house offers everything the discerning guest could wish for: privacy, relaxation and superb service delivered by multilingual staff which includes a team of Ivor Spencer trained butlers. Guests have a choice of dining options: Quilon, offering southern coastal Indian cuisine, Bank Westminster, Zander Bar and The Library. There are 82 suites and apartments, ranging from junior suites to the five-bedroom Prime Minister's Suite, which combine contemporary interior design with luxury hotel facilities. Deluxe suites offer award-winning bathrooms, whilst designated Ivor Spencer Suites have 16-hour personal butler service, limousine pick-up and an exclusive range of special amenities. Each suite provides sophisticated technology including two-line speaker telephones, voicemail, dataport, fax/copier/printer, CD and DVD player. Fully equipped kitchens as well as 24-hour room service are available. A team of talented chefs is also at hand to prepare private dinners. Guests can enjoy treatments at the exclusive Shiseido Qi Salon and a fully equipped gymnasium at the Club at St James Court.

Our inspector loved: The pure opulence experienced in each individual suite.

Directions: Nearest underground stations are St James's Park and Victoria.

Web: www.johansens.com/buckinghamgate
E-mail: info@51-buckinghamgate.co.uk
Tel: 020 7769 7766
Fax: 020 7233 5014

Price Guide:
suites £300–£975

CANNIZARO HOUSE

WEST SIDE, WIMBLEDON COMMON, LONDON SW19 4UE

Directions: The nearest tube and British Rail station is Wimbledon.

Web: www.johansens.com/cannizarohouse
E-mail: cannizarohouse@thistle.co.uk
Tel: 0870 333 9124
Fax: 020 8970 2753

Price Guide: (room only):
double/twin from £156
feature room from £184

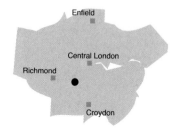

Cannizaro House, an elegant Georgian country house, occupies a tranquil position on the edge of Wimbledon Common, yet is only 18 minutes by train from London Waterloo and the Eurostar terminal. Cannizaro House restored as a superb hotel has, throughout its history, welcomed Royalty and celebrities such as George III, Oscar Wilde and William Pitt. The 18th century is reflected in the ornate fireplaces and mouldings, gilded mirrors and many antiques. All the hotel's 45 bedrooms are individually designed, with many overlooking beautiful Cannizaro Park. All of the 17 executive rooms have air-conditioning. Several intimate rooms are available for meetings and private dining, including the elegant Queen Elizabeth Room – a popular venue for wedding ceremonies. The Viscount Melville Suite offers air-conditioned comfort for up to 100 guests. There is a spacious south facing summer terrace as ideal for afternoon tea and receptions as it is for evening cocktails. The award-winning kitchen, produces the finest modern and classical cuisine, complemented by an impressive list of wines.

Our inspector loved: *The summer terrace - so perfect for Champagne and strawberries.*

ETROP GRANGE

THORLEY LANE, MANCHESTER AIRPORT, GREATER MANCHESTER M90 4EG

Hidden away near Manchester Airport lies Etrop Grange, a beautiful country house hotel and restaurant. The original house was built in 1780 and more than 200 years on has been lovingly restored. Today, the hotel enjoys a fine reputation for its accommodation, where the luxury, character and sheer elegance of the Georgian era are evident in every feature. The magnificent award winning restaurant offers a well balanced mix of traditional and modern English cuisine, complemented by an extensive selection of fine wines. Attention to detail ensures personal and individual service. In addition to the obvious advantage of having an airport within walking distance, the location of Etrop Grange is ideal in many other ways. With a comprehensive motorway network and InterCity stations minutes away, it is accessible from all parts of the UK. Entertainment for visitors ranges from the shopping, sport and excellent nightlife offered by the city of Manchester to golf, riding, clay pigeon shooting, water sports and outdoor pursuits in the immediate countryside. Cheshire also boasts an abundance of stately homes, museums and historical attractions.

Our inspector loved: *The complimentary chauffeured Jaguar to Manchester Airport.*

Directions: Leave M56 at junction 5 towards Manchester Airport. Follow signs for Terminal 2. Go up the slip road. At roundabout take first exit, take immediate left and hotel is 400yds on the right.

Web: www.johansens.com/etropgrange
E-mail: etropgrange@corushotels.com
Tel: 0161 499 0500
Fax: 0161 499 0790

Price Guide:
single £137–£145
double/twin £175–£205
suites £199

NEW

DIDSBURY HOUSE

DIDSBURY PARK, DIDSBURY VILLAGE, MANCHESTER M20 5LT

Directions: Exit the M56 at junction 1 and take the A34 towards Manchester. At the traffic lights turn left onto the A5145 towards Didsbury. At the second set of traffic lights turn right into Didsbury Park. The Hotel is on the left.

Web: www.johansens.com/didsburyhouse
E-mail: enquiries@didsburyhouse.co.uk
Tel: 0161 448 2200
Fax: 0161 448 2525

Price Guide:
single £98–£150
double/twin £118–£175
suite £195–£300

This stylish and contemporary small 'boutique' Hotel, in a leafy south Manchester suburb, is a careful refurbishment and extension of a Grade II listed, mid 19th century Victorian villa and coach house. It is the second town house hotel concept to be opened in the city by Eamonn and Sally O'Loughlin, the first being the acclaimed Eleven Didsbury Park. Their new hotel, just 100 yards away, is double the size and twice as stunning. It seduces guests immediately as they enter its beautiful hallway. The superb, original carved wooden staircase carries the eye up to a magnificent stained-glass window. Ornate ceilings and architraves, polished wooden floors and warm décor dominate the luxurious public rooms. The exquisite and romantic attic suite has separate His and Her cast-iron roll-top baths and His and Her seats in a huge shower and steam cubicle, while in every gorgeous en suite bedroom the bath fits 2. A top floor footbridge spans a central atrium and a charming lounge with ostrich-egg sized lights and pewter bar leads onto a secluded courtyard furnished with a restful and imaginative combination of steel, bamboo and water features. Gym, steam room and face, body and holistic treatments are available in the SO Spa. Breakfast and room service menu available in the evenings, but complimentary transport is provided for dining out.

Our inspector loved: *The stunning stained-glass window seen from both the front hall and atrium.*

BARNHAM BROOM

NORWICH, NORFOLK NR9 4DD

Barnham Broom is a golfers' paradise. Situated in 250 acres of the beautiful River Yare Valley 10 miles from the cathedral city of Norwich, it offers everything for the sporting enthusiast, and tranquillity for leisure seekers. The complex has two 18-hole golf courses of character and quality. The par 72 Valley course, dominated by water features and mature trees, was designed by Frank Pennink, one of Europe's most respected course architects, and is one of the finest in Norfolk. The par 71 Hill, designed by Pennink's protégé, Donald Steel, offers fine views of the surrounding countryside with the main challenge being the constant breezes and the many bunkers guarding the greens. In addition, there are excellent practice facilities, including 3 full-length academy holes, PGA professional tuition by the Peter Ballingall Golf School. Hotel guests enjoy a choice of 52 tastefully decorated en suite bedrooms with every comfort. The main restaurant, Flints, offers full à la carte and table d'hôte menus. Lighter meals and beverages are available all day at the Sports Bar and Café with 6ft satellite TV screen. A superb, newly equipped leisure centre features an indoor pool, spa bath, sauna, steam room, solarium and gym. Conference and banqueting suites.

Our inspector loved: The bedrooms have a fresh, country appeal.

Directions: Signposted from A47 in the East Midlands and A11 from London.

Web: www.johansens.com/barnhambroom
E-mail: enquiry@barnhambroomhotel.co.uk
Tel: 01603 759393
Fax: 01603 758224

Price Guide:
single from £90
double/twin from £110
four poster from £120
suite from £135

237

NEW

THE HOSTE ARMS HOTEL

THE GREEN, BURNHAM MARKET, NORFOLK PE31 8HD

Directions: Burnham Market is 2 miles from A149 on B1155.

Web: www.johansens.com/hostearms
E-mail: reception@hostearms.co.uk
Tel: 01328 738777
Fax: 01328 730103

Price Guide:
single £71–£115
doubles £96–£140
suites £120–£170
penthouse £200

Dating back to the 17th century and overlooking the green in the picturesque village of Burnham Market, The Hoste Arms has received many awards including 'Johansens Inn of the Year' and the 'Inn of the Year César Award' from the Good Hotel Guide. Paul Whittome and Manager Emma Tagg continue their quest to improve and upgrade services and facilities, achieved with the addition of a stylish and relaxed lounge and the new Gallery Restaurant. Jeanne Whittome has decorated the rooms throughout the Hotel in a simple yet individual and elegant style. All main dining areas are air-conditioned and the walled gardens, with electrically operated canopy and outside heating, provide an attractive area for diners to enjoy their meal. The excellent menu, created by head chef Andrew McPherson and his team, features an extensive amount of seafood and has British, French and Oriental touches. A selection of well-priced wines is offered alongside a private collection of Paul's favourites. There are several stately homes in the area such as Holkham Hall, Houghton Hall and Sandringham and for nature lovers there are bird sanctuaries and boat trips. Golf enthusiasts have Hunstanton, Brancaster and Cromer. Fully-equipped business meeting facilities are now available also. Special breaks available.

Our inspector loved: *That there is always something new and exciting here, this year The Zulu Suite.*

CONGHAM HALL

GRIMSTON, KING'S LYNN, NORFOLK PE32 1AH

Dating from the mid-18th century, this stately Manor House is set in acres of parkland, orchards and gardens. The conversion from country house to luxury hotel in 1982 was executed with care to enhance the elegance of the classic interiors. The hotel's renowned herb garden grows over 700 varieties of herb, many are used by the chef to create modern English dishes with the accent on fresh local produce and fish from the local Norfolk markets. The hotel's hives even produce the honey for your breakfast table. The beautiful flower displays, home-made pot pourri and roaring log fires blend together to create a welcoming and relaxing atmosphere. Congham Hall is the ideal base from which to tour the spectacular beaches of the north Norfolk coastline, Sandringham, Burnham Market and Holkham Hall.

Our inspector loved: The wonderful herb garden.

Directions: Go to the A149/A148 interchange north east of King's Lynn. Follow the A148 towards Sandringham/Fakenham/Cromer for 100 yards. Turn right to Grimston. The Hotel is then 2 miles on the left.

Web: www.johansens.com/conghamhall
E-mail: reception@conghamhallhotel.co.uk
Tel: 01485 600250
Fax: 01485 601191

Price Guide:
single from £99
double/twin from £150
suites from £230

PARK FARM COUNTRY HOTEL & LEISURE

HETHERSETT, NORWICH, NORFOLK NR9 3DL

Directions: By road, just off A11 on B1172, Norwich Airport eight miles, Norwich rail station six miles and Norwich bus station five miles.

Web: www.johansens.com/parkfarm
E-mail: enq@parkfarm–hotel.co.uk
Tel: 01603 810264
Fax: 01603 812104

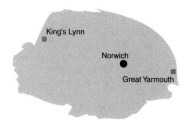

King's Lynn

Norwich

Great Yarmouth

Price Guide:
single £90-£125
double/twin £115-£150
suites £160-£180

Park Farm Hotel occupies a secluded location in beautifully landscaped grounds south of Norwich, once the second greatest city in England. There are executive rooms for additional comforts, with four poster beds and Jacuzzi baths. Additional bedrooms have been sympathetically converted from traditional and new buildings to reflect the style of the six rooms available in the main house. A superb leisure complex to suit all ages has been carefully incorporated alongside the original Georgian house to include heated swimming pool, sauna, steam room, solarium, spa bath, gymnasium, aerobics studio and a new beauty therapy area. The delightful Georgian restaurant is renowned for high standards of cuisine and service, with a wide selection of dishes and fine choice of wines. Conference facilities cater for up to 120 candidates, (24 hour and daily delegate rates available). Ideal location for wedding receptions. The Norfolk broads, the coast, Norwich open market, Castle museum and Cathedral are nearby. A self catering cottage is also available.

Our inspector loved: *The large new conservatory which is a popular spot for morning coffee & bar meals.*

FAWSLEY HALL

FAWSLEY, NR DAVENTRY, NORTHAMPTONSHIRE NN11 3BA

Set in the beautiful Northamptonshire countryside and surrounded by acres of rolling parkland with lakes, landscaped by Capability Brown, Fawsley Hall combines the charm and character of a gracious manor with the facilities and comforts of a modern hotel. The original Tudor Manor House opened as a hotel in 1998 but many traces of its illustrious past have been retained, such as the vaulted hall and Queen Elizabeth I chamber. 43 wonderfully decorated rooms offer a range of Tudor, Georgian, Victorian and 'classic modern' styles, many of which include four poster beds. The Knightley Restaurant has established a reputation as being the finest in Northamptonshire and the 'Old Laundry Bar' provides delicious light meals at lunchtime. The Hotel has 2 new health and beauty treatment rooms together with a fitness studio. 7 conference and syndicate rooms can accommodate up to 80 delegates and the attractive Salvin Suite can seat up to 140 for a private banquet or wedding reception. Places of historic interest include: Sulgrave Manor, ancestral home of George Washington; Althorp; Canons Ashby; Blenheim Palace; Silverstone; Towcester Racecourse; an Elizabethan manor house and Warwick Castle. Oxford and Stratford-upon-Avon are nearby.

Our inspector loved: The atmospheric great hall dating back to the Tudor period.

Directions: Fawsley Hall can be reached by the M40, junction 11 or the M1, junction16. Both are 10 miles from the Hotel.

Web: www.johansens.com/fawsleyhall
E-mail: reservations@fawsleyhall.com
Tel: 01327 892000
Fax: 01327 892001

Market Harborough

Northampton

Towcester

Price Guide:
single from £135
double/twin from £150
suite from £260

241

WHITTLEBURY HALL

WHITTLEBURY, NR TOWCESTER, NORTHAMPTONSHIRE NN12 8QH

Directions: 11 miles from M1 Jct15A. 18 miles from M40 Junction 10. Luton and Birmingham airports are within easy reach.

Web: www.johansens.com/whittleburyhall
E-mail: sales@whittleburyhall.co.uk
Tel: 01327 857857
Fax: 01327 857867

Price Guide:
single £125
double/twin £155
suite £260

Market Harborough

Northampton

Towcester

Whittlebury Hall is a modern building where the elegance of classic Georgian architecture has been complemented by contemporary furnishings and fabrics to create a truly fabulous hotel. The spacious bedrooms have all been elegantly decorated with a host of modern touches and thoughtful extras, whilst three superbly appointed, individually styled suites have a whirlpool spa bath and shower. The Silverstone Bar is aptly named with a host of motor racing memorabilia adorning the walls. Astons Restaurant offers a relaxed atmosphere with menus blending classic and contemporary cuisine with a dash of continental inspiration, complemented by fine wines from around the globe. The management training centre offers 12 suites and 24 dedicated syndicate rooms, all equipped with state-of-the-art audio visual equipment. Guests can relax and unwind at the Spa, where over 50 treatments are available in the health and beauty treatment suite. There is a 19-metre swimming pool, whirlpool spa, Turkish steam room, sauna and a 42-station StairMaster® gym, whilst the adjacent Whittlebury Park golf course offers preferred rates for guests. Motor racing enthusiasts can enjoy racing action at nearby Silverstone. Warwick Castle, Towcester racecourse and Oxford are all within a easy drive.

Our inspector loved: The extensive facilities and so close to the Silverstone race circuit.

MARSHALL MEADOWS COUNTRY HOUSE HOTEL

BERWICK-UPON-TWEED, NORTHUMBERLAND TD15 1UT

Marshall Meadows can truly boast that it is England's most northerly hotel, just a quarter of a mile from the Scottish border, an ideal base for those exploring the rugged beauty of Northumberland. A magnificent Georgian mansion standing in 15 acres of woodland and formal gardens, Marshall Meadows today is a luxurious retreat, with a country house ambience – welcoming and elegant. It has a burn and small waterfall with attractive woodland walks. This is not a large hotel, there are just nineteen bedrooms, each individually designed. Restful harmonious colour schemes, comfortable beds and the tranquillity of its surroundings ensure a good night's sleep! The lounge is delightful, with traditional easy chairs and sofas, overlooking the patio. Ideal for summer afternoon tea. The congenial "Duck & Grouse Bar" stocks forty whiskies and real ale. Marshall Meadows has a galleried restaurant where diners enjoy local game, fresh seafood and good wine. Private dining facilities are also available. Excellent golf, fishing and historic Berwick-on-Tweed are nearby.

Our inspector loved: *The close proximity to the sea.*

Directions: A1 heading North, take Berwick by-pass and at Meadow House roundabout, head towards Edinburgh. After 300 yards, turn right, indicated by white sign – hotel is at end of small side road.

Web: www.johansens.com/marshallmeadows
E-mail: stay@marshallmeadows.co.uk
Tel: 01289 331133
Fax: 01289 331438

Price Guide:
single £90
double/twin £120
suite £150

243

TILLMOUTH PARK

CORNHILL-ON-TWEED, NEAR BERWICK-UPON-TWEED, NORTHUMBERLAND TD12 4UU

Directions: Tillmouth Park is on the A698 Coldstream to Berwick-upon-Tweed road.

Web: www.johansens.com/tillmouthpark
E-mail: reception@tillmouthpark.f9.co.uk
Tel: 01890 882255
Fax: 01890 882540

Price Guide:
single £90–£160
twin/double £130–£195

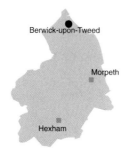

Berwick-upon-Tweed

Morpeth

Hexham

This magnificent mansion house, built in 1882 using stones from nearby Twizel Castle, offers the same warm welcome to visitors today as when it was an exclusive private house. Tillmouth Park is situated in 15 acres of mature parkland gardens above the river Till. The generously sized bedrooms are individually designed with period and antique furniture, and are fully appointed with bathrobes, toiletries, hairdryer and trouser press. Most bedrooms offer spectacular views of the surrounding countryside. The wood-panelled restaurant serves fine à la carte and table d'hôte menus offering contemporary British cuisine, while the Bistro is less formal. A well-chosen wine list and a vast selection of malt whiskies complement the cuisine. The elegant, galleried main hall offers comfort and there are open log fires throughout the house. Tillmouth Park is ideally situated for country pursuits, with fishing on the Tweed and Till and clay shooting available on the grounds. The area also abounds in fine golf courses. Coldstream and Kelso are within easy reach; the Northumbrian coast and Berwick are 15 minutes away, and Flodden Field, Lindisfarne and Holy Island are nearby. There are many stately homes to visit in the area including Floors, Alnwick, Manderston and Paxton.

Our inspector loved: The magnificent galleried main hall.

MATFEN HALL

MATFEN, NEWCASTLE-UPON-TYNE, NORTHUMBERLAND, NE20 0RH

Originally built in 1830 by Sir Edward Blackett, Matfen Hall opened as a hotel in 1999. Carefully restored by Sir Edward's descendants, Sir Hugh and Lady Blackett, this magnificent family seat lies in the heart of some of Northumberland's most beautiful countryside. Recently awarded Small Hotel of the Year in the Excellence in England awards Matfen Hall offers splendid facilities for conferences, weddings and leisure breaks. The Great Hall is awe-inspiring with its stained glass windows, massive pillars and stone floors, while each of the 31 bedrooms have their own individual character, combining modern features with traditional opulence. A huge open fireplace adds charm to the elegantly furnished Drawing Room and the unique, book-lined Library restaurant serves contemporary English cuisine and has recently been awarded 2 AA rosettes for the highest standard of cuisine and service. Matfen Hall enjoys stunning views over its own 18-hole golf course, laid out on a classic parkland landscape with manicured greens and fairways flanked by majestic trees. Rated as one of the finest in the North East, it provides a pleasurable test for players of all abilities. There is also a 9 hole par 3 golf course. The area offers plenty to explore, scenic coastal, rural and ancient sites are within comfortable driving distance. Newcastle-upon-Tyne is only 20 minutes away. Special breaks available.

Our inspector loved: The magnificent Baronial Hall.

Directions: From A1 take A69 towards Hexham. At Heddon on the Wall take B6318 towards Chollerford, travel 7 miles and turn right to Matfen.

Web: www.johansens.com/matfenhall
E-mail: info@matfenhall.com
Tel: 01661 886500
Fax: 01661 886055

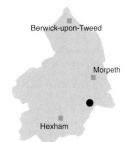

Price Guide:
single £97.50–£145
double £130–£235

LINDEN HALL

LONGHORSLEY, MORPETH, NORTHUMBERLAND NE65 8XF

Directions: From Newcastle take A1 north for 15 miles, then A697 toward Coldstream and Wooler. The hotel is 1 mile north of Longhorsley.

Web: www.johansens.com/lindenhall
E-mail: stay@lindenhall.co.uk
Tel: 01670 50 00 00
Fax: 01670 50 00 01

Price Guide:
single £74.50–£84.50
double/twin £108–£155
luxury rooms: £176–£184

Ivy-clad, hidden away among 450 acres of fine park and woodland in mid-Northumberland, Linden Hall is a superb Georgian country house within easy reach of Newcastle-upon-Tyne. An impressive mile-long drive sweeps up to its main door where, upon entering, the visitor will discover a relaxed, dignified atmosphere enhanced by gracious marble hearths, antiques and period pieces. Those wishing to escape the urban stress will be delighted to find every fitness and relaxation requirement catered for on the 18-hole golf course or at the health and beauty spa. Beauty therapy treatments, fitness and steam room, swimming pool, sun terrace and solarium are all available on the premises. The 50 bedrooms are individually and elegantly furnished. Some rooms have four-poster beds; each has its own private bathroom, supplied with thoughtful extras. The Linden Tree serves informal drinks and bar meals and the Dobson Restaurant, with panoramic views of the Northumberland coastline, serves delicious food, imaginatively prepared. Wedding ceremonies & receptions, banquets, dinner parties and business conferences can be held in comfort in any one of Linden Hall's conference and banqueting suites.

Our inspector loved: The wonderful clock in the reception area.

NEW

HOTEL DES CLOS - RESTAURANT 'SAT BAINS

OLD LENTON LANE, NOTTINGHAM, NOTTINGHAMSHIRE NG7 2SA

Guests arriving at this Victorian farmhouse conversion sense the welcoming ambience of the property's origins throughout its attractive interior. The hotel has been voted in the top 200 hotels in Great Britain & Ireland by the AA. The owners, the Ralley family, provide warm hospitality throughout your stay. The bedrooms are individually designed and well-equipped with an array of up-to-date amenities. The sumptuous Honeymoon suite is beautifully decorated with a Breton marriage bed as its centrepiece and antique furnishings. Guests must sample the award-winning cuisine in Restaurant 'Sat Bains, presided over by Head Chef Sat Bains, Roux Scholar 1999. The fine dishes are complemented by a wine list of over 100 bins including many excellent New World vintages. The Hotel Des Clos offers special weekend break packages. With its conference and special function rooms it is ideal for small intimate weddings. The National Watersports Centre, Trent Bridge Cricket Ground, Nottingham University, a well-equipped tennis centre and a large market are all nearby. Other notable landmarks are Nottingham Castle and Sherwood Forest.

Our inspector loved: A little France on the outskirts of Nottingham a place to enjoy excellent food and wine.

Directions: Leave M1 at Jct24 and follow A453 signposted Nottingham. As you approach the flyover stay in the middle lane, signposted Lenton Industrial Estate. Turn left at the roundabout and immediately left again the hotel is sign posted.

Worksop

Mansfield

Nottingham

Web: www.johansens.com/desclos
E-mail: info@hoteldesclos.com
Tel: 01159 866566
Fax: 01159 860343

Price Guide:
single £99.50
double £109.50–£119.50
suite £125–£150

LANGAR HALL

LANGAR, NOTTINGHAMSHIRE NG13 9HG

Directions: Langar is accessible via Bingham on the A52, or via Cropwell Bishop from the A46 (both signposted). The house adjoins the church and is hidden behind it.

Web: www.johansens.com/langarhall
E-mail: langarhall–hotel@ndirect.co.uk
Tel: 01949 860559
Fax: 01949 861045

Price Guide:
single £65–£9750
double/twin £130–£150
suite £175

Worksop

Mansfield

Nottingham

Set in the Vale of Belvoir, mid-way between Nottingham and Grantham, Langar Hall is the family home of Imogen Skirving. It was built in 1837 on the site of a great historic house, the home of Admiral Lord Howe. It stands in quiet seclusion overlooking gardens, where sheep graze among the ancient trees in the park. Below the croquet lawn lies a romantic network of medieval fishponds stocked with carp. Epitomising "excellence and diversity", Langar Hall combines the standards of good hotel-keeping with the hospitality and style of country house living. Having received a warm welcome, guests can enjoy the atmosphere of a private home that is much loved and cared for. The en suite bedrooms are individually designed and comfortably appointed. The public rooms feature fine furnishings and most rooms afford beautiful views of the garden, park and moat. Langar Hall is an ideal venue for small boardroom meetings. It is also an ideal base from which to visit Belvoir Castle, to see cricket at Trent Bridge, to visit students at Nottingham University and to see Robin Hood's Sherwood Forest. Dogs can be accommodated by arrangement.

Our inspector loved: *The informality of this lovely family house in a small village location, a treasure in the countryside.*

NEW

BIGNELL PARK HOTEL & RESTAURANT

CHESTERTON, BICESTER, OXFORDSHIRE OX26 1UE

In the lovely setting of the pretty village Chesterton, this friendly and welcoming Cotswold stone Hotel combines traditional old-world charm with the grace of a delightfully run country home. Originally an 18th century farmhouse, Bignell Park stands in 2½ acres of secluded, lawned gardens and orchard. Close by is the distinguished Kirtlington Polo Club and the historic market town and important hunting centre of Bicester. It is an ideal location for those wishing to explore a succession of enchanting, honey-coloured Cotswold villages and enjoy the attractions of Stratford-Upon-Avon, Warwick Castle, Oxford and Blenheim Palace, ancestral home to the Dukes of Marlborough. The tastefully refurbished en suite bedrooms, which include 3 four-posters, are spacious, attractively decorated and provide every facility to make visiting a pleasure. During winter months guests can relax before a roaring log fire in the comfortable and elegant drawing room which looks out over the garden. The candlelit restaurant, with wood-beamed ceiling, minstrels' gallery and open fire, has gained a deserved reputation. Head Chef Graham Thomson and his team carefully prepare imaginative and varied English/French menus to suit all tastes.

Our inspector loved: *The lovely dining room with its open fire original walls.*

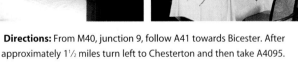

Directions: From M40, junction 9, follow A41 towards Bicester. After approximately 1½ miles turn left to Chesterton and then take A4095.

Web: www.johansens.com/bignellpark
E-mail: enq@bignellparkhotel.co.uk
Tel: 01869 362550
Fax: 01869 322729

Price Guide:
single £70–£90
double/twin £90–£110
four poster£135

THE BAY TREE HOTEL

SHEEP STREET, BURFORD, OXON OX18 4LW

The Bay Tree has been expertly refurbished so that it retains all its Tudor splendour while offering every modern facility. The oak-panelled rooms have huge stone fireplaces and a galleried staircase leads upstairs from the raftered hall. All the bedrooms are en suite, three of them furnished with four-poster beds and two of the five suites have half-tester beds. In the summer, guests can enjoy the delightful walled gardens, featuring landscaped terraces of lawn and flower beds. A relaxing atmosphere is enhanced by the staff's attentive service in the flagstoned dining room where the head chef's creative cuisine is complemented by a comprehensive selection of fine wines. Light meals are served in a country-style bar. Burford, often described as the gateway to the Cotswolds, is renowned for its assortment of antique shops and the Tolsey Museum of local history. The Bay Tree Hotel makes a convenient base for day trips to Stratford-upon-Avon, Stow-on-the-Wold and Blenheim Palace. Golf, clay pigeon shooting and riding can be arranged locally.

Directions: Burford is on the A40 between Oxford and Cheltenham. Proceed halfway down the hill into Burford, turn left into Sheep Street and The Bay Tree Hotel is 30 yards on your right.

Web: www.johansens.com/baytree
E-mail: bookings@cotswold–inns–hotels.co.uk
Tel: 01993 822791
Fax: 01993 823008

Price Guide:
single £119
double/twin £145–£175
suite £195–£220

Our inspector loved: The conservatory overlooking the traditional walled rose garden.

Banbury

Oxford

Henley-on-Thames

THE PLOUGH AT CLANFIELD

BOURTON ROAD, CLANFIELD, OXFORDSHIRE OX18 2RB

The Plough at Clanfield is an idyllic hideaway for the romantic at heart. Set on the edge of the village of Clanfield, typical of the Oxfordshire Cotswolds, The Plough dates from 1560 and is a fine example of well-preserved Elizabethan architecture. The hotel is owned and personally run by John and Rosemary Hodges, who have taken great care to preserve the charm and character of this historic building. As there are only 12 bedrooms, guests can enjoy an intimate atmosphere and attentive, personal service. All the bedrooms are beautifully appointed to the highest standard and all have en suite bathrooms. At the heart of the hotel is the Shires Restaurant, regarded as one of the finest in the area. The cuisine is superbly prepared and impeccably served, with an interesting selection of wines. Two additional dining rooms are available for private entertaining. The hotel is an ideal base from which to explore the Cotswolds or the Thames Valley. There are many historic houses and gardens in the area, as well as racing at Newbury and Cheltenham. Hotel closed 24th December to 7th January.

Our inspector loved: *This small family hotel that has been transformed by John and his wife Rosemary.*

Directions: The hotel is located on the edge of the village of Clanfield, at the junction of the A4095 and B4020, between the towns of Witney and Faringdon, some 15 miles to the west of the city of Oxford.

Web: www.johansens.com/ploughatclanfield
E-mail: ploughatclanfield@hotmail.com
Tel: 01367 810222
Fax: 01367 810596

Price Guide:
single £90
double £120–£130

PHYLLIS COURT CLUB

MARLOW ROAD, HENLEY-ON-THAMES, OXFORDSHIRE RG9 2HT

Directions: M40 junction 4 to Marlow or M4 junction 8/9 then follow signposts to Henley-on-Thames.

Web: www.johansens.com/phylliscourt
E-mail: sue.gill@phylliscourt.co.uk
Tel: 01491 570500
Fax: 01491 570528

Price Guide:
single £108
twin/double £126.50

Founded in 1906 by the owner of the house and a group of friends and London businessmen, the Club has an intriguing history spanning six centuries and involving royal patronage. Phyllis Court occupies an unrivalled position on the banks of the Thames and overlooking the Henley Royal Regatta course. Phyllis Court prides itself on retaining the traditions of its illustrious past while guests today who now stay in this fine historic residence can, in modern times, enjoy the highest standards of up to date hospitality. Oliver Cromwell slept here and he built the embankment wall; and it was here that William II held his first Royal Court. Years later, when the name Henley became synonymous with rowing, there came as patrons of the Royal Regatta Prince Albert, King George V and Edward, Prince of Wales. The character of the place remains unaltered in its hallowed setting, but the comfortable bedrooms, the restaurant, the "cellar" and the entire complement of amenities are of the latest high quality. What is more, they are available for all. Likely to be fully booked far ahead during the season. Ideal for meetings, functions and wedding parties.

Our inspector loved: *The views over the river Thames.*

THE COTSWOLD LODGE HOTEL

66A BANBURY ROAD, OXFORD OX2 6JP

Situated in a quiet conservation area just ½ mile away from Oxford is this picturesque Victorian building which has been restored in the style of a stately manor house. An ideal location for tourists and those on business, the Hotel offers a comfortable and relaxed environment. The Scholars bar is ideal for a light lunch or pre-dinner drink, and during winter, log fires enhance the cosy ambience. The elegant Fellows restaurant serves outstanding seasonal menus, with high quality ingredients a priority. Fresh fish and lobster come from Cornwall, sausages are made specially for the hotel, wild salmon is delivered from Scotland, and local lamb and game are used extensively. An impressive wine list ensures that there is something to suit all tastes and complement every meal. The tastefully furnished en suite bedrooms differ in size and style. The Cotswold Lodge happily caters for conferences on a daily or residential basis, and over the years has become renowned for its superb reputation in hosting wedding receptions. Staff are on hand to provide their expertise and tailor arrangements to suit individual requirements. The Banquet room accommodates up to 100 people and has access to a patio with fountain and walled garden.

Our inspector loved: *A superb hotel with very high standards, lovely bedrooms individually designed for luxury.*

Directions: From M40 junction 8, take A40 for Oxford; or junction 9, take A34; or from M4, junction 13, take A34 for Oxford.

Web: www.johansens.com/cotswoldlodge
E-mail: cotswoldlodgeuk@aol.com
Tel: 01865 512121
Fax: 01865 512490

Price Guide:
single £125
double/twin £175
suite from £295

NEW

WESTWOOD COUNTRY HOTEL

HINKSEY HILL, NR. BOARS HILL, OXFORD OX1 5BG

Directions: Located SW of Oxford. Take Oxford Ring Road, and where A34 meets the ring road at roundabout, follow signs for Wootton and Boars Hill. At the top of the hill the road bears to the left. The hotel is on the right.

Web: www.johansens.com/westwoodcountry
E-mail: reservations@westwoodhotel.co.uk
Tel: 01865 735 408
Fax: 01865 736 536

Price Guide:
single £65
double £95
four-poster £105

Banbury

Oxford

Henley-on-Thames

This delightful Edwardian Country House Hotel is set in four acres of landscaped gardens surrounded by an area of outstanding natural beauty. The Westwood Country Hotel is located in Boars Hill only 2 miles from Oxford city centre. The gardens, officially opened by the world-renowned botanist, David Bellamy, several years ago, provide a natural habitat for a large variety of wildlife. Owner Anthony Healy, himself a keen gardener, has created a vegetable and fruit garden which provides produce for the hotels' kitchen. The hotel has been tastefully and elegantly refurbished retaining and enhancing many of its original features. It provides 24 comfortable en suite bedrooms, including two beautiful four-poster rooms and a self-contained suite. The menu is imaginative and varied, and the wine list boasts selections from around the world. Dining is enjoyed in the comfortable Oaks restaurant overlooking the gardens. Blenheim Palace, The ancient city of Bath, Stratford-on-Avon and the Cotswold Route are all within a comfortable drive, as is London Heathrow airport.

Our inspector loved: *The terraced garden overlooking the woods.*

LE MANOIR AUX QUAT' SAISONS

GREAT MILTON, OXFORDSHIRE OX44 7PD

Situated in secluded grounds a few miles south of the historic city of Oxford. The restaurant and the contemporary classic hotel of Le Manoir aux Quat' Saisons are among the finest in Europe. Le Manoir is the inspired creation of Raymond Blanc whose extraordinary cooking has received the highest tributes from all international guides to culinary excellence. The Times uniquely gives Blanc's cooking 10 out of 10 and rates it 'the best in Britain'. The atmosphere throughout is one of understated elegance while all 32 bedrooms and suites offer guests the highest standards of comfort and luxury. Every need is anticipated, for service is a way of life here, never intrusive but always present. For dedicated 'foodies', Raymond Blanc's highly successful cookery school, is a must. Four-day courses are run from August to April and participation is restricted to ten guests to ensure the highest level of personal tuition. Participants stay at Le Manoir and their partners are welcome to stay free of charge although their meals and drinks are charged separately.

Our inspector loved: This centre of excellence - The garden vista's.

Directions: From London, M40 and turn off at junction 7 (A329 to Wallingford). From the North, leave M40 at junction 8A and follow signs to Wallingford (A329). After 1½ miles, turn right, follow the brown signs for Le Manoir aux Quat' Saisons.

Banbury

Oxford

Henley-on-Thames

Web: www.johansens.com/lemanoirauxquatsaisons
E-mail: lemanoir@blanc.co.uk
Tel: 01844 278881
Fax: 01844 278847

Price Guide:
double/twin £245–£450
suites £450–£1150

STUDLEY PRIORY

HORTON HILL, HORTON-CUM-STUDLEY, OXFORD, OXFORDSHIRE OX33 1AZ

Directions: From London leave M40 at Jct8. Follow A40 toward Oxford. Turn right for Horton-cum-Studley. Hotel is at the top of the hill.

Web: www.johansens.com/studleypriory
E-mail: res@studley-priory.co.uk
Tel: 01865 351203
Fax: 01865 351613

Price Guide:
single £105–£140
double/twin £140–£165
suite £275–£300

Banbury

Oxford

Henley-on-Thames

Set a few miles from the famous University City of Oxford, close to the beautiful villages and countryside of the Cotswolds and convenient for motorway connections via the nearby M40, Studley Priory is ideally suited for business and pleasure. The hotel exudes a sense of timelessness, its exterior little altered since Elizabethan times. The interior has been sympathetically updated to offer 18 lovely en suite bedrooms, each complemented by fine furnishings and luxurious bathrooms. The Elizabethan Suite offers a half tester bed dating from 1700, and many fine antiques remain in this historic property. The Croke Restaurant, which has received 3 AA Rosettes for its excellent cuisine, offers a seasonally changing menu of contemporary dishes created using only the finest local produce, complemented by an extensive wine list. Conference facilities are available for up to 50 people, and larger events, such as weddings, can be accommodated in an attached marquee. Nearby attractions include 2 fine golf courses, Blenheim Palace, the Manors of Waddesdon and Milton, The Cotswolds and Oxford, horse-racing at Cheltenham and Ascot, motor racing at Silverstone. Member of Small Luxury Hotels of the World.

Our inspector loved: The stunning food served in the Croke restaurant.

WESTON MANOR

WESTON-ON-THE-GREEN, OXFORDSHIRE OX25 3QL

Imposing wrought-iron gates flanked by sculptured busts surmounting tall grey stone pillars lead into the impressive entrance to this delightful old manor house, the showpiece of the lovely village of Weston-on-the-Green since the 11th century. The ancestral home of the Earls of Abingdon and Berkshire, and once the property of Henry VIII, Weston Manor stands regally in 12 acres of colourful gardens restored as a unique country house hotel of character. A peaceful retreat for visitors wishing to discover the delights of the surrounding Cotswold countryside and of Oxford, Woodstock, Blenheim Palace and Broughton Castle. Many of the Manor's 34 charming bedrooms, including four in a cottage and 16 in the old coach-house, retain antique furniture and all have garden views, private bathrooms and elegant surroundings. There is a croquet lawn and a secluded, heated outdoor swimming pool. Golf and riding are nearby. At the heart of the Manor is the restaurant, a magnificent vaulted and oak panelled Baronial Hall where delectable cuisine is served. Dining in such historic splendour is very much the focus of a memorable stay. Weston Manor is ideal for exclusive use house parties.

Our inspector loved: *The stunning topiary gardens.*

Directions: From the M40, exit at junction 9 onto the A34. Leave A34 on 1st exit, towards Oxford. After approximately one mile turn right onto the B340. Weston Manor is on the left.

Banbury

Oxford

Henley-on-Thames

Web: www.johansens.com/westonmanor
E-mail: reception@westonmanor.co.uk
Tel: 01869 350621
Fax: 01869 350901

Price Guide:
single £115
double/twin £154
suite £225

 ³⁴ ... ⁵⁰

THE SPREAD EAGLE HOTEL

CORNMARKET, THAME, OXFORDSHIRE OX9 2BW

Directions: Exit M40 at junction 6. Take B4009 to Chinnor and then B4445 to Thame. The hotel is on the left after the roundabout at the west end of Upper High Street.

Web: www.johansens.com/spreadeaglethame
E-mail: enquiries@spreadeaglethame.co.uk
Tel: 01844 213661
Fax: 01844 261380

Price Guide:
single £95
double/twin from £110

The historic market town of Thame with its mile long main street is a delightful town just six miles from the M40 and surrounded by beautiful countryside speckled with tiny, charming villages, many of them with cosy thatched cottages. The Spread Eagle has stood tall, square and imposingly in the heart of Thame since the 16th century and over the years has played host to Charles II, French prisoners from the Napoleonic wars, famous politicians and writers such as Evelyn Waugh. The former proprietor John Fothergill introduced haute cuisine to the provinces and chronicled his experiences in the best seller, 'An Innkeeper's Diary'. The book is still available at The Spread Eagle and the restaurant is named after him. It serves excellent English and French cuisine made with the freshest local produce. Seasonal changing menus are complemented by a well balanced wine list which includes some superb half-bottles of unusual vintages. Guests have 33 bedrooms to choose from, comprising two suites, 23 doubles, three twins and five singles. All are en suite, well equipped and tastefully decorated. Good conference facilities are available. The Spread Eagle is ideally situated for visits to many fascinating historic places such as Blenheim Palace and Waddesdon Manor.

Our inspector loved: *The French doors from the bedroom, opening onto a private garden.*

THE SPRINGS HOTEL & GOLF CLUB

NORTH STOKE, WALLINGFORD, OXFORDSHIRE OX10 6BE

The Springs is a grand old country house which dates from 1874 and is set deep in the heart of the beautiful Thames valley. One of the first houses in England to be built in the Mock Tudor style, it stands in six acres of grounds. The hotel's large south windows overlook a spring fed lake, from which it takes its name. Many of the luxurious bedrooms and suites offer beautiful views over the lake and lawns, while others overlook the quiet woodland that surrounds the hotel. Private balconies provide patios for summer relaxation. The Lakeside restaurant has an intimate atmosphere inspired by its gentle décor and the lovely view of the lake. The award-winning restaurant's menu takes advantage of fresh local produce and a well stocked cellar of international wines provides the perfect accompaniment to a splendid meal. Leisure facilities include a 18-hole par 72 golf course, Clubhouse and putting green, a swimming pool, sauna and touring bicycles. Oxford, Blenheim Palace and Windsor are nearby, and the hotel is conveniently located for racing at Newbury and Ascot and the Royal Henley Regatta.

Our inspector loved: The view from the restaurant on to the lake and the golf course.

Directions: From M40 take exit 6 onto B4009, through Watlington to Benson; turn left onto A4074 towards Reading. After ½ mile go right onto B4009. The hotel is ½ mile further on the right.

Banbury

Oxford

Henley-on-Thames

Web: www.johansens.com/springshotel
E-mail: info@thespringshotel.com
Tel: 01491 836687
Fax: 01491 836877

Price Guide:
single from £90
double/twin from £100
suite from £165

THE FEATHERS HOTEL

MARKET STREET, WOODSTOCK, OXFORDSHIRE OX20 1SX

Directions: From London leave the M40 at junction 8; from Birmingham leave at jct 9. Take A44 and follow the signs to Woodstock. The hotel is on the left.

Web: www.johansens.com/feathers
E-mail: enquiries@feathers.co.uk
Tel: 01993 812291
Fax: 01993 813158

Price Guide:
single £115
double/twin £130–£185
suite £235–£290

The Feathers is a privately owned and run town house hotel, situated in the centre of Woodstock, a few miles from Oxford. Woodstock is one of England's most attractive country towns, constructed mostly from Cotswold stone and with some buildings dating from the 12th century. The hotel, built in the 17th century, was originally four separate houses. Antiques, log fires and traditional English furnishings lend character and charm. There are 20 bedrooms, all of which have private bathrooms and showers. Public rooms, including the drawing room and study, are intimate and comfortable. The small garden is a delightful setting for a light lunch or afternoon tea and guests can enjoy a drink in the cosy courtyard bar, which has an open fire in winter. The antique-panelled restaurant is internationally renowned for its fine cuisine, complemented by a high standard of service and 3 AA Rosettes. The menu changes frequently and offers a wide variety of dishes, using the finest local ingredients. Blenheim Palace, seat of the Duke of Marlborough and birthplace of Sir Winston Churchill, is just around the corner. The Cotswolds and the dreaming spires of Oxford are a short distance away.

Our inspector loved: *This lovely hotel with beautiful window boxes outside each bedroom and secluded courtyard gardens.*

HAMBLETON HALL

HAMBLETON, OAKHAM, RUTLAND LE15 8TH

Winner of Johansens Most Excellent Country Hotel Award 1996, Hambleton Hall, originally a Victorian mansion, became a hotel in 1979. Since then its renown has continually grown. It enjoys a spectacular lakeside setting in a charming and unspoilt area of Rutland. The hotel's tasteful interiors have been designed to create elegance and comfort, retaining individuality by avoiding a catalogue approach to furnishing. Delightful displays of flowers, an artful blend of ingredients from local hedgerows and the London flower markets colour the bedrooms. In the restaurant, chef Aaron Patterson and his enthusiastic team offer a menu which is strongly seasonal. Grouse, Scottish ceps and chanterelles, partridge and woodcock are all available at just the right time of year, accompanied by the best vegetables, herbs and salads from the Hall's garden. The Croquet Pavilion, a two bedroom suite with living room and breakfast room is a luxurious addition to the accommodation options. For the energetic there are lovely walks around the lake and opportunities for tennis and swimming, golf, riding, bicycling, trout fishing, and sailing. Burghley House and Belton are nearby, as are the antique shops of Oakham, Uppingham and Stamford. Hambleton Hall is a Relais & Châteaux member.

Our inspector loved: *Standing on the terrace overlooking the beautiful gardens and magnificent views of Rutland water.*

Directions: In the village of Hambleton, signposted from the A606, 1 mile east of Oakham.

Web: www.johansens.com/hambletonhall
E-mail: hotel@hambletonhall.com
Tel: 01572 756991
Fax: 01572 724721

Price Guide:
single £155
double/twin £180–£345
suite £600

BARNSDALE LODGE

THE AVENUE, RUTLAND WATER, NR OAKHAM, RUTLAND, LE15 8AH

Directions: The Lodge is on A606 Oakham–Stamford road.

Web: www.johansens.com/barnsdalelodge
E-mail: barnsdale.lodge@btconnect.com
Tel: 01572 724678
Fax: 01572 724961

Price Guide:
single £69
double/twin £89
junior suite £10950

Oakham

Stamford

Uppingham

Situated in the ancient county of Rutland, amid unspoiled countryside, Barnsdale Lodge overlooks the rippling expanse of Rutland Water. After nine years, the expansion is finally complete and guests are invited to enjoy the hospitality offered by hosts The Hon. Thomas Noel and Robert Reid. A restored 17th century farmhouse, the atmosphere and style are distinctively Edwardian. This theme pervades throughout, from the courteous service to the furnishings, including chaises-longues and plush, upholstered chairs. The 45 en suite bedrooms, mostly on the ground floor, including two superb rooms specifically designed for disabled guests, evoke a mood of relaxing comfort. Traditional English cooking and fine wines are served. The chef makes all the pastries and cakes as well as preserves. Elevenses, buttery lunches, afternoon teas and suppers are enjoyed in the garden, conservatory, courtyard and à la carte dining rooms. There are 5 conference rooms and facilities for wedding receptions and parties. Interconnecting bedrooms, a baby-listening service and safe play area are provided for children. Robert Reid has strived to maintain the friendly intimacy of the lodge and is often on hand, offering advice and suggestions. Belvoir and Rockingham Castles are nearby. Rutland Water, a haven for nature lovers, offers several water sports. A Health Spa is planned for 2003.

Our inspector loved: *This very popular country hotel has affected many waistline with its homemade pastries and preserves....,and that includes the inspector!*

THE LAKE ISLE

16 HIGH STREET EAST, UPPINGHAM, RUTLAND LE15 9PZ

This small personally run restaurant and town house hotel is situated in the pretty market town of Uppingham, dominated by the famous Uppingham School and close to Rutland Water. The entrance to the building, which dates back to the 18th century, is via a quiet courtyard where a wonderful display of flowering tubs and hanging baskets greets you. In winter, sit in the bar where a log fire burns or relax in the upstairs lounge which overlooks the High Street. In the bedrooms, each named after a wine growing region in France and all of which are en suite, guests will find fresh fruit, home-made biscuits and a decanter of sherry. Those in the courtyard are cottage-style suites. Under the personal direction of chef Gary Thomas, the restaurant offers regular weekly changing menus using fresh ingredients from far afield. There is an extensive wine list of more than 200 wines ranging from regional labels to old clarets. Special 'Wine Dinners' are held throughout the year, enabling guests to appreciate this unique cellar. Burghley House, Rockingham speedway and Belvoir Castles are within a short drive.

Our inspector loved: *This super cosy little town house hotel with a lovely cottage courtyard garden.*

Directions: Uppingham is near the intersection of A47 and A6003. The hotel is on the High Street and is reached on foot via Reeves Yard and by car via Queen Street.

Oakham
Stamford
Uppingham

Web: www.johansens.com/lakeisle
E-mail: Info@LakeIsleHotel.com
Tel: 01572 822951
Fax: 01572 824400

Price Guide:
single £45–£65
double/twin £70–£75
suite £80–£85
family room £125

263

THE OLD VICARAGE HOTEL

WORFIELD, BRIDGNORTH, SHROPSHIRE WV15 5JZ

Directions: 8 miles west of Wolverhampton, 1 mile from A454, 2 miles from A442, 8 miles south of M54, junction 4.

Web: www.johansens.com/oldvicaragewolverhampton
E-mail: admin@the-old-vicarage.demon.co.uk
Tel: 01746 716497
Fax: 01746 716552

Price Guide:
£80–£110
double/twin £120–£175
suites £155–£175

This former Edwardian parsonage sits proudly on the crest of a hill overlooking the delightful conservation village of Worfield and glorious countryside. It is reached by a leafy lane leading into 2 acres of manicured lawned grounds and colourful gardens that offer a peaceful and relaxed environment. Guests can snugly enjoy this idyllic view from their rooms or the Hotel's spacious conservatory, a sun trap in summer, warmed by a roaring fire in winter. The interior of The Old Vicarage is elegant with tastefully decorated rooms liberally highlighted with polished period furniture, antique clocks, Moorcroft pottery and fine paintings. Bedrooms are charming, comfortable and individually furnished in Edwardian and Victorian styles to complement the features of the house. 4 Coach House rooms have French windows opening onto a private garden. Award-winning, imaginative menus, accompanied by an extensive wine list, are served in an intimate restaurant enhanced with generously proportioned, highly polished antique tables and sparkling silver. The Ironbridge Gorge Museum Complex, The Severn Valley Railway, stately homes, castles and National Trust gardens, attractive border towns and picturesque villages are among visitor attractions within easy reach.

Our inspector loved: *That the ambience of this hotel was very 21st century and welcoming.*

DINHAM HALL

LUDLOW, SHROPSHIRE SY8 1EJ

Tall, square, solid and stylish Dinham Hall is the epitome of a grand, late 18th century family home. Now an elegant Hotel, it stands prestigiously in the centre of the historic market town of Ludlow just a short stroll from the ruins of a massive sandstone castle built by Roger Montgomery, Earl of Shrewsbury, in 1085. An enviable location that provides guests with ready access to the town's broad streets, narrow lanes, graceful buildings and mellow beauty. Dinham offers a comfortable and relaxing atmosphere. Lounges are restful and warmed by open fires in winter and each of the 14 bedrooms offer a décor harmony of modern facilities with period design. Some have four-posters and 2 of the bedrooms are within a cottage in the garden grounds. The elegant and sumptuous restaurant serves succulent and creative French cuisine prepared by talented chef Olivier Bossut. While dining, guests can enjoy superb views over the walled garden and open countryside towards the Whitcliffe hills and Mortimer forests or when taking tea on the Hotel terrace during summer months. As well as browsing in the town's famed antique shops guests can delight in visiting Ludlow races, take lovely river walks, explore historic sites, play golf, fish or clay shoot locally.

Our inspector loved: The atmosphere of this hotel with its delightful small dining room serving enjoyable dishes of interest.

Directions: Ludlow is approached via A49. Dinham Hall is in the centre of town overlooking the castle.

Oswestry

Shrewsbury

Bridgnorth

Web: www.johansens.com/dinhamhall
E-mail: info@dinhamhall.co.uk
Tel: 01584 876464
Fax: 01584 876019

Price Guide:
single £70–£99
double/twin £130–£180

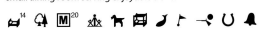

SHROPSHIRE - SHREWSBURY

PRINCE RUPERT HOTEL

BUTCHER ROW, SHREWSBURY, SHROPSHIRE SY1 1UQ

Directions: After leaving M54 follow signs to Shrewsbury town centre. Cross English Bridge and bear right up the Wyle Cop. After 70m turn sharp right into the cobblestoned Fish Street. The Prince Rupert is 150m ahead.

Web: www.johansens.com/princerupert
E-mail: post@prince-rupert-hotel.co.uk
Tel: 01743 499955
Fax: 01743 357306

Price Guide:
single £60–£75
double/twin £95
suite £130–£160

Oswestry

Shrewsbury

Bridgnorth

Ornamented by a pink sandstone castle and narrow cobbled streets lined with black-and-white Tudor buildings, Shrewsbury is an historic county town on the banks of the River Severn. The Prince Rupert Hotel is at its medieval heart. Once the 12th century home of Prince Rupert, grandson of King James I, it combines old world charm with the comfort, service and facilities expected in a premier hotel. Although spread over various old buildings with linking corridors, the overall feeling is that the hotel is intimate and small. The 70 tastefully refurbished en suite bedrooms, some with king-size four-poster beds, include 12th century beamed suites, have every home-from-home comfort and are surprisingly quiet for a town centre location. The elegant Royalist Restaurant with its oak-panelled walls, fireplaces and suits of armour is known for Head Chef Graeme Williams' cuisine. A brasserie, Chambers, is in the oldest part of the hotel, and light lunches and afternoon teas are served in the main lounge. The Health and Beauty Spa includes a Jacuzzi, steam shower, weights room and beauty salon. Attingham Park, Ironbridge Gorge, and Powys castles are within easy reach.

Our inspector loved: *The travel in time from ancient 12th century to 2002 experienced in this city centre hotel.*

MADELEY COURT

TELFORD, SHROPSHIRE TF7 5DW

This veritable gem of a residence has remained virtually unaltered since the 16th century, when it was mainly built, while the interior has been expertly restored to provide a unique style and elegance tuned to the requirements of private and business guests. Furnishings have been judiciously selected to enrich Madeley's period appeal; scatterings of fine fabrics, handsome antique pieces and elaborate fittings all accentuate the historic atmosphere and ensure that every guest leaves with an indelible impression. The bedrooms, whether located in the old part of the Court or in the newer wing, are quiet and full of character; all are en suite and offer interactive television; some have whirlpool baths and views over the lake. At the heart of this Grade I listed manor house is the original 13th-century hall where the restaurant is now located, serving inventive food, awarded 2 RAC Ribbons, with a wine list to match. Another dining option is the Cellar, which offers a more informal setting and the Lakeside Bar is open all day for refreshments and light snacks. Business meetings and private functions are happily catered for in the 3 rooms available. Places of interest nearby include Ironbridge Gorge, Shrewsbury, Powys Castle and Weston Park.

Our inspector loved: The bathroom in the turret, very intriguing.

Directions: 4 miles from Jct 4 off M54; follow A442 then B4373. Signposted Dawley then Madeley.

Web: www.johansens.com/madeleycourt
E-mail: admin@g6068.u-net.com
Tel: 01952 680068
Fax: 01952 684275

Price Guide: (room only)
single from £105
double/twin £120–£145
historic £137

STON EASTON PARK

STON EASTON, BATH, SOMERSET BA3 4DF

Directions: 11 miles south of Bath on the A37 between Bath and Wells.

Web: www.johansens.com/stoneastonpark
E-mail: stoneastonpark@stoneaston.co.uk
Tel: 01761 241631
Fax: 01761 241377

Price Guide:
single from £99
double/twin £185–£345
four-poster £245–£345

The internationally renowned hotel at Ston Easton Park is a Grade I Palladian mansion of notable distinction. A showpiece for some exceptional architectural and decorative features of its period, it dates from 1739 and has recently undergone extensive restoration, offering a unique opportunity to enjoy the opulent splendour of the 18th century. A high priority is given to the provision of friendly and unobtrusive service. The hotel has won innumerable awards for its décor, service and food. Jean Monro, an acknowledged expert on 18th century decoration, supervised the design and furnishing of the interiors, complementing the original features with choice antiques, paintings and objets d'art. Fresh, quality produce, delivered from all parts of Britain, is combined with herbs and vegetables from the Victorian kitchen garden to create English and French dishes. To accompany your meal, a wide selection of rare wines and old vintages is stocked in the house cellars. The grounds, landscaped by Humphry Repton in 1793, consist of romantic gardens and parkland. The 17th century Gardener's Cottage, close to the main house on the wooded banks of the River Norr, provides private suite accommodation.

Our inspector loved: *This gracious mansion offering luxury, relaxation and peace.*

DANESWOOD HOUSE HOTEL

CUCK HILL, SHIPHAM, NR WINSCOMBE, SOMERSET BS25 1RD

This tall, pebble-dashed Edwardian house nestles on the slopes of the Mendip Hills commanding spectacular views over the Somerset countryside towards the Bristol Channel and South Wales. Originally a homeopathic health hydro, it is now a hotel of distinction which has been in the enthusiastic ownership of David and Elise Hodges for almost 25 years. They have created a homely, welcoming and relaxing atmosphere and their continual pursuit of excellence has earned the hotel a reputation for comfort, culinary delights and service. The generous en suite bedrooms are individually designed, delightfully furnished and have every facility from colour TV to direct dial telephone. The Honeymoon Suite boasts a 7ft King-size bed while the Victorian Room has a Queen Anne four-poster. 5 recently added bedrooms open out onto the five acres of grounds and have private patios. Great emphasis is placed on using fresh produce and local meat and poultry for the superb dishes served in the period dining room, which has been awarded 2 AA Rosettes. Breakfast is in the sunny conservatory. Conference facilities. The hotel grounds offer direct access to the Mendip Walkway. Nearby are 5 18-hole golf courses, trout fishing, riding and several National Trust houses.

Our inspector loved: The elevated location commanding beautiful views over the Somerset countryside.

Directions: Shipham is signposted from the A38 Bristol-Bridgwater road. Go through the village towards Cheddar and the hotel is on the left.

Web: www.johansens.com/daneswoodhouse
E-mail: info@daneswoodhotel.co.uk
Tel: 01934 843145
Fax: 01934 843824

Price Guide:
single £89.50–£99.50
double/twin £105–£150
suites £150

Charlton House And The Mulberry Restaurant

CHARLTON ROAD, SHEPTON MALLET, NEAR BATH, SOMERSET BA4 4PR

Directions: A303, then A37 to Shepton Mallet. Take A361 towards Frome and find hotel drive on the right.

Web: www.johansens.com/charltonhouse
E-mail: enquiry@charltonhouse.com
Tel: 01749 342008
Fax: 01749 346362

Price Guide:
single £112.50–£155
double/twin £155–£225
suite £250–£355

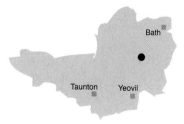

Bath

Taunton   Yeovil

This grand 17th century country manor, is now owned by Roger and Monty Saul, founders of the Mulberry Design Co. They have lovingly and skilfully created an exquisite hotel of the highest international standards without detracting from Charlton's own history and architecture. The reception rooms have wonderful proportions and are not overwhelmed by the sumptuous furnishings, fine antiques, brilliant rugs on polished floors, witty memorabilia and exciting paintings adorning their walls – veritable Aladdin's Caves! The bedrooms, are equally magical, totally luxurious and yet restful, with opulent bathrooms. Professional yet friendly staff play an important part both in the drawing room, with its marvellous intimate atmosphere and in the dramatic dining room and spacious conservatory presided over by award-winning chef, Adam Fellows. Fantastic cooking and sublime wines make every meal a sybaritic experience. The hotel prides itself on catering for "special occasions". Charlton House recreations include shove-halfpenny(!), croquet, a trout lake, tennis and strolling in the landscaped gardens. Nearby are Bath, Wincanton Races, sailing, golf, the Mendip Hills – and the Mulberry factory shop.

Our inspector loved: *The first class cuisine and total feel of relaxation.*

MOUNT SOMERSET COUNTRY HOUSE HOTEL

HENLADE, TAUNTON, SOMERSET TA3 5NB

This elegant Regency residence, awarded 2 Rosettes and 3 stars, stands high on the slopes of the Blackdown Hills, overlooking miles of lovely countryside. The Hotel is rich in intricate craftsmanship and displays fine original features. Its owners have committed themselves to creating an atmosphere in which guests can relax, confident that all needs will be catered for. The bedrooms are sumptuously furnished and many offer views over the Quantock Hills. All of the bedrooms have luxurious bathrooms and some have spa baths. Light lunches, teas, coffees and home-made cakes can be enjoyed in the beautifully furnished drawing room, whilst in the restaurant the finest food and wines are served. A team of chefs work together to create dishes which exceed the expectations of the most discerning gourmet. Adjacent to the Hotel, the President's Health Club, with its large heated indoor pool and fully-equipped gym, is available for use by hotel guests. Places of interest nearby include Glastonbury Abbey, Wells Cathedral and the vibrant city of Exeter.

Our inspector loved: *Driving along the winding approach and finding total comfort within this gracious residence.*

Directions: At the M5 exit at junction 25, join the A358 towards Ilminster. Just past Henlade turn right at the sign for Stoke St. Mary. At the T-junction turn left, the Hotel drive is 150 yards on the right.

Web: www.johansens.com/mountsomerset
E-mail: info@mountsomersethotel.co.uk
Tel: 01823 442500
Fax: 01823 442900

Price Guide:
single from £95–£125
double/twin from £110–£135
suites £155–£170

BINDON COUNTRY HOUSE HOTEL

LANGFORD BUDVILLE, WELLINGTON, SOMERSET TA21 0RU

Directions: 15 minutes from M5/J26, drive to Wellington take B3187 to Langford Budville, through village, right towards Wiveliscombe, then right at junction. Pass Bindon Farm and after 450 yards turn right.

Web: www.johansens.com/bindoncountryhouse
E-mail: stay@bindon.com
Tel: 01823 400070
Fax: 01823 400071

Price Guide:
single £95
double/twin £105–£205
suite from £135

This splendid baroque country house has a motto over the west wing door which, although put there in the 1860s, is appropriate today. 'Je trouve bien' is the perfect sentiment for this hotel, albeit in an old setting. Mark and Lynn Jaffa have meticulously restored Bindon. It is tranquil and private, surrounded by seven acres of gardens and woodland. New arrivals immediately have a feeling of well-being, as they respond to greetings from their hosts and drop into sofas in the charming lounge. There are just twelve beautifully proportioned, luxurious bedrooms, all extremely comfortable with many 'extras' including robes in the well-designed bathrooms. The handsome panelled Jacobean bar is convivial and it is advisable to reserve a table in the Wellesley Restaurant, as its reputation is far flung. The graceful setting and excellent wines accompanying the exquisitely presented gourmet dishes make dining a memorable occasion. Country pursuits – fishing, riding, shooting and golf are nearby and Bindon has its own pool, tennis court and croquet lawn. Wells Cathedral and stately homes are there to visit.

Our inspector loved: The peace, tranquillity and total overall comfort.

NEW

THE SWAN HOTEL

SADLER STREET, WELLS, SOMERSET BA5 2RX

This truly historic hotel with charm and an ambience all of its own combines English tradition and architectural splendour. Dating back to the 15th century, The Swan nestles in the shadow of the 12th century west front of the magnificent Wells Cathedral, a short walk from Vicars Close, the oldest complete medieval street in Western Europe. Formerly a major Posting House, it has been sympathetically restored and extended with an ongoing refurbishment plan to ensure every comfort and facility whilst retaining the beauty, ambience, elegance and attentive personal service of the past. Reflecting its background and character The Swan offers superb accommodation in a relaxing environment. There are open log fires with York stone surrounds, heavy ceiling beams, highly polished panelling, fine paintings and antiques galore. Individually styled, en suite bedrooms have every 21st century amenity. Most are lavishly adorned with exquisite period furniture and many boast original four poster beds. Downstairs, guests can enjoy an uninterrupted read or chat over tea in the spacious lounge and sip cocktails in a cosy bar overlooking the Cathedral prior to sampling acclaimed traditional and modern cuisine in the dining room. Cheddar Gorge, Wookey Hole Caves and many historic houses and gardens are within easy reach.

Directions: Exit the M5 at junction 22. On reaching Wells, follow the signs for hotels and deliveries. Once in Sadler Street the Hotel is on the right.

Web: www.johansens.com/swanwells
E-mail: swan@bhere.co.uk
Tel: 01749 836300
Fax: 01749 836301

Price Guide: (room only)
single from £70-£84
double/twin from £78-£114

Our inspector loved: The location overlooking the Cathedral grounds.

NEW

SWINFEN HALL HOTEL

SWINFEN, NR LICHFIELD, STAFFORDSHIRE WS14 9RE

Directions: Exit the M42 at junctions 9 or 10. Swinfen Hall is set back from the A38, 2 miles south of Lichfield.

Web: www.johansens.com/swinfenhall
E-mail: swinfenhall@virgin.net
Tel: 01543 481494
Fax: 01543 480341

Price Guide: (including continental breakfast)
single from £110
double/twin from £125
suite from £170

Stoke-on-Trent

Stafford

Cannock

Swinfen Hall was built with immense extravagance in 1757 under the direction of the local architect Benjamin Wyatt and the same extravagance has been faithfully lavished on the building recently in a magnificent restoration programme. Awarded 4 stars by the AA and RAC, the Hotel is the epitome of luxury and elegance and is totally complementary to the building's beautiful architecture. The grand entrance hall with stuccoed ceiling and balustraded minstrel's gallery provide an impressive welcome to the Hotel and the elegant atmosphere continues throughout with each room being gracefully and sensitively appointed to its period origins. The 2 RAC Ribbons and 2 AA Rosettes awarded Four Seasons restaurant is panelled in oak from floor to ceiling and is a dramatic backdrop to some wonderfully prepared dishes using seasonal and locally grown ingredients. The Hotel provides an idyllic setting for wedding ceremonies and the ballroom can accommodate up to 120 for a spectacular wedding breakfast whilst the private dining room (the original dining room of the house) can be hired for private parties between 10 and 20 guests. Strikingly, this oasis of luxury is also only 20 minutes from Birmingham City centre and airport.

Our inspector loved: *Its unspoilt style creating excellent hospitality.*

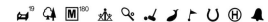

HOAR CROSS HALL HEALTH SPA RESORT

HOAR CROSS, NR YOXALL, STAFFORDSHIRE DE13 8QS

Surrounded by beautiful countryside, lakes and exquisite formal gardens with water features, exotic plants and beautiful flowers, Hoar Cross Hall is a secluded haven and the perfect venue for those who want a peaceful environment in which to be pampered. Oak panelling, tapestries, rich furnishings and paintings adorn the interior and an impressive library, with 3,000 books to browse through, has Spanish leather walls. A stunning Jacobean staircase leads to luxurious bedrooms, all with crown tester or four poster beds and elegant design. Penthouses have private saunas and balconies overlooking the treetops. Breathtaking gilded ceilings and William Morris wallpaper in the original ballroom set the scene for the dining room, where a superb à la carte menu is offered. A tasty breakfast and buffet lunch is served in the Plantation Restaurants overlooking the pools. There are unlimited ways in which visitors can de-stress at Hoar Cross Hall; yoga, meditation, tai chi, aqua-aerobics and dance classes are all available and outdoor pursuits include tennis, croquet, archery and a fantastic golf academy. Trained professionals are ready to assist and the spa consists of hydrotherapy baths, flotation therapy, saunas, a gymnasium and steam rooms.

Our inspector loved: *The totally calming and relaxing ambiance and the amazing water 'Grotto.'*

Directions: From Lichfield turn off the A51 onto the A515 towards Ashbourne. Go through Yoxall and turn left to Hoar Cross.

Web: www.johansens.com/hoarcrosshall
E-mail: info@hoarcross.co.uk
Tel: 01283 575671
Fax: 01283 575652

Price Guide: (fully inclusive price including treatments per person)
single £155-£185
double/twin £175-£210

WENTWORTH HOTEL

WENTWORTH ROAD, ALDEBURGH, SUFFOLK IP15 5BD

Directions: Aldeburgh is on A1094 just 7 miles from the A12 between Ipswich and Lowestoft.

Web: www.johansens.com/wentworth
E-mail: stay@wentworth–aldeburgh.co.uk
Tel: 01728 452312
Fax: 01728 454343

Price Guide:
single £70
double/twin £116

The Wentworth Hotel is ideally situated opposite the beach at Aldeburgh on Suffolk's unspoilt coast. Aldeburgh has maritime traditions dating back to the 15th century which are still maintained today by the longshore fishermen who launch their boats from the shore. It has also become a centre for music lovers: every June the Aldeburgh International Festival of Music, founded by the late Benjamin Britten, is held at Snape Maltings. Privately owned by the Pritt family since 1920, the Wentworth has established a reputation for comfort and service, good food and wine, for which many guests return year after year. Relax in front of an open fire in one of the hotel lounges, or sample a pint of the famous local Adnam's ales in the bar, which also serves meals. Many of the 37 elegantly furnished en suite bedrooms have sea views. The restaurant offers an extensive menu for both lunch and dinner and there is a comprehensive wine list. The garden terrace is the perfect venue for a light lunch alfresco. Nearby, the Minsmere Bird Sanctuary will be of interest to nature enthusiasts, while for the keen golfer, two of Britain's most challenging courses are within easy reach of the hotel at Aldeburgh and Thorpeness. Closed from December 27 to early new year.

Our inspector loved: The lovely pictures & the proximity to the sea.

ANGEL HOTEL

BURY ST EDMUNDS, SUFFOLK IP33 1LT

Being the most historic Coaching Inn in East Anglia, the hotel was immortalised by Charles Dickens, has welcomed King Louis Phillippe of France nad more recently Pierce Brosnan. On one of the prettiest squares in England, visitors will have the immediate impression of a hotel that is loved and nurtured by its owners. In the public rooms, guests will appreciate the carefully chosen ornaments and pictures, fresh flowers and log fires. The hotel has numerous suites and four poster bedrooms, some with air conditioning. All bedrooms are individually furnished and decorated and all have en suite bathrooms. The elegant dining room has been awarded 2 Rosettes by the AA for excellent food and service. Overlooking the ancient abbey, the restaurant serves classic English cuisine, including local speciality dishes and succulent roasts. The Angel can offer a wide range of quality conference and banqueting facilities catering for private dinners, meetings and weddings from 10–60 persons. The hotel is within an hour of the east coast ferry ports and 45 minutes from Stansted Airport. Nearby there is racing at Newmarket and several golf courses within easy reach. Bury St Edmunds is an interesting and historic market town and an excellent centre for touring the surrounding area.

Our inspector loved: The dining room, dramatic yet elegant which compliments this historic building.

Directions: Follow signs to Historic Centre.

Web: www.johansens.com/angelburysted
E-mail: sales@angel.co.uk
Tel: 01284 714000
Fax: 01284 714001

Price Guide:
single from £83
double/twin from £93
suite from £133

277

RAVENWOOD HALL COUNTRY HOTEL & RESTAURANT

ROUGHAM, BURY ST EDMUNDS, SUFFOLK IP30 9JA

Directions: 2 miles East of Bury St. Edmunds off the A14.

Web: www.johansens.com/ravenwoodhall
E-mail: enquiries@ravenwoodhall.co.uk
Tel: 01359 270345
Fax: 01359 270788

Price Guide:
single £73–£98
double/twin: £96–£133

Bury St Edmunds

Newmarket

Ipswich

Nestling within 7 acres of lovely lawns and woodlands deep in the heart of Suffolk lies Ravenwood Hall. Now an excellent country house hotel, this fine Tudor building dates back to 1530 and retains many of its original features. The restaurant, still boasting the carved timbers and huge inglenook from Tudor times, creates a delightfully intimate atmosphere in which to enjoy imaginative cuisine. The menu is a combination of adventurous and classical dishes, featuring some long forgotten English recipes. The Hall's extensive cellars are stocked with some of the finest vintages, along with a selection of rare ports and brandies. A cosy bar offers a less formal setting in which to enjoy some unusual meals. Comfortable bedrooms are furnished with antiques, reflecting the historic tradition of the Hall, although each is equipped with every modern facility. A wide range of leisure facilities is available for guests, including a hard tennis court, a croquet lawn and heated swimming pool. There are golf courses and woodland walks to enjoy locally; hunting and shooting can be arranged. Places of interest nearby include the famous medieval wool towns of Lavenham and Long Melford; the historic cities of Norwich and Cambridge are within easy reach.

Our inspector loved: *The huge inglenook fireplaces and the informal reminders of a private country estate.*

NEW

THE ICKWORTH HOTEL

HORRINGER, BURY ST EDMUNDS, SUFFOLK IP29 5QE

This stylish and contemporary Hotel is the newly opened East Wing of the Ickworth House and estate, formerly home of the Marquess of Bristol and left in legacy to the National Trust in 1956. It is surrounded by some 1,800 acres of glorious parkland with views from the Hotel overlooking the beautifully manicured lawns and the Italian garden. The Hotel prides itself on its winning combination of contemporary style and elegance whilst ensuring guests' every comfort. The traditional and the modern sit side-by-side in stunning effect, the overall atmosphere is one of peace and tranquillity without pomposity. An ideal venue for business as well as pleasure, there are a number of syndicate and private dining rooms available, including the stunning Chinese Room with its hand-painted wallpaper. The Aquae Sulis Spa offers a range of natural treatments, facials and massages to aid relaxation, and with excellent children's clubs and babysitting facilities this is also an excellent retreat for parents and children alike. 3 tempting restaurants offer a winning selection of relevant dishes, choose either the elegant dining room for formal evening dinner, the buzzy Italian Café Inferno for pizza and light lunches with the children or the Grand Conservatory for cucumber sandwiches and a relaxed afternoon tea.

Our inspector loved: *The selection of artwork, particularly the imaginative contemporary slant on traditional portraiture.*

Directions: From the A14 at Bury St Edmunds take the A143 in the direction of Haverhill.

Web: www.johansens.com/ickworth
E-mail: info@ickworthhotel.com
Tel: 01284 735350
Fax: 01284 736300

Price Guide:
double/twin £150-£270
suite from £350

THE MARLBOROUGH HOTEL

HENLEY ROAD, IPSWICH, SUFFOLK IP1 3SP

Directions: At Junction of A12/A14 take Tesco exit, continue to A1214, turn left into A1214 (direction Woodbridge) over double mini roundabout to lights, then turn right into Henley Road.

Web: www.johansens.com/marlborough
E-mail: sales@themarlborough.co.uk
Tel: 01473 226789/257677
Fax: 01473 226927

Price Guide:
single from £71
double/twin from £86
suite £114

Set in a stunning residential area in the environs of Ipswich, the Marlborough is a renovated Victorian hotel whose owners, the Gough family, guarantee a friendly and hospitable ambience. The interior is a model of modern stylishness, with rich coloured décor complementing the comfortable furnishings, freshly picked flowers and breathtaking pictures. Chef Shaun Thurlow serves Rosette-winning fare, emphasising the freshness of the local produce, in an elegant and beautifully-decorated room which overlooks the magnificent garden. Some of the hotel's individually-designed bedrooms have delightful balconies with views of the garden, while all are spacious and have modern bathrooms. Visitors can take advantage of windsurfing and walking at Alton, with nearby Woodbridge a haven for sailing. Christchurch Park and its Tudor mansion, formerly the home of Thomas Wolsey, are practically next door. Within easy driving distance are the rugged Suffolk coastline, historic Aldeburgh and the world-famous Snape Maltings. The Marlborough Hotel is also on the edge of beautiful Constable Country.

Our inspector loved: *The cheerful interior which was matched by the friendly ambience.*

BELSTEAD BROOK HOTEL

BELSTEAD ROAD, IPSWICH, SUFFOLK IP2 9HB

An oasis on the edge of Ipswich, Belstead Brook Hotel is surrounded by nine acres of landscaped gardens and woodlands. It combines the charm and tranquillity of the original 16th century country house with every modern day comfort. Bedrooms are pleasantly furnished and many overlook the garden. Guests may use the luxurious swimming pool with sauna, steam room, large Jacuzzi, separate pool for children and a well-equipped gymnasium. There are new executive garden rooms with allocated parking. The award-winning restaurant offers a choice of menus, complemented by a comprehensive cellar. For weddings, conferences or banquets, the hotel offers private dining rooms and a choice of purpose-built meeting and syndicate rooms to accommodate up to 130 guests or delegates. The hotel is an ideal base from which to explore the delights of Suffolk. These include Southwold, Aldeburgh, Woodbridge, the estuaries of the Deben and the Orwell, the wool towns of Lavenham and Long Melford and the countryside of the Stour Valley, made famous by John Constable.

Our inspector loved: The country house style but with all the benefits of a modern property.

Directions: From A12/A14 junction take A1214 to Ipswich West. At first roundabout turn right to Belstead and follow the brown signs to the hotel.

Web: www.johansens.com/belsteadbrook
E-mail: sales@belsteadbrook.co.uk
Tel: 01473 684241
Fax: 01473 681249

Price Guide:
double/twin £80–£104.75
suites £150

HINTLESHAM HALL

HINTLESHAM, IPSWICH, SUFFOLK IP8 3NS

Directions: Hintlesham Hall is 4 miles west of Ipswich on the A1071 Sudbury road.

Web: www.johansens.com/hintleshamhall
E-mail: reservations@hintleshamhall.com
Tel: 01473 652334
Fax: 01473 652463

Price Guide:
single £98–£120
double/twin £110–£235
suite £225–£375

The epitome of grandeur, Hintlesham Hall is a house of evolving styles: its splendid Georgian façade belies its 16th-century origins, to which the red-brick Tudor rear of the hall is a testament. The Stuart period also left its mark, in the form of a magnificent carved-oak staircase leading to the north wing of the hall. The combination of styles works extremely well, with the lofty proportions of the Georgian reception rooms contrasting with the timbered Tudor rooms. The décor throughout is superb – all rooms are individually appointed in a discriminating fashion. Iced mineral water, toiletries and towelling robes are to be found in each of the comfortable bedrooms. The herb garden supplies many of the flavours for the well-balanced menu which will appeal to the gourmet and the health-conscious alike, complemented by a 300-bin wine list. Bounded by 175 acres of rolling countryside, leisure facilities include the Hall's own 18-hole championship golf course, new state of the art gymnasium, sauna, steam room, spa bath, tennis, croquet, snooker and a health and beauty suite with a full range of E'Spa products available at weekends and by arrangement during the week. Guests can also explore Suffolk's 16th-century wool merchants' villages, its pretty coast, 'Constable country' and Newmarket.

Our inspector loved: *Great cookery days and wine dinners.*

BLACK LION HOTEL & RESTAURANT

CHURCH WALK, THE GREEN, LONG MELFORD, SUFFOLK CO10 9DN

One of Long Melford's oldest Inns, The Black Lion glories in its superb position overlooking the Green, and the Village with its elegant broad street and imposing church. Having been in existence for over 300 years, the Hotel recently entered a fresh era in its illustrious history. Under new owner Craig Jarvis a transformation has taken place, with rich colours, comfortable antique furniture and welcoming open fires all creating a charming country house ambience. Flanked by the stately homes of Kentwell and Melford Hall, good sized bedrooms are furnished with antiques and offer individual design plus modern facilities, some have picturesque views. The menu, based on traditional dishes with a modern approach, may be sampled casually in the Lounge Bar or more formally in the Restaurant each providing superb presentation and excellent food. The Victorian walled garden is an ideal setting to enjoy lunches and cream teas. A prolifery of antique emporiums, interesting shops, picturesque country walks and stately homes are within walking distance of the Inn, and many other places of interest are just a short drive away. Racegoers will find The Black Lion a perfect base from which to attend Newmarket, while those simply longing to get away from it all could not wish for a more peaceful and inviting country retreat.

Our inspector loved: *Not wanting to move from the comfy sofas in front of the big log fire.*

Directions: From A14 take A134 in direction of Sudbury. Hotel overlooks Long Melford village green.

Web: www.johansens.com/blacklion

E-mail:
Tel: 01787 312356
Fax: 01787 374557

Price Guide:
single from £75
double/twin from £95
suite from £130

BEDFORD LODGE HOTEL

BURY ROAD, NEWMARKET, CB8 7BX

Directions: From M11 exit at Junction 9 onto A11. Follow signs to Newmarket. From the Clock Tower in centre of Town go straight across two mini roundabouts onto the Bury Road. The hotel is ¼ mile on the left.

Web: www.johansens.com/bedfordlodge
E-mail: info@bedfordlodgehotel.co.uk
Tel: 01638 663175
Fax: 01638 667391

Price Guide: (incl breakfast and VAT)
single from £105
double/twin from £140
suites £130–£205

This elegant hotel stands in three acres of glorious secluded gardens, adjacent to paddocks and training stables and just a short walk from Newmarket town centre. Formerly a Georgian hunting lodge built for the Duke of Bedford in the late 18th century, it offers a striking combination of both classic and modern styles. The atmosphere is relaxing and the service impeccable. This is horse racing country and the sport of kings is reflected throughout the hotel. A picture of Roxanna, the most famous mare of 18th-century England, hangs in the attractive hallway beyond the bar that bears her name. The newly refurbished bedrooms are carefully designed and offer a range of modern facilities. Contemporary dining in an elegant and charming ambience is offered in the award-winning Orangery restaurant with magnificent trompe-l'oeil fruit trees. Guests can relax in the hotel's superb leisure complex, which includes an indoor swimming pool, sauna, spa pool, solarium and fully equipped air-conditioned gym. Beauty treatments by prior arrangement. The University City of Cambridge, Suffolk and South Norfolk are all within easy reach. Weekend package from £75 per person per night (incl. dinner, bed and breakfast and VAT).

Our inspector loved: *The stylish bedrooms and superb comfortable beds.*

SWYNFORD PADDOCKS HOTEL AND RESTAURANT

SIX MILE BOTTOM, NR NEWMARKET, SUFFOLK CB8 0UE

This classical white mansion standing in glorious gardens and idyllic countryside with racehorses grazing its pastures has a romantic history. In 1813 it was the scene of a passionate love affair between Lord Byron and the wife of the owner, Colonel George Leigh. Swynford was converted into a hotel 20 years ago. It has a country house atmosphere with antique furniture, open fires and attention to detail of times gone by. Each individually decorated, en suite bedroom has colour television, clock radio alarm, telephone, mini-bar and many other amenities. The lounge bar overlooks the gardens and the dining room offers an imaginative menu, changed regularly to incorporate the season's fresh produce. The award-winning restaurant has been awarded two RAC Dining Awards and two AA Rosettes. Conference facilities are available and a luxury marquee for private and special functions. Tennis, putting and croquet are within the grounds and guided tours of Newmarket with a look at the horseracing world can be arranged. Heliquisine: For a special occasion guests are chauffeur driven in a limousine to Cambridge airport for a helicopter ariel view of the surrounding towns, then land for a superb lunch at the hotel.

Our inspector loved: *That it is just minutes away from the famous racecourse, but in a country location overlooking a beautiful stud.*

Directions: From M11, exit at jct 9 and take A11 towards Newmarket. After 10 miles join A1304 signed Newmarket. Hotel is on left after ¾ of a mile.

Web: www.johansens.com/swynfordpaddocks
E-mail: info@swynfordpaddocks.com
Tel: 01638 570234
Fax: 01638 570283

Price Guide:
single £110
double/twin £135–£155
suite £175

THE SWAN HOTEL

MARKET PLACE, SOUTHWOLD, SUFFOLK IP18 6EG

Directions: Southwold is off the A12 Ipswich–Lowestoft road. The Swan Hotel is in the town centre.

Web: www.johansens.com/swansouthwold
E-mail: swan.hotel@adnams.co.uk
Tel: 01502 722186
Fax: 01502 724800

Price Guide:
single £70
double/twin £120
suite £185

Rebuilt in 1659, following the disastrous fire which destroyed most of the town, The Swan was remodelled in the 1820s, with further additions in 1938. The hotel provides all modern services while retaining its classical dignity and elegance. Many of the antique-furnished bedrooms in the main hotel offer a glimpse of the sea, while the garden rooms – decorated in a more contemporary style – are clustered around the old bowling green. The Drawing Room has the traditional character of an English country house and the Reading Room upstairs is perfect for quiet relaxation or as the venue for a private party. The daily menu offers dishes ranging from simple, traditional fare through the English classics to the chef's personal specialities as well as a full a la carte menu. An exciting selection of wines is offered. Almost an island, Southwold is bounded on three sides by creeks, marshes and the River Blyth – making it a paradise for birdwatchers and nature lovers. Hardly changed for a century, the town, built around a series of greens, has a fine church, lighthouse and golf course. Music lovers flock to nearby Snape Maltings for the Aldeburgh Festival.

Our inspector loved: *The comfortable lounge - I could have relaxed all day.*

SECKFORD HALL

WOODBRIDGE, SUFFOLK IP13 6NU

Seckford Hall dates from 1530 and it is said that Elizabeth I once held court there. The hall has lost none of its Tudor grandeur. Furnished as a private house with many fine period pieces, the panelled rooms, beamed ceilings, carved doors and great stone fireplaces are displayed against the splendour of English oak. Local delicacies such as the house speciality, lobster, feature on the à la carte menu. The original minstrels gallery can be viewed in the banqueting hall, which is now a conference and function suite designed in keeping with the general style. The Courtyard area was converted from a giant Tudor tithe barn, dairy and coach house. It now incorporates ten charming cottage-style suites and a modern leisure complex, which includes a heated swimming pool, exercise machines, spa bath and beauty salon. The hotel is set in 34 acres of tranquil parkland with sweeping lawns and a willow-fringed lake and guests may stroll about the grounds or simply relax in the attractive terrace garden. There is a 18-hole golf course, where equipment can be hired, and a gentle walk along the riverside to picturesque Woodbridge, with its tide mill, antique shops and yacht harbours. Visit the site of the Sutton Hoo buriel ship site and new museum. Constable country and the Suffolk coast are nearby.

Directions: Remain on the A12 Woodbridge bypass until the blue-and-white hotel sign.

Web: www.johansens.com/seckfordhall
E-mail: reception@seckford.co.uk
Tel: 01394 385678
Fax: 01394 380610

Price Guide:
single £79–£130
double/twin £120–£170
suite £150–£170

Our inspector loved: The first sight of this beautiful tudor building.

PENNYHILL PARK HOTEL

LONDON ROAD, BAGSHOT, SURREY GU19 5EU

Bagshot has been a centre of hospitality since the early Stuart sovereigns James I and Charles I had a hunting lodge there. Pennyhill Park Hotel continues to uphold that tradition. Created in 1849, this elegant mansion reflects its journey through Victorian and Edwardian times while providing every modern amenity. The bedrooms are outstanding: no two are identical, and infinite care has been invested in creating practical rooms with distinctive features. Impeccable service is to be expected, as staff are trained to classical, Edwardian standards. Haute cuisine and a listing of fine wines is offered in the wonderful oak panelled Latymer Room or less formal eating is available in the sparkling St James Restaurant. Recreational facilities are available within the grounds, which span 120 acres and include landscaped gardens, a 9-hole golf course, a swimming pool, a three acre lake, gym, rugby/football pitch, archery, jogging and walking path. Pennyhill Park is conveniently located only 27 miles from central London and not far from Heathrow, Windsor Castle, Ascot, Wentworth and Sunningdale.

Directions: From the M3, exit 3, take A322 towards Bracknell. Turn left on to A30 signposted to Camberley. ¾ mile after Bagshot; turn right 50 yards past the Texaco garage.

Web: www.johansens.com/pennyhillpark
E-mail: enquiries@pennyhillpark.co.uk
Tel: 01276 471774
Fax: 01276 473217

Price Guide:
single from £205.62
double/twin from £217.37
suite from £352.50
apartments from £411.25

Our inspector loved: *Marble, marble and more marble - extravagant and stunning interiors.*

WOODLANDS PARK HOTEL

WOODLANDS LANE, STOKE D'ABERNON, COBHAM, SURREY KT11 3QB

Set in 15 acres of wooded lawns, Woodlands Park Hotel, part of the Arcadian Hotel Group, is an ideal location for touring the surrounding Surrey and Berkshire countryside or for those seeking a base on the edge of Greater London. At the turn of the century, the then Prince of Wales and the famous actress Lillie Langtry were frequent visitors to this splendid Victorian mansion. Well-equipped en suite bedrooms retain an appealing Victorian theme and ambience, despite having been refurbished to the highest modern standards. Each offers its guests luxury, comfort and every up-to-date amenity. The Oak Room Restaurant, awarded 2 AA Rosettes, serves English and French cuisine in elegant surroundings, whilst in Quotes Brasserie you will discover a wide selection of dishes from the speciality menu, designed for those who prefer less formal dining. Small meeting rooms can be reached from the Grand Hall and can accommodate between 10 and 60 for private dinners or meetings, while the Prince of Wales Suite seats up to 260. Nearby are Wisley Gardens, Hampton Court and Brooklands Museum. Kempton Park, Epsom and Sandown are within a short distance for those who enjoy racing.

Our inspector loved: Room 57.

Directions: On the M25, take junction 9 or 10. The hotel is east of Cobham at Stoke d'Abernon on the A245.

Web: www.johansens.com/woodlandsparkcobham
E-mail: info@woodlandspark.co.uk
Tel: 01372 843933 or 0800 9 177 877
Fax: 01372 842704

Price Guide: (Room only)
single £150–£185
twin/double £170–£260
suites £270–£460

289

Great Fosters

STROUDE ROAD, EGHAM, SURREY TW20 9UR

Directions: M25/J13, head for Egham and watch for brown 'Historic Buildings' signs.

Web: www.johansens.com/greatfosters
E-mail: enquiries@greatfosters.co.uk
Tel: 01784 433822
Fax: 01784 472455

Price Guide:
single from £120
double/twin from £155
suite from £280

Probably built as a Royal Hunting lodge in Windsor Forest, very much a stately home since the 16th century, today Great Fosters is a prestigious hotel within half an hour of both Heathrow Airport and central London. Its past is evident in the mullioned windows, tall chimneys and brick finials, while the Saxon moat – crossed by a Japanese bridge – surrounds three sides of the formal gardens, complete with topiary, statuary and a charming rose garden. Within are fine oak beams and panelling, Jacobean chimney pieces, superb tapestries and a rare oakwell staircase leading to the Tower. Some of the guest rooms are particularly magnificent – one Italian styled with gilt furnishings and damask walls, others with moulded ceilings, beautiful antiques and Persian rugs. Guests relax in the bar, then enjoy good English and French cooking and carefully selected wines, either in the Oak Room Restaurant or the Tithe Barn with its vaulted roof. Celebrations, meetings and weddings take place in the elegant Orangery and impressive Painted Hall, the ceiling a riot of exotic birds and animals. Great Fosters is close to polo in Windsor Great Park, racing at Ascot, golf at Wentworth, boating in Henley and pageantry at Windsor Castle, Runnymede and Hampton Court.

Our inspector loved: *The newly created dining room and the many ongoing improvements to this fine old building and its ancient setting.*

LANGSHOTT MANOR

LANGSHOTT, HORLEY, SURREY RH6 9LN

The peace and seclusion of this beautiful Manor House, tucked away down a quiet country lane amidst 3 acres of lovely garden, belies its proximity to London's Gatwick Airport, only 10 minutes away by car. Retaining the essential feel of a fine Elizabethan house, Langshott has recently been sympathetically expanded to encompass an attractive new dining room with views over ponds and gardens. Additional to the main house, superb bedrooms have been created in both the Coach House Mews and the Moat Mews. The Manor prides itself on outstanding levels of hospitality, service, cuisine and comfort acknowledged by 3 AA Red Stars and an RAC Gold Ribbon. Each of the bedrooms are decorated in individual style, all of them offer exceptional standards of provision exemplified by luxurious towelling robes and comfy slippers. There are Egyptian cotton sheets on the beds, hot water bottles to go in the beds and home-made cookies beside the beds. There are romantic and honeymoon breaks and if you are flying from Gatwick special arrangements include 2 weeks car parking and a chauffeured car to the airport.

Our inspector loved: Everything.

Directions: From the A23 at Horley take Ladbroke Road immediately north of the Chequers Hotel roundabout. The Manor is ¾ of a mile (1 kilometre) on the right.

Web: www.johansens.com/langshottmanor
E-mail: admin@langshottmanor.com
Tel: 01293 786680
Fax: 01293 783905

Price Guide:
single from £185
double/twin £220–£260
suite £290

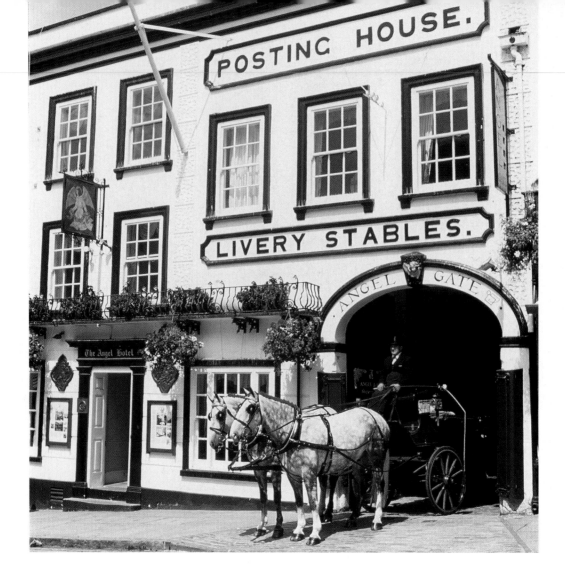

THE ANGEL POSTING HOUSE AND LIVERY

91 THE HIGH STREET, GUILDFORD, SURREY GU1 3DP

The Angel, a delightful historic coaching inn on the old Portsmouth road, now a luxurious small hotel, has stood on the cobbled High Street in the centre of Guildford since the 16th century. This timber-framed building has welcomed many famous visitors, including Lord Nelson, Sir Francis Drake, Jane Austen and Charles Dickens. Today, with easy access to Gatwick, Heathrow, the M4, M3 and M25, it is ideally placed for both business and leisure weekends. Relax with afternoon tea in the galleried lounge with its oak-beamed Jacobean fireplace and 17th-century parliament clock; a welcome retreat from the bustle of the nearby shops. Following the trend of townhouses, only room and breakfast are offered but guests have an extensive choice of restaurants within a few minutes stroll from the hotel. The charming bedrooms and suites are all unique and named after a famous visitor. Excellent communications, presentation facilities and 24-hour service make this a good choice for business meetings. Guests can enjoy complimentary use of modern leisure club facilities just a short drive away.

Directions: From M3 jct3 take A322; or from M25 jct10 take A3. The Angel is in the centre of Guildford, within the pedestrian priority area – guests should enquire about vehicle access and parking when booking.

Web: www.johansens.com/angelpostinghouse
E-mail: angelhotel@hotmail.com
Tel: 01483 564555
Fax: 01483 533770

Price Guide: (room only)
double/twin £140–£165
suite £185–£205

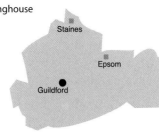

Our inspector loved: The pedestrianised High Street location - with good shopping all round.

LYTHE HILL HOTEL & SPA

PETWORTH ROAD, HASLEMERE, SURREY GU27 3BQ

Cradled by the Surrey foothills in a tranquil setting is the enchanting Lythe Hill Hotel & Spa. It is an unusual cluster of ancient buildings – parts of which date from the 14th century. While most of the beautifully appointed accommodation is in the more recently converted part of the hotel, there are five charming bedrooms in the Tudor House, including the Henry VIII room with a four-poster bed dated 1614. There are two delightful restaurants, the Auberge de France offers classic French cuisine in the oak-panelled room which overlooks the lake and parklands, and the 'Dining Room' has the choice of imaginative English fare. An exceptional wine list offers over 200 wines from more than a dozen countries. A splendid Egyptian featured leisure facility includes a 16 x 8 metre swimming pool, steam room and sauna, gym, hairdressing, treatment rooms and a nail bar. National Trust hillside adjoining the hotel grounds provides interesting walking and views over the surrounding countryside. The area is steeped in history, with the country houses of Petworth, Clandon and Uppark to visit as well as racing at Goodwood and polo at Cowdray Park. Brighton and the south coast are only a short drive away.

Our inspector loved: The fabulous Spa in a countryside setting.

Directions: Lythe Hill lies about 1½ miles from the centre of Haslemere, east on the B2131.

Web: www.johansens.com/lythehill
E-mail: lythe@lythehill.co.uk
Tel: 01428 651251
Fax: 01428 644131

Price Guide: (room only)
single from £98
double/twin from £125
suite from £150

Staines

Epsom

Guildford

293

FOXHILLS

STONEHILL ROAD, OTTERSHAW, SURREY KT16 0EL

This magnificent 400 acre estate is a delightful environment for any discerning traveller, whatever their interests may be. Named after the 18th century foreign secretary, Charles James Fox, Foxhills comprises of a large Manor House, elegant suites, three golf courses, numerous tennis courts, indoor and outdoor swimming pools, three restaurants and a host of health and fitness facilities including a gymnasium and a spa or beauty salon. The 38 bedrooms, located in a superb courtyard setting, are the essence of comfort; elegantly furnished and offering all the latest amenities, they are designed in a number of styles; some have gardens whilst others are on two floors. The two restaurants pride themselves in their culinary excellence. Inside the Manor itself, the award-winning restaurant serves fine cuisine and is renowned for the Sunday buffet – a gourmet's delight! The sport and health facilities at Foxhills are particularly impressive and with 20 qualified instructors on hand, guests may wish to acquire a new skill such as racquetball or T'ai Chi. Those wishing to be pampered will enjoy the sauna, steamroom and the fine beauty salon. Awarded 4 stars by the AA.

Directions: From M25 Jct 11, follow signs to Woking. After a dual carriageway, turn left into Guildford Road. 3rd exit at roundabout and immediately right into Foxhills Road. Turn left at the end of the road, Foxhills is on the right.

Web: www.johansens.com/foxhills
E-mail: reservations@foxhills.co.uk
Tel: 01932 704500
Fax: 01932 874762

Price Guide: (room only)
double/twin from £160
suite from £225

Our inspector loved: The astonishing range of leisure provision.

NUTFIELD PRIORY

NUTFIELD, REDHILL, SURREY RH1 4EN

Built in 1872 by the millionaire MP, Joshua Fielden, Nutfield Priory is an extravagant folly embellished with towers, elaborate carvings, intricate stonework, cloisters and stained glass, all superbly restored to create an unusual country house hotel. Set high on Nutfield Ridge, the priory has far-reaching views over the Surrey and Sussex countryside, while being within easy reach of London and also Gatwick Airport. The elegant lounges and library have ornately carved ceilings and antique furnishings. Unusually spacious bedrooms – some with beams – enjoy views over the surrounding countryside. Fresh fruit is a thoughtful extra. The Cloisters Restaurant provides a unique environment in which to enjoy the high standard of cuisine, complemented by an extensive wine list. Conferences and private functions can be accommodated in the splendid setting of one of the hotel's 10 conference rooms. The Priory Health and Leisure Club, adjacent to the hotel, provides all the facilities for exercise and relaxation that one could wish for, including a swimming pool, sauna, spa, solarium, gym, steam room and extensive beauty treatments.

Our inspector loved: *The very grand Victorian proportions and gothic features.*

Directions: Nutfield is on the A25 between Redhill and Godstone and can be reached easily from junctions 6 and 8 of the M25. From Godstone, the Priory is on the left just after the village.

Web: www.johansens.com/nutfieldpriory
E-mail: nutbooking@aol.com
Tel: 01737 824400
Fax: 01737 823321

Price Guide:
single from £145
double/twin £170–£200
suite £205–£265

OATLANDS PARK HOTEL

146 OATLANDS DRIVE, WEYBRIDGE, SURREY KT13 9HB

Directions: From M25 junction 11, follow signs to Weybridge. Follow A317 through High Street into Monument Hill to mini-roundabout. Turn left into Oatlands Drive; hotel is 50 yards on left.

Web: www.johansens.com/oatlandspark
E-mail: info@oatlandsparkhotel.com
Tel: 01932 847242
Fax: 01932 842252

Price Guide: (room only)
single £135–£190
double/twin £180–£200
suite from £215

Records of the Oatlands estate show that Elizabeth I and the Stuart kings spent time in residence in the original buildings. The present mansion dates from the late-18th century and became a hotel in 1856: famous guests included Émile Zola, Anthony Trollope and Edward Lear. The hotel stands in acres of parkland overlooking Broadwater Lake, with easy access to Heathrow, Gatwick and central London. Although it caters for the modern traveller, the hotel's historic character is evident throughout. The accommodation ranges from superior rooms to large de luxe rooms and suites. The elegant, high-ceilinged Broadwater Restaurant is the setting for creative à la carte menus with dishes to suit all tastes. A traditional roast is served every Sunday lunchtime. The six air-conditioned meeting rooms and up-to-date facilities include video conferencing and are complemented by the professional conference team. Theme evenings, such as Henry VIII banquets, are a speciality. Many sporting and leisure activities are offered including a new 9 hole, par 27, golf course.

Our inspector loved: *The new English oak panelling.*

WHITE LODGE COUNTRY HOUSE HOTEL

SLOE LANE, ALFRISTON, EAST SUSSEX BN26 5UR

Nestled in 5 acres of landscaped grounds, in the heart of the Cuckmere Valley, the White Lodge Country House Hotel offers a friendly welcome and excellent service in relaxed and peaceful surroundings. This recently refurbished Hotel has individually styled bedrooms, some with four poster beds. All have private facilities, colour television and a hospitality tray, many have views over Alfriston and the South Downs. The elegant Orchid Restaurant offers guests a diverse menu of traditional dishes, served in a relaxing atmosphere and is complemented by a well-stocked cellar. Guests can relax in the cosy lounges or the drawing room which have real log fires in the winter. Murder Mystery evenings and other events are held at the Hotel on a regular basis. Outdoor activities might include lazing in the Hotel gardens, enjoying a game of croquet or putting, or taking a pleasant stroll into the village of Alfriston with its olde worlde shops and The National Trust property The Clergy House. Glynebourne, Lewes, Eastbourne and Brighton are only a short drive away.

Our inspector loved: The views over Alfriston and the Downs.

Directions: Alfriston is on the B2108 between the A27/A259. The Hotel is well signed from the village centre.

Web: www.johansens.com/whitelodgecountryhouse
E-mail: sales@whitelodge–hotel.com
Tel: 01323 870265
Fax: 01323 870284

Price Guide:
single from £50
double/twin from £100
suite from £130

POWDERMILLS HOTEL

POWDERMILL LANE, BATTLE, EAST SUSSEX TN33 0SP

Situated outside the historic Sussex town famous for the 1066 battle, PowderMills is an 18th century listed country house which has been skilfully converted into an elegant hotel. Nestling in 150 acres of parks and woodland, the beautiful and tranquil grounds feature a 7-acre specimen fishing lake. Wild geese, swans, ducks, kingfishers and herons abound. Privately owned and run by Douglas and Julie Cowpland, the hotel has been carefully furnished with locally acquired antiques. On cooler days, log fires burn in the entrance hall and drawing room. The bedrooms – ten with four-posters – are all individually furnished and decorated. The Orangery Restaurant offers fine classical cooking by chef James Penn. Guests may dine on the terrace in summer, looking out over the swimming pool and grounds. Light meals and snacks are available in the library. The location an is ideal base from which to explore the beautiful Sussex and Kent countryside and there are many villages and small towns in the area.

Directions: From centre of Battle take the Hastings road south. After ¼ mile turn right into Powdermill Lane. After a sharp bend, the entrance is on the right; cross over the bridge and lakes to reach the hotel.

Web: www.johansens.com/powdermills
E-mail: powdc@aol.com
Tel: 01424 775511
Fax: 01424 774540

Price Guide:
single from £80
double/twin £105–£175

Our inspector loved: The new rooms overlooking the lake - don't miss a trip in the old launch.

Brighton
Hastings
Eastbourne

BUXTED PARK COUNTRY HOUSE HOTEL

BUXTED, NR UCKFIELD, EAST SUSSEX TN22 4AY

Few settings are more tranquil than Buxted Park's rural location, close to Ashdown Forest. Built in 1725, the attractive Georgian Mansion has been sympathetically restored to its former glory of time gone by, when Queen Victoria and Queen Mary were both regular visitors. Set in 312 acres of stunning gardens and parkland, the hotel also boasts extensive trout lakes, with fly-fishing available. There are 44 spacious bedrooms, most with delightful views of the gardens and estate, which is home to herds of fallow deer. The Orangery Restaurant situated in the restored Victorian conservatory provides rare and elegant surroundings in which to enjoy the excellent food and wines. There are several impressive and comfortable lounges to choose from as well as the magnificent ballroom, which opens out into the Coat of Arms Lounge. The hotel is equipped with a small health club, which has a gym, sauna, steam room, spa bath and treatment rooms (prior reservations required). Two night leisure breaks are available from £70 per person per night.

Our inspector loved: The romance of its having been a harem!

Directions: The entrance to the hotel is located on the A272, east of its junction with the A22

Web: www.johansens.com/buxtedpark
E-mail: res.bph@arcadianhotels.co.uk
Tel: 01825 732711
Fax: 01825 732770

Price Guide:
single from £95
double/twin from £135
suites from £185

THE GRAND HOTEL

KING EDWARD'S PARADE, EASTBOURNE, EAST SUSSEX BN21 4EQ

Directions: A22 from London. A259 from East or West. Hotel is at the western end of the seafront.

Web: www.johansens.com/grandeastbourne
E-mail: reservations@grandeastbourne.com
Tel: 01323 412345
Fax: 01323 412233

Price Guide:
single £125–£385
double/twin £159–£210
suite £210–£410

Hastings
Brighton
Eastbourne

The Grand Hotel is a fine property, steeped in history, which evokes the charm and splendour of the Victorian era. The majestic facade complements the elegant interior whilst the reception rooms are beautifully appointed with rich fabrics and ornaments. Many of the 152 bedrooms are of vast proportions: all being refurbished to include every comfort with attractive bathrooms. The hotel has numerous areas in which to relax and a good choice of restaurants and bars. 'The Mirabelle' in particular achieves exceptional standards of fine dining. The array of new leisure facilities includes both indoor and outdoor pools, gymnasium, sauna, solarium, spa bath, steam room, snooker tables and a hair salon and 8 beauty rooms. Guests may choose to try the nearby racquet and golf clubs. For the meeting organiser, the hotel offers an impressive range of rooms which can cater for a number of business purposes from a board meeting for 12 to a larger conference for up to 300 delegates. Those seeking a peaceful retreat will be pleased with the tranquil atmosphere of Eastbourne. Pastimes include walks along the Downs, sea fishing and trips to the two nearby theatres.

Our inspector loved: *The stunning sea views and superb 'grand hotel' service.*

ASHDOWN PARK HOTEL AND COUNTRY CLUB

WYCH CROSS, FOREST ROW, EAST SUSSEX RH18 5JR

Ashdown Park is a grand, rambling 19th century mansion overlooking almost 200 acres of landscaped gardens to the forest beyond. Built in 1867, the hotel is situated within easy reach of Gatwick Airport, London and the South Coast and provides the perfect backdrop for every occasion, from a weekend getaway to a honeymoon or business convention. The hotel is subtly furnished throughout to satisfy the needs of escapees from urban stress. The 107 en suite bedrooms are beautifully decorated – several with elegant four-poster beds, all with up-to-date amenities. The Anderida restaurant offers a thoughtfully compiled menu and wine list, complemented by discreetly attentive service in soigné surroundings. Guests seeking relaxation can retire to the indoor pool and sauna, pamper themselves with a massage, before using the solarium, or visiting the beauty salon. Alternatively, guests may prefer to amble through the gardens and nearby woodland paths; the more energetic can indulge in tennis, croquet or use the Fitness Studio and Beauty Therapy. There is also an indoor driving range, a lounge/bar and an 18-hole par 3 golf course with an outdoor driving range.

Our inspector loved: *The enormous Fairway studio suites.*

Directions: East of A22 at Wych Cross traffic lights on road signposted to Hartfield.

Web: www.johansens.com/ashdownpark
E-mail: reservations@ashdownpark.com
Tel: 01342 824988
Fax: 01342 826206

Price Guide:
single £125–£315
double/twin £159–£310
suite £340

NEWICK PARK

NEWICK, NEAR LEWES, EAST SUSSEX BN8 4SB

Directions: The nearest motorway is the M23, jct 11.

Web: www.johansens.com/newickpark
E-mail: bookings@newickpark.co.uk
Tel: 01825 723633
Fax: 01825 723969

Price Guide:
single £95–£120
double/twin £165–235

This magnificent Grade II listed Georgian country house, set in over 200 acres of breath-taking parkland and landscaped gardens, overlooks the Longford River and lake and the South Downs. Whilst situated in a convenient location near to the main road and rail routes and only 30 minutes away from Gatwick Airport, Newick Park maintains an atmosphere of complete tranquillity and privacy. The en suite bedrooms are decorated in a classic style and contain elegant antique furnishings. The exquisite dining room offers a wide choice of culinary delights, carefully devised by the Head Chef, Billy Butcher. The convivial bar complements the restaurant with its delicate style and understated elegance. The friendly staff ensure that guests receive a warm welcome and an outstanding level of comfort. The house and grounds are ideal for weddings or conferences and may be hired for exclusive use by larger groups. The Dell gardens, planted primarily in Victorian times, include a rare collection of Royal Ferns. Vibrant and diverse colours saturate the lawns during the changing seasons, courtesy of the various flowers and shrubs encompassing the gardens. The activities on the estate itself include fishing, shooting and tennis, whilst nearby distractions include the East Sussex Golf Club and racing at Goodwood.

Our inspector loved: The utterly tranquil landscaped setting.

HORSTED PLACE COUNTRY HOUSE HOTEL

LITTLE HORSTED, EAST SUSSEX TN22 5TS

Horsted Place enjoys a splendid location amid the peace of the Sussex Downs. This magnificent Victorian Gothic Mansion, which was built in 1851, overlooks the East Sussex National golf course and boasts an interior predominantly styled by the celebrated Victorian architect, Augustus Pugin. In former years the Queen and Prince Philip were frequent visitors. Guests today are invited to enjoy the excellent service offered by a committed staff. Since the turn of 2001, and under new management, the bedrooms have been refurbished to provide luxurious décor and every modern comfort, whilst all public areas have been refurbished and upholstered. Dining at Horsted is guaranteed to be a memorable experience. Chef Allan Garth offers a daily fixed price menu as well as the seasonal à la carte menu. The Horsted Management Centre is a suite of air-conditioned rooms which have been specially designed to accommodate theatre-style presentations and training seminars or top level board meetings. Places of interest nearby include Royal Tunbridge Wells, Lewes and Glyndebourne. For golfing enthusiasts there is the added attraction of the East Sussex National Golf Club, one of the finest golf complexes in the world.

Our inspector loved: The magnificent Pugin staircase, and everything else to match.

Directions: The hotel entrance is on the A26 just short of the junction with the A22, two miles south of Uckfield and signposted towards Lewes.

Web: www.johansens.com/horstedplace
E-mail: hotel@horstedplace.co.uk
Tel: 01825 750581
Fax: 01825 750459

Price Guide:
double/twin from £130
suite from £220

303

DALE HILL

TICEHURST, NR WADHURST, EAST SUSSEX TN5 7DQ

Directions: From the M25, junction 5, follow the A21 to Flimwell. Then turn right onto the B2087. Dale Hill is on the left.

Web: www.johansens.com/dalehill
E-mail: info@dalehill.co.uk
Tel: 01580 200112
Fax: 01580 201249

Price Guide:
single £85–£105
double/twin £100–£140
suites: £140-£180

Situated in over 350 acres of fine grounds, high on the Kentish Weald, Dale Hill is a modern hotel which combines the best in golfing facilities with the style and refinement desired by discerning guests. The décor is enhanced by soft coloured fabrics and carpets, creating a summery impression throughout the year. Golfers have the choice of two 18-hole courses, a gently undulating, 6,093 yards par 70 and a new, challenging championship-standard course designed by former U.S. Masters champion Ian Woosnam. Just 20 minutes drive away, under the same ownership as the hotel, is the Nick Faldo designed Chart Hills course hailed as 'the best new course in England'. Packages allow guests to play both championship courses. Diners enjoy glorious views in a choice of restaurants where traditional award winning cuisine is complemented by a fine wine list and service. The fully equipped health club features a heated swimming pool and a range of health, beauty and fitness facilities. Dale Hill is only a short drive from Tunbridge Wells and its renowned Pantiles shopping walk. Also nearby are medieval Scotney Castle, which dates back to 1380, Sissinghurst, a moated Tudor castle with gardens and Bewl Water, renowned for fly-fishing and water sports.

Our inspector loved: The view from the dining room.

AMBERLEY CASTLE

AMBERLEY, NR ARUNDEL, WEST SUSSEX BN18 9ND

A former winner of the Johansens Country Hotel award, Amberley Castle is this year celebrating its 900 year history. Set between the rolling South Downs and the peaceful expanses of the Amberley Wildbrooks, its towering battlements give breathtaking views and massive 14th Century curtain walls and the mighty portcullis bear silent testimony to a fascinating past. Proprietors, Joy and Martin Cummings, have transformed this medieval fortress into a unique country castle hotel. They offer a warm, personal welcome and their hotel provides the ultimate in contemporary luxury, while retaining an atmosphere of timelessness. Five distinctive new suites were added recently in the Bishopric by the main gateway. Each room is individually designed and has its own Jacuzzi bath. The exquisite 12th-century Queen's Room is the perfect setting for the creative cuisine of head chef James Peyton and his team. Amberley Castle is a natural first choice for romantic or cultural weekends, sporting breaks or confidential executive meetings. Roman ruins, antiques, stately homes, castle gardens, horse racing and history 'everywhere' you look, all within a short distance. It is easily accessible from London and the major air and channel ports.

Our inspector loved: The portcullis-will it descend and keep us there forever?

Directions: Amberley Castle is on the B2139, off the A29 between Bury and Storrington. Look out for the Union flag, which clearly marks the driveway.

Web: www.johansens.com/amberleycastle
E-mail: info@amberleycastle.co.uk
Tel: 01798 831992
Fax: 01798 831998

Price Guide: (Room only)
double/twin £145–£300
suite £275–£325

BAILIFFSCOURT

CLIMPING, WEST SUSSEX BN17 5RW

Directions: Three miles south of Arundel, off the A259.

Web: www.johansens.com/bailiffscourt
E-mail: bailiffscourt@hshotels.co.uk
Tel: 01903 723511
Fax: 01903 723107

Price Guide:
single from £135
double £160–£255
suite £295–£375

Bailiffscourt is a perfectly preserved 'medieval' house, built in the 1930s using authentic material salvaged from historic old buildings. Gnarled 15th century beams and gothic mullioned windows combine to recreate a home from the Middle Ages. Set in 30 acres of beautiful pastures and walled gardens, it provides guests with a wonderful sanctuary in which to relax or work. The bedrooms are all individually decorated and luxuriously furnished, with many offering four poster beds, open log fires and beautiful views over the surrounding countryside. The restaurant offers a varied menu and summer lunches can be taken alfresco in a rose-clad courtyard or the walled garden. A good list of well-priced wines accompanies meals. Private dining rooms are available for weddings, conferences and meetings and companies can hire the hotel as their 'country house' for 2 or 3 days. Bailiffscourt, is surrounded by tranquil parkland with a golf practice area, heated outdoor pool and tennis courts. Climping Beach, 100 yards away, is ideal for windsurfing. Nearby are Arundel with its castle, Chichester and Goodwood.

Our inspector loved: The unique timeless enviroment.

NEW

HOTEL DU VIN & BISTRO

SHIP STREET, BRIGHTON BN1 1AD

The Hotel du Vin group, which since 1994, has successively excited visitors and residents of Winchester, Tunbridge Wells, Bristol and Birmingham with its alternative hotel style, has arrived in Brighton and opens in the autumn of 2002. They have completely transformed a well-located but neglected area to introduce to the south coast their very individual formula of relaxed eating, fine wines and supremely comfortable bedrooms in what is now a stunning building. Immediately off the sea front and adjacent to the famous Lanes with its myriad of inviting little shops, this will be a real treat. Inside, the various public areas will provide several choices for relaxing; the fine wine bar will offer 15 wines by the glass and bourbon as the featured drink, the main bistro opens onto the pavement and on sunny days lunch in the inner courtyard will be available. The cellar dining room is one of 2 private dining areas and the original wine cellar can be seen and tastings will be on offer as well as tours round the walk-in cigar humidor. Brighton positively explodes with exhilarating, sophisticated, quirky, colourful and vibrant things to see and do; enjoy the exotic beauty of The Royal Pavilion, visit the Regency Town House or experience how the Edwardians lived at Preston Manor. The Brighton Festival each May is the biggest Arts Fiesta in England.

Our inspector loved: The indoor and outdoor eating options and shopping in the lanes close by.

Directions: Take the A23 to Brighton city centre then follow the signposts to the Seafront. At the roundabout opposite Brighton pier turn right and drive past Ship Street taking the next right onto Middle Street until it meets Ship Street. Turn right into Ship Street and the Hotel is at the end of the road.

Web: www.johansens.com/hotelduvinbrighton
E-mail: info@hotelduvin.com
Tel: 01273 718588
Fax: 01273 718599

Price Guide: (room only)
double/twin from £115
suite from £185

THE MILLSTREAM HOTEL

BOSHAM, NR CHICHESTER, WEST SUSSEX PO18 8HL

Directions: South of the A259 between Chichester and Havant.

Web: www.johansens.com/millstream
E-mail: info@millstream-hotel.co.uk
Tel: 01243 573234
Fax: 01243 573459

Price Guide:
single £79–£89
double/twin £125–£130
suite £169–£175

A village rich in heritage, Bosham is depicted in the Bayeux Tapestry and is associated with King Canute, whose daughter is buried in the local Saxon church. Moreover, sailors from the world over navigate their way to Bosham, which is a yachtsman's idyll on the banks of Chichester Harbour. The Millstream consists of a restored 18th-century malthouse and adjoining cottages linked to The Grange, a small English manor house. Individually furnished bedrooms are complemented by chintz fabrics and pastel décor. Period furniture, a grand piano and bowls of freshly cut flowers feature in the drawing room. A stream meanders past the front of the beautiful gardens. Cross the bridge to the two delightful new suites in "Waterside" the thatched cottage. Whatever the season, care is taken to ensure that the composition and presentation of the dishes reflect high standards. An appetising luncheon menu is offered and includes local seafood specialities such as: dressed Selsey crab, the Millstream's own home-smoked salmon and grilled fresh fillets of sea bass. During the winter, good-value 'Hibernation Breaks' are available.

Our inspector loved: *The shortbread and friendly welcome*

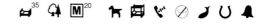

OCKENDEN MANOR

OCKENDEN LANE, CUCKFIELD, WEST SUSSEX RH17 5LD

Set in 9 acres of grounds in the centre of the Tudor village of Cuckfield on the Southern Forest Ridge, this hotel is an ideal base from which to discover Sussex and Kent, the Garden of England. First recorded in 1520, Ockenden Manor has become a hotel of great charm and character. The bedrooms all have their own individual identity: climb your private staircase to Thomas or Elizabeth, look out across the glorious Sussex countryside from Victoria's bay window or choose Charles, with its handsome four-poster bed. The elegant wood panelled restaurant with its beautiful handpainted ceiling is the perfect setting in which to enjoy the chef's innovative cooking. An outstanding, extensive wine list offers, for example, a splendid choice of first-growth clarets. Spacious and elegantly furnished, the Ockenden Suite welcomes private lunch and dinner parties. A superb conservatory is part of the Ockenden Suite, this opens on to the lawns, where marquees can be set up for summer celebrations. The gardens of Nymans, Wakehurst Place and Leonardslee are nearby, as is the opera at Glyndebourne.

Our inspector loved: The restaurant ceiling and flowers everywhere.

Directions: In the centre of Cuckfield on the A272. Less than 3 miles east of the A23.

Web: www.johansens.com/ockendenmanor
E-mail: ockenden@hshotels.co.uk
Tel: 01444 416111
Fax: 01444 415549

Price Guide:
single from £105
double/twin from £160
suite from £290

GRAVETYE MANOR

NEAR EAST GRINSTEAD, WEST SUSSEX RH19 4LJ

Directions: From the M23 junction10 onto A264 towards East Grinstead, at the Duke's Head roundabout take 3rd exit signposted Haywards Heath B2028. 1 miLe south of Turner's Hill village. Gravetye Manor is signposted on the left.

E-mail: info@gravetyemanor.co.uk
Tel: 01342 810567
Fax: 01342 810080

Price Guide:
single £150–£235
double/twin £190–£360

This fine Elizabethan stone mansion is situated on a sheltered hill top site above a trout lake and encircled by 1,000 acres of forest just 30 miles away from Hyde Park Corner. William Robinson, the great English gardener bought the Manor and its extensive grounds in 1884 and it was here at Gravetye that he developed his pioneering ideas for the creation of the English natural garden. Peter Herbert has owned Gravetye since 1958 and with meticulous care has restored and extended the house with stone from the original quarry and oak from the surrounding forests. Guests enjoy an exceptional level of comfort, service and gastronomic pleasure in this traditional English manor house set in gardens of outstanding beauty whose designer had few peers. The bedrooms are well furnished, comfortable and individually designed and decorated to capture the spirit of this great house and to secure the best views of the gardens, meadows and forest beyond. The oak panelled restaurant offers both table d'hote and á la carte menus complemented by wines from the cellar that contains a formidable 500 bins. Places of interest nearby include Glyndebourne Opera, Chartwell and Royal Ashdown Golf Club.

Our inspector loved: *The sense of complete tranquillity.*

ALEXANDER HOUSE HOTEL

EAST STREET, TURNER'S HILL, WEST SUSSEX RH10 4QD

A previous winner of Johansens Most Excellent Service award, Alexander House is a magnificent mansion with its own secluded 175 acres of parkland, including a gently sloping valley which forms the head of the River Medway. Records trace the estate from 1332 when a certain John Atte Fen made it his home. Alexander House is now a modern paragon of good taste and excellence. Spacious rooms throughout this luxurious hotel are splendidly decorated to emphasise their many original features and the bedrooms are lavishly furnished to the highest standards of comfort. The House is renowned for its delicious classic English and French cuisine, rare wines and vintage liqueurs. Music recitals and garden parties feature among a full programme of special summer events and the open fires and cosy atmosphere make this the ideal place to pamper yourself in winter. The many facilities include a resident beautician. Transport can take guests to Gatwick Airport in under 15 minutes. Antique shops, National Trust properties, museums and the Royal Pavilion in Brighton are nearby. Gardens close by include Wakehurst Place, Nymans and Leonardslee.

Our inspector loved: *The glittering chandeliers and opulence.*

Directions: Alexander House lies on the B2110 road between Turner's Hill and East Grinstead, six miles from junction 10 of the M23 motorway.

Web: www.johansens.com/alexanderhouse
E-mail: info@alexanderhouse.co.uk
Tel: 01342 714914
Fax: 01342 717328

Price Guide:
single from£150
double from £170
twin/junior suite from £250

SOUTH LODGE HOTEL

LOWER BEEDING, NR HORSHAM, WEST SUSSEX RH13 6PS

Directions: On A281 at Lower Beeding, south of Horsham. Gatwick airport 12 miles. Nearest motorway M23 Jct11.

Web: www.johansens.com/southlodge
E-mail: enquiries@southlodgehotel.co.uk
Tel: 01403 891711
Fax: 01403 891766

Price Guide: (room only)
double/twin £195–£265
suite/premier rooms £350–£380

South Lodge is a magnificent country house hotel, which has successfully captured the essence of Victorian elegance. With one of the most beautiful settings in rural Sussex, unrivalled views may be enjoyed over the South Downs from the hotel's elevated position. The mansion was originally built by Frederick Ducane Godman, a 19th-century botanist and explorer, and the hotel's wonderful 90 acre grounds are evidence of his dedication. Many original features have been preserved, wood panelling throughout the hotel and open fires in the reception rooms. The 40 individually designed bedrooms are luxuriously equipped with every modern requirement. There is also a beautiful cottage within the grounds – The Bothy, with two double and two single rooms, kitchen, bathrooms, lounge, conservatory and dining room. It is set in its own garden and can be used for leisure and conference purposes. The Camellia Restaurant has seasonally changing menus complemented by an international wine list. A variety of leisure facilities include a fitness centre, snooker room, croquet, tennis and clay pigeon shooting (shooting and archery by prior arrangement), as well as golf at South Lodge's two 18-hole championship courses.

Our inspector loved: The grand hotel ambience in a country house setting.

THE ANGEL HOTEL

NORTH STREET, MIDHURST, WEST SUSSEX GU29 9DN

The Angel Hotel is a stylishly restored 16th century coaching inn which has earned widespread praise from its guests, the national press and guidebooks. Sympathetically renovated to combine contemporary comfort with original character, The Angel bridges the gap between town house bustle and country house calm. To the front, a handsome Georgian façade overlooks the High Street, while at the rear, quiet rose gardens lead to the parkland and ruins of historic Cowdray Castle. There are 28 bedrooms, all offering private bathrooms and modern amenities. Individually furnished with antiques, many rooms feature original Tudor beams. The newly created Brasserie restaurant offers an excellent value contemporary menu. For corporate guests the hotel offers two attractive meeting rooms, a business suite, presentation aids and secretarial services. Racegoers will find it very convenient for Goodwood and theatregoers for the internationally acclaimed Chichester Festival Theatre. The historic market town of Midhurst is well placed for visits to Petworth House, Arundel Castle and the South Downs.

Our inspector loved: *The bustle of locals lunching.*

Directions: From the A272, the hotel is on the left as the town centre is approached from the east.

Web: www.johansens.com/angelmidhurst
E-mail: angel@hshotels.co.uk
Tel: 01730 812421
Fax: 01730 815928

Price Guide:
single £80–£115
double/twin £110–£150

THE SPREAD EAGLE HOTEL & HEALTH SPA

SOUTH STREET, MIDHURST, WEST SUSSEX GU29 9NH

Directions: Midhurst is on the A286 between Chichester and Milford.

Web: www.johansens.com/spreadeaglemidhurst
E-mail: spreadeagle@hshotels.co.uk
Tel: 01730 816911
Fax: 01730 815668

Price Guide:
single £80–£180
double/twin £110–£210

Dating from 1430, when guests were first welcomed here, The Spread Eagle Hotel is one of England's oldest hotels and is steeped in history. Following a recent refurbishment, the hotel is the essence of opulence and those wishing to be pampered will enjoy the superb fitness facilities and excellent standard of service. Located in either the main building or the market house, the 39 en suite bedrooms, some with four-poster beds, are well-appointed with soft furnishings and fine ornaments. A roaring log fire attracts guests into the historic lounge bar, ideal for relaxing in the afternoons or enjoying an apéritif. Sumptuous modern British cuisine may be savoured in the candlelit restaurant, complemented by an extensive wine list. Weddings, banquets and meetings are held in the Jacobean Hall and Polo Room. The Aquila Health Spa is an outstanding facility featuring a blue tiled swimming pool as its centrepiece. A Scandinavian sauna, Turkish steam room, hot tub, fitness centre and a range of beauty treatments, aromatherapy and massage are also offered. The stately homes at Petworth, Uppark and Goodwood are all within a short drive, with Chichester Cathedral, the Downland Museum and Fishbourne Roman Palace among the many local attractions. Cowdray Park Polo Club is only 1 mile away.

Our inspector loved: The ancient buildings and the up-to-date spa.

THE VERMONT HOTEL

CASTLE GARTH, NEWCASTLE-UPON-TYNE, TYNE & WEAR NE1 1RQ

Situated next to the historic Castle and overlooking the famous Tyne Bridge, The Vermont boasts an unrivalled position and impressive façade. Winner of the RAC Blue Ribbon and the AA Courtesy & Care Award, it was converted from the County Hall into a 12-storey hotel in 1993, and today its charm lies in an attentive service which makes guests feel welcome and pampered. With classical décor and stylish design throughout, all bedrooms offer maximum comfort, whilst pleasant public areas provide ample space for further relaxation. Morning coffee or afternoon tea is served in the Lounge, and the traditional Redwood Bar with its fireplace and sofas is the ideal venue to meet for a drink. For food, The Bridge Restaurant is informal with great views, while the Blue Room has won awards for its service and modern classical cuisine. All menus are complemented by a carefully chosen wine list. For those wishing to sample the atmosphere of the Quayside, Martha's Bar and Courtyard on the ground floor is the entrance to the bars, restaurants and bustling nightlife. The first floor of Martha's is also available for private hire. Located in the heart of the city, The Vermont is the ideal base from which to explore Newcastle's excellent shops as well as the surrounding areas of Northumberland, Durham and The Borders.

Our inspector loved: Peaceful luxury next to the castle in the centre of Newcastle.

Directions: Close to the A1(M), and 7 miles from Newcastle International Airport.

Web: www.johansens.com/vermont
E-mail: info@vermont-hotel.co.uk
Tel: 0191 233 1010
Fax: 0191 233 1234

Price Guide:
single £155
double £175
suites £210

NAILCOTE HALL

NAILCOTE LANE, BERKSWELL, NR SOLIHULL, WARWICKSHIRE CV7 7DE

Directions: Situated 6 miles south of Birmingham International Airport/ NEC on the B4101 Balsall Common–Coventry road.

Web: www.johansens.com/nailcotehall
E-mail: info@nailcotehall.co.uk
Tel: 02476 466174
Fax: 02476 470720

Price Guide:
single £150
double/twin £160
suite £195–£275

Nailcote Hall is a charming Elizabethan country house hotel set in 15 acres of gardens and surrounded by Warwickshire countryside. Built in 1640, the house was used by Cromwell during the Civil War and was damaged by his troops prior to the assault on Kenilworth Castle. Ideally located in the heart of England, Nailcote Hall is within 15 minutes' drive of the castle towns of Kenilworth and Warwick, Coventry Cathedral, Birmingham International Airport/Station and the NEC. Situated at the centre of the Midlands motorway network, Birmingham city centre, the ICC and Stratford-upon-Avon are less than 30 minutes away. Leisure facilities include indoor swimming pool, gymnasium, solarium and sauna. Outside there are all-weather tennis courts, pétanque, croquet, a challenging 9-hole par-3 golf course and putting green (host to the British Championship Professional Short Course Championship). In the intimate Tudor surroundings of the Oak Room restaurant, the chef will delight you with superb cuisine, while the cellar boasts an extensive choice of international wines. En suite bedrooms offer luxury accommodation and elegant facilities are available for conferences, private dining and corporate hospitality.

Our inspector loved: The lovely oak dining room.

NUTHURST GRANGE

HOCKLEY HEATH, WARWICKSHIRE B94 5NL

The most memorable feature of this friendly country house hotel is its outstanding restaurant. David Randolph and his Head Chef Ben Davies have won many accolades for their imaginative menus, described as 'English, cooked in the light French style'. Diners can enjoy their superb cuisine in one of the three adjoining rooms which comprise the restaurant and form the heart of Nuthurst Grange. The rest of the house is no less charming – the spacious bedrooms have a country house atmosphere and are appointed with extra luxuries such as an exhilarating air-spa bath, a trouser press, hairdryer and a safe for valuables. For special occasions there is a room furnished with a four-poster bed and a marble bathroom. There are fine views across the 7½ acres of landscaped gardens. Executive meetings can be accommodated at Nuthurst Grange – within a 12 mile radius of the hotel lie central Birmingham, the NEC, Stratford-upon-Avon, Coventry and Birmingham International Airport. Sporting activities available nearby include golf, canal boating and tennis.

Our inspector loved: *Relaxing in the jacuzzi bath.*

Directions: From M42 exit 4 take A3400 signposted Hockley Heath (2 miles, south). Entrance to Nuthurst Grange Lane is ¼ mile south of village. Also, M40 (exit 16 – southbound only), take first left, entrance 300 yards.

Web: www.johansens.com/nuthurstgrange
E-mail: info@nuthurst-grange.com
Tel: 01564 783972
Fax: 01564 783919

Price Guide:
single £139
double/twin £159–£179
suite £189

MALLORY COURT

HARBURY LANE, BISHOPS TACHBROOK, LEAMINGTON SPA, WARWICKSHIRE CV33 9QB

Directions: 2 miles south of Leamington Spa on Harbury Lane, just off B4087 Bishops Tachbrook-Leamington Spa road, Harbury Lane runs from B4087 towards Fosse Way. M40 Jct13 from London/Jct14 from Birmingham.

Web: www.johansens.com/mallorycourt
E-mail: reception@mallory.co.uk
Tel: 01926 330214
Fax: 01926 451714

Price Guide:
double single occupancy from £165
double from £195
suite from £295

Surrounded by ten acres of attractive gardens, Mallory Court affords a stunning vista across the beautiful Warwickshire countryside. Offering every home comfort, arriving guests are enveloped by the welcoming ambience and peace and quiet of a private house rather than a hotel. The public rooms are bedecked with floral arrangements and during the winter season, afternoon tea may be enjoyed in the comfortable lounges beside the burning log fires. The luxurious bedrooms are enhanced by soft fabrics, thick carpets and en suite facilities. The sun lounge is at its most inviting throughout the summer months when it opens onto the terrace. Guests may enjoy a chilled drink whilst listening to the soft tones of the piano before rambling through the 10 acre garden which features a rose garden, herbaceous border and an ornamental stream. The dishes served in the elegant restaurant are a fusion of classical and modern British flavours. Diners may begin with chicken liver and foie gras parfait with truffle dressing, followed by pan-fried monkfish with mussels and a saffron sauce and ending with a baked custard tart with plum compôte. The hotel is set in a particularly historic area: stately homes, castles and gardens abound.

Our inspector loved: *The cosy drawing room with wonderful floral decorations.*

ALVESTON MANOR

CLOPTON BRIDGE, STRATFORD-UPON-AVON, WARWICKSHIRE CV37 7HP

Legend has it that the first performance of Shakespeare's A Midsummer's Night Dream was given under the ancient cedar tree standing in the grounds of this historic and charming hotel. Alveston Manor is conveniently situated on the south side of the River Avon a short walk from the town centre. With its wood-framed façade, leaded windows, pointed roof peaks and tall, ornate chimneys it is an imposing sight to visitors and passing travellers. The interior is enhanced by tasteful décor, rich furnishings, antiques, fine pictures and striking floral displays. There is also a delightful, delicate aroma created by years of polish on original oak panelling and an Elizabethan staircase. Guests can relax in total peace and enjoy an appealing period charm that sympathetically encompasses every modern day comfort. The en suite bedrooms are fitted to a high standard, with many of the bedrooms being situated in the adjoining modern Warwick and Charlecote Wings. A selection of suites and feature rooms are located in the original Manor House. Pre-dinner apéritifs can be sipped in an intimate cocktail bar before the enjoyment of a superbly prepared dinner.

Our inspector loved: The internal courtyard garden, where guests can sit and relax.

Directions: Exit M40 at junction 15 and take A46 and A439 towards Stratford. Join the one-way system towards Banbury and Oxford. Alveston Manor is at the junction of A422/A3400.

Web: www.johansens.com/alvestonmanor
E-mail: alvestonmanor@heritage-hotels.co.uk
Tel: 0870 400 8181
Fax: 01789 414095

Price Guide:
single from £61
double/twin from £121
suite from £185

BILLESLEY MANOR

BILLESLEY, ALCESTER, NR STRATFORD-UPON-AVON, WARWICKSHIRE B49 6NF

Directions: Leave M40 at exit 15, follow A46 towards Evesham and Alcester. 4 miles beyond Stratford-upon-Avon turn right to Billesley.

Web: www.johansens.com/billesley
E-mail: bookings@billesleymanor.co.uk
Tel: 01789 279955
Fax: 01789 764145

Price Guide:
single £115
double/twin £170
suite £220

This magnificent 16th-century Manor House is set in 11 acres of its own private parkland and has a unique topiary garden and sun terrace. Centuries of history and tradition welcome guests to this beautiful hotel. Billesley Manor has 62 beautiful bedrooms, including four-poster rooms and suites, all of which are en suite and many with stunning gardens views. Cuisine of the highest standards is served in the Stuart restaurant, awarded 2 AA Rosettes. A selection of rooms for private dining are available for family, friends or business guests. The 'Cedar Barns' offer a new dimension in conference facilities incorporating state-of-the-art equipment in unique and impressive surroundings. An impressive indoor heated swimming pool, tennis courts, six-hole pitch and putt course, croquet lawn and rough ground are available. The organisation of corporate events such as clay pigeon shooting, archery and quad biking are also on offer. Weekend breaks are available – ideal for visiting the Royal Shakespeare Theatre, Warwick Castle, Ragley Hall and the Cotswolds. Situated in the heart of England, minutes away from Shakespeare's Stratford-upon-Avon and only 23 miles from Birmingham International Airport, the hotel can be easily accessed by air, rail and road.

Our inspector loved: *The wonderful topiary garden.*

ETTINGTON PARK

ALDERMINSTER, STRATFORD-UPON-AVON, WARWICKSHIRE CV37 8BU

The foundations of Ettington Park date back at least 1000 years. Mentioned in the Domesday Book, Ettington Park rises majestically over 40 acres of Warwickshire parkland, surrounded by terraced gardens and carefully tended lawns, where guests can wander at their leisure to admire the pastoral views. The interiors are beautiful, their striking opulence enhanced by flowers, beautiful antiques and original paintings. Amid these elegant surroundings guests can relax totally, pampered with every luxury. On an appropriately grand scale, the 48 bedrooms and superb leisure complex, comprising an indoor heated swimming pool, spa bath, and sauna, make this a perfect choice for the sybarite. The menu reflects the best of English and French cuisine, served with panache in the dining room, with its elegant 18th century rococo ceiling and 19th century carved family crests. The bon viveur will relish the fine wine list. Splendid conference facilities are available: the panelled Long Gallery and 14th century chapel are both unique venues. Clay pigeon shooting, archery and fishing can be arranged on the premises.

Our inspector loved: This stunning gothic style building with wonderful gardens.

Directions: From M40 junction 15 (Warwick) take A46, A439 signposted Stratford, then left-hand turn onto A3400. Ettington Park is five miles south of Stratford-upon-Avon off the A3400.

Web: www.johansens.com/ettingtonpark
E-mail: ettington@arcadianhotels.co.uk
Tel: 01789 450123
Fax: 01789 450472

Price Guide:
single from £125
double/twin from £185
suites from £265

THE WELCOMBE HOTEL AND GOLF COURSE

WARWICK ROAD, STRATFORD-UPON-AVON, WARWICKSHIRE CV37 0NR

Directions: 5m from exit 15 of M40, on A439. 1m from Stratford-upon-Avon.

Web: www.johansens.com/welcombe
E-mail: sales@welcombe.co.uk
Tel: 01789 295252
Fax: 01789 414666

Price Guide:
single £120–£160
double/twin £160–£310
suite £275–£750

Only minutes from the motorway network, yet peacefully set amid its own 157 acres parkland estate, the Welcombe Hotel & Golf Course is the leading hotel in the heart of England. Continuous refurbishment of the 1869 mansion has resulted in a stunning hotel and championship 18-hole golf course. The magnificent public areas include an oak-panelled lounge, immaculate cocktail bar and light and airy 2 AA Rosette restaurant, where finest contemporary cuisine is matched by a well-balanced wine list. The setting is extremely elegant, with breathtaking views over the gardens to the parkland beyond. Accommodation includes suites, gallery rooms and bedrooms, all appointed to the highest standards and beautifully decorated. Superb private rooms are available for conferences, board meetings and product launches. All enjoy natural daylight and three feature French doors onto a terrace overlooking the gardens. Corporate golf events can be arranged on the hotel's own course, with brand new clubhouse facilities including private function rooms, bistro style restaurant, changing rooms and professional golf shop. Floodlit tennis courts are on site with superb country walks in the Welcombe Hills. Stratford-upon-Avon, Royal Shakespeare Theatres, The Cotswolds and Warwick Castle are nearby.

Our inspector loved: *The magnificent views from the clubhouse onto the golf course.*

WROXALL ABBEY ESTATE - WROXALL COURT

BIRMINGHAM ROAD, WROXALL, NR.WARWICK, WARWICKSHIRE CV35 7NB

Wroxall Abbey Estate is a collection of listed buildings including Wroxall Court and Wroxall Mansion and nestles in 27 acres of beautiful landscaped gardens, which was once the home of Sir Christopher Wren. The Hotel offers unrivalled service and quality for both business and pleasure amidst the peace and tranquillity of glorious Warwickshire countryside. Wroxall Court's 22 individually designed bedrooms are furnished with stylish fabrics and boast every modern comfort one would expect from such a unique venue. Delicious, imaginative cuisine is served in the Bistro which has an inviting, informal atmosphere, whilst Tapestries is ideal for receptions and Christmas parties. A fabulous historic clock tower tops the Court. Within the gardens are the ruins of the Abbey and Wren's Chapel which date back to c.1141, the latter displays breathtaking stained-glass and a brick tower. Services are held in the Chapel every Sunday and it is a romantic place to exchange wedding vows. Sonnets is Wroxall Mansion's fine dining restaurant and seats up to 80 guests. A further 40 spacious bedrooms and suites, function rooms, panelled snooker room and bar, spa and indoor pool are undergoing refurbishment for completion in the forthcoming months. Guests can enjoy the delights of nearby Warwick and its castle, with Stratford-upon-Avon and the Cotswolds only a short distance away.

Our inspector loved: The spacious bedroom with its mezzanine lounge.

Directions: From the M42, exit at junction 5 onto the A4141 to Knowle. Continue towards Warwick.for about 10 miles. Drive through Chadwick End and the entrance to Wroxall Abbey Estate is approx 2 miles further on, on the right.

Web: www.johansens.com/wroxallcourt
E-mail: info@wroxallestate.com
Tel: 01926 484470
Fax: 01926 485206

Price Guide:
single £49–£99
double/twin £75–£99
suite £149–£249

THE GLEBE AT BARFORD

CHURCH STREET, BARFORD, WARWICKSHIRE CV35 8BS

"Glebe" means belonging to the Church, which explains why this beautiful Georgian country house is in a unique and quiet position next to the church in Barford, an attractive village in Warwickshire. It is a Grade II listed building, dating back to 1820, with an unusual central atrium and surrounded by gardens. The bedrooms are spacious, comfortable and peaceful. They have all the accessories expected by today's travellers. The restaurant is in an elegant, conservatory, green plants adding cool colour. There are excellent table d'hôte and à la carte menus and the wine list has been carefully selected to complement the dishes. The Glebe is an ideal venue for private celebrations and corporate events as it has several well-equipped conference rooms – the Bentley Suite seats 120 people for a banquet and the Directors Suite, with leather armchairs, is ideal for a discreet strategy meeting. Those wishing to be pampered will be pleased with the new beauty and sunbed room. Guests appreciate the Glebe Leisure Club with a pool, gymnasium, sauna, steam room and spa facilities. They can play tennis and golf nearby. Ideally situated for Warwick and Stratford races.

Directions: M40 exit Junction 15 A429 signed Barford & Wellesbourne. Turning left at mini-roundabout, the hotel is on the right just past the church.

Web: www.johansens.com/glebeatbarford
E-mail: sales@glebe.co.uk
Tel: 01926 624218
Fax: 01926 624625

Price Guide:
single £98
double/twin £118
suite £150

Nuneaton

Leamington Spa

Stratford upon Avon

Our inspector loved: *The light airy atmosphere of the Orangery Restaurant overlooking the garden.*

ARDENCOTE MANOR HOTEL AND COUNTRY CLUB

LYE GREEN ROAD, CLAVERDON, WARWICKSHIRE CV35 8LS

Under private ownership, this former Gentlemen's residence, which was built around 1860, has been sympathetically refurbished and substantially extended to provide a luxury hotel with all modern amenities and comforts, whilst retaining its traditional elegance and appealing intimacy. Set in 42 acres of landscaped grounds in the heart of Shakespeare country, it offers beautifully appointed en suite accommodation – many rooms have glorious views of the lake and gardens – fine cuisine and extensive sports and leisure facilities, including indoor pool and spa bath, outdoor whirlpool, sauna and steamrooms, squash and tennis courts, two fully equipped gymnasia and a 9-hole golf course. The Ardencote Spa is also at the disposal of guests, offering an extensive range of therapeutic, stress relief and holistic treatments. Ardencote Manor's award winning restaurant, the Lakeside Lodge, offers an exciting and innovative menu under the direction of Head Chef Simon Douglas. Places of interest nearby include the NEC, Warwick Castle (discounted tickets available through hotel), Stratford-upon-Avon and the Cotswolds. Weekend breaks available.

Our inspector loved: *The log cabin where you can dine overlooking the water and the golf course.*

Directions: From M40 follow signs to Henley-in-Arden. Lye Green Road is off A4189 Henley-in-Arden/Warwick Road at Claverdon Village Green.

Web: www.johansens.com/ardencote
E-mail: hotel@ardencote.com
Tel: 01926 843111
Fax: 01926 842646

Nuneaton

Leamington Spa
Stratford upon Avon

Price Guide:
single £105
double £145

LUCKNAM PARK, BATH

COLERNE, CHIPPENHAM, WILTSHIRE SN14 8AZ

Directions: 15 minutes from M4, junctions 17 and 18, located between A420 and A4 near the village of Colerne.

Web: www.johansens.com/lucknampark
E-mail: reservations@lucknampark.co.uk
Tel: 01225 742777
Fax: 01225 743536

Price Guide: (room only)
single from £165;
double/twin from £205
suite from £445

For over 250 years Lucknam Park has been a focus of fine society and aristocratic living, something guests will sense immediately upon their approach along the mile-long avenue lined with beech trees. Built in 1720, this magnificent Palladian mansion is situated just six miles from Bath on the southern edge of the Cotswolds. The delicate aura of historical context is reflected in fine art and antiques dating from the late Georgian and early Victorian periods. Award winning food can be savoured in the elegant restaurant, at tables laid with exquisite porcelain, silver and glassware, accompanied with wines from an extensive cellar. Set within the walled gardens of the hotel is the Spa, comprising an indoor pool, sauna, solarium, steam room, whirlpool spa, gymnasium, beauty salon and snooker room. Numerous activities can be arranged on request, including hot-air ballooning, golf and archery. The Lucknam Park Equestrian Centre, which is situated on the estate, welcomes complete beginners and experienced riders and takes liveries. Bowood House, Corsham Court and Castle Combe are all nearby. Lucknam Park is now a member of Relais et Châteaux.

Our inspector loved: *The service and friendliness of the staff - nothing is too much trouble.*

WOOLLEY GRANGE

WOOLLEY GREEN, BRADFORD-ON-AVON, WILTSHIRE BA15 1TX

Woolley Grange is a 17th century Jacobean stone manor house set in 14 acres of formal gardens and paddocks. Standing on high ground, it affords southerly views of The White Horse at Westbury and beyond. Furnished with flair and an air of eccentricity, the interior décor and paintings echo the taste of owners Nigel and Heather Chapman. Woolley Grange has gained a reputation for outstanding cuisine. Using local farm produce and organically grown fruit and vegetables from the Victorian kitchen gardens, the chef has created a sophisticated style of country house food which aims to revive the focus on flavours. Children are particularly welcome; the owners have 4 of their own and they do not expect their young visitors to be 'seen but not heard.' In the Victorian coach house there is a huge games room and a well-equipped nursery with a full-time nanny available to look after guests' children 10–6pm every day. A children's lunch and tea are provided daily. Nearby attractions include medieval Bradford-on-Avon, Georgian Bath, Longleat and prehistoric Stonehenge. Riding can be arranged.

Our inspector loved: The Victorian style bathrooms.

Directions: From Bath on the A363, fork left at Frankleigh House after town sign. From Chippenham take the A4 to Bath, fork left on the B3109 then turn left after town sign.

Web: www.johansens.com/woolleygrange
E-mail: info@woolleygrange.com
Tel: 01225 864705
Fax: 01225 864059

Price Guide:
single £95
double/twin £105–£200
suite from £175–£270

THE MANOR HOUSE HOTEL & GOLF CLUB

CASTLE COMBE, CHIPPENHAM, WILTSHIRE SN14 7HR

Nestling in the heart of one of England's prettiest villages deep in the Southern Cotswolds, the 14th-century Manor House at Castle Combe is one of Britain's most architecturally beautiful and idyllically set country house hotels. Ivy-clad stone walls and mullioned windows, oak panelling, log fires and antique furniture blend sympathetically with the individually designed bedrooms, many of which feature four poster beds, original beams and exposed walls. Cottage style simpler rooms are found in the Mews Cottages. Set in the 300-acre estate of wooded valley and downland is the Peter Allis and Clive Clark 6340 yard, par 73, championship golf course, one of the most spectacular and challenging courses in the South of England Delightful walks in the surrounding countryside or a stroll through the estate, unchanged for almost 200 years, are a magical experience. With its enchanting gardens and parkland, a gently flowing trout stream and the romance of a terraced Italian garden, the Manor House provides peace and tranquillity, together with a friendly atmosphere and award-winning cuisine and hospitality.

Our inspector loved: The wonderful setting in one of Britain's most idyllic villages.

Directions: A 15-minute drive from junctions 17 & 18 of the M4, or 20 minutes from the M5/M4 intersection. 12 miles from the beautiful Georgian city of Bath and only 2 hours drive from central London. Approached directly from A420 and B4039.

Web: www.johansens.com/manorhousecastlecombe
E-mail: enquiries@manor-housecc.co.uk
Tel: 01249 782206
Fax: 01249 782159

Price Guide: (room only)
single/double/twin from £145
suite £265–£500

Swindon

Warminster

Salisbury

THE OLD RECTORY

CRUDWELL, NR MALMESBURY, WILTSHIRE SN16 9EP

Surrounded by a large garden and with a grand entrance, Victorian pond and Cotswold stone walls, this picturesque hotel was originally a 14th-century house and has a welcoming atmosphere complemented by friendly, professional staff. Flagstone floors, open fireplaces, fresh flowers and lush décor all contribute to the plush and cosy rooms, which are enhanced by the exceptional combination of modern conveniences with antique grandeur and all the comforts of home. All the newly refurbished en suite bedrooms are individually and luxuriously furnished, some with window seats overlooking the beautifully landscaped gardens. The larger bedrooms benefit from stunning four-poster beds and luxurious spa baths. The superb award winning 3 AA rosette cuisine, uses mostly organic ingredients and is lovingly created by the hotel's brigade of chefs headed by Peter Fairclough, who is a member of the prestigous Master Chefs of Great Britain. There is a choice between two dining locations: the formal, oak-panelled restaurant with beams and period detail or the airy and light conservatory, which is perfect for private lunch or dinner parties. Apéritifs and coffee are served outside around the pond when the weather is sunny and warm. Leisure pursuits such as horse riding and golf are a short distance away, and guests can explore Bath, the surrounding Cotswold towns and countryside.

Our inspector loved: The beautifully appointed rooms and lovely garden.

Directions: From M4 Jct17 take A429 to Cirencester; the hotel is opposite The Plough next to the church.

Web: www.johansens.com/oldrectorycrudwell
E-mail: office@oldrectorycrudwell.co.uk
Tel: 01666 577194
Fax: 01666 577853

Price Guide:
single £75
double/twin from £98

HOWARD'S HOUSE

TEFFONT EVIAS, SALISBURY, WILTSHIRE SP3 5RJ

Directions: From London, turn left off A303. 2 miles after the Wylye intersection follow signs to Teffont and on entering the village join the B3089. Howard's House is signposted.

Web: www.johansens.com/howardshouse
E-mail: enquiries@howardshousehotel.com
Tel: 01722 716392
Fax: 0722 716820

Price Guide:
single £90
double/twin £145–£165

Tucked away in the depths of rural Wiltshire and surrounded by 2 acres of beautiful gardens the fragrance of jasmine exudes through the open windows of the House and the tinkling of the fountain in the lily pond can be gently heard. This charming small country house hotel, run by Noële and Bill Thompson, is located in the quitessential English hamlet of Teffon Evias, just 9 miles from Stonehenge. Howard's House is a haven of tranquillity for those seeking to escape the noise and stress of the modern world. The bedrooms are delightfully appointed, with additional touches of fresh fruit, home-made buscuits, plants and up-to-date magazines. The 3 Rosettes awarded restaurant is the height of elegance and serves modern British cuisine providing dishes of national acclaim. Cooked with flair and imagination and using home-grown and the best local produce, al fresco dining can be enjoyed during the summer. During the winter guests may curl up by the genuine log fire with a good book and a glass of vintage port. Whatever the time of year you are guaranteed the ultimate in country house hospitality. Howard's House is ideally situated for visiting Stonehenge, Old Sarum, Salisbury Cathedral, Wilton House and Stourhead Gardens.

Our inspector loved: *The lovely setting in one of the most picturesque villages.*

THE PEAR TREE AT PURTON

CHURCH END, PURTON, SWINDON, WILTSHIRE SN5 4ED

Dedication to service is the hallmark of this excellent honey-coloured stone hotel nestling in the Vale of the White Horse between the Cotswolds and Marlborough Downs. Owners Francis and Anne Young are justly proud of its recognition by the award of the RAC's Blue Ribbon for excellence. Surrounded by rolling Wiltshire farmland, The Pear Tree sits majestically in 7½ acres of tranquil grounds on the fringe of the Saxon village of Purton, famed for its unique twin towered Parish Church and the ancient hill fort of Ringsbury Camp. Each of the 17 individually and tastefully decorated bedrooms and suites is named after a character associated with the village, such as Anne Hyde, mother of Queen Mary II and Queen Anne. All are fitted to a high standard and have digital television, hairdryer, trouser press, a safe and a host of other luxuries. The award-winning conservatory restaurant overlooks colourful gardens and is the perfect setting in which to enjoy good English cuisine prepared with style and flair. Cirencester, Bath, Oxford, Avebury, Blenheim Palace, Sudeley Castle and the Cotswolds are all within easy reach.

Our inspector loved: The light and airy conservatory dining room.

Directions: From M4 exit 16 follow signs to Purton and go through the village until reaching a triangle with Spar Grocers opposite. Turn right up the hill and the Pear Tree is on the left after the Tithe Barn.

Web: www.johansens.com/peartree
E-mail: relax@peartreepurton.co.uk
Tel: 01793 772100
Fax: 01793 772369

Price Guide:
single £110
double/twin £110–£130
suites £130

BISHOPSTROW HOUSE

WARMINSTER, WILTSHIRE BA12 9HH

Directions: Bishopstrow House is south east of Warminster on the B3414 from London via the M3.

Web: www.johansens.com/bishopstrowhouse
E-mail: enquiries@bishopstrow.co.uk
Tel: 01985 212312
Fax: 01985 216769

Price Guide:
single £99
double/twin £160–£245
suite from £330

Bishopstrow House is the quintessential Georgian mansion. It combines the intimacy of a grand country hotel retreat with all the benefits of modern facilities and the luxury of the Ragdale Spa, which offers a superb range of beauty, fitness and relaxation therapies in addition to Michaeljohn's world famous hair styling. A Grade II listed building, Bishopstrow House was built in 1817 and has been sympathetically extended to include indoor and outdoor heated swimming pools, a gymnasium and a sauna. The attention to detail is uppermost in the library, drawing room and conservatory with their beautiful antiques and Victorian oil paintings. The bedrooms are grandly furnished; some have opulent marble bathrooms and whirlpool baths. Skilfully prepared modern British food is served in the Mulberry Restaurant, with lighter meals available in the Mulberry Bar and the conservatory which overlooks 27 acres of gardens. There is fly fishing on the hotel's private stretch of the River Wylye, golf at 5 nearby courses, riding, game and clay pigeon shooting. Longleat House, Wilton House, Stourhead, Stonehenge, Bath, Salisbury and Warminster are within easy reach.

Our inspector loved: The leisure facilities.

THE BROADWAY HOTEL

THE GREEN, BROADWAY, WORCESTERSHIRE WR12 7AA

The Broadway Hotel stands proudly in the centre of the picturesque Cotswold village of Broadway where every stone evokes memories of Elizabethan England. Once used by the Abbots of Pershore, the hotel was formerly a 16th-century house, as can be seen by its architecture which combines the half timbers of the Vale of Evesham with the distinctive honey-coloured and grey stone of the Cotswolds. It epitomises a true combination of old world charm and modern day amenities with friendly, efficient service. All bedrooms provide television, telephone and tea and coffee making facilities. Traditional English dishes and a peaceful ambience are offered in the beamed Courtyard Restaurant. There is an impressive variety of à la carte dishes complemented by good wines. The congenial Jockey Club bar is a pleasant place to enjoy a drink. The Hotel overlooks the village green at the bottom of the main street where guests can browse through shops offering an array of fine antiques. On a clear day, 13 counties of England and Wales can be viewed from Broadway Tower. Snowhill, Burford, Chipping Campden, Bourton-on-the-Water, Stow-on-the-Wold and Winchcombe as well as larger Cheltenham, Worcester and Stratford are within easy reach.

Our inspector loved: Sitting in the conservatory overlooking the courtyard with its trickling fountain.

Directions: From London M40 to Oxford, A40 to Burford, A429 through Stow-on-the-Wold, then A44 to Broadway.

Web: www.johansens.com/broadwayworcestershire
E-mail: bookings@cotswold–inns–hotels.co.uk
Tel: 01386 852401
Fax: 01386 853879

Price Guide:
single £75–£85
double £118–£138

333

DORMY HOUSE

WILLERSEY HILL, BROADWAY, WORCESTERSHIRE WR12 7LF

This former 17th century farmhouse has been beautifully converted into a delightful hotel which retains much of its original character. With its oak beams, stone-flagged floors and honey-coloured local stone walls it imparts warmth and tranquillity. Dormy House provides a wealth of comforts for the most discerning guest. Each bedroom is individually decorated – some are furnished with four-poster beds – and suites are available. Head Chef, Alan Cutler, prepares a superb choice of menus and Tapestries Restaurant offers an extensive wine list with a diverse range of half bottles. The versatile Dormy Suite is an ideal venue for conferences, meetings or private functions – professionally arranged to individual requirements. The hotel has its own leisure facilities which include a games room, gym, sauna/steam room, croquet lawn and putting green. Mountain bikes are available for hire. Broadway Golf Club is adjacent. The locality is idyllic for walkers. Stratford-upon-Avon, Cheltenham Spa, Hidcote Manor Garden and Sudeley Castle are all within easy reach. USA representative: Josephine Barr, 1-800-323-5463. Closed 2 days at Christmas.

Our inspector loved: *The quiet rural location.*

Directions: Hotel is 1/2 mile off A44 between Moreton-in-Marsh and Broadway. Taking the turning signposted Saintbury, the hotel is first on left past picnic area

Web: www.johansens.com/dormyhouse
E-mail: reservations@dormyhouse.co.uk
Tel: 01386 852711
Fax: 01386 858636

Price Guide:
single £110
double/twin £150–£160
suite £195

Kidderminster

Worcester

Evesham

BROCKENCOTE HALL

CHADDESLEY CORBETT, NR KIDDERMINSTER, WORCESTERSHIRE DY10 4PY

The Brockencote estate consists of 70 acres of landscaped grounds surrounding a magnificent hall. There is a gatehouse, half-timbered dovecote, lake, some fine European and North American trees and an elegant conservatory. The estate dates back over three centuries and the style of the building reflects the changes which have taken place in fashion and taste. The hotel has been awarded 3 AA Red Stars, 4 RAC dining awards and is Heart of England Tourist Board Midlands Hotel of the Year 1998. At present, the interior combines classical architectural features with contemporary creature comforts. As in most country houses, each of the bedrooms is different: all have their own character, complemented by tasteful furnishings and décor. The friendly staff provide a splendid service under the supervision of owners Alison and Joseph Petitjean. The Hall specialises in traditional French cuisine with occasional regional and seasonal specialities. Brockencote Hall is an ideal setting for those seeking peace and quiet in an unspoilt corner of the English countryside. Located a few miles south of Birmingham, it is convenient for business people and sightseers alike and makes a fine base for touring historic Worcestershire. Special rates available Sunday to Saturday.

Our inspector loved: *The very homely atmosphere.*

Directions: Exit 4 from M5 or exit 1 from M42 (southbound). Brockencote Hall is set back from A448 at Chaddesley Corbett between Bromsgrove and Kidderminster.

Web: www.johansens.com/brockencotehall
E-mail: info@brockencotehall.com
Tel: 01562 777876
Fax: 01562 777872

Price Guide:
single £120–£140
double/twin £145–£180

THE EVESHAM HOTEL

COOPER'S LANE, OFF WATERSIDE, EVESHAM, WORCESTERSHIRE WR11 1DA

It is the somewhat unconventional atmosphere at the Evesham Hotel that stays in the memory. Originally a Tudor farmhouse, the hotel was extended and converted into a Georgian mansion house in 1809. Unusually, it combines an award-winning welcome for families with the relaxed but efficient style required by business users. For the past quarter of a century it has been successfully run by the Jenkinson family. Each of the 40 en suite bedrooms is furnished complete with a teddy bear and a toy duck for the bath. The restaurant offers delicious cuisine from a very imaginative and versatile menu, accompanied by a somewhat unique "Euro-sceptic" wine list (everything but French and German!). The drinks selection is an amazing myriad. The indoor swimming pool has a seaside theme. The peace of the 2½ acre garden belies the hotel's proximity to the town – a 5 minute walk away. In the gardens are six 300 year-old mulberry trees and a magnificent cedar of Lebanon, planted in 1809. The hotel is a good base from which to explore the Cotswolds, Stratford-upon-Avon and the Severn Valley. Closed at Christmas.

Our inspector loved: This family orientated hotel with its quirky features.

Directions: Cooper's Lane lies just off Waterside (the River Avon).

Web: www.johansens.com/evesham
E-mail: reception@eveshamhotel.com
Tel: 01386 765566
Fax: 01386 765443

Price Guide:
single £68–£79
double/twin £108
family £160

Kidderminster

Worcester

Evesham

COLWALL PARK

COLWALL, NEAR MALVERN, WORCESTERSHIRE WR13 6QG

This delightful hotel is in the centre of the village and set against a background of the Malvern Hills – to which it has direct access from its mature gardens. It also has the privilege of almost a private railway station, (just over 2 hours from Paddington). The hotel is thriving under new management who have undertaken a thorough renovation of the hotel without spoiling its character. The bedrooms are pristine and comfortable and suites have been introduced – including one for families with an amusing children's bedroom. A bottle of the local Hereford water is always at hand. Residents enjoy the library (which can accommodate private dinners for 8 people), the first floor 'video' snug and the inviting panelled Lantern bar where light meals are ordered from attentive bar staff. The Seasons Restaurant has table settings of delicate china and fine crystal. The kitchen is in the hands of a creative chef, offering a gourmet fine dining restaurant to 2 AA Rosette standard. Interesting international wines are listed. The ballroom, ideal for corporate events, leads onto the garden where wedding groups pose by the beautiful lime tree. Special breaks feature Cheltenham Races and Malvern Theatre weekends. Hotel sports are boules and croquet.

Our inspector loved: *Its homely feel and convenient location for the M5.*

Directions: M5/J7, A442 then A449. Colwall village is on B4218 between Malvern and Ledbury.

Web: www.johansens.com/colwallpark
E-mail: hotel@colwall.com
Tel: 01684 540000
Fax: 01684 540847

Price Guide:
single £65-£80
double/twin £110–£130
suite £150

THE COTTAGE IN THE WOOD

HOLYWELL ROAD, MALVERN WELLS, WORCESTERSHIRE WR14 4LG

The Malvern Hills once the home and inspiration for England's most celebrated composer Sir Edward Elgar, are the setting for The Cottage in the Wood. With its spectacular outlook across the Severn Valley plain, this unique hotel won acclaim from the Daily Mail for the best view in England. The main house was originally the Dower House to the Blackmore Park estate and accommodation is offered here and in Beech Cottage, an old scrumpy house – and the Coach House. The cottage-style furnishings give an intimate and cosy impression and the smaller Coach House rooms have suntrap balconies and patios. Owned and run by the Pattin family for over 14 years, the atmosphere is genuinely warm and relaxing. A regularly changing modern English menu is complemented by an almost obsessional wine list of 600 bins. If this causes any over-indulgence, guests can walk to the tops of the Malvern Hills direct from the hotel grounds. Nearby are the Victorian spa town of Great Malvern, the Three Counties Showground and the Cathedral cities of Worcester, Gloucester and Hereford.

Our inspector loved: Its wonderful location with breathtaking views.

Directions: Three miles south of Great Malvern on A449, turn into Holywell Road by post box and hotel sign. Hotel is 250 yards on right.

Web: www.johansens.com/cottageinthewood
E-mail: proprietor@cottageinthewood.co.uk
Tel: 01684 575859
Fax: 01684 560662

Price Guide:
single £79–£90
double/twin £95–£165

SALFORD HALL HOTEL

ABBOTS SALFORD, NR EVESHAM, WORCESTERSHIRE WR11 5UT

Between Shakespeare's Stratford-upon-Avon, the rolling Cotswolds and the Vale of Evesham is the Roman village of Abbot's Salford. Steeped in history, Salford Hall is a romantic Grade I listed manor house. It was built in the late 15th century as a retreat for the monks of Evesham Abbey and the imposing stone wing was added in the 17th century. Essentially unchanged, stained glass, a priest hole, exposed beams, oak panelling and original decorative murals are examples of the well-preserved features of the interior. The period charm is doubly appealing when combined with modern comforts, gracious furnishings, delicious food and an extensive selection of fine wines. Reflecting the past associations of the hall, the bedrooms are named after historical figures and all are individually appointed with oak furniture and luxury fittings. Guests may relax in the conservatory lounge or on the sunny terrace within the walled flower garden. The Hawkesbury room was formerly a medieval kitchen. Facilities include snooker, a sauna and a solarium. Special weekends are arranged for hot-air ballooning, horse-racing, touring the Cotswolds, discovering Shakespeare and murder mysteries. Closed for Christmas.

Our inspector loved: This Tudor mansion with lots of character.

Directions: Abbot's Salford is 8 miles west of Stratford-upon-Avon on B439 towards The Vale of Evesham.

Web: www.johansens.com/salfordhall
E-mail: reception@salfordhall.co.uk
Tel: 01386 871300
Fax: 01386 871301

Price Guide:
single £85–118
double/twin £118–140

WILLERBY MANOR HOTEL

WELL LANE, WILLERBY, HULL, EAST YORKSHIRE HU10 6ER

Directions: Take the M62 towards Hull which runs into the A63, turn off onto the A164 in the direction of Beverley. Follow the signs to Willerby and then Willerby Manor.

Web: www.johansens.com/willerbymanor
E-mail: info@willerbymanor.co.uk
Tel: 01482 652616
Fax: 01482 653901

Price Guide:
single £45–£86
double/twin £72–£130

Originally the home of the Edwardian shipping merchant, Sir Henry Salmon, Willerby Manor was bought in the early 1970s by John Townend, a Wine Merchant from Hull. The elegance of the hotel, as its stands today, is testament to the careful work of the Townend family over the years. Furnished in a stylish manner, the public rooms are the essence of comfort. The 51 bedrooms are beautifully decorated with colour co-ordinated fabrics and soft furnishings. Every modern amenity is provided as well as an array of thoughtful extras such as fresh floral arrangements. Restaurant Icon serves modern English food and is complemented by an extensive well-chosen wine list from the House of Townend. A more informal ambience pervades the Everglades Brasserie where guests may savour bistro-style meals and beverages. Fitness enthusiasts will be delighted with the well-equipped Health Club which includes a spacious gymnasium, whirlpool spa bath, an exercise studio with daily classes and a beauty treatment room. The hotel is in a convenient location for those wishing to explore the cities of Hull and York.

Our inspector loved: *The family wine shop "Hot Wines" next door to reception.*

THE DEVONSHIRE ARMS COUNTRY HOUSE HOTEL

BOLTON ABBEY, SKIPTON, NORTH YORKSHIRE BD23 6AJ

The Devonshire reflects its charming setting in the Yorkshire Dales: a welcome escape from a busy and crowded world, peace and quiet, beautiful countryside – the perfect place in which to relax. The hotel is owned by the Duke and Duchess of Devonshire and is set in rolling parkland on their 30,000 acre Bolton Abbey Estate in the Yorkshire Dales National Park. The Duchess of Devonshire personally supervises the decoration of the interiors which include antiques and paintings from their family home at Chatsworth. Fine dining led by Head Chef Michael Wignall in the elegant Burlington Restaurant is complemented by an impressive wine list. Alternatively there is the less informal atmosphere of the Devonshire Brasserie and Bar with its lively décor and contemporary art. The Devonshire Club housed in a converted 17th century barn offers a full range of leisure, health and beauty therapy facilities. There is plenty to do and see on the hotel's doorstep from exploring the ruins of the 12th century Augustinian Bolton Priory to fly fishing on the river Wharfe. Managing Director, Jeremy Rata, together with General Manager Stuart Procter, lead an enthusiastic team committed to providing a high standard of service and hospitality.

Our inspector loved: The unique glass fronted wine rooms offering a choice of over 1200 bins of fine and rare wines.

Directions: Off the A59 Skipton–Harrogate road at junction with the B6160.

Web: www.johansens.com/devonshirearms
E-mail: sales@thedevonshirearms.co.uk
Tel: reservations 01756 718111
Fax: 01756 710564

Price Guide:
single £145–£285
double/twin £195–£300
suite £345

CRATHORNE HALL

CRATHORNE, NR YARM, NORTH YORKSHIRE TS15 0AR

Directions: From A19 Thirsk–Teesside road, turn to Yarm and Crathorne. Follow signs to Crathorne village; hotel is on left. Teesside Airport and Darlington rail station are both seven miles; a courtesy collection service is available.

Web: www.johansens.com/crathornehall
E-mail: enquiries@crathornehall.com
Tel: 01642 700398
Fax: 01642 700814

Price Guide:
single £70–£125
double/twin £140–£295

Crathorne Hall was the last great stately home built in the Edwardian era. Now a splendid country house hotel, it is set in 15 acres of woodland overlooking the River Leven and the Cleveland Hills. True to their original fashion, the interiors have elegant antique furnishings complementing the grand architectural style. There is no traffic to wake up to here: just the dawn chorus, all the comforts of a luxury hotel and if desired, a champagne breakfast in bed. From a simple main course to a gastronomic dinner, the food is of the highest quality, complemented by a comprehensive wine list. Whether catering for conferences, product launches, wedding receptions or a quiet weekend for two, professional, courteous service is guaranteed. In the grounds, guests can play croquet, follow the jogging trail or try clay-pigeon shooting with a tutor on a layout designed to entertain the beginner and test the expert. Leisure activities such as clay shooting, golf, ballooning and racing circuit driving can be arranged. The Yorkshire Dales, Durham and York are nearby. Special breaks available.

Our inspector loved: *The feeling of Edwardian splendour and the panoramic views over Leven Valley.*

THE BALMORAL HOTEL

FRANKLIN MOUNT, HARROGATE, NORTH YORKSHIRE HG1 5EJ

The Balmoral is a delightful privately owned individual hotel near the heart of the elegant spa town of Harrogate. All the bedrooms are individually decorated and furnished offering the highest standards of comfort. Ten rooms have four-posters, each in a different style. The Windsor Suite even boasts its own whirlpool bath. Guests enjoy the fascinating memorabilia on various themes throughout the Hotel and they can relax in the exquisite Harry's Bar or enjoy a quiet drink in the cosy Snug before taking dinner in Villu Toots. The extensive modern Mediterranean menu embraces both the traditional and unexpected, popular with non-residents. The wine list is equally diverse with fine vintages rubbing shoulders with more youthful newcomers. Guests can enjoy the use of the Academy – one of the finest Health & Fitness Centres in the North, five minutes from the Hotel. Special Spa Breaks throughout the year. Harrogate is famed for its antique and fashion shops, art galleries and Herriot country and the many historic homes and castles in the area.

Our inspector loved: *The ceramic cats on all the beds and Trudie the owners dog.*

Directions: From Harrogate Conference Centre, follow the Kings Road up and the hotel is ½ mile on the right.

Web: www.johansens.com/balmoral
E-mail: info@balmoralhotel.co.uk
Tel: 01423 508208
Fax: 01423 530652

Price Guide:
single £80–£105
double/twin £98–£120
suites £140– £220

GRANTS HOTEL

SWAN ROAD, HARROGATE, NORTH YORKSHIRE HG1 2SS

Directions: Swan Road is in the centre of Harrogate, off the A61 to Ripon.

Web: www.johansens.com/grants
E-mail: enquiries@grantshotel–harrogate.com
Tel: 01423 560666
Fax: 01423 502550

Price Guide:
single £99–£115
double/twin £110–£160
suites £165

Towards the end of the last century, Harrogate became fashionable among the gentry, who came to 'take the waters' of the famous spa. Today's visitors have one advantage over their Victorian counterparts – they can enjoy the hospitality of Grants Hotel, the creation of Pam and Peter Grant. Their friendly welcome, coupled with high standards of service, ensures a pleasurable stay. All the bedrooms are attractively decorated and have en suite bathrooms. Downstairs, guests can relax in the comfortable lounge or take refreshments out to the terrace gardens. Drinks and light meals are available at all times from Harry Grant's Bar and dinner is served in the French café-style Chimney Pots Bistro, complete with brightly coloured check blinds and cloths and lots of humorous 'Beryl Cook' pictures. Cuisine is basically traditional rustic with a smattering of Oriental influence complemented by the mouth-watering home-made puddings. Located less than five minutes' walk from Harrogate's Conference and Exhibition Centre, Grants offers its own luxury meeting and syndicate rooms, the Herriot Suite. The Royal Pump Room Museum and the Royal Baths Assembly Rooms are nearby. Guests have free use of 'The Academy Health and Leisure Club. 'Super value breaks available.

Our inspector loved: *The Beryl Cook pictures in the Bistro.*

RUDDING PARK HOTEL & GOLF

RUDDING PARK, FOLLIFOOT, HARROGATE, NORTH YORKSHIRE HG3 1JH

Rudding Park's award winning hotel is just 2 miles from Harrogate town centre. Its setting is superb, surrounded by 230 acres of parkland. The hotel has an elegant façade and entrance, approached by a sweeping driveway. The Regency period house offers fine conference and banqueting rooms, while the adjoining hotel has been brilliantly designed and built to harmonise with the original mansion. A warm welcome awaits guests in the pleasant foyer, with its big fireplace and easy chairs. The bedrooms are spacious, with contemporary cherry wood furniture, relaxing colour schemes, many modern accessories and lovely views over the estate. Guests can relax in the Mackaness Drawing Room. The stylish two AA Rosetted Clocktower Restaurant and Bar are inviting and on sunny days they extend onto the terrace. The food is delicious and the wine list extensive. Leisure facilities are excellent – there is an 18-hole par 72 parkland golf course which has played host to the PGA Mastercard tour series. The golf academy and driving range are ideal for lessons and practise. Hotel guests are welcome to use a local award winning gym and health club.

Our inspector loved: *The mature parkland golf course surrounding the hotel.*

Directions: Rudding Park is accessible from the A1 north or south, via A661, being just off A658.

Web: www.johansens.com/ruddingpark
E-mail: sales@ruddingpark.com
Tel: 01423 871350
Fax: 01423 872286

Price Guide:
single £120–£155
double/twin £150–£185
suite from £280

HOB GREEN HOTEL AND RESTAURANT

MARKINGTON, HARROGATE, NORTH YORKSHIRE HG3 3PJ

Directions: Turn left signposted Markington off the A61 Harrogate to Ripon road, the hotel is one mile after the village on the left.

Web: www.johansens.com/hobgreen
E-mail: info@hobgreen.com
Tel: 01423 770031
Fax: 01423 771589

Price Guide:
single £85–£95
double/twin £100–£125
suite £130

Set in 870 acres of farm and woodland this charming 'country house' hotel is only a short drive from the spa town Harrogate and the ancient city of Ripon. The restaurant has an excellent reputation locally with only the finest fresh local produce being used, much of which is grown in the hotel's own garden. The interesting menus are complemented by an excellent choice of sensibly priced wines. All twelve bedrooms have been individually furnished and tastefully equipped to suit the most discerning guest. The drawing room and hall, warmed with log fires in cool weather, are comfortably furnished with the added attraction of fine antique furniture, porcelain and pictures. Situated in the heart of some of Yorkshire's most dramatic scenery, the hotel offers magnificent views of the valley beyond from all the main rooms. York is only 23 miles away. There is a wealth of cultural and historical interest nearby with Fountains Abbey and Studley Royal water garden and deer park a few minutes' drive. The Yorkshire Riding Centre is in Markington Village. Simply relax in this tranquil place where your every comfort is catered for. Special breaks available.

Our inspector loved: *The large vegetable and herb garden.*

THE BOAR'S HEAD HOTEL

THE RIPLEY CASTLE ESTATE, HARROGATE, NORTH YORKSHIRE HG3 3AY

Imagine relaxing in a luxury hotel at the centre of a historic private country Estate in England's incredibly beautiful North Country. The Ingilby family who have lived in Ripley Castle for 28 generations invite you to enjoy their hospitality at The Boar's Head Hotel. There are 25 luxury bedrooms, individually decorated and furnished, most with king-size beds. The Restaurant menu is outstanding, presented by a creative and imaginative kitchen brigade and complemented by a wide selection of reasonably priced, good quality wines. There is a welcoming bar serving traditional ales straight from the wood and popular bar meal selections. When staying at The Boar's Head, guests can enjoy complimentary access to the delightful walled gardens and grounds of Ripley Castle, which include the lakes and a deer park. A conference at Ripley is a different experience – using the idyllic meeting facilities available in the castle, organisers and delegates alike will appreciate the peace and tranquillity of the location which also offers opportunities for all types of leisure activity in the Deer Park.

Our inspector loved: The pretty, historic village of Ripley.

Directions: Ripley is very accessible, just 10 minutes from the conference town of Harrogate, 20 minutes from the motorway network, and Leeds/Bradford Airport, and 40 minutes from the City of York.

Web: www.johansens.com/boarsheadharrogate
E-mail: reservations@boarsheadripley.co.uk
Tel: 01423 771888
Fax: 01423 771509

Price Guide:
single £99–£120
double £120–£140

SIMONSTONE HALL

HAWES, NORTH YORKSHIRE DL8 3LY

Directions: Hawes is on A684. Turn north on Buttertubs Pass towards Muker. Simonstone Hall is ½ mile on the left

Web: www.johansens.com/simonstonehall
E-mail: email@simonstone.demon.co.uk
Tel: 01969 667255
Fax: 01969 667741

Price Guide:
single £55–£90
double/twin £110–£180

Fine cuisine, comfort, peace and tranquillity combine with breathtaking scenery to make any stay at Simonstone Hall totally memorable. This former 18th century hunting lodge has been lovingly restored and furnished with antiques to create an idyllic retreat for its guests. The Hall stands in 5 acres of beautiful landscaped gardens with an adjacent 14,000 acres of grouse moors and upland grazing. Many period features have been retained such as the panelled dining room, mahogany staircase with ancestral stained glass windows and a lounge with ornamental fireplace and ceilings. The bedrooms are of the highest standards and offer every modern comfort including four-poster and sleigh beds. In the restaurant, guests savour the freshest local produce presented with flair and imagination, whilst enjoying stunning views across Upper Wensleydale. An excellent wine list is available to complement any dish. Informal meals are served in the Game Tavern which provides a particularly warm and local atmosphere. Simonstone Hall, with its fine views, is the perfect base for enjoying and exploring the hidden Yorkshire Dales. The area abounds with ancient castles, churches and museums. Hardraw Force, England's highest single drop waterfall which can be heard from the gardens, is only a walk away.

Our inspector loved: The wonderful setting.

THE PHEASANT

HAROME, HELMSLEY, NORTH YORKSHIRE YO62 5JG

The Pheasant, rich in oak beams and open log fires, offers two types of accommodation, some in the hotel and some in a charming, 16th-century thatched cottage. The Binks family, who built the hotel and now own and manage it, have created a friendly atmosphere which is part of the warm Yorkshire welcome that awaits all guests. The bedrooms and suites are brightly decorated in an attractive, cottage style, and are all complete with en suite facilities. Traditional English cooking is the speciality of the restaurant; many of the dishes are prepared using fresh fruit and vegetables from the hotel's garden. During the summer, guests may relax on the terrace overlooking the pond. A new indoor heated swimming pool is an added attraction. Other sporting activities available locally include swimming, riding, golf and fishing. York is a short drive away, as are a host of historic landmarks including Byland and Rievaulx Abbeys and Castle Howard of Brideshead Revisited fame. Also nearby is the magnificent North York Moors National Park. Dogs by arrangement. Closed Christmas, January and February.

Our inspector loved: *Watching the ducks on the pond.*

Directions: From Helmsley, take the A170 towards Scarborough; after ¼ mile turn right for Harome. The hotel is near the church in the village.

Web: www.johansens.com/pheasanthelmsley
Tel: 01439 771241
Fax: 01439 771744

Price Guide: (including five-course dinner)
single £68–£75
double/twin £136–£150

HAZLEWOOD CASTLE HOTEL

PARADISE LANE, HAZLEWOOD, TADCASTER, NR LEEDS & YORK, NORTH YORKSHIRE LS24 9NJ

Directions: Off the A64 east of the A1 Leeds/York intersection.

Web: www.johansens.com/hazelwoodcastle
E-mail: info@hazlewood-castle.co.uk
Tel: 01937 535353
Fax: 01937 530630

Price Guide:
single from £110
double/twin £175–£275
suites £195–£300

Scarborough

Harrogate

York

Behind the restored 13th-century façade of this fascinating castle lies a vibrant and professional hotel, where outstanding cuisine and flawless hospitality are offered in magnificent surroundings. Famed for its gourmet food, the hotel houses its own cookery school, where John Benson-Smith, formerly a Masterchef Judge, gives lively demonstrations. The hotel has two excellent restaurants, the informal Prickly Pear and the chic Restaurant 1086, as well as a range of facilities for private dining. A distinct panache is lent to the atmosphere of a banquet set in the Old Dining Room and State Drawing Rooms, and Restaurant 1086, the signature restaurant of John Benson-Smith, can be hired to add charismatic zest to a dinner party. Hazlewood Castle is well designed to accommodate corporate or private events, whilst providing a sense of privilege and individuality for its guests. Its fortified buildings include the impressive Great Hall and the Chapel of St Leonards, ideal for musical occasions, amongst its many convivial reception rooms. The beautifully decorated bedrooms reflect the perfect balance of tradition and design that is evident throughout the hotel. Numerous activities include golf and clay pigeon shooting. Special weekend breaks available.

Our inspector loved: *The Victoria room, which has gold wallpaper from Queen Victoria's private bathroom at the Great Exhibition in 1851.*

SWINTON PARK

MASHAM, NR RIPON, NORTH YORKSHIRE HG4 4JH

Swinton Park, with its battlement-topped turrets and a round tower coloured green with climbing ivy, is a Grade II* listed 'castle' dating from the late 1600s. The heart of the building is essentially Regency style, but heavily disguised by the Victorians with the addition of turrets and castellations. Sold by the Earl of Swinton in 1980, but recently bought back by the family and extensively refurbished, it is a luxurious hotel with every comfort and up-to-date facility. Rising picturesquely against the skyline, it is set in 200 acres of deer-stocked parkland and formal gardens surrounded by a 20,000-acre family estate ½ mile from the market town of Masham. The ground floor rooms enjoy sweeping views over the parkland, lake and gatehouse and are all furnished with antiques and family portraits. The guest rooms sharing the first and second floors are individually designed on the theme of a Yorkshire town, dale, castle, abbey or garden. Four are suites and the turret room is on two floors with a wonderful free standing rain bath. Superb British cuisine is served in an elegant dining room which features a gold leaf ceiling and sumptuous décor. Guests can enjoy country pursuits and golf, mountain biking, off roading and model boat racing. There is a spa in the hotel's conservatory.

Directions: Masham is off A6108 between Leyburn and Ripon.

Web: www.johansens.com/swintonpark
E-mail: enquiries@swintonpark.com
Tel: 01765 680900
Fax: 01765 680901

Price Guide:
single £100–£250
double/twin £100–£250
suites £250–£350

Our inspector loved: The parkland setting of this family's castle.

HACKNESS GRANGE

NORTH YORK MOORS NATIONAL PARK, SCARBOROUGH, NORTH YORKSHIRE YO13 0JW

Directions: Take A64 York road until left turn to Seamer on to B1261, through to East Ayton and Hackness.

Web: www.johansens.com/hacknessgrange
E-mail: hacknessgrange@englishrosehotels.co.uk
Tel: 01723 882345
Fax: 01723 882391

Price Guide:
single £60–£90
double/twin £90–£160
suite £190

The attractive Georgian Hackness Grange country house lies at the heart of the dramatic North York Moors National Park – miles of glorious countryside with rolling moorland and forests. Set in acres of private grounds, overlooking a tranquil lake, home to many species of wildlife, Hackness Grange is a haven of peace and quiet for guests. There are charming bedrooms in the gardens and courtyard together with de luxe rooms in the main house. For leisure activities, guests can enjoy 9-hole pitch 'n' putt golf, tennis and an indoor heated swimming pool. Hackness Grange is an ideal meeting location for companies wishing to have exclusive use of the hotel for VIP gatherings. The attractive Derwent Restaurant with its quality décor, paintings and Rosette, is the setting for lunch and dinner. Here you will enjoy creatively prepared delicious cuisine, which is partnered by a wide choice of international wines. When you choose to stay at Hackness Grange you will find you have chosen well – a peaceful and relaxing location with so much to see and do: for example, visit Great Ayton, birthplace of Captain Cook.

Our inspector loved: *The ducks and wildlife around the lake.*

WREA HEAD COUNTRY HOTEL

SCALBY, NR SCARBOROUGH, NORTH YORKSHIRE YO13 0PB

Wrea Head Country Hotel is an elegant, beautifully refurbished Victorian country house built in 1881 and situated in 14 acres of wooded and landscaped grounds on the edge of the North York Moors National Park, just three miles from Scarborough. The house is furnished with antiques and paintings and the oak-panelled front hall with its inglenook fireplace with blazing log fires in the winter, is very welcoming. All the bedrooms are individually decorated to the highest standards, with most having delightful views of the gardens. The elegant Four Seasons Restaurant is renowned for serving the best traditional English fare using fresh local produce and has a reputation for outstanding cuisine. There are attractive meeting rooms, each with natural daylight, ideal for private board meetings and training courses requiring privacy and seclusion. Scarborough is renowned for its cricket, music and theatre. Wrea Head is a perfect location from which to explore the glorious North Yorkshire coast and country and you can take advantage of special English Rose breaks throughout the year.

Our inspector loved: *The large collection of Pietro Annigoni paintings in the main hall.*

Directions: Follow the A171 north from Scarborough, past the Scalby Village, until the hotel is signposted. Follow the road past the duck pond and then turn left up the drive.

Web: www.johansens.com/wreaheadcountry
E-mail: wreahead@englishrosehotels.co.uk
Tel: 01723 378211
Fax: 01723 355936

Price Guide:
single from £75
double/twin £120–£190
suite £190

353

AMBASSADOR HOTEL

123–125 THE MOUNT, YORK, NORTH YORKSHIRE YO24 1DU

Built in 1826 for a wealthy York merchant, this elegant Georgian haven has been attractively refurbished by Sallie Gray, retaining the style and elegance of that glorious era. Each of the 25 beautiful bedrooms have been individually style and decorated, all of them have private bath or shower rooms, direct dial telephones, data points, television, trouser press, courtesy trays, radios, hairdryers and big fluffy towels. The classically decorated Grays Restaurant has been awarded numerous accolades and awards for its excellent cuisine, for which only the finest of local foods is being used. The extensive gardens at the rear of The Ambassador are a wonderful place to relax and unwind. York City centre is a short stroll away as is York's magnificent racecourse. For residents, there is ample parking available at the front and rear of the hotel. The Ambassador is a perfect conference and meeting venue, recognising that a successful meeting reflects a professional image. The conference rooms are a superb range of unique character and, with high ceilings and natural daylight, create a serene but businesslike atmosphere. Special breaks available.

Directions: From the A64 turn onto the A1036 signposted York. Go past the racecourse; The Ambassador is on the right before the traffic lights.

Web: www.johansens.com/ambassadorhotel
E-mail: stay@ambassadorhotel.co.uk
Tel: 01904 641316
Fax: 01904 640259

Price Guide:
single £98–£110
double/twin £118–£140

Our inspector loved: The friendliness and thoughtfulness of the staff.

THE GRANGE HOTEL

1 CLIFTON, YORK, NORTH YORKSHIRE YO30 6AA

Set near the ancient city walls, just a short walk from the world famous Minster, this sophisticated Regency town house has been carefully restored and its spacious rooms richly decorated. Beautiful stone-flagged floors lead to the classically styled reception rooms. The flower-filled Morning Room is welcoming, with its deep sofas and blazing fire in the winter months. Double doors between the panelled library and drawing room can be opened up to create a dignified venue for parties, wedding receptions or business entertaining. Prints, antiques and English chintz in the bedrooms reflect the proprietor's careful attention to detail. The Ivy Restaurant has an established reputation for first-class gastronomy, incorporating the best in modern British and French cuisine. The Seafood bar has two murals depicting racing scenes. The Brasserie is open for lunch Monday to Saturday and dinner every night until after the theatre closes most evenings. For conferences, a computer and fax are available as well as secretarial services. Brimming with history, York's list of attractions includes the National Railway Museum, the Jorvik Viking Centre and the medieval Shambles.

Our inspector loved: *The stunning orchid arrangement in the York stone-paved front hall.*

Directions: The Grange Hotel is on the A19 York–Thirsk road, 400 yards from the city centre.

Web: www.johansens.com/grangeyork
E-mail: info@grangehotel.co.uk
Tel: 01904 644744
Fax: 01904 612453

Price Guide:
single £105–£150
double/twin £135–£195
suite £230

MIDDLETHORPE HALL

BISHOPTHORPE ROAD, YORK, NORTH YORKSHIRE YO23 2GB

Directions: Take A64 (T) off A1 (T) near Tadcaster, follow signs to York West, then smaller signs to Bishopthorpe.

Web: www.johansens.com/middlethorpehall
E-mail: info@middlethorpe.com
Tel: 01904 641241
Fax: 01904 620176

Price Guide:
single £124–£165
double/twin £190–£300
suite from £260–£370

Harrogate

Scarborough

York

Middlethorpe Hall is a delightful William III house, built in 1699 for Thomas Barlow, a wealthy merchant and was for a time the home of Lady Mary Wortley Montagu, the 18th century diarist. The house has been immaculately restored by Historic House Hotels who have decorated and furnished it in its original style and elegance. There are beautifully designed bedrooms and suites in the main house and the adjacent 18th century courtyard. The restaurant, which has been awarded 3 Rosettes from the AA, offers the best in contemporary English cooking. A health and beauty Spa with an indoor swimming pool opened in 1999. Middlethorpe Hall, which is a member of Relais & Chateaux Hotels, stands in 20 acres of parkland and overlooks York Racecourse yet is only 1½ miles from the medieval city of York with its fascinating museums, restored streets and world-famous Minster. From Middlethorpe you can visit Yorkshire's famous country houses, like Castle Howard, Beningbrough and Harewood, the ruined Abbeys of Fountains and Rievaulx and explore the magnificent Yorkshire Moors. Helmsley, Whitby and Scarborough are nearby. Special breaks available.

Our inspector loved: *The Spa which is situated in the adjacent cottages.*

Mount Royale Hotel

THE MOUNT, YORK, NORTH YORKSHIRE YO24 1GU

Two elegant William IV houses have been restored to their former glory to create the Mount Royale Hotel, which is personally run by the Oxtoby family. Comfortable bedrooms are furnished with imagination, all in an individual style. Each of the garden rooms opens onto the garden and has its own verandah. Downstairs, the public rooms are filled with interesting items of antique furniture, objets d'art and gilt-framed paintings. To the rear of the building, overlooking the gardens, is the new Sous Le Mont Restaurant, specialising in modern English cuisine. Amenities include steam room, sauna, solarium and Julie Clarke's health and beauty treatment centre. With a delightful English garden and heated outdoor pool, the one acre grounds are a peaceful haven just minutes from York's centre. York is a historic and well-preserved city, famous for its Minster and medieval streets. Also within walking distance is York racecourse, where the flat-racing season runs from May to October. Lovers of the great outdoors will find the Yorkshire Dales and North York Moors a 45 minute drive away. Only small dogs by arrangement.

Our inspector loved: *The new Sous Le Mont Restaurant with its extensive and comprehensive wine list.*

Directions: From A64, turn onto the A1036 signposted York. Go past racecourse; hotel is on right before traffic lights.

Web: www.johansens.com/mountroyale
E-mail: reservations@mountroyale.co.uk
Tel: 01904 628856
Fax: 01904 611171

Price Guide:
single £85–£115
double/twin £105–£150
suites £155

THE WORSLEY ARMS HOTEL

HOVINGHAM, NEAR YORK, NORTH YORKSHIRE YO62 4LA

Directions: Hovingham is on the B1257, eight miles from Malton and Helmsley. 20 minutes North of York.

Web: www.johansens.com/worsleyarms
E-mail: worsleyarms@aol.com
Tel: 01653 628234
Fax: 01653 628130

Price Guide:
single £65–£85
double/twin £95–£165

The Worsley Arms is an attractive stone-built Georgian spa hotel in the heart of Hovingham, a pleasant and unspoiled Yorkshire village with a history stretching back to Roman times. The hotel, which overlooks the village green and is set amid delightful gardens, was built in 1841 by the baronet Sir William Worsley is now owned and personally run by Anthony and Sally Finn. Hovingham Hall, the Worsley family and childhood home of the Duchess of Kent, is nearby. Elegant furnishings and open fires create a welcoming atmosphere. The spacious sitting rooms are an ideal place to relax over morning coffee or afternoon tea. The award-winning Restaurant offers creatively prepared dishes, including game from the estate, cooked and presented with flair. Guests can visit the wine cellar to browse or choose their wine for dinner. The Cricketers bar provides a more informal setting to enjoy modern cooking at its best. The en suite bedrooms range in size and have recently all been redecorated. There is plenty to do nearby, including tennis, squash, jogging, golf and scenic walks along nature trails. Guests can explore the beautiful Dales, the North Yorkshire Moors and the spectacular coastline or discover the abbeys, stately homes and castles nearby.

Our inspector loved: *Choosing wine for dinner in the wine cellar.*

MONK FRYSTON HALL HOTEL

MONK FRYSTON, NORTH YORKSHIRE LS25 5DU

A short distance from the A1 and almost equidistant from Leeds and York, this mellow old manor house hotel, built in 1740, is ideal for tourists, business people and those looking for an invitingly secluded spot for a weekend break. The mullioned and transom windows and the family coat of arms above the doorway are reminiscent of Monk Fryston's fascinating past. In 1954 the Hall was acquired by the late Duke of Rutland, who has created an elegant contemporary hotel, while successfully preserving the strong sense of heritage and tradition. The bedrooms, ranging from cosy to spacious, have private en suite bathrooms and are appointed to a high standard. A generous menu offers a wide choice of traditional English dishes with something to suit all tastes. From the Hall, the terrace leads down to an ornamental Italian garden which overlooks a lake and is a delight to see at any time of year. Wedding receptions are held in the oak-panelled Haddon Room with its splendid Inglenook fireplace. The Rutland Room provides a convenient venue for meetings and private parties. York is 17 miles, Leeds 13 miles and Harrogate 18 miles away.

Our inspector loved: *The oak panelled front hall with open fire.*

Directions: The Hall is three miles off the A1, on the A63 towards Selby in the centre of Monk Fryston.

Web: www.johansens.com/monkfrystonhall
E-mail: reception@monkfryston-hotel.com
Tel: 01977 682369
Fax: 01977 683544

Price Guide:
single £88–£135
double/twin £109–£155

HELLABY HALL HOTEL

OLD HELLABY LANE, NR ROTHERHAM, SOUTH YORKSHIRE S66 8SN

The impressive 17th century façade of Hellaby Hall has been an unmistakable feature of the South Yorkshire skyline since 1692, when it was built by Ralph Fretwell on his return from Barbados. Today this award-winning Hotel continues to nurture its excellent reputation, combining historic charm with luxurious and modern facilities. All 52 bedrooms are tastefully furnished in a variety of styles, including the romantic four poster suite with its magnificent bed, private lounge and dining area. Elsewhere, guests can relax in the oak-panelled lounge where friendly staff are on hand to ensure that any stay is as comfortable as possible. The light and spacious Attic Restaurant is perfect for intimate celebrations or business lunches and an informal Italian restaurant with south west facing courtyard provides a popular alternative and alfresco dining. A selection of rooms can host corporate meetings or dining events and some are now licensed to hold civil wedding ceremonies. The Hotel also comprises of Bodyscene, a £2 million state-of-the-art health and leisure club with swimming pool and steam room, a large fitness suite and dedicated gym instructor and beauty team.

Directions: From the M18, exit at junction 1 and take the A631 towards Bawtry. The Hotel is ½ mile on the left.

Web: www.johansens.com/hellabyhall
E-mail: sales@hellabyhallhotel.co.uk
Tel: 01709 702701
Fax: 01709 700979

Price Guide:
single £45–£120
double/twin £79–£160
suite £165–£190

Our inspector loved: The large health and leisure club.

CHARNWOOD HOTEL

10 SHARROW LANE, SHEFFIELD, SOUTH YORKSHIRE S11 8AA

The Charnwood Hotel is a listed Georgian mansion dating from 1780. Originally owned by John Henfrey, a Sheffield Master Cutler, it was later acquired by William Wilson of the Sharrow Snuff Mill. Restored in 1985, this elegant 'country house in town' is tastefully furnished, with colourful flower arrangements set against attractive décor. The no smoking bedrooms are all individually decorated and the Woodford suite is designed specifically to meet the requirements of a family. Brasserie Leo has a relaxed atmosphere serving traditional English and French cuisine. The Library and Henfrey's are ideal for private dining or small meetings and larger functions are catered for in the Georgian Room and Coach House. Also there are 19 self catering apartments nearby. While approximately a mile from Sheffield city centre, with its concert hall, theatre and hectic night-life, Charnwood Hotel is also convenient for the Peak District National Park. Meadowhall shopping centre and Sheffield Arena are a short ride away.

Our inspector loved: The lively atmosphere in Brasserie Leo.

Directions: Sharrow Lane is near the junction of London Road and Abbeydale Road, 1½ miles from city centre. Junction 33 from the M1.

Web: www.johansens.com/charnwood
E-mail: reception@charnwoodhotel.co.uk
Tel: 0114 258 9411
Fax: 0114 255 5107

Price Guide:
single £68–£102
double/twin £83–£120

WHITLEY HALL HOTEL

ELLIOTT LANE, GRENOSIDE, SHEFFIELD, SOUTH YORKSHIRE S35 8NR

Carved into the keystone above one of the doors is the date 1584, denoting the start of Whitley Hall's lengthy country house tradition. In the bar is a priest hole, which may explain the local belief that a tunnel links the house with the nearby 11th century church. In the 18th century, the house was a prestigious boarding school, with Gothic pointed arches and ornamentation added later by the Victorians. Attractively refurbished, Whitley Hall is now a fine hotel with all the amenities required by today's visitors. Stone walls and oak panelling combine with richly carpeted floors and handsome decoration. A sweeping split staircase leads to the bedrooms, all of which have en suite bathrooms. Varied yet unpretentious cooking is served in generous portions and complemented by a wide choice from the wine cellar, including many clarets and ports. Peacocks strut around the 30 acre grounds, which encompass rolling lawns, mature woodland and two ornamental lakes. Banquets and private functions can be held in the conference suite.

Our inspector loved: *The peacocks fanning their tails in the garden.*

Directions: Leave M1 at junction 35, following signs for Chapeltown (A629), go down hill and turn left into Nether Lane. Go right at traffic lights, then left opposite Arundel pub, then immediately right into Whitley Lane. At fork turn right into Elliott Lane; hotel is on left.

Web: www.johansens.com/whitleyhall
E-mail: reservations@whitleyhall.com
Tel: 0114 245 4444
Fax: 0114 245 5414

Price Guide:
single £65–£95
double/twin £80–£115

HOLDSWORTH HOUSE

HOLDSWORTH ROAD, HOLMFIELD, HALIFAX, WEST YORKSHIRE HX2 9TG

Holdsworth House is a retreat of quality and charm standing three miles north of Halifax in the heart of Yorkshire's West Riding. Built in 1633, it was acquired by the Pearson family 40 years ago. With care, skill and professionalism they have created a hotel and restaurant of considerable repute. The interior, with its polished panelling and open fireplaces, has been carefully preserved and embellished with fine antique furniture and ornaments. The comfortable lounge opens onto a pretty courtyard and overlooks the herb garden and gazebo. The restaurant comprises three beautifully furnished rooms, ideal for private dinner parties. Exciting modern English and Continental cuisine is meticulously prepared and presented, complemented by a thoughtfully compiled wine list. The restaurant has two AA Rosette. Each cosy bedroom has its own style, from the four split-level suites to the two interconnecting rooms for families. This is the perfect base from which to explore the Pennines, the Yorkshire Dales and Haworth, home of the Brontë family. Weekend breaks available. Closed at Christmas.

Our inspector loved: *The cosy, oak-panelled, award winning restaurant.*

Directions: From M1 Jct42 take M62 west to Jct26. Follow A58 to Halifax (ignore signs to town centre). At Burdock Way roundabout take A629 to Keighley; after 1½ miles go right into Shay Lane; hotel is one mile on right.

Web: www.johansens.com/holdsworthhouse
E-mail: info@holdsworthhouse.co.uk
Tel: 01422 240024
Fax: 01422 245174

Price Guide:
single £87–£130
double/twin £110 –£140
suite £140–£150

363

HALEY'S HOTEL & RESTAURANT

SHIRE OAK ROAD, HEADINGLEY, LEEDS, WEST YORKSHIRE LS6 2DE

Directions: Two miles north of Leeds City Centre off the main A660 Otley Road – the main route to Leeds/Bradford Airport, Ilkley and Wharfedale.

Web: www.johansens.com/haleys
E-mail: info@haleys.co.uk
Tel: 0113 278 4446
Fax: 0113 275 3342

Price Guide:
single from £110
double/twin from £145
suite from £230

Just two miles from Leeds City Centre, yet set in a quiet leafy lane in the Headingley conservation area close to the cricket ground and the university, Haley's is truly the Country House Hotel in the City. Each of the 29 guest rooms offers the highest levels of comfort and is as individual as the fine antiques and rich furnishings which grace the hotel. A new addition to the existing accommodation is Bedford House, the elegant Victorian Grade II listed building next door which contains seven outstandingly furnished and beautifully equipped modern bedrooms, including two suites, one with its own private entrance. The Bramley Room and Library are popular venues for private meetings, lunch or dinner parties. Haley's Restaurant has an enviable reputation, holding two AA Rosettes. An imaginative menu of modern English cuisine is accompanied by a fine wine list. Leeds offers superb shopping (including Harvey Nichols) and the Victorian Arcades. Opera North and the theatres combine with Haley's superb accommodation and food to provide entertaining weekends.

Our inspector loved: A peaceful retreat in the leafy suburbs.

QUEBECS, THE LEEDS TOWN HOUSE

9 QUEBEC STREET, LEEDS, WEST YORKSHIRE LS1 2HA

Newly opened in February 2002, excellently located right in the centre of the city of Leeds, near City Square, this chic Victorian Hotel has been beautifully restored with stunning original Victorian features. Classic tones and sumptuous surroundings reflect the grandeur of the breathtaking architecture of the building and 5 awe-inspiring stained glass windows, depicting the coats of arms of the principal towns of Yorkshire, light a magnificent winding oak staircase. Guests will admire the delicately carved panels of the circular Oak Room and the elegant style of the Hotel's public rooms. Opulent air conditioned bedrooms are exquisitely furnished and have sleek granite and chrome bathrooms. Attention to detail with fresh fruit, crisp Egyptian cotton linen and luxury toiletries make a truly comfortable stay. Leeds is steeped in history and culture and there are numerous museums and galleries to visit. There is excellent shopping, with many designer shops a few minutes walk away and a number of fine restaurants to choose from. The Hotel is an ideal base for exploring the beautiful Yorkshire Dales, Moors and Brontë country. Superb business facilities make this venue perfect for any small corporate occasion.

Our inspector loved: *The panelled Oak Room with carved faces in the panelling.*

Directions: From the M1 follow signs for Leeds and exit the M621 at junction 3. Continue following signs for Leeds city centre, underneath the railway bridge and pass the traffic lights. Pass city square on your right into Quebec Street and Quebecs is on the left.

Web: www.johansens.com/quebecs
E-mail: res_quebecs@etontownhouse.com
Tel: 0113 244 8989
Fax: 0113 244 9090

Price Guide:
single £125
double/twin £135–£170
suite £185–£225

CHEVIN COUNTRY PARK HOTEL

YORKGATE, OTLEY, WEST YORKSHIRE LS21 3NU

Directions: From A658 between Bradford and Harrogate, take the Chevin Forest Park road, then left into Yorkgate for Chevin Park.

Web: www.johansens.com/chevinlodge
E-mail: reception@chevinlodge.co.uk
Tel: 01943 467818
Fax: 01943 850335

Price Guide:
single £65–£120
double/twin £110–£140

A quite unique hotel – you would probably need to travel to Scandinavia to discover a similar hotel to Chevin Park. Built entirely of Finnish logs and surrounded by birch trees, it is set in 50 acres of lake and woodland in the beauty spot of Chevin Forest Park. The spacious, carefully designed bedrooms are tastefully furnished with pine and some have patio doors leading to the lakeside gardens. In addition, there are several luxury lodges tucked away in the woods, providing alternative accommodation to the hotel bedrooms. Imaginative and appetising meals are served in the beautiful balconied restaurant, which overlooks the lake. Chevin Lodge offers conference facilities in the Woodlands Suite which is fully- equipped for all business requirements. The Leisure Club has a 11 x 7 metres swimming pool, spa bath, sauna, solarium and gym. There is also a games room, all weather tennis court and jogging trails that wind through the woods. Leeds, Bradford and Harrogate are within 20 minutes' drive. Special weekend breaks are available.

Our inspector loved: *A small piece of Finland in Yorkshire.*

WOOD HALL

TRIP LANE, LINTON, NR WETHERBY, WEST YORKSHIRE LS22 4JA

Off the A1/M1 link about 15 miles due west of York, built of stone from the estate, Wood Hall, part of the Arcadian Hotel Group, is an elegant Georgian country house overlooking the River Wharfe. Its grounds, over 100 acres in all, are approached along a private drive that winds through a sweep of parkland. The sumptuously furnished drawing room and the oak-panelled bar, with its gentlemen's club atmosphere, lead off the grand entrance hall. Superb floral displays, gleaming chandeliers and immaculately designed interiors hint at the careful attention that has been lavished on Wood Hall. Gastronomes will relish the excellent à la carte menu, which combines contemporary Anglo-French style with attractive presentation. The mile-long private stretch of the Wharfe offers up trout and barbel to the keen angler, while miles of walks and jogging paths encompass the estate. There is a leisure club including a swimming pool, spa bath, steam room, gymnasium and treatment salon. Near to the National Hunt racecourse at Wetherby, York, Harrogate, Leeds, the Dales and Harewood House are only a short distance away. Special breaks available.

Our inspector loved: *The stunning view of the hotel as you drive up the long driveway.*

Directions: From Wetherby, take the A661 towards Harrogate. Take turning for Sicklinghall and Linton, then left for Linton and Wood Hall. Turn right opposite the Windmill public house; hotel is 1½ miles further on.

Leeds
Bradford
Huddersfield

Web: www.johansens.com/woodhall
E-mail: woodhall@arcadianhotels.co.uk
Tel: 01937 587271 or 0800 9 177 877
Fax: 01937 584353

Price Guide:
single from £98
double/twin from £110

Aichner Clodi GGK

PERFECT HOSPITALITY BEGINS

WITH PERFECT FORM.

Classic furniture from Selva is the calling card of exclusive establishments.
By creating uniquely stylish surroundings, Selva spoils
not only your guests, but you, as well: with custom solutions,
creative ideas, and the most modern logistics. We would be happy to make
an appointment for you to visit our hotel furnishings showroom in Bolzano.

HOTEL STYLE
A brand of Selva Style International

Channel Islands

Recommendations in the Channel Islands appear on pages 369-373

For further information on the Channel Islands, please contact:

Guernsey Tourist Board
PO Box 23, St Peter Port, Guernsey GY1 3AN
Tel: +44 (0)1481 723552
Internet: www.guernseytouristboard.com

Jersey Tourism
Liberation Square, St Helier, Jersey JE1 1BB
Tel: +44 (0)1534 500777
Internet: www.jtourism.com

Sark Tourism
Harbour Hill, Sark, Channel Islands GY9 0SB
Tel: +44 (0)1481 832345
Internet: www.sark-tourism.com

Herm
The White House Hotel, Herm Island via Guernsey GY1 3HR
Tel: +44 (0)1481 722159
Internet: www.herm-island.com

or see **pages 466-469** for details of
local attractions to visit during your stay.

Images from www.britainonview.com

CHÂTEAU LA CHAIRE

ROZEL BAY, JERSEY JE3 6AJ

Directions: The hotel is signposted off the main coastal road to Rozel Bay, six miles north east of St Helier.

Web: www.johansens.com/chateaulachaire
E-mail: res@chateau-la-chaire.co.uk
Tel: 01534 863354
Fax: 01534 865137

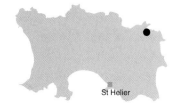

St Helier

Price Guide:
single from £100
double/twin from £132
suites from £231

Nestling on the Rozel Valley's sunny slopes is Château La Chaire, an elegantly proportioned Victorian house surrounded by terraced gardens. Built in 1843, the Château has been enhanced and transformed into a luxurious hotel providing its guests with a superb blend of superior comfort, service and cuisine. Each of the bedrooms has been furnished to the highest standards and offers an impressive array of personal comforts; many en suite bathrooms feature Jacuzzis. The same attention to detail is evident in the public rooms, such as the splendid rococo lounge. Exceptional personal service is acknowledged by the RAC Gold Ribbon award. Both adventurous and traditional dishes can be enjoyed in the oak panelled setting of La Chaire restaurant. Seafood is a speciality, but there is plenty of choice to cater for all tastes. Awarded 3AA Red Stars and 2 AA Rosettes. A few minutes from the hotel is the picturesque Rozel Bay, a bustling fishing harbour with safe beaches close by. The island's capital, St Helier, is just six miles away. Local tours, golf, fishing and riding are among the many leisure activities that the hotel's staff will be happy to arrange for guests.

Our inspector loved: The sumptuous seafood.

THE ATLANTIC HOTEL

LE MONT DE LA PULENTE, ST BRELADE, JERSEY JE3 8HE

This is a stunning luxury hotel that offers elegance, grace, comfort, exquisite cuisine and impeccable service. It is excellent in every way, from majestic interior pillars and magnificent wood panelling to sumptuous furnishings, warm décor and perfect location. The Atlantic stands regally in 3 acres of private grounds alongside the La Moye Golf Course overlooking the 5-mile sweep of St Ouen's Bay. A multi-million pound refurbishment of the hotel including the enlargement of bedrooms and remodelling of the building's exterior to give a 'marine' flavour, has resulted in even more venue quality and the hotel's elevation to 5-Sun status by Jersey Tourism. No expense has been spared in refurnishing the bedrooms, suites and garden studios. Tastefully decorated, they offer occupants the highest standard of facilities and comfort together with splendid views of the sea or the golf course. Most prestigious and stylish is the spacious Atlantic Suite with its own entrance hall, living room, guest cloakroom and service pantry in addition to the en suite master bedroom. The delightful, award-winning restaurant overlooks the open-air swimming pool and sun terrace. Head Chef Ken Healy specialises in modern British cooking and produces excellent and imaginative menus.

Our inspector loved: The koi carp under the stairs.

Directions: Off a private drive off the A13 at La Pulente, 2 miles from the airport.

Web: www.johansens.com/atlantic
E-mail: info@theatlantichotel.com
Tel: 01534 744101
Fax: 01534 744102

St Helier

Price Guide:
single £140–£170
double/twin £185–£270
suite £260–£445

HOTEL L'HORIZON

ST BRELADE'S BAY, JERSEY, JE3 8EF, CHANNEL ISLANDS

Directions: In the heart of St Brelade's Bay, ten minutes from the airport. Price guide.

Web: www.johansens.com/lhorizon
E-mail: hotelhorizon@jerseymail.co.uk
Tel: 01534 743101
Fax: 01534 746269

Price Guide:
rooms £130–£200
suite from £340

St Helier

A premier hotel in the Channel Islands, L'Horizon is situated on Jersey's lovely St Brelade's Bay. Its south facing position ensures that the hotel enjoys many hours of sunshine. A variety of reception areas provides guests with a choice of environments in which to sit and relax. Comfortable and spacious bedrooms offer every modern amenity and many enjoy a wonderful view across the bay. All sea facing bedrooms have balconies. There are three restaurants, each noted for its individual style, the traditional and elegant Crystal Room, fine dining in the intimate Grill Room and the relaxed atmosphere of the pool side Brasserie. L'Horizon has won many international accolades and its menus are compiled from the best fresh Jersey produce and from speciality ingredients from the world's top markets. In summer, relax and sip your favourite cocktails enjoying the panoramic views from the terrace. Guests are invited to take advantage of the superb facilities of the Club L'Horizon, which include a mini gym, large swimming pool, steam room, and sauna. Activities available nearby are swimming, walking and golf. There are three 18-hole golf courses on the island. Seafarers can go on boat trips round the island or across to Guernsey, Alderney, Herm, Sark and France. Special breaks available.

Our inspector loved: *Watching the surfers from the bedroom balcony.*

LONGUEVILLE MANOR

ST SAVIOUR, JERSEY JE2 7WF

Three generations of the Lewis family have welcomed guests to this 13th-century Manor, which is today a very fine and prestigious hotel. Ever attentive staff, superb public rooms, exquisite bedrooms and sumptuous cuisine, which in 2002 earned the Manor's restaurant its 9th consecutive Michelin star, suggest the standards you may expect. Guests dine in either the elegant oak-panelled room or the spacious garden room. Many of the fruits, vegetables and herbs for the kitchen are grown in the hotel's walled garden or the traditional greenhouse which provides fresh produce throughout the seasons - it even has a banana tree! The wine list offers a selection by Longueville's Master Sommelier, and includes gems from the New World, great vintages from the best of the French châteaux and superb Champagnes. Continued upgrading has seen the introduction of delightful new suites, both in the main house and in the restored garden cottage, along with a small meeting and private dining facility. The large heated pool has an adjoining bar, where guests may enjoy a light alfresco meal during the summer. Tennis can be played on the synthetic grass court whilst the lawn is ideal for croquet. Guests may stroll through the magnificent garden with its picturesque lake, home to black swans and mandarin ducks.

Our inspector loved: *The welcoming smiles and the leopard on the bath and the food and the wine and the flowers and ...*

Directions: On A3, 1 mile from St Helier.

Web: www.johansens.com/longuevillemanor
E-mail: longman@itl.net
Tel: 01534 725501
Fax: 01534 731613

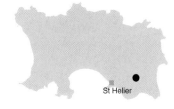
St Helier

Price Guide:
single from £175
double/twin £200–£380
suite £400–£670

www.hildon.com

HILDON
STILL NATURAL MINERAL WATER
SPORT
The ultimate refreshment for
leisure & sport.

For further information on Ireland, please contact:

The Irish Tourist Board
St Andrews Church
Suffolk Street
Dublin 2
Tel: +353 (0)1 602 4000
Internet: www.ireland.travel.ie

Northern Ireland Tourist Board
St Anne's Court
59 North Street
Belfast BT1 1NB
Tel: +44 (0)28 9024 6609
Internet: www.nitb.com

or see **pages 466-469** for details of
local attractions to visit during your stay.

DROMOLAND CASTLE

NEWMARKET-ON-FERGUS, SHANNON AREA, CO CLARE

Directions: Take the N18 to Newmarket-on-Fergus, go two miles beyond the village and the hotel entrance is on the right-hand side.

Web: www.johansens.com/dromolandcastle
E-mail: sales@dromoland.ie
Tel: 00 353 61 368144
Fax: 00 353 61 363355

Price Guide: (room only)
double/twin €204–€459
suite €433–€879

Dromoland Castle, just 8 miles from Shannon Airport, is one of the most famous baronial castles in Ireland, dating from the 16th century. Dromoland was the ancestral seat of the O'Briens, direct descendants of Irish King Brian Boru. Priceless reminders of its past are everywhere: in the splendid wood and stone carvings, magnificent panelling, oil paintings and romantic gardens. The 100 en suite guest rooms and suites are all beautifully furnished. Stately halls and an elegant dining room are all part of the Dromoland experience. The Dromoland International Centre is one of Europe's most comprehensive conference venues, hosting groups of up to 450. Classical cuisine is prepared by award-winning chef David McCann. Fishing, 18 hole golf, clay pigeon shooting and Full Health and Beauty Centre are all available on the estate, whilst activities nearby include horse riding and golf on some of Ireland's other foremost courses. The castle is an ideal base from which to explore this breathtakingly beautiful area. Dromoland Castle is a member of Preferred Hotels & Resorts World Wide.

Our inspector loved: *The unique Dromoland experience in a stunning setting.*

HAYFIELD MANOR HOTEL

PERROTT AVENUE, COLLEGE ROAD, CORK, IRELAND

From the tall, pillared entrance and richly curtained sash windows, to the 2 acres of mature gardens, this Hotel is the essence of style. Hayfield Manor, is a veritable country manor estate within a comfortable walk from the heart of Ireland's second largest city. Situated adjacent to University College Cork, the Hotel provides seclusion and privacy maintaining the atmosphere of unhurried tranquillity established since its Georgian days. The magnificently furnished lounge, with its soft sofas and chairs, ornate open fire and vases of fragrant fresh flowers, is particularly restful. Every modern comfort is to hand and none more so than in the 87 spacious and elegant guest rooms, which boast marble bathrooms with fluffy robes and baskets brimming with toiletries. A health club, exclusive to hotel residents only, has views across the garden and before or after a swim in the palm-surrounded pool you can work-out in the gym, enjoy the steam room or relax in the outdoor jacuzzi. Gourmet cuisine served in the intimate Manor Room Restaurant has a wonderful ambience and high standard of service. Hayfield Manor is the sister property of Joe and Margaret Scally's charming town centre hotel in Killarney, The Killarney Royal. Golf, riding and fishing are nearby as are Blarney Castle, Kinsale and Cobh Heritage Centre.

Our inspector loved: *The Georgian elegance in a secluded part of Ireland's second largest city.*

Directions: 1 mile from city centre.

Web: www.johansens.com/hayfieldmanor
E-mail: enquiries@hayfieldmanor.ie
Tel: 00 353 21 4845900
Fax: 00 353 21 4316839

Price Guide: (including tax & service charge)
double/twin €320–€365
suite €380–€560
master suite €990

THE MILL PARK HOTEL

THE MULLINS, DONEGAL TOWN, CO DONEGAL, IRELAND

Situated in picturesque Donegal town, surrounded by stunning scenery and the Bay of Donegal, the historic Mill Park Hotel is the ultimate in luxury. All rooms are spacious with high ceilings, whilst a cosy atmosphere is created by the open fireplaces and comfortable furnishings. Large, luxurious bedrooms are individually and imaginatively decorated complete with all modern conveniences. Local seafood specialities such as Bruckless Bay oysters and crab as well as fresh fish from the fishing port of Killybegs are featured on the excellent à la carte menu. There is also an excellent choice of vegetarian meals and a comprehensive wine list. A modern, impressively spacious Leisure Club offers an indoor heated swimming pool, fitness rooms and a sun bed. Golf can be arranged at the world-renowned championship course, Murvagh, or the many other excellent courses in the vicinity. Other leisure pursuits include horse riding, angling, walking, surfing, swimming and other water sports. Guests can visit Donegal's mediaeval castle or explore the spectacular North Western scenery. The hotel can accommodate meetings, conferences and events.

Directions: Take N15 to Donegal town.

Web: www.johansens.com/millpark
E-mail: millparkhotel@eircom.net
Tel: 00 353 73 22880
Fax: 00 353 73 22640

Price Guide:
single €125
double/twin €165
suite €220

Our inspector loved: *The general air of informality and cheerfulness.*

378

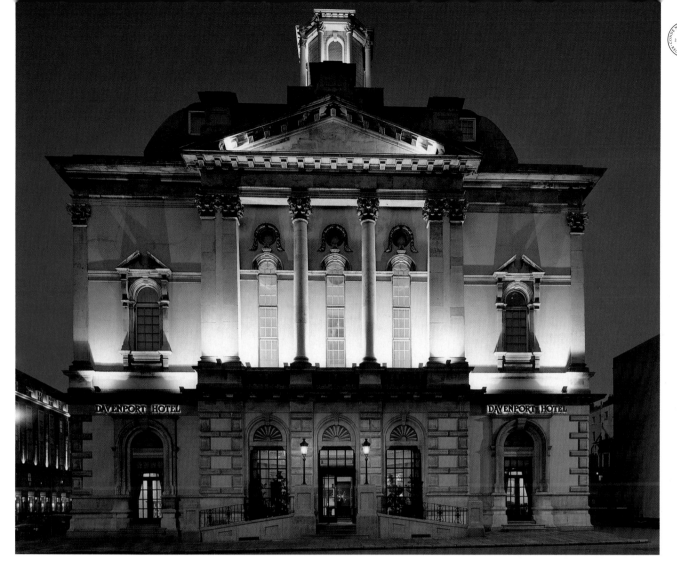

THE DAVENPORT HOTEL

MERRION SQUARE, DUBLIN 2, IRELAND

Built in 1863 as a Gospel Hall, The Davenport still boasts the dramatic façade that graced the original building and is now an elegant boutique style hotel. Conveniently located in the heart of Georgian Dublin, it is surrounded by tall, graceful architecture and wide, surburban streets. Designed with both the tourist and business traveller in mind, The Davenport is modern and stylish; the bedrooms are cool and spacious with every modern amenity, whilst the junior suites contain an additional executive desk with direct line fax machine and laser printer. Large conferences or small meetings can both be catered for here, with The Gandon Suite accommodating up to 400 whilst The Boardroom with its natural daylight and air conditioning is ideally suited to smaller, high level discussions. Lanyons Restaurant offers the finest cuisine amidst a stunning Georgian interior, whilst the Presidents Bar is a warm and comfortable retreat in which to relax and contemplate the various presidents and associations of bygone days. Merrion Square really is central to all that Dublin has to offer: The National Gallery; The Natural History Museum; Irish Parliament and Trinity College or the fine shopping district of Grafton Street and Stephen's Green.

Our inspector loved: The atmosphere in the Presidents Bar.

Directions: Located at Merrion Square in the heart of Dublin.

Web: www.johansens.com/davenport
E-mail: davenportres@ocallaghanhotels.ie
Tel: 00 353 1 607 3500
Fax: 00 353 1 661 5663
US toll free: 1 800 569 9983

Price Guide:
double/twin €298
suite €380

MERRION HALL

54-56 MERRION ROAD, BALLSBRIDGE, DUBLIN 4

Directions: From the city centre take Merrion Road; the Hotel is on the left hand side overlooking the RDS Convention Centre, near Lansdowne Road, and is linked to major tourist sites and the business district by the DART electric train.

Web: www.johansens.com/merrionhall
E-mail: merrionhall@iol.ie
Tel: 00 353 1 668 1426
Fax: 00 353 1 668 4280

Price Guide:
single €99–€130
double/twin €124–€190
suite €159–€240

Balbriggan

Dublin

Dun Laoghaire

This exclusive Edwardian property is located close to the RDS Convention centre just minutes from downtown Dublin. Merrion Hall shares its neighbourhood with the world's embassies in the fashionable Ballsbridge area of Dublin City. Executive bedrooms, some with four poster suites, offer air conditioning, whirlpool spas and all the modern comforts expected by the discerning traveller. The hotel's library stocks a fine selection of Irish and international literature, whilst afternoon teas and fine wines are served in the main drawing room. A feature of this Edwardian town house is a very special breakfast, which can be enjoyed overlooking mature secluded gardens. There are also numerous restaurants within a short stroll of the hotel, leaving guests utterly spoilt for choice. There is a direct luxury coach link to and from Dublin airport. Residents have complimentary parking on the grounds. The Hotel can arrange golfing packages and scenic tours.

Our inspector loved: *The convenient location of this Edwardian house.*

THE MERRION HOTEL

UPPER MERRION STREET, DUBLIN 2, IRELAND

The Merrion is Dublin's most luxurious hotel and a historic landmark. It has been imaginatively and brilliantly conceived, four superb Grade I Georgian terrace houses meticulously restored. There is also an elegant Garden Wing. The interior decorations are impressive, authentically reflecting the Georgian era by the choice of wall colours, specially commissioned fabrics and well researched antiques. By contrast, a private collection of 20th-century art is displayed throughout the hotel, and the neo-classic stairwell has a series of contemporary murals. Every guest room is luxurious, some situated in the Garden Wing, with views over the two gardens – delightful with box hedges, statuary and fountains, approached from the drawing rooms in summer. The Merrion offers a choice of two handsome bars, the larger a fascinating 18th century cellar, the other more intimate and two restaurants, the legendary Restaurant Patrick Guilbaud in a dramatic setting and 'Morningtons', offering traditional dishes with an Irish influence. The Merrion has a state-of-the-art meeting and private dining facility, perfect for hosting banquets. Guests relax in The Tethra Spa, which has an 18m pool, gymnasium and salons for pampering.

Our inspector loved: *The discreet but friendly service.*

Directions: City Centre. The hotel has valet parking.

Web: www.johansens.com/merrion
E-mail: info@merrionhotel.com
Tel: 00 353 1 603 0600
Fax: 00 353 1 603 0700

Price Guide: (room only)
single €300–€380
double/twin €325–€415
suite €610–€995

Balbriggan

Dublin

Dun Laoghaire

STEPHEN'S GREEN HOTEL

ST STEPHEN'S GREEN, DUBLIN 2, IRELAND

Directions: The hotel lies alongside St. Stephen's Green, between St. Stephen's Green Shopping Centre and the National Concert Hall.

Web: www.johansens.com/stephensgreen
E-mail: stephensgreenres@ocallaghanhotels.ie
Tel: 00 353 1 607 3600
Fax: 0 353 1 661 5663
US toll free: 1 800 569 9983

Price Guide:
double/twin €315
suite €380–€765

Balbriggan

Dublin

Dun Laoghaire

Once a collection of Georgian buildings, the Stephen's Green Hotel is a stunning mix of classical architecture and clean, modern style. Stuccoed ceilings and elegant dado rails combine with bold stripes and strong colours to create an atmosphere that is reflective of the cosmopolitan city that Dublin has become, yet still offers a tranquil and dignified escape from life outside. The "Magic Glasses" bar and "Pie Dish" restaurant both take their names from the lesser-known writings of George Fitzmaurice, the Irish playwright, and again reflect the ethos of the hotel incorporating classical style within a contemporary setting. Bistro style cuisine of the 21st century is also cleverly combined with traditional Irish fayre in the "Pie Dish", which is a warm and inviting place to dine after a day in the city. Dublin has rapidly become one of the world's most popular cities, and its diversity is key to its attraction. From bustling street markets to splendid Georgian buildings, cultural museums to horseracing tracks there really is something for everyone, and all within easy access of the hotel.

Our inspector loved: *The views across Stephen's Green Park, a park in the city centre.*

SHEEN FALLS LODGE

KENMARE, CO. KERRY, IRELAND

You could be forgiven for expecting a magic carpet instead of a plane to land you at Sheen Falls Lodge – one of the Emerald Isle's most romantic and luxurious hotels. Standing amidst a vast estate of green countryside and well-kept gardens, with the sparkling Sheen River tumbling down the falls. The Lodge is a magnificent mansion, and the interior, with its country house ambience, is evocative of the past. The Library, with traditional leather furniture, holds many fine books and the spacious lounges have warm colour schemes, log fires and generous sofas. Flowers, lovely antiques and memorabilia enhance the atmosphere. The guest rooms are exquisite, luxuriously appointed and decorated in soft restful shades. They have opulent bathrooms. Dining here starts with the privilege of touring the extensive wine cellar with the sommelier to select a great vintage to accompany a magnificent meal – local salmon, lobster or duck perhaps. Riding, tennis, croquet, fishing, shooting and billiards are 'house' sports. The Lodge also has a superb Health Spa and fitness centre, with indoor heated swimming pool. Nearby are several excellent golf courses, marvellous walking, bikes to hire and deep sea fishing can be arranged.

Our inspector loved: The walk round the outstanding wine cellar.

Directions: From Kenmare follow N71 in the direction of Glengarrif and turn left after the Suspension Bridge. Dublin airport is about 5 hours drive away, Shannon airport is 2½ hours travelling time, Cork airport is approx 1½ hours and Kerry airport is 50 minutes away.

Web: www.johansens.com/sheenfallslodge
E-mail: info@sheenfallslodge.ie
Tel: 00 353 64 41600
Fax: 00 353 64 41386

Price Guide:
Deluxe Room €280–€425
suite €450–€640

KILLARNEY PARK HOTEL

KENMARE PLACE, KILLARNEY, CO KERRY, IRELAND

Directions: In the centre of Killarney.

Web: www.johansens.com/killarneypark
E-mail: info@killarneyparkhotel.ie
Tel: 00 353 64 35555
Fax: 00 353 64 35266

Price Guide:
single €240–€360
double/twin €240–€360
suites €340–€700

Ballybunion

Dingle

Killarney

Warm, soothing décor, plush sofas by log fires, subdued lighting, flower displays and discreet, efficient service make visitors believe they have wandered into a Victorian country home. This particular home is located near the town centre, a stone's throw from almost everything Killarney has to offer yet with the hospitality associated with bygone times. Killarney Park is a premier hotel of character, luxury and style where a sense of opulence abounds. Fine antique furniture, thoughtful colour schemes and lavish soft furnishings create an atmosphere of comfort in the individually designed guestrooms and the suites with splendid sitting areas and open fires. A private entrance hall enhances the sense of exclusivity and privacy. Large chandeliers hang from the ornate ceiling in the Park Restaurant, which echoes a time of courteous dining. The cuisine is award-winning, the service excellent. A pianist plays softly in the background. Drinks can be savoured around a magnificent marble fireplace in the richly curtained Drawing Room, and quiet moments can be enjoyed in the well-stocked library. There is also a panelled billiards room and a Health Spa featuring a Grecian-style pool and a range of leisure, fitness and beauty facilities. Golf, fishing, riding and shooting can be arranged nearby.

Our inspector loved: *The spacious bedrooms where no expense has been spared to provide comfort.*

PARKNASILLA HOTEL

GREAT SOUTHERN HOTEL, PARKNASILLA, CO. KERRY, IRELAND

County Kerry has an equitable climate from the warm Gulf Stream. Parknasilla is a splendid Victorian mansion surrounded by extensive parkland and subtropical gardens leading down to the seashore. New arrivals appreciate the graceful reception rooms which, like the luxurious bedrooms, look out on the mountains, across the verdant countryside or down to Kenmare Bay. Wonderful damask and chintz harmonize with the period furniture and thoughtful 'extras' have been provided. The bathrooms are lavishly appointed. George Bernard Shaw's many visits are reflected in the names of the inviting Doolittle Bar and the elegant Pygmalion Restaurant. The sophisticated menus always include fish fresh from the sea and the international wine list will please the most discerning guests. Corporate activities and private celebrations are hosted in the traditional Shaw Library or handsome Derryquin Suite. Leisure facilities abound: a private 9-hole golf course with challenging championship courses close by, riding, water sports, sailing, clay pigeon shooting and archery. Parknasilla has 7 recommended walks through the estate and its own motor yacht for cruises round the coast. Indoors there is a superb pool, sauna, steam room, Jacuzzi, hot tub, hydrotherapy seaweed baths, aromatherapy and massage

Our inspector loved: The sensitive moderisation of this Victorian favourite.

Directions: The hotel is south west of Killarney off N70.

Web: www.johansens.com/parknasilla
E-mail: res@parknasilla.gsh.com
Tel: 00 353 64 45122
Fax: 00 353 64 45323

Price Guide: (room only)
single/double/twin €230
suite €400

KILLASHEE HOUSE HOTEL

KILLASHEE, NAAS, CO KILDARE, IRELAND

Directions: 30 minutes from Dublin on N7/M7 to Naas, then 1 mile along R448 Kilcullen Road.

Web: www.johansens.com/killashee
E-mail: reservations@killasheehouse.com
Tel: 00 353 45 879277
Fax: 00 353 45 879266

Price Guide: (per person sharing)
single from €144
double/twin from €99
suite €110–€210

Celbridge

Naas

Kildare

Originally a Victorian hunting lodge in 1861, Killashee House still bears the coats of arms of its founders, the Moore family. It has since changed hands many times, been the victim of fire, and housed a preparatory school for boys, before being sold to its current owners in 1998. Today it is a glorious hotel situated within 80 acres of gardens and woodland, just 30 minutes from Dublin. There are 84 luxurious and comfortable guest rooms including 12 suites and 6 Presidential rooms, many with four-poster beds and stunning views of the gardens and, sometimes, the Wicklow Mountains. Every bedroom has multi-line telephone, data port and voicemail. The conference facilities are at the forefront of modern technology with sophisticated audio-visual equipment as well as video conferencing and fibre optic data ports. Killashee House Country Club which includes a 25m pool is the ultimate in luxury and sheer relaxation. The National Stud and the racecourses of Curragh, Punchestown and Naas are all within easy reach, whilst there is an exceptional selection of championship golf courses nearby, including the K Club and the Curragh. There is car racing at Mondello Park, and the Japanese and St Fiachra's Gardens provide a tranquil setting for horticultural enthusiasts.

Our inspector loved: *The country house atmosphere, only a short journey from the city.*

MOUNT JULIET

THOMASTOWN, CO. KILKENNY, IRELAND

Mount Juliet is an architectural gem, a magnificent 18th century Georgian mansion standing proudly on the banks of the River Nore in the heart of a lush 1,500 acre estate that teems with natural activity. The entrance doorway leads into an impressive hall featuring elaborate stucco work with bas-reliefs on walls and ceilings. A feeling of opulence pervades all reception rooms, the bars recall a glorious equestrian past whilst the homeliness of the library and drawing rooms provide comfortable venues for relaxation. Afternoon tea or a pre-dinner glass of champagne can be enjoyed in the elegant Majors Room. Jewel in the crown, however, is the exquisite Lady Helen Dining Room, famed for its original stucco plasterwork, pastoral views and superb cuisine. Chef Peter Brennan produces gourmet delights that have earned a RAC Gold Ribbon and 2 AA Rosettes. The Hotel's 32 en suite guest rooms are individually designed, light and airy, comfortable and full of the character and charm that reflects quiet good taste and refinement. Centre of activity for guests is Hunters Yard, which is situated on the edge of a championship golf course, which hosted the American Express World Golf Championships in September 2002. It envelopes all of the estate's sporting and leisure life together with stylish dining and 16 en suite 'Club' style guest rooms offering total privacy and access to the sybaritic new spa.

Directions: 16 miles from Kilkenny on the N9 via N10.

Web: www.johansens.com/mountjuliet
E-mail: info@mountjuliet.ie
Tel: 00 353 56 73000
Fax: 00 353 56 73019

Price Guide:
single €290
double/twin €470
suite €560

Our inspector loved: The outstanding golf course and sporting facilities.

ASHFORD CASTLE

CONG, CO MAYO

Directions: 30 minutes from Galway on the shore of Lough Corrib, on the left when entering the village of Cong.

Web: www.johansens.com/ashfordcastle
E-mail: ashford@ashford.ie
Tel: 00 353 92 46003
Fax: 00 353 92 46260

Price Guide:
single/twin/double €204–€489
suite €543–€947

Ashford Castle is set on the northern shores of Lough Corrib amidst acres of beautiful gardens and forests. Once the country estate of Lord Ardilaun and the Guinness family, it was transformed into a luxury hotel in 1939. The castle's Great Hall is lavishly decorated with rich panelling, fine period pieces, objets d'art and masterpiece paintings. Guest rooms are of the highest standards and many feature high ceilings, enormous bathrooms and delightful lake views. The main dining room offers superb continental and traditional menus, while the gourmet restaurant, The Connaught Room, specialises in excellent French cuisine. Before and after dinner in the Dungeon Bar guests are entertained by a harpist or pianist. Ashford Castle offers a full range of country sports, including fishing on Lough Corrib, clay pigeon shooting, riding, an exclusive 9-hole golf course and Ireland's only school of falconry. The hotel has a modern health centre comprising a whirlpool, sauna, steam room, fully equipped gymnasium and conservatory. Ashford is an ideal base for touring the historic West of Ireland, places like Kylemore Abbey, Westport House and the mediaeval town of Galway.

Our inspector loved: *The stunning views across Lough Corrib.*

KNOCKRANNY HOUSE HOTEL

KNOCKRANNY, WESTPORT, CO MAYO, IRELAND

Situated on secluded grounds overlooking the picturesque Heritage town of Westport, Knockranny House Hotel enjoys unrivalled views of Croagh Patrick, Clew Bay and the Atlantic Ocean. This Victorian style hotel is privately owned and managed by Adrian and Geraldine Noonan, who guarantee the best in Irish hospitality. The 54 charming bedrooms and suites are tastefully furnished and offer luxury, comfort and every up-to-date convenience. The Executive Suites have four-poster beds, spa baths, a sunken lounge area with panoramic views and all the trimmings of pure luxury. Fresh flowers in spring to roaring open log fires in winter create a relaxing ambience with every possible comfort. La Fougère Restaurant offers imaginative modern Irish cuisine with International influences, complimented by a selection of fine wines. Activities such as golf, fishing, sailing, horse riding and much more can be enjoyed in the dramatic surrounding countryside, whilst a climb to the top of Croagh Patrick makes an exhilarating day's journey. The ideal location to combine business with pleasure, Knockranny offers extensive conference and banqueting facilities for up to 400. The Conference Suites are fully air-conditioned with state-of-the-art communication and audiovisual equipment.

Our inspector loved: The stunning view of the mountain Croagh Patrick and the Atlantic Ocean from the circular dining room windows.

Directions: Left off the N60 before entering Westport town.

Web: www.johansens.com/knockranny
E-mail: info@khh.ie
Tel: 00 353 982 8600
Fax: 00 353 982 8611

Price Guide:
single from €175
double/twin €230
suite €294

NUREMORE HOTEL AND COUNTRY CLUB

CARRICKMACROSS, CO MONAGHAN, IRELAND

Directions: The Hotel is ideally located on the main N2 road between Dublin and Monaghan, only 1½ hours from both Dublin and Belfast.

Web: www.johansens.com/nuremore
E-mail: nuremore@eircom.net
Tel: 00 353 42 9661438
Fax: 00 353 42 9661853

Price Guide:
single €150–€200
double/twin €220–€260
suite €250–€300

Monaghan

Castleblayney

Carrickmacross

Nestling on the outskirts of Carrickmacross, Nuremore Hotel and Country Club is set in 200 acres of rolling countryside with beautifully landscaped gardens. Its wide range of facilities include a swimming pool, tennis courts, treatment rooms and a health club featuring a gymnasium, spa bath, sauna and steam room. The Hotel's renowned 18 hole championship golf course makes superb use of the surrounding lakes and landscape and has been described as one of the most picturesque parkland courses in the country. Resident professional, Maurice Cassidy, is on hand to offer advice and tuition. All 72 bedrooms and suites are beautifully appointed to ensure a generous feeling of personal space and guests can sample the classic European cuisine with Irish and French influences, prepared by award winning chef Raymond McArdle. The restaurant has been listed in Food & Wine magazine and it also features in the Bridgestone Guide to Ireland's best 100 restaurants. Nuremore's impressive conference centre constantly evolves to ensure it remains at the cutting edge for business events. Conference and syndicate rooms boast natural lighting, AV equipment, air conditioning, fax and ISDN lines. A dedicated conference team ensures that all functions run smoothly.

Our inspector loved: The extensive sporting and health facilities and newly refurbished swimming pool.

DUNBRODY COUNTRY HOUSE & RESTAURANT

ARTHURSTOWN, NEW ROSS, CO WEXFORD, IRELAND

Once home to the Marquess of Donegal, this beautiful Georgian country house hotel stands in the heart of 20 acres of woodland and gardens on the dramatic hook peninsula of Ireland's sunny south-east coast. The charming interior is adorned with comfortable furniture, furnishings and paintings, fresh flowers, potted plants and crackling log fires in period fireplaces during cooler months. Owners Kevin and Catherine Dundon have perfected the art of relaxed elegance. Public rooms are large and comfortable with views over to distant parkland. Bedrooms and suites are understated opulence: spacious, delightfully decorated, superbly appointed and with a high standard of facilities including luxurious bathrooms. Kevin acquired star-status as Master Chef in Canada and creates gastronomic delights for a discerning clientele in an elegant dining room overlooking the lawned garden. The Dunbrody Cookery school also offers residential cookery courses and demonstrations. Also highly acclaimed is the late breakfast which is served daily until noon. Waterford and Wexford are close, as are Tintern Abbey, Dunbody Abbey and a multitude of sandy coves. Croquet and clay pigeon shooting is on site, golf, riding and fishing nearby.

Our inspector loved: *The international influence in Kevin Dundon's fine cooking.*

Directions: From Wexford take R733 to Duncannon and Arthurstown. Dunbrody is on the left coming into Arthurstown village.

Web: www.johansens.com/dunbrody
E-mail: dunbrody@indigo.ie
Tel: 00 353 51 389 600
Fax: 00 353 51 389 601

Price Guide:
single €120–€150
double/twin €195–€300
suite €300–€390

MARLFIELD HOUSE

GOREY, CO WEXFORD

Directions: On the Gorey–Courtown road R742, just over a mile east of Gorey.

Web: www.johansens.com/marlfieldhouse
E-mail: info@marlfieldhouse.ie
Tel: 00 353 55 21124
Fax: 00 353 55 21572

Price Guide:
single from €130
double/twin €235–€255
state rooms from €425–€730

Staying at Johansens award-winning Marlfield House is a memorable experience. Set in 34 acres of woodland and gardens, this former residence of the Earl of Courtown preserves the Regency lifestyle in all its graciousness. Built in 1820 and situated just 55 miles south of Dublin, it is recognised as one of the finest country houses in Ireland and is supervised by its welcoming hosts and proprietors, Raymond and Mary Bowe and their daughter Margaret. The State Rooms have been built in a very grand style and have period fireplaces where open fires burn even in the cooler weather. All of the furniture is antique and the roomy beds are draped with sumptuous fabrics. The bathrooms are made of highly polished marble and some have large freestanding bathtubs. There is an imposing entrance hall, luxurious drawing room and an impressive curved Richard Turner conservatory. The kitchen's gastronomic delights have earned it numerous awards. Located two miles from fine beaches and within easy reach of many golf courses, the house is central to many touring high points: Glendalough, Waterford Crystal and Powerscourt Gardens and the medieval city of Kilkenny. Closed mid-December to the end of January.

Our inspector loved: *The instant calming influence caused by the Bowe family's devotion to quality.*

KELLY'S RESORT HOTEL

ROSSLARE, CO WEXFORD, IRELAND

Situated beside the long, sandy beach at Rosslare, Kelly's is very much a family hotel, now managed by the fourth generation of Kellys. With a firm reputation as one of Ireland's finest hotels, based on a consistently high standard of service, Kelly's extends a warm welcome to its guests, many of whom return year after year. The public rooms are tastefully decorated and feature a collection of carefully selected paintings. All bedrooms are en suite have been refurbished in the last four years. The hotel restaurant is highly regarded for its superb cuisine and great attention to detail. An extensive wine list includes individual estate wines imported from France. To complement Chef Aherne's fine cuisine Kelly's have a French Bar/Bistro "La Marine", which is an inspired assemblage of design and offers the ideal venue for pre-dinner drinks. Ireland's numerous endevour awards for tourism. For exercise and relaxation, guests have the use of the hotel's Aqua Club, with two swimming pools and a range of water and health facilities with extensive range of treatments, 'swimming lounge', plunge pool and canadian hot tub, also a beauty salon. Golfers have courses at Rosslare, St Helens' Bay and Wexford, which has an excellent shopping centre. Places of interest nearby include the Irish National Heritage Park at Ferrycarrig.

Our inspector loved: *The complete family resort with something for every age.*

Directions: Follow signs to Rosslare.

Web: www.johansens.com/kellysresort
E-mail: kellyhot@iol.ie
Tel: 00 353 53 32114
Fax: 00 353 53 32222

Price Guide:
single €84–€90
double/twin €148–€187

Hunter's Hotel

NEWRATH BRIDGE, RATHNEW, CO WICKLOW

Hunter's Hotel, one of Ireland's oldest coaching inns, has been established since the days of post horses and carriages. Run by the Gelletlie family for five generations, the hotel has a long-standing reputation for hospitality, friendliness and excellent food. The restaurant is known for its roast joints, its locally caught fish and its home-grown vegetables. The hotel gardens above the river Vartry are a delightful scene for enjoying afternoon tea, lunch or dinner. All the reception rooms retain the character of bygone days with antique furniture, open fires, fresh flowers and polished brass. Most of the 16 attractive en suite bedrooms overlook the award-winning gardens. Business meetings and seminars for up to 25 delegates are held in the new Garden Room. Hunter's is an ideal base from which to visit Mount Usher gardens, Powerscourt Gardens, Russborough House, Glendalough, Killruddery House, Avondale House and the other attractions of Co. Wicklow, "The Garden of Ireland", where a Garden Festival is held each year in May/June. Local amenities include twenty 18-hole golf courses within half an hour's drive, most notably Druid's Glen and the highly regarded European. Horse riding and hill walking are other pursuits which can be arranged.

Directions: Take N11 to Rathnew; turn left just before village on Dublin side.

Web: www.johansens.com/hunters
E-mail: reception@hunters.ie
Tel: 00 353 404 40106
Fax: 00 353 404 40338

Price Guide:
single€88.90–€108
double/twin €177.80–€215.90

Bray

Dunlavin

Wicklow

Our inspector loved: *The friendly family atmosphere to eat and drink in this traditional inn.*

SCOTLAND

Recommendations in Scotland appear on pages 395-439

For further information on Scotland, please contact:

Visit Scotland
23 Ravelston Terrace, Edinburgh EH4 3TP
Tel: +44 (0)131 332 2433
Internet: www.visitscotland.com

or see **pages 466-469** for details of
local atractions to visit during your stay.

Images from www.britainonview.com

395

ARDOE HOUSE HOTEL AND RESTAURANT

SOUTH DEESIDE ROAD, BLAIRS, ABERDEEN AB12 5YP

Directions: Leave Aberdeen on A92 south and join B9077 south Deeside Road at the Bridge of Dee.

Web: www.johansens.com/ardoehouse
E-mail: ardoe@macdonald-hotels.co.uk
Tel: 01224 860600
Fax: 01224 861283

Price Guide:
single £70–£160
double/twin £90–£170
suite £130–£170

Built in 1878 by a local manufacturer for his wife, the majestic, turreted Ardoe House is designed in the Scottish Baronial style favoured by Queen Victoria for Balmoral Castle. Situated within its own beautifully landscaped grounds with magnificent views over the River Dee and open countryside, Ardoe House has the style of an elegant country mansion with all modern comforts. Rich oak panelling, ornate ceilings and stained glass windows abound. The Great Hall reception area is truly spectacular, the richly furnished public rooms are relaxing and there are various small secluded areas where guests can privately enjoy a glass of malt whisky. Every bedroom has a pleasant and comfortable atmosphere and whatever your taste in cuisine, the fare available in the hotel's 2 AA Rosettes award-winning restaurant will more than match expectations. Ardoe House is only 10 minutes from Aberdeen City Centre yet is a fine gateway to tour Royal Deeside. Guests will enjoy complimentary use of a fully equipped leisure centre, which comprises an 18m x 8m swimming pool, sauna, steam room, state-of-the-art gymnasium, aerobics studio, blitz room and four health and beauty treatment rooms. Short break rates which include dinner and breakfast are available on request.

Our inspector loved: *The mix of Historic House and Modern Hotel, good food, very comfortable rooms and splendid leisure & function facilities.*

DARROCH LEARG HOTEL

BRAEMAR ROAD, BALLATER, ABERDEENSHIRE AB35 5UX

Four acres of leafy grounds surround Darroch Learg, sited on the side of the rocky hill which dominates Ballater. The hotel, which was built in 1888 as a fashionable country residence, offers panoramic views over the golf course, River Dee and Balmoral Estate to the fine peaks of the Grampian Mountains. Oakhall, an adjacent mansion built in Scottish baronial style and adorned with turrets, contains five of the 18 bedrooms ideal for private groups. All bedrooms are individually furnished and decorated, providing modern amenities. The reception rooms in Darroch Learg are similarly elegant and welcoming, a comfortable venue in which to enjoy a relaxing drink. Log fires create a particularly cosy atmosphere on chilly nights. The beautifully presented food has been awarded 3AA Rosettes. A wide choice of wines, AA "Wine List of the Year for Scotland", complements the cuisine, which is best described as modern and Scottish in style. To perfect the setting, there is a wonderful outlook south towards the hills of Glen Muick. The wealth of outdoor activities on offer include walking, riding, mountain-biking, loch and river fishing, gliding and skiing. The surrounding areas are interesting with an old ruined Kirk and ancient Celtic stones. A few miles away stands Balmoral Castle, the Highland residence of the British sovereign.

Our inspector loved: One would be hard-pressed to find better food and wine than what is readily available here.

Directions: At the western edge of Ballater on the A93.

Web: www.johansens.com/darrochlearg
E-mail: nigel@darrochlearg.co.uk
Tel: 013397 55443
Fax: 013397 55252

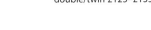

Price Guide:
single £62.50–£82.50
double/twin £125–£155

ENMORE HOTEL

MARINE PARADE, KIRN, DUNOON, ARGYLL PA23 8HH

Directions: Kirn is on the A815, north-west of Dunoon (A885). A continuous car-ferry crosses to and from Gourock across the Firth of Clyde.

Web: www.johansens.com/enmore
E-mail: enmorehotel@btinternet.com
Tel: 01369 702230
Fax: 01369 702148

Price Guide:
single £59–£89
double/twin £79–£158

Known as the jewel on the Clyde, the waterfront town of Dunoon on the Cowal peninsula is often regarded as the gateway to the Western Highlands yet only ¾ hour from Glasgow airport. Enmore Hotel is an attractive house, built in 1785 as a summer retreat for a wealthy cotton merchant. It has since been fully restored by owners David and Angela Wilson. Pretty country wallpaper and bright fabrics characterise the bedrooms, with fluffy towelling robes and flowers among the extras. One of the bedrooms has a double whirlpool bath complete with underwater lighting and another has a four-poster bed with a jacuzzi. In the restaurant, the emphasis is on the use of fresh, local produce to create traditional Scottish dishes. Typical choices may include Arbroath smokies, haggis soup, kippers or the best fillet steaks available in Scotland. Chef-patron David Wilson offers a five-course table d'hôte along with an à la carte menu each evening. 2 international-standard squash courts are available. Dunoon is well equipped with recreational amenities, including bowling, tennis, sailing and a championship golf course.

Our inspector loved: The magical views across the water.

ARDANAISEIG

KILCHRENAN BY TAYNUILT, ARGYLL PA35 1HE

This romantic small luxury hotel, built in 1834, stands alone in a setting of almost surreal natural beauty at the foot of Ben Cruachan. Directly overlooking Loch Awe and surrounded by wild wooded gardens, Ardanaiseig is evocative of the romance and history of the Highlands. Skilful restoration has ensured that this lovely old mansion has changed little since it was built. The elegant drawing room has log fires, bowls of fresh flowers, superb antiques, handsome paintings and marvellous views of the islands in the Loch and of faraway mountains. The traditional library, sharing this outlook, is ideal for postprandial digestifs. The charming bedrooms are peaceful, appropriate to the era of the house, yet equipped thoughtfully with all comforts. True Scottish hospitality is the philosophy of the Ardanaiseig Restaurant, renowned for its inspired use of fresh produce from the Western Highlands. The wine list is magnificent. Artistic guests enjoy the famous 100 acre Ardanaiseig gardens and nature reserve, filled with exotic shrubs and trees brought back from the Himalayas over the years. Brilliant rhododendrons and azaleas add a riot of colour. The estate also offers fishing, boating, tennis and croquet (snooker in the evenings) and exhilarating hill or lochside walks.

Directions: Reaching Taynuilt on A85, take B845 to Kilchrenan .

Web: www.johansens.com/ardanaiseig
E-mail: ardanaiseig@clara.net
Tel: 01866 833333
Fax: 01866 833222

Price Guide:
single £80–£125
double/twin £108–£250

Our inspector loved: *The roaring log fire on a cold winter's night.*

STONEFIELD CASTLE

TARBERT, LOCH FYNE, ARGYLL PA29 6YT

Directions: Take the A83, Stonefield Castle is less than 2 miles from Tarbert.

Web: www.johansens.com/stonefield
E-mail: enquiries@stonefieldcastle.co.uk
Tel: 01880 820836
Fax: 01880 820929

Price Guide:
single £85–£115
double/twin £170–£190
suite £220

The beauty of the Scottish countryside has been the source for a wealth of poetry over innumerable years and there can be few better examples than the setting of Stonefield Castle. Nestled within 60 acres of its own woodland, the Castle stands high on the Kintyre peninsula overlooking the craggy Argyll coastline and Loch Fyne. Famed for their fisheries and smoke-houses this area has much to be proud of and guests sitting in the award-winning restaurant will have a heady combination of exemplary Scottish cuisine overlooking the most spectacular scenery on the West Coast. The Castle was built in 1837 for a member of the famous Campbell clan and it stands today as a fine example of Scottish Baronial architecture, with long elegant windows, gothic turrets and imposing castellations. Each of its 33 bedrooms has been carefully designed to ensure that this period elegance is retained and indeed some of the original pieces of furniture remain in the Hotel. The woodland gardens at Stonefield lure horticulturalists from far and wide to see its rare examples of exotic rhododendrons and shrubs whilst the spectacular scenery of the local countryside makes this a stunning backdrop for summer walks or cosy autumn retreats.

Our inspector loved: *Some of the finest views in Scotland.*

ISLE OF ERISKA

LEDAIG, BY OBAN, ARGYLL PA37 1SD

One could not ask for more peace, tranquillity or seclusion than at this small, comfortable Hotel standing regally alone on a private island off the unspoilt west coast of Scotland. Tracks and trails criss-cross through the abundant flora and fauna of the island's 300 acres of wildlife habitat. Its badger colonies are famous, long-horned Highland cattle lord its grasslands and grey seals flourish in the surrounding waters. Reached from the mainland by its own vehicle bridge, the Isle of Eriska Hotel appears more remote than its 2 hour drive from Edinburgh or Glasgow may suggest. Inside, the solid stone walls over which the blue and white flag of St. Andrew proudly flutters, there is a welcoming atmosphere combined with a calming presence that is emphasised by warm décor and fine furnishings. The library, luxurious drawing room and dining room with its excellently prepared and presented cuisine lie at the heart of the Hotel. A large, log fire greets visitors to the rich, oak panelled hall. 19 en suite, delightfully decorated bedrooms offer every amenity, most have splendid views over gardens that provide the house with an abundance of flowers and the kitchen with fresh herbs. For extra relaxation guests can enjoy a six hole golf course and a spa with sauna, gym and heated swimming pool.

Our inspector loved: *The friendly and welcoming attention from the owners and staff.*

Directions: From Edinburgh and Glasgow, drive to Tyndrum via Crianlarich, the A85 towards Oban. At Connel proceed by bridge on the A828 for 4 miles to the north of Benderloch Village. Then follow signs.

Oban

Dunoon

Campbelltown

Web: www.johansens.com/isleoferiska
E-mail: office@eriska-hotel.co.uk
Tel: 01631 720371
Fax: 01631 720531

Price Guide:
single £185
double/twin £240–£290
suites £450

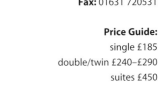

BALCARY BAY HOTEL

AUCHENCAIRN, NR CASTLE DOUGLAS, DUMFRIES & GALLOWAY DG7 1QZ

Directions: Located off the A711 Dumfries–Kirkcudbright road, two miles out of Auchencairn on the Shore Road.

Web: www.johansens.com/balcarybay
E-mail: reservations@balcary-bay-hotel.co.uk
Tel: 01556 640217/640311
Fax: 01556 640272

Price Guide:
single £63
double/twin £112–£130

Enjoying a very warm climate due to its proximity to the Gulf Stream, Balcary Bay is one of Scotland's more romantic and secluded hideaways, yet only ½ hour from the bustling market town of Dumfries. As you sit in the lounge overlooking Balcary Bay, the dong of birds and the gently lapping waves compete for your attention. Guests will be greeted by genuine Scottish hospitality, which includes the provision of modern facilities with a traditional atmosphere, imaginatively prepared local delicacies such as lobsters, prawns and salmon, plus the reassuring intimacy of a family-run hotel. This hotel is a true haven for those wishing to get away from their hectic lives, and an ideal break for a romantic weekend. This exciting corner of Scotland offers numerous great coastal and woodland walks, whilst nearby are several 9 and 18-hole golf courses at Colvend, Kirkcudbright, Castle Douglas, Southerness and Dumfries. There are also salmon rivers and trout lochs, sailing, shooting, riding and bird watching facilities. The area abounds with National Trust historic properties and gardens. Seasonal short breaks and reduced inclusive rates for 3 and 7 nights.

Our inspector loved: *The views from this hotel, which complete the feeling of total escape.*

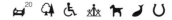

CALLY PALACE HOTEL

GATEHOUSE OF FLEET, DUMFRIES & GALLOWAY DG7 2DL

Set in over 150 acres of forest and parkland, on the edge of Robert Burns country, this 18th century country house has been restored to its former glory by the McMillan family, the proprietors since 1981. On entering the hotel, guests will initially be impressed by the grand scale of the interior. Two huge marble pillars support the original moulded ceiling of the entrance hall. All the public rooms have ornate ceilings, original marble fireplaces and fine reproduction furniture. Combine these with grand, traditional Scottish cooking and you have a hotel par excellence. The 55 en suite bedrooms have been individually decorated. Some are suites with a separate sitting room; others are large enough to accommodate a sitting area. An indoor leisure complex, completed in the style of the marble entrance hall, includes heated swimming pool, Jacuzzi, saunas and solarium. The hotel has an all-weather tennis court, a putting green, croquet and a lake. Also, for exclusive use of hotel guests is an 18-hole golf course, par 70, length 5,802 yards set around the lake in the 150 acre grounds. Special weekend and over-60s breaks are available out of season. Closed January and mid week in February.

Our inspector loved: *The great golf course.*

Directions: Sixty miles west of Carlisle, 1–1½ miles from Gatehouse of Fleet junction on the main A75 road.

Web: www.johansens.com/callypalace
E-mail: info@callypalace.co.uk
Tel: 01557 814341
Fax: 01557 814522

Price Guide: (including dinner)
single £85–£129
double/twin £160–£184
(minimum stay 2 nights)

KIRROUGHTREE HOUSE

NEWTON STEWART, WIGTOWNSHIRE DG8 6AN

Directions: The hotel is signposted one mile outside Newton Stewart on the A75.

Web: www.johansens.com/kirroughtreehouse
E-mail: info@kirroughtreehouse.co.uk
Tel: 01671 402141
Fax: 01671 402425

Price Guide:
single £70–£99
double/twin £130–£150
suite £165

Winner of the Johansens Most Excellent Service Award 1996, Kirroughtree House is situated in the foothills of the Cairnsmore of Fleet, on the edge of Galloway Forest Park. The hotel stands in eight acres of landscaped gardens, where guests can relax and linger over the spectacular views. This striking mansion was built by the Heron family in 1719 and the oak-panelled lounge with open fireplace reflects the style of that period. From the lounge rises the original staircase, from which Robert Burns often recited his poems. Each bedroom is well furnished – guests may choose to spend the night in one of the hotel's spacious de luxe bedrooms with spectacular views over the surrounding countryside. Many guests are attracted by Kirroughtree's culinary reputation – only the finest produce is used to create meals of originality and finesse. This is a good venue for small conferences. Pitch-and-putt, lawn tennis and croquet can be enjoyed in the grounds. Residents can play golf on the many local courses and also have use of our sister hotel's exclusive 18-hole course at Gatehouse of Fleet. Trout and salmon fishing can be arranged nearby, as can rough shooting and deer stalking during the season. Short breaks available. Closed 3 January to mid February.

Our inspector loved: *The beautiful gardens and display of rhododendrons.*

THE DRYFESDALE HOTEL

LOCKERBIE, DUMFRIESSHIRE DG11 2SF

Built in 1782, this former manse was converted into a country house hotel in the early 1950s. Situated in one of the most beautiful and peaceful settings in the area of Annandale, yet only a few minutes from the M74, this family-run hotel has greatly enhanced its standards. There is very much a happy ambience throughout. The lounges and bar are comfortably relaxing, while the individually decorated bedrooms are of a luxury standard. The Kirkhill restaurant, which has been awarded 2 rosettes by the AA, serves the best regional produce. Amongst the many attractions in the surrounding area are Samye Ling Tibetan centre and Temple at Eskdalemuir, Drumlanrigg Castle near Thornhill and the beautiful Galloway coastline passing Shambellie House museum at New Abbey, Gem Rock museum at Cree Town and Threave gardens near Castle Douglas. Dumfries is situated 20 minutes to the west of Lockerbie, the home of Robbie Burns monument and museum, historic buildings and shopping centre. A 20-minute drive to the south of Lockerbie takes you to the historic city of Carlisle, with cathedral and the Lanes shopping centre. The beautiful Cumbrian lakes and mountains are within driving distance as are the cities of Glasgow and Edinburgh. The Dryfesdale Hotel is a Member of Taste of Scotland.

Our inspector loved: *A peaceful oasis yet only minutes from theM74 motorway.*

Directions: Dryfesdale Hotel is situated on junction 17 of the M74, approximately 27 miles north of Carlisle.

Web: www.johansens.com/dryfesdale
E-mail: reception@dryfesdalehotel.co.uk
Tel: 01576 202427
Fax: 01576 204187

Price Guide:
single £65–£85
double/twin £90–£120
suites £120

405

THE BONHAM

35 DRUMSHEUGH GARDENS, EDINBURGH EH3 7RN

Directions: The Hotel is situated in the city's West End.

Web: www.johansens.com/bonham
E-mail: reserve@thebonham.com
Tel: 0131 623 6060
Fax: 0131 226 6080

Price Guide:
single: £140–£165
double/twin £165–£240
suites £295–£325

This award-winning, boutique-style Hotel is situated just a few minutes walk from the West End of Edinburgh and is equally suitable for a restful weekend or a high-intensity business trip. Many of the original Victorian features of the 3 converted town houses have been maintained. The interior has been designed to create a contemporary ambience within the classic timelessness of a Victorian town house. Each room has been elegantly and dramatically created with modern furniture and art, using rich, bold colours to produce tasteful oversized abundance throughout. The Bonham promises to offer a traditional feel with a modern twist, coupled with impeccable standards and individuality. Purely for pleasure, each of the 48 bedrooms offers 55 channel cable TV, a mini-bar and e-TV, which provides a complete PC capability, Internet and e-mail access as well as DVD video and CD player. The Events Room is a perfect setting for a range of select meetings and private dining. Restaurant at The Bonham, the most timeless contemporary restaurant in Edinburgh, serves distinct European inspired cuisine which is complemented by provocative wines. Along with its famous castle and numerous shops, Edinburgh houses Scotland's national galleries and some splendid museums.

Our inspector loved: *The design and décor which have blended the new with the old so well.*

BRUNTSFIELD HOTEL

69 BRUNTSFIELD PLACE, EDINBURGH EH10 4HH

This elegant Victorian townhouse first became a hotel in the 1920s, and has maintained a reputation for its special charm and character ever since. Located just a few minutes from the hustle and bustle of the city centre, guests arriving here will relish the peace and tranquillity of its setting overlooking the leafy Bruntsfield Links; one of Edinburgh's oldest golfing areas and now an elegant park. The traditional Victorian architecture is mirrored inside the building with carefully decorated bedrooms and lounges to ensure that a welcoming ambience of warmth and comfort is maintained throughout the hotel. There are 75 carefully appointed bedrooms, many of which have delightful views, some of Bruntsfield Links, or Edinburgh Castle or beyond towards Edinburgh's Old Town; and there are also a number of larger rooms with four poster beds. The King's Bar offers speciality beers and ales throughout the day, as well as a wide-ranging menu for lunch and supper. The delightfully named Potting Shed restaurant prides itself on its casual yet comfortable atmosphere and offers an award-winning selection of modern dishes using local produce, as well as a balanced range of light snacks served by attentive yet unobtrusive staff.

Our inspector loved: The new bedrooms are large and comfortable and blend well with th old building.

Directions: Join the A702 city bypass, exit at Lothianburn to Bruntsfield Place. The hotel overlooks Bruntsfield Links Park.

Web: www.johansens.com/bruntsfield
E-mail: sales@thebruntsfield.co.uk
Tel: 0131 229 1393
Fax: 0131 229 5634

Price Guide:
single £79-£120
double/twin £120-£200

CHANNINGS

15 SOUTH LEARMONTH GARDENS, EDINBURGH EH4 1EZ

Channings is located on a quiet cobbled street only 10 minutes walk from the centre of Edinburgh, with easy access to the shops on Princes Street and the timeless grandeur of Edinburgh Castle. Formerly 5 Edwardian town houses, the original features have been restored with flair and consideration and the atmosphere is like that of an exclusive country club. With an ambience of country-style tranquillity, guests can relax in one of the lounges with coffee or afternoon tea served by the friendliest of staff. For those who like to browse, the Hotel has an interesting collection of antique prints, furniture, objets d'art, periodicals and books. The atmosphere is perfect for discreet company meetings, small conferences and private or corporate events. These may be held in the oak-panelled Library or Kingsleigh. Fine dining at Channings can be experienced in the exclusive Channings Restaurant which boasts distinctive food in a warm and welcomng ambience. Alternatively, Ochre Vita, is a delight with its vibrant and flavoursome Mediterranean food and wines.

Directions: Go north-west from Queensferry Street, over Dean Bridge on to Queensferry Road. Take the 3rd turning on the right down South Learmonth Avenue, then turn right at the end into South Learmonth Gardens.

Web: www.johansens.com/channings
E-mail: reserve@channings.co.uk
Tel: 0131 332 3232
Fax: 0131 332 9631

Price Guide:
single £130–£160
double/twin £170–£205
four poster £195–£210
suite £245–£250

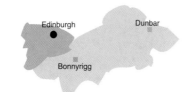

Our inspector loved: *The location; as close to the centre as you can get yet still overlooking green grass.*

THE HOWARD

34 GREAT KING STREET, EDINBURGH EH3 6QH

Situated in the heart of Edinburgh this 5 star Hotel, originally built as a private house, ensures that each guest is made to feel special and experiences traditional Georgian pampering as if a guest in a private home. Visitors take a step back in time when staying at The Howard where attention to detail and the 'personal touch' is of paramount importance. A dedicated butler is on hand to tend to guests' every need; from unpacking bags to serving afternoon tea and will even arrange a social itinerary for exploring nearby Edinburgh where chic designer boutiques are just 7 minutes walk away in George Street and connections by train and Edinburgh airport are close by. Some of the 18 individually decorated bedrooms boast freestanding roll top baths, jacuzzi and power and double showers and 3 exclusive suites have their very own terraced gardens and private entrances. 24 hour room service is available and dinner may be served in the comfort of guests' own rooms, by their personal butler, from the à la carte menu. Alternatively, 'Dining at The Atholl' is an unforgettable experience where the dedicated team of chefs serve meticulously prepared cuisine. The Howard offers an elegant Georgian setting ideal for personal entertaining and private corporate gatherings.

Our inspector loved: *The timeless elegance in one of Edinburgh's smartest streets.*

Directions: From Queen Street turn north into Dundas Street, then take the second right into Great King Street. The Hotel is on the left.

Web: www.johansens.com/howardedinburgh
E-mail: reserve@thehoward.com
Tel: 0131 315 2220
Fax: 0131 557 6515

Price Guide:
single £175–£275
double £235–£295
junior suite £325–£355
suite £365–£475

PRESTONFIELD HOUSE

PRIESTFIELD ROAD, EDINBURGH EH16 5UT

Directions: Approaching Edinburgh from the south, follow the City bypass to the Sheriffhall roundabout and take the A7. At Cameron Toll roundabout go straight across and turn right at third set of traffic lights onto Priestfield Road.

Web: www.johansens.com/prestonfieldhouse
E-mail: info@prestonfieldhouse.com
Tel: 0131 668 3346
Fax: 0131 668 3976

Price Guide:
single £145–£245
double/twin £145–£245
suite £325

13 acres of landscaped gardens and a challenging golf course encompass the grounds and parklands of this fine estate. Built in 1687 for the Lord Provost of Edinburgh, Prestonfield House is one of Scotland's finest historic mansions and part of its great architectural heritage. The interior has retained many of its original 17th and 18th century features and houses the family's collection of paintings and antique furniture. An ornate ceiling forms the centrepiece in the Tapestry Room whilst the room next door is entirely panelled in 17th century Spanish leather. The spacious bedrooms are beautifully appointed and are located in either the original house or in the new extension. Every room enjoys spectacular views across the surrounding landscape and gardens which makes it hard to believe that Prestonfield is a city centre hotel, only 5 minutes by taxi from the centre of Edinburgh. The Old Dining Room serves a mouth-watering à la carte menu comprising of traditional cuisine such as grilled turbot steak and fillet of guinea fowl. 5 private rooms, varying in size, may be hired for parties, meetings or special occasions.

Our inspector loved: *The city location with country views all around.*

THE ROXBURGHE

38 CHARLOTTE SQUARE, EDINBURGH EH2 4HG

Offering some of the finest Georgian architecture in Scotland, this hotel provides an ideal base from which to explore the city of Edinburgh. Having undergone an extensive period of renovation in 1999, The Roxburghe has added a distinctly modern wing, carefully designed to complement the Georgian architecture of Adam's original terraced houses. Overlooking Charlotte Square, the classic rooms retain fine period detailing. The rooms in the modern wing are held in contemporary design, with an open aspect across the handsome George Street. The south-facing rooms on the top floor have stunning views across the rooftops to Edinburgh Castle. The Roxburghe's Rosette awarded restaurant is situated in a beautiful Georgian drawing room overlooking Charlotte Square. The cuisine is a blend of classical British style with the best flavours of the world beyond, complemented by a selection of wines from both the old and new worlds. The fitness facilities include a pool, fitness centre, sauna, steam room and solarium. Many rooms are suitable for conference and meeting purposes. Special packages include two to five day beauty breaks with massages and facial treatments. George Street, Prince's Street and Edinburgh Castle are all within easy walking distance.

Our inspector loved: *The relaxing lounges overlooking Edinburgh's Charlotte Square.*

Directions: The hotel is 5 minutes from Waverley Station and 20 minutes from Edinburgh Airport.

Web: www.johansens.com/roxburgheedinburgh
E-mail: roxburghe@csmm.co.uk
Tel: 0131 240 5500
Fax: 0131 240 5555

Price Guide:
single £110
double/twin £150
suite £240

THE SCOTSMAN

20 NORTH BRIDGE, EDINBURGH, EH1 1YT

Directions: Set in the city centre, on North Bridge between Princes Street and High Street.

Web: www.johansens.com/scotsman
E-mail: reservations@scotsmanhotel.com
Tel: 0131 556 5565
Fax: 0131 652 3652

Price Guide:
double/twin £125–£350
suite £195–£400

Located on Edinburgh's historic North Bridge, a few minutes stroll from Princes Street and The Royal Mile, the exclusive Scotsman was converted from The Scotsman newspaper's baronial offices and boasts innovative design, stylish décor and attention to detail. Their efficient, friendly service, together with warm Scottish hospitality, makes this special venue difficult to beat. Guests have a choice of 2 restaurants; the informal North Bridge Brasserie which has a fun atmosphere and excellent food and at the foot of a dazzling marble staircase, the Hotel's new restaurant, Vermilion, delivers timeless classics using quality ingredients. Individually designed bedrooms make use of magnificent Scottish Estate tweeds, they are extremely comfortable with state-of-the-art entertainment systems and luxurious bathrooms. A modern interpretation of a traditional hotel drawing room provides a tranquil setting in which to relax and have a drink. Alternatively, the breakfast room bar contains immaculate replicas of the Versailles chandeliers. The Hotel has a leisure club and spa with a large indoor pool. Conference facilities are available. Edinburgh Castle is nearby and the shopping on Princes Street is outstanding. Visitors will love the renowned Edinburgh Festival, which takes place during the summer months.

Our inspector loved: *The amazing mix of contemporary styles blending so well with the style of this grand old building.*

NEW

THE RUSACKS

PLIMOUR LINKS, ST. ANDREWS, FIFE KY16 9JQ

Set in the magnificent Kingdom of Fife and surrounded by outstanding beauty and interest, The Rusacks enjoys a prestigious position overlooking the 18th green of St. Andrews Golf Course. The Hotel opened in 1887, has witnessed many famous moments in golfing history and has been host to sports and music legends. Voted one of the top ten golfing hotels in the world, The Rusacks epitomizes all that is good in traditional Scottish hospitality and hotel-keeping. Open fireplaces with roaring log fires, antiques and splendid décor create an atmosphere of authentic Victorian charm and luxury. The 68 bedrooms are beautifully appointed and have breathtaking views, some overlook the golf course and The West Sands. Awarded 2 AA Rosettes for Outstanding Cuisine, the restaurant offers fine Scottish fare specializing in seafood and game of distinctive flavour. An impressive malt whisky collection can be tasted in the Old Course Bar. St. Andrews is also home to Scotland's first university and boasts over 1,000 years of history. Guests can visit museums, climb St. Rule's Tower for a panoramic vista or cycle to surrounding farms and villages in East Fife. There are 2 beautiful beaches in the town and the nearby Fife Coastal Path includes many picturesque coastal hamlets, amazing cliffs and beaches.

Our inspector loved: The airy public rooms and panoramic views over the links from this classic Hotel.

Directions: The Rusacks sits adjacent to the coastal A91, 26 miles from junction 8 of the M90.

Web: www.johansens.com/rusacks
E-mail: general.rusacks@macdonald-hotels.co.uk
Tel: 01334 474321
Fax: 01334 477896

Price Guide:
single £55–£145
double/twin £140–£290
suite £180–£380

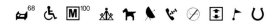

413

NEW

STRATHBLANE COUNTRY HOUSE HOTEL

MILNGAVIE ROAD, STRATHBLANE G63 9EH

Directions: Leave Glasgow on A809 and approximately 3 miles north of Milngavie turn right onto B821 for Strathblane. Alternatively, leave Glasgow on A879, join A81 towards Mugdock, Blanefield and Netherton before turning west onto B821.

Web: www.johansens.com/strathblane
E-mail: strathblane.info@countryhotels.net
Tel: 01360 770491
Fax: 01360 770345

Price Guide:
single £45–£65
double/twin £90–£120

The rugged Trossachs, stomping ground of historically infamous Rob Roy McGregor, are 20 minutes away. Loch Lomond, Stirling Castle and bustling Glasgow are an extra 10 minutes drive. The whole region oozes a breathtaking beauty of lochs and forest-covered hills of history and charm. Strathblane Country House nestles cosily in this environment within the shadow of the majestic Campsie Hills and surrounded by 15 acres of mature woodland and gardens. Built in 1846 and traditionally Scottish, the Hotel has a reputation for ambience, warmth, friendliness and the high quality of lunch and dinner cuisine produced by award-winning chef Martin Hollis. His menus are extensive and only the finest of local produce is considered for his kitchen. Each of Strathblane's en suite bedrooms tastefully reflect the elegance of a by-gone age whilst providing all the luxury expected from today's discerning visitor. An elegant lounge and drawing room are relaxing venues for quiet fireside chats or pre and post-dinner drinks. Horse riding and fishing can be enjoyed nearby and Mugdock Country Park is approximately 1 mile away.

Our inspector loved: So close to Glasgow, yet out in the country.

NEW

MUCKRACH LODGE HOTEL & RESTAURANT

DULNAIN BRIDGE, BY GRANTOWN-ON-SPEY, INVERNESS-SHIRE PH26 3LY

Set in 10 acres of landscaped grounds and surrounded by woods and estate, this former sporting lodge, Muckrach, has a relaxed and informal ambience with an awe-inspiring backdrop of the surrounding Cairngorm Mountains, the River Spey and a 16th century castle. Quality of service is paramount in this relaxing Hotel, where a comfortable atmosphere has been lovingly created with plump sofas, log fires and fresh flowers. The finest quality ingredients are served in the Hotel's excellent restaurant, which offers fresh fish and superb Scottish beef, complemented by a distinguished wine cellar and rare malts. There is a large selection of books, magazines and games to enjoy by the fireside or for the more energetic, the beautiful National Park offers stunning heather moors, ancient forests and sparkling rivers and lochs. Muckrach Lodge is the ideal base for touring the Highlands, Loch Ness, Inverness and the picturesque Morayshire coastal villages. The Malt Whisky and Castle Trails are extremely interesting and Strathspey's turbulent history can be discovered by visiting the area's cathedrals, forts and museums. Nearby there are galleries, antiques, bird watching and superb golf with Royal Dornoch, Nairn, Boat of Garten and others. Alternatively climbing and watersport activities are available.

Our inspector loved: The relaxed style and the abscence of pretentiousness.

Directions: Muckrach Lodge is 3 miles South West of Grantown-on-Spey on the B9102 and A95, through Dulnain Bridge Village on the A938.

Web: www.johansens.com/muckrachlodge
E-mail: stay@muckrach.co.uk
Tel: 01479 851257
Fax: 01479 851325

Price Guide:
single £60–£85
double/twin £120–£140

BUNCHREW HOUSE HOTEL

INVERNESS, SCOTLAND IV3 8TA

Directions: From Inverness follow signs to Beauly, Dingwall on the A862. One mile from the outskirts of Inverness the entrance to Bunchrew House is on the right.

Web: www.johansens.com/bunchrewhouse
E-mail: welcome@bunchrew–inverness.co.uk
Tel: 01463 234917
Fax: 01463 710620

Price Guide:
single £85–£145
double/twin £150–£199

John O'Groats
Portree
Inverness
Fort William

This splendid 17th century Scottish mansion, owned by Graham and Janet Cross, is set amidst 20 acres of landscaped gardens and woodlands on the shores of the Beauly Firth. Guests can enjoy breathtaking views of Ben Wyvis and the Black Isle, while just yards from the house the sea laps at the garden walls. Bunchrew has been carefully restored to preserve its heritage, while still giving its guests the highest standards of comfort and convenience. A continual schedule of refurbishment is on-going. The bedrooms are beautifully furnished and decorated to enhance their natural features. The elegant panelled drawing room is the ideal place to relax at any time, while during the winter log fires lend it an added appeal which has given the hotel 4 Star status. In the candle-lit restaurant the traditional cuisine includes prime Scottish beef, fresh lobster and langoustines, locally caught game and venison and freshly grown vegetables which has been rewarded with two AA Rosettes. A carefully chosen wine list complements the menu. Local places of interest include Cawdor Castle, Loch Ness, Castle Urquhart and a number of beautiful glens. For those who enjoy sport there is skiing at nearby Aviemore, sailing, cruising, golf, shooting and fishing.

Our inspector loved: *To return to this oasis outside town with fresh refurbishments, thriving with great care from the owners.*

THE GLENMORISTON TOWN HOUSE HOTEL & LA RIVIERA RESTAURANT

NESS BANK, INVERNESS IV2 4SF

In the heart of the magnificent Scottish Highlands and a short walk from the town centre, the delightful award-winning Glenmoriston Hotel, with its breathtaking views, is superbly located on the banks of the River Ness. Totally refurbished, this Hotel has been designed with a strong Italian influence and exudes a wonderful sense of warmth and serenity. Sumptuous fabrics and luxurious comfort create an atmosphere of quiet elegance in the cosy public areas and in contrast, the light infused conservatory is an oasis of peace, perfect for relaxing whilst enjoying a coffee or a delicious light lunch. Individually designed bedrooms are stylishly decorated with spacious bathrooms and offer all modern facilities. The mouth-watering cuisine, which consists of quality local produce, twinned with a Tuscan flair, is served in the traditional La Riviera Restaurant or the more contemporary surroundings of La Terrazza. The menu is complemented by a wide selection of excellent wines. Fully-equipped business and group facilities are available. Glenmoriston is an ideal base for exploring the Scottish Highlands and Inverness' shopping and theatre districts.

Our inspector loved: *This stylish refurbishment – how fitting for the new city of Inverness to be home to this tasteful hotel.*

Directions: On the opposite side of the river to the Eden Court Theatre, the Hotel is best approached from Bank St, straight across the crossroads on the north side of the bridge.

Web: www.johansens.com/glenmoriston
E-mail: glenmoriston@cali.co.uk
Tel: 01463 223777
Fax: 01463 712378

John O'Groats

Portree

Inverness

Fort William

Price Guide:
single £85–£105
double/twin £95–£135

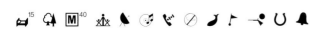

417

NEW

GLENMORANGIE HOUSE AT CADBOLL

FEARN, BY TAIN, ROSS-SHIRE IV20 1XP

Directions: Approximately 33 miles north from Inverness on the A9, turn right at the B9175 signposted to Balintore and Hilton. Drive through Hilton to the end of the lane then follow the signposts.

Web: www.johansens.com/glenmorangie
E-mail: relax@glenmorangieplc.co.uk
Tel: 01862 871671
Fax: 01862 871625

Price Guide: (including dinner & wines)
single £110–£135
double/twin £220–£270
suite £370

John O'Groats

Portree

Inverness

Fort William

Private and exclusive, the enchanting Glenmorangie House is situated on the broad plain of the Easter Ross Seaboard and has a palpable sense of peace and tranquillity. A warm and hospitable welcome is given and the beautiful artworks, polished wood and freshly cut flowers create a serene ambience that is sublime. Guests will feel at home in the comfortable overstuffed sofas and cosy log fires of the Morning Room, where there is an extensive selection of fine malt whisky available. The 9 individually appointed bedrooms are tastefully designed with comfort as a priority and feature stunning views across the delicately manicured lawns and gardens. Fresh fish, local game, vegetables and fruits of the season are creatively combined to create delightful classical and modern dishes with a homely touch. These sumptuous meals are served in the elegant communal dining room. For leisure there is salmon and trout fishing, game shooting and pony trekking. Guests may quietly stroll along the unspoilt beaches or visit the working distillery of Glenmorangie. For the golf enthusiasts, there are numerous excellent golf courses nearby as well as the championship Royal Dornoch Golf Course.

Our inspector loved: *The delightful bedrooms, comfortable lounges and a lovely communal dinner to round off the evening.*

CUILLIN HILLS HOTEL

PORTREE, ISLE OF SKYE IV51 9QU

Spectacular views of the majestic Cuillin Mountains and Portree Bay on the beautiful Isle of Skye make this Hotel the perfect choice for any discerning visitor. Originally built in the 1870's as a hunting lodge, the Hotel benefits from 15 acres of private mature grounds, which creates a secluded setting and tranquil atmosphere. Quality and comfort is a priority, reflected in the beautiful furniture and decor of the lounge, where guests can relax in front of the log fire and sample the extensive choice of malt whiskys. Spacious bedrooms are elegantly furnished and decorated to the highest standard with all modern conveniences. Imaginative and traditional cuisine combine to create award- winning delights, which are served in the stylish restaurant overlooking the Bay. Guests may feast on highland game, lobster, scallops and other deliciously fresh local produce as well as tasty home-made desserts. An interesting selection of informal meals is served in the bar. The Island's rich history can be discovered through its castles, museums and visitor centres. There is an abundance of beautiful unspoilt coastal paths and woodland walks nearby. The town of Portree is a mere 10 minutes walk away.

Our inspector loved: The considerable investment recently has lifted the rooms to a higher plane and bathrooms are state of the art.

Directions: Skye can be reached by bridge from Kyle of Localsh or by ferry from Mallaig or Glenelg. From Portree take the A855 to Staffin. After $1/2$ mile take the road to Budhmor.

Web: www.johansens.com/cuillinhills
E-mail: office@cuillinhills.demon.co.uk
Tel: 01478 612003
Fax: 01478 613092

Price Guide:
single £45–£95
double/twin £90–£190

DALHOUSIE CASTLE AND SPA

NR EDINBURGH, BONNYRIGG EH19 3JB

Directions: From Edinburgh A7 south, through Newtongrange. Right at the Junction onto B704, hotel is ¾ mile.

Web: www.johansens.com/dalhousiecastle
E-mail: enquiries@dalhousiecastle.co.uk
Tel: 01875 820153
Fax: 01875 821936
Conference fax: 01875 823365

Price Guide:
single from £90
double £120–£280

For over 700 years Dalhousie Castle has nestled in beautiful parkland, providing warm Scottish hospitality. There are fascinating reminders of a rich and turbulent history, such as the 2 AA Rosette Vaulted Dungeon Restaurant; a delightful setting in which to enjoy classical French and traditional Scottish 'Castle Cuisine'. 13 of the 27 Castle bedrooms are historically themed and include the James VI, Mary Queen of Scots, Robert the Bruce, William Wallace and The "de Ramseia" suite houses the 500 year old "Well". There are also 5 en suite bedrooms in the 100 year old Lodge. Five carefully renovated function rooms provide a unique setting for conferences, banquets and weddings for up to 120 delegates or guests. Extensive parking and a helipad are on site. Only 7 miles from Edinburgh City Centre and just 14 miles from the International Airport. The Castle is a Scottish Tourist Board 4 Stars classification and Taste of Scotland approved. The new Aqueous Spa includes a hydro pool, Laconium, Ottoman and treatment rooms. The Orangery Restaurant offers contemporary Scottish/European dining. Activities including falconry and clay pigeon shooting can be arranged given prior notice as well as golf at nearby courses.

Our inspector loved: *The contrast between lunch in the bright, modern conservatory and dinner in the vaulted cellar.*

BORTHWICK CASTLE

BORTHWICK, NORTH MIDDLETON, MIDLOTHIAN EH23 4QY

To the south of Edinburgh, off the A7, stands historic Borthwick Castle Hotel, a 20 minute drive from Scotland's capital. Built in 1430 by the Borthwick family, this ancient stronghold has witnessed many of the great events of Scotland's history at first hand. Notably, the safe keeping of Mary Queen of Scots following her wedding to the Earl of Bothwell and a forceful visitation by Oliver Cromwell in 1650. At Borthwick Castle there are 10 bedchambers, each with en suite facilities and 6 with four-poster beds. In the evening, guests dine in the magnificent setting of the candle-lit Great Hall where a four-course set menu is prepared by the chef. The cooking is traditional Scottish, serving fresh local produce. A comprehensive wine list is complemented by a fine selection of malt whiskies. While the castle caters for banquets of up to 65 guests, it especially welcomes those in search of that intimate dinner for 2. In either case, the experience is unforgettable. Open from March to January 3rd.

Our inspector loved: The magical high cielings in the Great Hall with its roaring fire.

Directions: 12 miles south of Edinburgh on the A7. At North Middleton, follow signs for Borthwick. A private road then leads to the castle.

Web: www.johansens.com/borthwickcastle
E-mail: borthwickcastle@hotmail.com
Tel: 01875 820514
Fax: 01875 821702

Price Guide:
single £80–£100
double/twin £135–£195

NEW

KNOCKOMIE HOTEL

GRANTOWN ROAD, FORRES, MORAYSHIRE IV36 2SG

Directions: Knockomie Hotel is located ½ mile south of Forres on the A940 to Grantown on Spey

Web: www.johansens.com/knockomiehotel
E-mail: stay@knockomie.co.uk
Tel: 01309 673146
Fax: 01309 673290

Price Guide:
single £75-£115
double/twin £90 £160
suites £180

Dating back some 150 years, this elegant house owes much of its defining style to the Arts and Crafts movement, that in 1914 transformed the house into what it is today. Paying guests are recorded as early as the 1840s, although its metamorphosis into a stylish hotel is somewhat more recent! With just 15 bedrooms, the hotel has a winning combination of personal service and intimate atmosphere combined with an extremely stylish and elegant interior, that ensures guests can relax from the moment they arrive and enjoy the local hospitality. This is Malt Whisky country and Knockomie has a fine collection for guests to savour, although a trip to one of the local distilleries is a must. It is a beautiful region with Loch Ness on the west and Speyside to the east Country pursuits are plentiful including shooting, fishing and golf which can all be arranged by the hotel; whilst the less sporting can enjoy trips to nearby Brodie and Cawdor castles. At the end of such a day, guests can look forward to a relaxing drink in the comfortable surroundings of the bar, followed by a carefully prepared dinner from a menu that boasts a successful balance of traditional Scottish ingredients and lighter recipes.

Our inspector loved: *The unexpected pleasure of coming across this stylish hotel nicely positioned outside the town.*

GLENEAGLES

AUCHTERARDER, PERTHSHIRE PH3 1NF

Known as the 'great palace in the glen' this luxurious hotel nestles in the heart of the Ochil Hills on the edge of the Highlands in the White Muir of Auchterarder. From its Georgian-style windows and lush green grounds guests can marvel at views of Ben Lomond and the Grampians. Gleneagles is enveloped by clean, crisp air and an artistic landscape capped by an ever-changing sky of blue, violet and autumnal gold. It is a haven of comfort and impeccable service. The interior has been redesigned and refurbished with 21st-century amenities, whilst offering the charm and atmosphere of a Scottish country house. The elegant public rooms are enhanced by superb antique furniture. The 262 bedrooms and 13 suites have every home-from-home comfort and stunning views across Gleneagles' lawns, estate and golf courses; some have hand-woven carpets, crystal chandeliers, tasseled silk hangings and four-poster beds. Guests may dine in the sophisticated Michelin-starred Andrew Fairlie and Strathearn restaurants, whilst a cosy bar serves light lunches and afternoon teas. Championship golf facilities and a variety of country sports and pursuits can be enjoyed. Superb leisure facilities. Less than 50 miles from Edinburgh and Glasgow airports.

Our inspector loved: *this ever-improving star of Scottish hotels, great food options, polished service and everything to do , golfside.*

Directions: From the north, leave A9 at the exit for A823 and follow sign for Gleneagles Hotel. From the south, turn off M9/A9 at junction with A823 signed Crieff and Gleneagles.

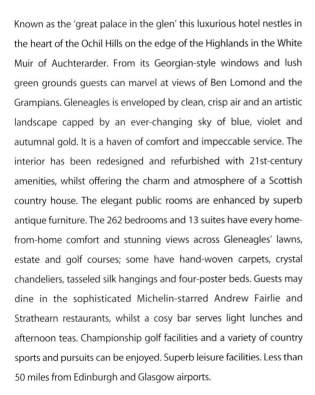

Web: www.johansens.com/gleneagles
E-mail: resort.sales@gleneagles.com
Tel: 01764 662231
Fax: 01764 662134

Price Guide:
single £215
double/twin £320

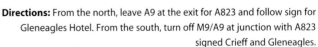

KINLOCH HOUSE HOTEL

BY BLAIRGOWRIE, PERTHSHIRE PH10 6SG

Directions: The hotel is 3 miles west of Blairgowrie, off the A923 Dunkeld road.

Web: www.johansens.com/kinlochhouse
E-mail: reception@kinlochhouse.com
Tel: 01250 884237
Fax: 01250 884333

Price Guide: (including dinner)
single £110
double/twin £220–£260
suite from £285

Winner of the 1994 Johansens Country Hotel Award, Kinloch House is an elegant example of a Scottish country home built in 1840. Set in 25 acres, including a magnificent walled garden and wooded parkland grazed by Highland cattle, it offers panoramic views to the south over Marlee Loch to the Sidlaw Hills beyond. It has a grand galleried hall with an ornate glass ceiling and fine paintings and antiques in the reception rooms. Chef Bill McNicoll and his team have established Kinloch House as one of the top dining venues in Scotland and his daily changing menus are complemented by the very extensive wine list. The cocktail bar, which stocks over 155 malt whiskies, is adjacent to the conservatory and is a focal point of the hotel. In August 1997 a fully equipped Health and Fitness Centre was opened for the exclusive use of guests. The Shentall Family offer a warm personal welcome to all their guests, whether they come simply to enjoy the beauty of the area, or to take advantage of the local pursuits of golf, hill walking, fishing and shooting. For the sightseer, Glamis Castle, Scone Palace and Blair Castle are among the area's attractions. 3 AA Rosettes and 3 AA Red Stars. Closed at Christmas.

Our inspector loved: The overall quality of this mini grand hotel, offering much in spaciousness, great upkeep and lovely food.

THE ROYAL HOTEL

MELVILLE SQUARE, COMRIE, PERTHSHIRE PH6 2DN

Set in an area of outstanding natural beauty, this former inn was once frequented by personalities such as Rob Roy McGregor and Queen Victoria, whose stay bestowed the name of The Royal Hotel on Comrie's major inn. Its homely yet luxurious and elegant atmosphere is enhanced by open log fires, period furnishings and genuine Highland hospitality provided by the cheerful staff and the Milsom family, who also own the Tufton Arms Hotel, Appleby. Each of the 11 bedrooms has been individually designed and shows exceptional attention to detail. An ideal place to unwind, the comfortable Lounge Bar is popular for pre-dinner drinks which include a choice of over 130 whiskies. Guests may enjoy Scottish cuisine and fine wines in the conservatory-style Brasserie or the more intimate Royal Restaurant, where Chef David Milsom and his team, awarded an AA Rosette, create delicious dishes based on fresh local produce. The hotel is located amidst superb walking country; guests can go for gentle walks in the nearby Glens and across the hills and moorlands. The hotel has its own stretch of the river Earn for fishing, and horse riding and fowl or clay pigeon shooting can be arranged. Comrie is surrounded by excellent golf courses, which range from scenic Highland layouts to idyllic parkland settings, such as the famous Gleneagles.

Our inspector loved: The blend of informality, correctness and style.

Directions: Located in the centre of the village.

Web: www.johansens.com/royalcomrie
E-mail: reception@royalhotel.co.uk
Tel: 01764 679200
Fax: 01764 679219

Price Guide:
single £75
double £120
suite £160

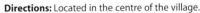

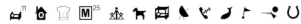

DALMUNZIE HOUSE

SPITTAL O'GLENSHEE, BLAIRGOWRIE, PERTHSHIRE PH10 7QG

Directions: Dalmunzie is on the A93 at the Spittal O'Glenshee, south of Braemar.

Web: www.johansens.com/dalmunziehouse
E-mail: dalmunzie@aol.com
Tel: 01250 885224
Fax: 01250 885225

Price Guide:
single £43–£65
double/twin £66–£118

Dalmunzie House is beautifully tucked away high in the Scottish Highlands, 18 miles north of Blairgowrie and 15 miles south of Braemar. Standing in its own mountainous 6,000-acre sporting estate, it is run by Simon and Alexandra Winton. Guests come to enjoy the relaxed family atmosphere which, together with unobtrusive service and attention, ensures a comfortable stay. The bedrooms are individual in character, some with antiques, others romantically set in the turrets of the house, all tastefully decorated. Delicately cooked traditional Scottish fare is created from local ingredients fresh from the hills and lochs. The menu changes daily and meals are served in the dining room, accompanied by wines from the well-stocked cellar. Among the sporting activities available on site are golf (the 9-hole course is one of the highest in Britain) and shooting for grouse, ptarmigan and black game. Other country pursuits include river and loch fishing, clay pigeon shooting, mountain biking, stalking for red deer and pony-trekking. Glenshee Ski Centre is 6 miles away: it offers cross-country and downhill skiing. Closer to home, the hotel games room provides more sedate pastimes for all the family. Closed late November to 28 December. Special winter/skiing rates.

Our inspector loved: *This stunningly located traditional hotel with a plethora of leisure opportunities on site or close by.*

CROMLIX HOUSE

KINBUCK, BY DUNBLANE, NR STIRLING FK15 9JT

Set in a 2,000 acre estate in the heart of Perthshire, just off the A9, the STB 5 Star Cromlix House is a rare and relaxing retreat. Built as a family home in 1874, much of the house remains unchanged including many fine antiques acquired over the generations. Proprietors David and Ailsa Assenti are proud of their tradition of country house hospitality. The individually designed bedrooms and spacious suites have been redecorated with period fabrics to enhance the character and fine furniture whilst retaining the essential feeling of a much loved home. Unpretentious, restful and most welcoming, the large public rooms have open fires. In the restaurant, the finest local produce is used. Cromlix is an ideal venue for small exclusive conferences and business meetings. The private Chapel is a unique feature and perfect for weddings. The hotel won the Andrew Harpers European Hideaway 2000 Award. Extensive sporting and leisure facilities include trout and salmon fishing and game shooting in season. There are several challenging golf courses within easy reach including Gleneagles, Rosemount, Carnoustie and St Andrews. The location is ideal for touring the Southern Highlands, with Edinburgh and Glasgow only an hour away.

Our inspector loved: The peaceful atmosphere where it's easy to believe you are in your own luxury house.

Directions: Cromlix House lies four miles north of Dunblane, north of Kinbuck on B8033 and four miles south of Braco.

Web: www.johansens.com/cromlixhouse
E-mail: reservations@cromlixhouse.com
Tel: 01786 822125
Fax: 01786 825450

Price Guide:
single £125–£195
double/twin £215–£255
suite with private sitting room £245–£360

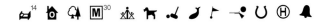

427

KINFAUNS CASTLE

NR PERTH, PERTHSHIRE PH2 7JZ

Directions: The hotel is two miles from Perth on the A90 Dundee Road.

Web: www.johansens.com/kinfaunscastle
E-mail: email@kinfaunscastle.co.uk
Tel: 01738 620777
Fax: 01738 620778

Price Guide:
single £125–£190
double £190–£230
suite £280–£320

Set within 26 acres of parkland and landscaped gardens, Kinfauns Castle stands on a promontory overlooking the River Tay. The castle, built by Lord Gray in the 1820s is located immediately off the A90 Dundee Road, just two miles from Perth. The new Directors, Mr and Mrs James A. Smith, made a commitment to the restoration of the wonderful building, the historical seat of Lord Gray. James Smith was until recently Vice-President of Central Asia for Hilton International. The 16 suites and rooms are individually decorated and reflect the quality, comfort and ambience one expects of a luxury country house. The public rooms feature the rich Victorian décor which has survived the Castle's 70 years as a hikers' hotel. One particular lounge sports a William Morris hunting scene paper whilst another contains a Dragon Boat Bar, brought back from Taipai by the present owner. Chef Jeremy Brazelle leads an award-winning brigade serving an exquisite fusion of modern Scottish and classical French cuisine produced from the finest locally-sourced ingredients. The area abounds with castles and sites of historic interest: Scone Palace and Glamis Castle are only a few miles away. Salmon fishing on the River Tay, golf, shooting and riding are easily available.

Our inspector loved: *The mixture of history and splendid grandeur interestingly intermingled with Oriental artefacts.*

BALLATHIE HOUSE HOTEL

KINCLAVEN, STANLEY, PERTHSHIRE PH1 4QN

Set in an estate overlooking the River Tay near Perth, Ballathie House Hotel offers Scottish hospitality in a house of character and distinction. Dating from 1850, this mansion has a French baronial façade and handsome interiors. Overlooking lawns which slope down to the riverside, the drawing room is an ideal place to relax with coffee and the papers, or to enjoy a malt whisky after dinner. The premier bedrooms are large and elegant, while the standard rooms are designed in a cosy, cottage style. On the ground floor there are several bedrooms suitable for guests with disabilities. Local ingredients such as Tay salmon, Scottish beef, seafood and piquant soft fruits are used by chef Kevin MacGillivray winner of the title "Scottish Chef of the Year 1999–2000", to create menus catering for all tastes. The hotel has two rosettes for fine Scottish cuisine. Activities available on the estate include salmon fishing, river walks, croquet and putting. The new Riverside Rooms are ideal for both house guests or sportsmen. The area has many good golf courses. Perth, Blairgowrie and Edinburgh are within an hour's drive. STB 4 star. Dogs in certain rooms only. 2 day breaks from £89 including dinner.

Our inspector loved: Something of the grand hotel in rural Perthshire, with polished service and classic comforts.

Directions: From the A93 at Beech Hedges, signposted for Kinclaven and Ballathie, or off the A9, 2 miles north of Perth, take the Stanley Road. The hotel is 10 miles north of Perth.

Web: www.johansens.com/ballathiehouse
E-mail: email@ballathiehousehotel.com
Tel: 01250 883268
Fax: 01250 883396

Price Guide:
single £75–£110
double/twin £150–£210
suite £220–£250

Pitlochry

Perth

Kinross

GLEDDOCH HOUSE

LANGBANK, RENFREWSHIRE PA14 6YE

Directions: M8 towards Greenock; take B789 Langbank/ Houston exit. Follow signs to left and then right after ½ mile; hotel is on left.

Web: www.johansens.com/gleddochhouse
E-mail:
Tel: 01475 540711
Fax: 01475 540201

Price Guide:
single £99
double/twin £150
suite £185

Once the home of a Glasgow shipping baron, Gleddoch House stands in 360 acres, with dramatic views across the River Clyde to Ben Lomond and the hills beyond. The individually appointed bedrooms all have en suite facilities and some have four-poster beds. Executive rooms and suites and family rooms are also available. Other amenities include a new conference centre with meeting rooms to cater for up to 120 delegates theatre style. The Garden Restaurant is renowned for its award-winning modern Scottish cuisine and is complemented by a comprehensive wine list. On the estate a series of activities are available such as golf, clay pigeon shooting, archery and off-road driving, making Gleddoch an ideal venue to host corporate events. Additionally the equestrian centre caters for all levels, from trekking to pony rides and individual tuition. Gleddoch's location offers an experience of a bygone era yet amid the sophistication that today's traveller requires. A range of short breaks, golfing packages and gourmet events are available throughout the year. Glasgow Airport is only 10 minutes drive away and the City Centre, 20 minutes.

Our inspector loved: *The spectacular views across the River Clyde from the hotel's elevated position.*

EDNAM HOUSE HOTEL

BRIDGE STREET, KELSO, ROXBURGHSHIRE TD5 7HT

Overlooking the River Tweed, in 3 acres of gardens, Ednam House is one of the region's finest examples of Georgian architecture. This undulating, pastoral countryside was immortalised by Sir Walter Scott. Ednam House has been owned and managed by the Brooks family for over 70 years, spanning 4 generations. Although the grandiose splendour may seem formal, the warm, easy-going atmosphere is all-pervasive. The lounges and bars are comfortably furnished and command scenic views of the river and grounds. All 32 bedrooms are en suite, individually decorated and well-equipped. In the elegant dining room which overlooks the river, a blend of traditional and creative Scottish cuisine, using fresh local produce, is served. The wine list is very interesting and reasonably priced. Ednam House is extremely popular with fishermen, the Borders being renowned for its salmon and trout. Other field sports such as stalking, hunting and shooting can be arranged as can riding, golfing and cycling. Local landmarks include the abbeys of Kelso, Melrose, Jedburgh and Dryburgh. The Hotel is closed Christmas and New Year.

Our inspector loved: *The repartee in the bar when the fishermen get together after a long day on the Tweed.*

Directions: From the south, reach Kelso via A698; from the north, via A68. The Hotel is just off the market square by the river.

Web: www.johansens.com/ednamhouse
E-mail: contact@ednamhouse.com
Tel: 01573 224168
Fax: 01573 226319

Price Guide:
single from £67
double/twin £89–£124

431

THE ROXBURGHE HOTEL & GOLF COURSE

KELSO, ROXBURGHSHIRE TD5 8JZ

Directions: The hotel is at Heiton, just off the A698 Kelso–Jedburgh road.

Web: www.johansens.com/roxburghekelso
E-mail: hotel@roxburghe.net
Tel: 01573 450331
Fax: 01573 450611

Price Guide:
single £120
double/twin £175
4-poster £215
suite £265

Converted by its owners, the Duke and Duchess of Roxburghe, into a luxury hotel of character and charm, The Roxburghe is situated in over 200 acres of rolling grounds on the bank of the River Teviot. There are 22 bedrooms, including four poster rooms and suites, and like the spacious reception rooms, they are furnished with care and elegance. The menu, which is changed daily, reflects the hotel's position at the source of some of Britain's finest fish, meat and game – salmon and trout from the waters of the Tweed, or grouse, pheasant and venison from the Roxburghe estate – complemented with wines from the Duke's own cellar. Fine whiskies are served in the Library Bar, with its log fire and leather-bound tomes. The Beauty Clinic brings to guests the régimes of Decleor, Paris. Surrounding the hotel is the magnificent Roxburghe Golf Course, designed by Dave Thomas. This parkland course, host to Scottish Juniors Open is the only championship golf course in the Scottish Borders. A full sporting programme can be arranged, including fly and coarse fishing, and falconry. The shooting school offers tuition in game and clay shooting. Seven great country houses are within easy reach including Floors Castle, the home of the Duke and Duchess of Roxburghe.

Our inspector loved: *A championship golf course on the doorstep.*

CASTLE VENLAW

EDINBURGH ROAD, PEEBLES, EH45 8QG

Just 40 minutes from the city of Edinburgh, yet within the peaceful Borders countryside, the Castle sits majestically on the slopes of Venlaw Hill overlooking the royal and ancient town of Peebles. Originally built as a private house in 1782, it was bought by John and Shirley Sloggie in 1997 and has undergone major refurbishment. Now recognised as one of the leading 4 star hotels in the area, Castle Venlaw keeps the country house tradition alive and offers an air of elegance and relaxed informality. From the welcoming Library with its oak panelling and log fire to the 12 bedrooms – all named after Scotland's finest malt whiskies – great care has been taken to preserve the Castle's charm and character. Guests can choose from a range of suites and at the top of the tower a family suite comes complete with children's den. The spacious and airy 2 AA Rosette restaurant provides the perfect ambience in which to enjoy menus where delicious local produce such as Borders salmon, lamb and game are given an International flavour. Outside, acres of beautiful woodland grounds can be explored, golf or fishing enjoyed and the history in the ruined Abbeys and historic houses can be appreciated. Edinburgh, Glasgow and Stirling are within easy reach. Short breaks, including dinner, are available throughout the year starting from £65.

Our inspector loved: *The exceptionally large rooms, the peace and quiet and the proximity to Edinburgh.*

Directions: From Edinburgh, follow the A703 to Peebles. After the 30mph sign, the Hotel drive is signposted on the left. From Peebles, follow the A703 to Edinburgh, the Hotel drive is on the right after ¾ mile.

Web: www.johansens.com/venlaw
E-mail: enquiries@venlaw.co.uk
Tel: 01721 720384
Fax: 01721 724066

Price Guide:
single £60–£85
double/twin £120–£180

ENTERKINE HOUSE

ANNBANK, BY AYR, AYRSHIRE KA6 5AL

Directions: From the A77 trunk road take the B742 signposted to Annbank and proceed via Mossblown bypassing Annbank on the road to Coylton. Enterkine Estate is 50 metres on the left past Annbank.

Web: www.johansens.com/enterkine
E-mail: mail@enterkine.com
Tel: 01292 521608
Fax: 01292 521582

Price Guide: (including dinner)
single £180
double/twin £300

The mysterious Enterkine, situated in 310 acres of woodland, meadows and valley is an unforgettable experience of peace and beauty. A winding tree-lined avenue leads to an elegant 1930's country house that boasts impressive views over the Ayr Valley. Inside, the Hotel is decorated with delightful soft furnishings and tasteful colour co-ordination to create a warm and welcoming ambience. The log fire and oval shaped library, stuffed full of interesting books, are perfect for a lazy day. Privacy and exclusivity is a priority and the staff place emphasis on individual service and comfort. The 6 stylish bedroom suites, with luxurious bathrooms, are extremely spacious, light and stunningly decorated with subtle colours and opulent fabrics, each in an individual style. Guests may sample the world-class cuisine that offers the best Scottish ingredients. Corporate events and parties can be catered for and golf, shooting and fishing are available. Close by, Culzean Castle is a fascinating visit or guests may wish to visit the nearby championship courses at Royal Troon and Prestwick. The countryside along the coastal road from Ayr to Turnberry is spectacular.

Our inspector loved: *The absolute attention to detail at every turn.*

GLENAPP CASTLE

BALLANTRAE, SCOTLAND KA26 0NZ

Glenapp is more of an experience rather than 'just another hotel'. As you turn through the castle gates, Glenapp stands proudly in front of you; imposing, exciting and inviting. The owners, Fay and Graham Cowan, offer a truly Scottish welcome to their glorious Ayrshire home. They bought Glenapp in a state of neglect and spent six years refurbishing it to combine the requirements of the discerning guest with the classic style of the house. No expense has been spared, from the stone fireplaces carved with the family crest to the Castle's own monogrammed china. Head Chef Laurent Gueguen will prepare exciting, innovative 6-course dinners, complemented by specially selected fine wines. The castle retains many original features as well as personally selected oil paintings and antique furnishings throughout bedrooms, lounges and oak panelled hallways. The 17 en suite bedrooms are spacious, individually decorated, and furnished to the highest standard, all offering either views of the garden or coastline. The 30-acre gardens contain many rare trees and shrubs and an impressive Victorian glasshouse and walled garden. Tennis and croquet are available in the grounds. Guests may play golf on the many local courses including championship courses, and shoot or fish on local estates.

Our inspector loved: Everything about it. It's just a different world.

Directions: Glenapp Castle is approximately 15 miles north of Stranraer or 35 miles south of Ayr on A77.

Troon

Ayr

Girvan

Web: www.johansens.com/glenappcastle
E-mail: enquiries@glenappcastle.com
Tel: 01465 831212
Fax: 01465 831000

Price Guide: (all inclusive)
luxury double/twin £440
suite £480
master room £550

MACDONALD CRUTHERLAND HOUSE HOTEL

STRATHAVEN ROAD, EAST KILBRIDE G75 0QZ

Directions: From M74, exit at Jct5. Take A726 to East Kilbride and follow signs for Strathaven.

Web: www.johansens.com/macdonaldcrutherlandhouse
E-mail: crutherland@macdonald–hotels.co.uk
Tel: 01355 577000
Fax: 01355 220855

Price Guide:
single £95–£128
double/twin £105–£150
suites £160–£210

Standing in 37 acres of garden and woodland just outside the market town of Strathaven, which became prosperous in the middle ages because of the silk industry, the Crutherland is a fine example of a great Scottish house restored in superb style. It is extravagantly decorated and boasts every luxury whilst evoking an age of elegance. The Crutherland House was built in 1705 as a dower house for the Lady Dowager from Torrance Castle, which was situated in what is now Calderglen Country Park. After being home to many families it was converted into a hotel in 1964 and recently had a £6million refurbishment which has enhanced and added to every facility. Each of the 75 spacious bedrooms has views over the grounds and all comforts from satellite television to hospitality tray and 24-hour service. The best of Scottish and international cuisine is served in the award winning restaurant. The leisure club features an 18-metre swimming pool, high-tech gymnasium, sauna and four beauty treatment rooms. The hotel also offers extensive business meeting facilities including 11 conference suites. Glasgow is within easy reach and Caldergren Country Park, Strathclyde Park and Kittochside Museum of Scottish Country Life are worth relaxing visits.

Our inspector loved: *The high standards of housekeeping throughout the hotel.*

FOREST HILLS HOTEL

KINLOCHARD BY ABERFOYLE, THE TROSSACHS FK8 3TL

The majestic Forest Hills Hotel is idyllically situated in 25 acres of mature wooded landscaped gardens overlooking beautiful Loch Ard in the foothills of the Trossachs, scattered with tumbling burns, rocky waterfalls, winding pathways and meandering forest trails. It is a stunning, history-steeped scenic location where guests can completely unwind and enjoy sumptuous comfort, warming log fires in winter or watching the summer sun illuminating Ben Lomond across the waters whilst sipping a cooling drink on the terrace. Forest Hills is excellent in every way, particularly its service, friendliness and hospitality. The 54 elegantly furnished en suite bedrooms have every facility that visitors could wish for. There are two dining options available. Enjoy a mouth-watering meal in the elegant Garden Restaurant. or sample the grill menu in the more informal Rafters Bar & Bistro. The newly refurbished leisure centre has a heated swimming pool, sauna, steam room, gym and a full size curling rink (curling rink available August to June). For the more adventurous, quadbiking, canoeing, windsurfing, sailing on the Loch, mountain biking, archery, fly fishing and guided ghost walks can be arranged. Beauty treatments are available.

Our inspector loved: This great retreat that is so easy to get to from surrounding main towns.

Directions: From the M9, exit at junction10. Take the A873 to Aberfoyle and then join the B892 to Kinlochard.

Web: www.johansens.com/foresthills
E-mail: forest_hills@macdonald-hotels.co.uk
Tel: 01877 387277
Fax: 01877 387307

Price Guide:
single £68–£90
double/twin £95–£135
suite £145–£185

437

THE NORTON HOUSE HOTEL

INGLISTON, EDINBURGH EH28 8LX

Directions: From Edinburgh take A8 past airport and hotel is ½ mile on the left. From Glasgow, follow M8 to Junction 2, take the first exit off the roundabout following signs for Ratho, take the first left, then left again following signs to Ratho, then left at the top of the hill, where hotel is signposted.

Web: www.johansens.com/nortonhouseedinburgh
E-mail: nortonhouse@arcadianhotels.co.uk
Tel: 0131 333 1275 or 0800 9 177 877
Fax: 0131 333 5305

Price Guide:
single £115–£150
double/twin £140–£165
suites £165–£200

This Victorian mansion, dating back to 1840, is a part of the Arcadian Hotel Group. Situated in 55 acres of mature parkland, Norton House combines modern comforts with elegance. The 47 en suite bedrooms are bright and spacious, with many facilities, including a video channel and satellite TV. Influenced by the best Scottish and French traditions, the menu offers a balanced choice. Moments away, through leafy woodlands, a former stable block has been converted into The Gathering Bistro and Bar, where drinks and snacks are available to family and friends. Set in a walled garden, it is an ideal venue for the barbecues which are a regular feature in the summer months. The Patio, Veranda and Boardroom lend a sense of occasion to small gatherings, while the Linlithgow Suite can cater for large-scale events such as banquets, weddings and conferences. Norton House is conveniently 1 mile from Edinburgh Airport and 6 miles from the city centre, it is also a base from which to explore the Trossachs, Borders and Lothians

Our inspector loved: *The feeling of tranquillity, even when the Hotel is busy.*

HOUSTOUN HOUSE

UPHALL, NR EDINBURGH, SCOTLAND EH52 6JS

Houstoun House is a beautiful, unspoilt example of a 16th-century Scottish laird's house, which has been complemented by a number of sympathetically designed new buildings. The gardens include a great cedar tree, grown from seed brought from the Lebanon by one of the early lairds, and the 20 acres of grounds and woodland are adjacent to Uphall Golf Course where guests can play by arrangement. The house is divided into three buildings – the Tower, containing the dining rooms and vaulted bar, the Woman House, joined to the Tower by a stone-flagged courtyard, and the Steading, formerly the estate factor's house. Guest rooms range from standard, to family, to four-poster rooms and suites, and some are specifically adapted for the disabled. All are elegantly furnished and well equipped, and have views of the gardens or the Ecclesmachan Hills. The wood-panelled dining rooms enjoy an excellent reputation for cuisine, while the Leisure Club offers a relaxed and informal Italian Bistro. Health and fitness facilities include a hi-tech gymnasium, 18-metre pool, beauty salon and all-weather tennis court. The city of Edinburgh and its airport are close by, as are access routes to Glasgow and Perth.

Our inspector loved: *The skillful blending of an old house with the modern facilities required from a new hotel.*

Directions: From M8 Jct 3 (Livingston), turn right at first roundabout, follow signs for Broxburn – A89 left at traffic lights on A899 to Uphall.

Web: www.johansens.com/houstounhouse
E-mail: events.houstoun@macdonald-hotels.co.uk
Tel: 01506 853831
Fax: 01506 854220

Price Guide: (exclusive of Breakfast)
single £90–£140 double/twin £120–£180
suites £140–£180

WALES – CYMRU

Recommendations in Wales appear on pages 441-459

For further information on Wales, please contact:

Wales Tourist Board
Brunel House, 2 Fitzalan Road, Cardiff CF24 0UY
Tel: +44 (0)29 2049 9909
Web: www.visitwales.com

North Wales Tourism
Tel: +44 (0)1492 531731
Web: www.nwt.co.uk

Mid Wales Tourism
Tel: (Freephone) 0800 273747
Web: www.mid-wales-tourism.org.uk

Tourism South & West Wales
Tel: +44 (0)1792 781212

or see **pages 466-469** for details of
local atractions to visit during your stay.

Images from www.britainonview.com

441

LLECHWEN HALL

ABERCYNON, NR LLANFABON, CARDIFF, MID GLAMORGAN CF37 4HP

Directions: Exit M4 at junction 32 and follow A470 towards Merthyr Tydfil for approximately 11 miles. Join A472 towards Nelson and then A4054 towards Cilfynydd. The hotel is on the left after ½ mile.

Web: www.johansens.com/Llechwenhall
E-mail: llechwen@aol.com
Tel: 01443 742050
Fax: 01443 742189

Price Guide:
single £54.50–£65.50
double/twin £75–£106

Visitors step back in time when they enter this lovely 17th-century Welsh Long-House with its Victorian frontage standing in 6 acres of mature gardens on the hillside overlooking the Aberdare and Merthyr valleys. There are four-foot thick walls with narrow embrasures, low ceilings, stout-blackened oak beams, huge fireplaces and stone-roofed outbuildings. Careful restoration and sympathetic refurbishment over the years, since being purchased as a near derelict building in 1988, has created a 3-star country house hotel with an award-winning restaurant. The 20 superbly appointed bedrooms are individually decorated and furnished to provide a truly comfortable environment. Guests have a choice of restaurants for memorable dining. Outstanding, freshly prepared cusine, with seasonal changes to the menu, is served either in the intimate atmosphere of the oak beamed restaurant in part of the original Welsh Long-House, or in the light and airy Victorian dining room with its stunning views across the valleys. Pre and after dinner drinks can be enjoyed in an elegant cocktail lounge. The Hotel is just a 20 minute drive from Cardiff and 15 minutes from the foothills of the Brecon Beacons.

Our inspector loved: The sympathetic restoration of this 17th century Welsh Long-House providing an oasis of comfort in spectacular surroundings.

YNYSHIR HALL

EGLWYSFACH, MACHYNLLETH, CEREDIGION SY20 8TA

Once owned by Queen Victoria, Ynyshir Hall is a captivating Georgian manor house that perfectly blends modern comfort and old-world elegance. Its 12 acres of landscaped gardens are set alongside the Dovey Estuary, one of Wales' most outstanding areas of natural beauty. The hotel is surrounded by the Ynyshir Bird Reserve. Hosts Rob and Joan Reen offer guests a warm welcome and ensure a personal service, the hallmark of a good family-run hotel. Period furniture and opulent fabrics enhance the 9 charming bedrooms. The suites, including a four-poster room and ground floor room, are particularly luxurious. The interiors are exquisitely furnished throughout with sofas, antiques, contemporary colour schemes, oriental rugs and original paintings. These works of art are the creation of Rob, an acclaimed artist. The artistry continues in the kitchen where local seafood, game and vegetables from the garden are used to create superb modern interpretations of classic French cuisine. The imaginative Michelin starred dishes prepared by Les Rennie, comprise a wonderful balance of colours, textures and flavours. Awarded The Catey's Independent Hotel of the Year 2002, Welsh Hotel of the Year 2001 by the AA . Winner of Johansens 'Most Excellent Restaurant Award 1999'. Landmarks include Cader Idris, Wales' 2nd highest mountain. Closed in January.

Our inspector loved: *The pan fried fois gras- what a dish!*

Directions: Off main road between Aberystwyth and Machynlleth.

Web: www.johansens.com/ynyshirhall
E-mail: info@ynyshir-hall.co.uk
Tel: 01654 781209
Fax: 01654 781366

Price Guide:
single £110–£180
double/twin £125–£180
suite £210–£275

443

BODYSGALLEN HALL

LLANDUDNO, NORTH WALES LL30 1RS

Directions: On A470 1 mile from the intersection with the A55. Llandudno is a mile further on the A470.

Web: www.johansens.com/bodysgallenhall
E-mail: info@bodysgallen.com
Tel: 01492 584466
Fax: 01492 582519

Price Guide:
single £109–£180
double/twin £145–£260
suite £170–£270

Bodysgallen Hall, owned and restored by Historic House Hotels, lies at the end of a winding drive in 200 acres of wooded parkland and beautiful formal gardens. Magnificent views encompass the sweep of the Snowdonia range of mountains and the hotel looks down on the imposing medieval castle at Conwy. This Grade I listed house was built mainly in the 17th century, but the earliest feature is a 13th century tower, reached by a narrow winding staircase, once used as a lookout for soldiers serving the English kings of Conwy and now a safe place from which to admire the fabulous views. The hotel has 19 spacious bedrooms in the house and 16 delightful cottage suites in the grounds. Two of the finest rooms in the house are the large oak-panelled entrance hall and the first floor drawing room, both with splendid fireplaces and mullioned windows. The restaurant has been awarded 4 RAC Dining Awards and menus feature delicious dishes using fresh local ingredients. The Bodysgallen Spa comprises a spacious swimming pool, steam room, sauna, solaria, gym, beauty salons and a club room. The hotel is ideally placed for visiting the many historic castles and stately homes in North Wales. Famous golf courses adorn the coastline. Bodysgallen Hall is a member of Relais & Chateaux Hotels.

Our inspector loved: The luxury and facilties of this historic hotel.

St Tudno Hotel & Restauarant

NORTH PROMENADE, LLANDUDNO LL30 2LP

Celebrating its 30th year under the ownership of Janette and Martin Bland, this is without doubt one of the most delightful small hotels to be found on the coast of Britain. St. Tudno Hotel, a former winner of the Johansens Hotel of the Year Award for Excellence, offers a very special experience. Elegantly and lovingly furnished with meticulous attention to detail, the Hotel offers a particularly warm welcome from the owners and their caring, friendly staff. Each beautifully co-ordinated bedroom has been individually designed with many thoughtful extras, half are equipped with spa baths. The bar lounge and sitting room, which overlook the sea, have an air of Victorian charm. Regarded as one of Wales' leading restaurants, the air-conditioned Garden Room has won 3 AA Rosettes for its excellent cuisine for the ninth consecutive year. This AA Red Star Hotel has won a host of other prestigious awards: Best Seaside Resort Hotel in Great Britain; Welsh Hotel of the Year; national winner of the AA's Warmest Welcome Award; the British Tea Council Tea Places Award of Excellence 1996–1998; the AA's Wine Award for Wales and even an accolade for having the Best Hotel Loos in Britain! St. Tudno is ideally situated for visits to Snowdonia, Conwy and Caernarfon Castles, Bodnant Gardens and Anglesey. Golf, riding, swimming, dry-slope skiing and tobogganing can all be enjoyed locally.

Directions: On the promenade opposite the pier entrance and gardens. Car parking and garaging is available for up to 12 cars.

Web: www.johansens.com/sttudno
E-mail: sttudnohotel@btinternet.com
Tel: 01492 874411
Fax: 01492 860407

Llandudno
Colwyn Bay
Betws-y-Coed

Price Guide:
single from £70
double/twin £100–£196
suite from £220

Our inspector loved: *Its wonderful, caring way with all its guests.*

PALÉ HALL

PALÉ ESTATE, LLANDDERFEL, BALA, GWYNEDD LL23 7PS

Directions: Situated off the B4401 Corwen to Bala Road, Palé Hall is 4 miles from Llandrillo.

Web: www.johansens.com/palehall
E-mail: enquiries@palehall.co.uk
Tel: 01678 530285
Fax: 01678 530220

Price Guide:
single £69–£125
double/twin £100–£185

Set in acres of peaceful, tranquil woodland on the edge of Snowdonia National Park, Palé Hall is a magnificent building, beautifully preserved by its current owners and gives guests the opportunity to sample true country house lifestyle. Shooting parties are a regular occurrence on the surrounding estates, whilst clay shooting and fishing on The Dee are available on site. A new venture with Land Rover Experience also enables guests to experience off road driving in their preferred choice of 4 wheel drive, whilst the less adventurous can walk for miles in the Hotel's beautiful estate. The staff at Palé Hall carefully maintain the beautiful period interior of the building including the galleried staircase and painted ceilings, which have survived largely due to the Hotel's unusual electricity system. Supplied by a turbine powered by water, the Hotel's 18 electric fires were left burning during 22 years of unoccupancy! Queen Victoria and Winston Churchill have stayed at the Hall. The 17 individually designed suites with luxurious bathrooms have breathtaking views of the surrounding scenery. The restaurant has 2 AA Rosettes and serves seasonal table d'hôte menus complemented by a fine wine selection. Exclusive use is available for conferences, product launches and weddings.

Our inspector loved: Its tranquillity, an oasis away from the pressures of modern life.

PENMAENUCHAF HALL

PENMAENPOOL, DOLGELLAU, GWYNEDD LL40 1YB

Climbing the long tree lined driveway you arrive at Penmaenuchaf Hall to behold its idyllic setting. With stunning panoramic views across the spectacular Mawddach Estuary and wooded mountain slopes in the distance, this handsome Victorian mansion is truly an exceptional retreat. Set within the Snowdonia National Park, the 21-acre grounds encompass lawns, a formal sunken rose garden, a water garden and woodland. The beautiful interiors feature oak and mahogany panelling, stained-glass windows, log fires in winter, polished Welsh slate floors and freshly cut flowers. There are 12 luxurious bedrooms, some with four-poster and half-tester beds and all with interesting views. In the restaurant guests can choose from an imaginative menu prepared with the best seasonal produce and complemented by an extensive list of wines. An elegant panelled dining room can be used for private dinners or meetings. Penmaenuchaf Hall is perfect for a totally relaxed holiday. For recreation, guests can fish for trout and salmon along ten miles of the Mawddach River or take part in a range of water sports. They can also enjoy scenic walks, visit sandy beaches and historic castles and take trips on narrow-gauge railways.

Our inspector loved: The warmth of welcome given to guest arriving for lunch.

Directions: The hotel is off the A493 Dolgellau–Tywyn road, about two miles from Dolgellau.

Web: www.johansens.com/penmaenuchafhall
E-mail: relax@penhall.co.uk
Tel: 01341 422129
Fax: 01341 422787

Price Guide:
single £75–£115
double/twin £116–£176

PORTMEIRION AND CASTELL DEUDRAETH

PORTMEIRION, GWYNEDD LL48 6ET

Directions: Portmeirion is signposted off the A487 mid-way between Penrhyndeudrath and Porthmadog.

Web: www.johansens.com/portmerion
E-mail: hotel@portmeirion–village.com
Tel: 01766 770000
Fax: 01766 771331

Price Guide: (room only)
single £100–£140
double/twin £120–£180
suite £150–£230

Portmeirion is a private village created by Welsh architect Sir Clough Williams-Ellis from 1926 to 1976. His aim was to show how a naturally beautiful place could be developed without spoiling its original charm. Portmeirion attracted a celebrated clientèle from the start – writers such as George Bernard Shaw, H G Wells, Bertrand Russell and Noel Coward were habitués. The village contains several interesting shops and a beauty salon and is surrounded by acres of sub-tropical woodlands and miles of sandy beaches. The hotel is based upon the Victorian mansion facing the estuary which houses the main restaurant, bar and several lounges. The village accommodation also contains several oak-panelled conference rooms, which are also licensed for civil weddings. During 2000, the hotel gained the Wales Tourist Board's top five star grading. Of Portmeirion's 51 rooms, 14 are located in the hotel's main building, 26 in the village and 11 in Castell Deudraeth, (pictured left). Castell Deudraeth, located mid-way along Portmeirion's drive, also has a brasserie-style restaurant and bar together with exhibition facilities and a Victorian garden.

Our inspector loved: *The magical setting and contrasting options of accommodation.*

THE TREARDDUR BAY HOTEL

LON ISALLT, TREARDDUR BAY, ANGLESEY LL65 2UN

For both business traveller and holidaymaker, here is one of the most delightful retreats to be found on the Anglesey coast. The comfortable and welcoming Trearddur Bay Hotel is situated opposite a 'Blue Flag Beach' and enjoys panoramic views across the sandy bay. This prime location is conveniently just 1³/₄ miles from the fully completed A55 North Wales Expressway, which makes the Hotel a comfortable drive from the Midlands, Yorkshire and the North West. Guests have the choice of a variety of sporting and leisure facilities from kayaking, diving and sailing to bird watching, walking and golf. Close by are places of historical interest such as a medieval chapel, Beaumaris Castle and a Celtic burial mound. For a day out with a difference, take the 99 minute fast ferry service to Ireland from the nearby port of Holyhead. Inside the Hotel's sparkling white exterior are spacious en suite bedrooms, with first-class furnishings and facilities. All of the 16 charming studio suites have sea views and many boast their own private balconies. Morning coffee and afternoon tea are served in a relaxing lounge, while aperitifs can be enjoyed in an elegant cocktail bar as a prelude to sampling culinary delights from the restaurant's extensive table d'hôte menu. A heated indoor swimming pool is a popular alternative to the Irish Sea.

Our inspector loved: Dining in the restaurant overlooking the bay whilst enjoying the beautifully cooked local fish.

Directions: From Bangor, when the A55 Expressway terminates at Holyhead, at the first roundabout turn left onto the B4545, signposted Trearddur. Continue for 1³/₄ miles. Turn right at the Power Garage onto Lon Isallt. The Hotel is 350 yards on the right.

Web: www.johansens.com/trearddurbay
E-mail: enquiries@trearddurbayhotel.co.uk
Tel: 01407 860301
Fax: 01407 861181

Price Guide:
single £82–£105
double/twin £120–£150
studio suite £140

LLANSANTFFRAED COURT HOTEL

LLANVIHANGEL GOBION, ABERGAVENNY, MONMOUTHSHIRE NP7 9BA

Llansantffraed Court is a perfect retreat from the fast pace of modern life. This elegant Georgian-style country house hotel, part of which dates back to the 14th century, is set in spacious grounds on the edge of the Brecon Beacons and the Wye Valley. Guests are provided with the highest level of personal, yet unobtrusive service. Most of the tastefully decorated and luxuriously furnished bedrooms offer views over the hotel's garden, and ornamental trout lake. While one has a four poster bed, others feature oak beams and dormer windows. An excellent reputation is enjoyed by the 2 AA Rosette restaurant; the menus reflect the changing seasons and the availability of fresh local produce. Exquisite cuisine is complemented by fine wines. Afternoon tea can be taken in the lounge, where guests enjoy a blazing log fire during the cooler months and savour the views of the South Wales countryside. A range of excellent facilities is available for functions, celebrations and meetings. Llansantffraed Court is an ideal base for exploring the diverse history and beauty of this area and there are plenty of opportunities to take advantage of energetic or relaxing pursuits, including, golf, trekking, walking, and salmon and trout fishing.

Directions: From M4 J24 (Via A449) off B4598 (formerly A40 old road) Leave A40 D/C at Abergavenny or Raglan. Follow signs to Clytha and the hotel is approx 4½ miles away.

Web: www.johansens.com/llansantffraedcourt
E-mail: reception@llch.co.uk
Tel: 01873 840678
Fax: 01873 840674

Price Guide:
single from £72
double/twin from £90
suites £157

Our inspector loved: *This elegant Georgian hotel surrounded by rolling parkland as far as the eye can see.*

LAMPHEY COURT HOTEL

LAMPHEY, NR TENBY, PEMBROKESHIRE SA71 5NT

This magnificent Georgian mansion, is idyllically situated in acres of grounds bordered by the beautiful Pembrokeshire National Park and just one mile from some of Britain's finest coastal scenery and beaches. Warm, friendly and efficient service is enriched by comfortable furnishings and decor. There are deluxe and superior bedrooms within the hotel and purpose built Coach House studios provide the extra space required by families. The restaurant serves traditional flavours and local produce including such pleasures as Teifi salmon and Freshwater Bay lobster. Lighter meals and snacks can be taken in the elegant Conservatory. The wide range of facilities in the superb leisure centre include an indoor heated swimming pool, jacuzzi, sauna and a gymnasium. There are aerobics classes, yoga, fitness programmes and beauty therapy and massage by appointment. Golf, sailing, fishing and yacht charter are all nearby. Well worth a visit is picturesque Tenby, the cliffside chapel of St Govan's, the Bishops Palace at Lamphey and Pembroke's impressive castle.

Our inspector loved: *The extensive leisure centre offering an indoor swimming pool, well equipped gymnasium, sauna and solarium.*

Directions: From M4, exit at Junction 49 onto the A48 to Carmarthen. Then follow the A477 and turn left at Milton Village for Lamphey.

Web: www.johansens.com/courtpembroke
E-mail: info@lampheycourt.co.uk
Tel: 01646 672273
Fax: 01646 672480

Price Guide:
single £74–£85
double/twin £100–£140

Warpool Court Hotel

ST DAVID'S, PEMBROKESHIRE SA62 6BN

Directions: The hotel is signposted from St David's town centre.

Web: www.johansens.com/warpoolcourt
E-mail: warpool@enterprise.net
Tel: 01437 720300
Fax: 01437 720676

Price Guide:
single from £75
double/twin from £132

Originally built as St David's Cathedral Choir School in the 1860s, Warpool Court enjoys spectacular scenery at the heart of the Pembrokeshire National Park, with views over the coast and St Bride's Bay to the islands beyond. First converted to a hotel over 40 years ago, continuous refurbishment has ensured all its up-to-date comforts are fit for the new century. All 25 bedrooms have immaculate en suite bathrooms and most enjoy sea views. The 2 AA Rosette restaurant enjoys a splendid reputation. Imaginative menus, including vegetarian, offer a wide selection of modern and traditional dishes. Local produce, including Welsh lamb and beef, is used whenever possible, with crab, lobster, sewin and sea bass caught just off the coast. Salmon and mackerel are smoked on the premises. The hotel gardens are ideal for a peaceful stroll or an after-dinner drink in the summer. There is a covered heated swimming pool (open April to end of October) and all-weather tennis court in the grounds. A path from the hotel leads straight on to the Pembrokeshire Coastal Path, with its rich variety of wildlife and spectacular scenery. Boating and water sports are available locally. St David's Peninsula offers a wealth of history and natural beauty and has inspired many famous artists. closed in January.

Our inspector loved: *The spectacular views of the coast from the dining room complementing the superb 2 Rosette cuisine.*

PENALLY ABBEY

PENALLY, TENBY, PEMBROKESHIRE SA70 7PY

Penally Abbey, a beautiful listed Pemrokeshire country house, offers comfort and hospitality in a secluded setting by the sea. Standing in five acres of gardens and woodland on the edge of Pembrokeshire National Park, the hotel overlooks Carmarthen Bay and Caldey Island. The bedrooms in the main building and in the adjoining coach house are well furnished, many with four-poster beds. The emphasis is on relaxation – enjoy a late breakfast and dine at leisure. Fresh seasonal delicacies are offered in the candlelit restaurant, with its chandeliers and colonnades. Guests can enjoy a game in the snooker room or relax in the elegant sunlit lounge, overlooking the terrace and gardens. In the grounds there is a wishing well and a ruined chapel – the last surviving link with the hotel's monastic past. Water-skiing, surfing, sailing, riding and parascending are available nearby. Sandy bays and rugged cliffs are features of the Pembrokeshire coastal park.

Our inspector loved: *The gothic splendour of the hotel with its magnificent sea views over Tenby golf course and Carmarthen Bay.*

Directions: Penally Abbey is situated adjacent to the church on Penally village green.

Fishguard

Tenby

Pembroke

Web: www.johansens.com/penallyabbey
E-mail: penally.abbey@btinternet.com
Tel: 01834 843033
Fax: 01834 844714

Price Guide:
single £128
double/twin £128–£144
suite £144

NANT DDU LODGE HOTEL

CWM TAF, BRECON BEACONS NR BRECON, POWYS, WALES CF48 2HY

Directions: On the A470, 12 miles south of Brecon, 6 miles north of Merthyr Tydfil.

Web: www.johansens.com/nantddulodge
E-mail: enquiries@nant-ddu-lodge.co.uk
Tel: 01685 379111
Fax: 01685 377088

Price Guide:
single £55–£68
double/twin £70–£90

Welshpool

Llandrindod Wells

Brecon

This award-winning country hotel and inn offers excellent value for money in the lovely unspoilt heart of the Brecon Beacons National Park. Its proprietors, the Ronson family, extend a warm welcome and the bustling, informal atmosphere has proved to be popular since they began running the Nant Ddu in 1992. The Nant Ddu is renowned for its exceptional contemporary décor and superb cuisine. Each individually designed bedroom displays inventiveness and style, and the very best are the new river rooms which come complete with queen size or four poster beds, sofas and video players. An atmospheric bar provides an intimate environment for drinking and eating, as food can be served here or in the Bistro style restaurant. The extensive menu offers a surprising array of traditional and creative dishes, and changes daily according to the availability of top quality ingredients. Views from the hotel are spectacular, and it boasts its own well kept lawns which broaden out into the green hills of the surrounding area. Country walks are a must, but there is also much to explore in Wales' many castles and cathedrals. For shopping, Cardiff city centre is just 35 minutes away. A luxury health spa with 18m pool, hydropool, gym and treatment rooms wiil be available in February 2003.

Our inspector loved: *The modern and vibrant décor.*

LLANGOED HALL

LLYSWEN, BRECON, POWYS, WALES LD3 0YP

The history of Llangoed Hall dates back to 560 AD when it is thought to have been the site of the first Welsh Parliament. Inspired by this legend, the architect Sir Clough Williams-Ellis, transformed the Jacobean mansion he found here in 1914 into an Edwardian country house. Situated deep in a valley of the River Wye, surrounded by a walled garden, the hotel commands magnificent views of the Black Mountains and Brecon Beacons beyond. The rooms are warm and welcoming, furnished with antiques and oriental rugs and on the walls, an outstanding collection of paintings acquired by the owner, Sir Bernard Ashley. The luxurious and spacious bedrooms enjoy fine views of the Wye Valley. Llangoed's restaurant is one of the principal reasons for going there. Classic but light, the Michelin starred menus represent the very best of modern cuisine, complemented by a cellar of more than 300 wines. Exclusive use of the entire hotel can be made available for board meetings. Outdoor pursuits include golf, riding, shooting and some of the best mountain walking and gliding in Britain. For expeditions, there are Hay-on-Wye and its bookshops, the border castles, Hereford and Leominster. Children over 8 are welcome. There are 3 heated kennels for dogs. The hotel is a member of Welsh Rarebits.

Our inspector loved: Its aristocratic faded grandeur.

Directions: 9 miles west of Hay, 11 miles north of Brecon on A470

Web: www.johansens.com/llangoedhall
E-mail: Llangoed_Hall_Co_Wales_UK@compuserve.com
Tel: 01874 754525
Fax: 01874 754545

Price Guide:
single from £110
double/twin from £145
suite from £295

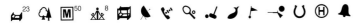

GLIFFAES COUNTRY HOUSE HOTEL

CRICKHOWELL, POWYS NP8 1RH

Directions: Gliffaes is signposted from the A40, 2½ miles west of Crickhowell.

Web: www.johansens.com/gliffaescountryhouse
E-mail: calls@gliffaeshotel.com
Tel: 01874 730371
Fax: 01874 730463

Price Guide:
single from £57–£77.50
double/twin £119–£170

Visitors may be surprised to discover a hotel featuring distinctive Italianate architecture midway between the Brecon Beacons and the Black Mountains. Gliffaes Country House Hotel is poised 150 feet above the River Usk and commands glorious views of the surrounding hills and valley. The elegantly furnished, Regency style drawing room is an ideal place to relax and leads to a large conservatory and on to the terrace, from which guests may enjoy the magnificent scenery. In addition to a panelled sitting room, there is a billiard room with a full-size table. In the dining room modern British style cuisine combines with local produce to create an imaginative daily changing menu. The Gliffaes fishery includes every type of water, from slow-flowing flats to fast-running rapids, on 3½ miles of the River Usk renowned for its wild brown trout and salmon fishing. The 33 acre hotel grounds have rare trees and shrubs as well as lawns for putting and croquet. There are two Golf courses within easy reach. Riding can be arranged nearby. Open throughout the year. There are now conference facilities available in the grounds. Cardiff and Bristol airports are within a 50 mile radius.

Our inspector loved: *The view overlooking the river, and the carpet of wild flowers on the path to the waters edge.*

LAKE VYRNWY HOTEL

LAKE VYRNWY, LLANWDDYN, MONTGOMERYSHIRE SY10 0LY

High on the hillside within 24,000 acres the Hotel commands breathtaking views of mountains, lakes and moorland. An R.S.P.B. sanctuary, the estate provides a wealth of wildlife and represents true peace and tranquillity, surrounded by lawns, an abundance of rhododendrons, woods and meadowlands. Built in 1860, its heritage has been maintained for over a hundred years as a retreat for all lovers of nature and fine dining. All 35 bedrooms are individually furnished and decorated, many with antiques and some have jacuzzis, balconies, four posters or suites. Dedicated meeting and private dining facilities are available and the new lounge has access onto an open deck terrace offering wonderful views over the lake. A Taste of Wales member and the 2 Rosettes awarded candlelit restaurant offers a seasonally changing menu; everything from the marmalade to the petits-fours are created in the Vyrnwy kitchens. Lighter informal lunches and afternoon teas are served overlooking a unique view. With 24,000 acres of sporting rights the Hotel owns some of Wales' best fishing. Other persuits include sailing, cycling, tennis, quad trekking, clay shooting, archery and some beautiful walking trails. Riders can bring their own horses, which can be accommodated in the livery and kennels for dogs are also available.

Our inspector loved: A location second to none with an ambiance to match.

Directions: From Shrewsbury take the A458 to Welshpool, then turn right onto B4393 just after Ford (signposted to Lake Vyrnwy 28 miles).

Web: www.johansens.com/lakevyrnwy
E-mail: res@lakevyrnwy.com
Tel: 01691 870 692
Fax: 01691 870 259

Welshpool

Llandrindod Wells

Brecon

Price Guide:
single £90–£155
double/twin £120–£190
suite £190–£220

457

THE LAKE COUNTRY HOUSE

LLANGAMMARCH WELLS, POWYS LD4 4BS

Directions: From the A483, follow signs to Llangammarch Wells and then to the hotel.

Web: www.johansens.com/lakecountryhouse
E-mail: info@lakecountryhouse.co.uk
Tel: 01591 620202
Fax: 01591 620457

Price Guide:
single/double/twin £135–£160
suite £185–£215

Welshpool

Llandrindod Wells

Brecon

A welcoming Welsh Country house set in its own 50 acres with rhododendron lined pathways, riverside walks and a large well stocked trout lake. Within the hotel, airy rooms filled with fine antiques, paintings and fresh flowers make this the perfect place to relax. Delicious home-made teas are served everyday beside log fires. From the windows, ducks and geese can be glimpsed wandering in the gardens which cascade down to the river. In the award winning restaurant, fresh produce and herbs from the gardens are used for seasonal Country House menus, complemented by one of the finest wine lists in Wales. Each of the supremely comfortable bedrooms or suites with beautifully appointed sitting rooms are furnished with the thoughtful attention to details seen throughout the hotel. Guests can fish for trout or salmon on the four miles of river which runs through the grounds and the 3 acre lake regularly yields trout of five pounds and over. The grounds are a haven for wildlife: herons, dippers and kingfishers skim over the river, there are badgers in the woods and swans and waterfowl abound. There is a large billiard room in the hotel and a 9 hole par three golf course, tennis court, croquet lawn and putting green. Awarded an AA 3 Red star and RAC Blue Ribbon.

Our inspector loved: *The excellent team, who make this a very pleasant hotel full of history.*

MISKIN MANOR COUNTRY HOUSE HOTEL

MISKIN, NR CARDIFF CF72 8ND

Although its history dates back to the 11th century, Miskin Manor first became a hotel only in 1986, following extensive restoration and refurbishment. Only 10 minutes' drive from central Cardiff and Cardiff Bay and set amid 22 acres of undisturbed parkland, criss-crossed with streams, peace and seclusion are guaranteed. The uncommonly spacious reception rooms have fine fireplaces, panelled walls and elaborate plasterwork ceilings, all enhanced by rich drapery and comfortable furniture. All of the bedrooms have en suite bathrooms and full facilities. In the 1920s, one of the de luxe suites was occupied by the Prince of Wales (later King Edward VIII), a room which is now aptly named the Prince of Wales suite. First-class Welsh cuisine is served in the restaurant, awarded an AA Rosette and complemented by a comprehensive wine list. Just a short walk away from the hotel, within the grounds, the popular Health Club boasts a glass-backed squash court, badminton, swimming pool and extensive gymnasium, while more gentle pursuits are provided by the solarium, sauna and steam room as well as refreshment facilities and a crèche. Celebrations, conferences and functions can be catered for, with professional and quality services assured.

Our inspector loved: The inspector loved the ambience of this friendly hotel, rich with character from the superb restorations of their 11th century origins.

Directions: From junction 34 of the M4, towards Llantrisant. Drive is ¼ a mile north of the M4.

Web: www.johansens.com/miskinmanorcountryhouse
E-mail: info@miskin–manor.co.uk
Tel: 01443 224204
Fax: 01443 237606

Price Guide:
single from £94
double/twin £126–£136.50
suite £152.50–£195

Tchibo,
Awaken the senses...

Fresh ground coffee, and equipment solutions wherever, whenever

Contact

Local Call 0845 600 8244   Fax 01372 748196   E-mail sales@tchibo.co.uk

Tchibo Coffee International, Tchibo House, Blenheim Road, Epsom, Surrey KT19 9AP www.tchibo.co.uk

Tchibo

MINI LISTINGS COUNTRY HOUSES

Condé Nast Johansens are delighted to recommend over 280 country houses, small hotels and inns across Great Britain.
Call 0800 269 397 or see the order forms on page 517 to order guides.

England

Bath & North East Somerset

Apsley House - 141 Newbridge Hill, Bath,
Somerset BA1 3PT. Tel: 01225 336966

Bath Lodge Hotel - Norton St Philip, Bath,
Somerset BA2 7NH. Tel: 01225 723040

The Carpenters Arms - Stanton Wick, Nr Pensford,
Somerset BS39 4BX. Tel: 01761 490202

The County Hotel - 18/19 Pulteney Road, Bath,
Somerset BA2 4EZ. Tel: 01225 425003

Oldfields - 102 Wells Road, Bath, Somerset BA2 3AL.
Tel: 01225 317984

Tasburgh House - Warminster Road, Bath BA2 6SH.
Tel: 01225 425096

Villa Magdala - Henrietta Road, Bath, Somerset BA2 6LX.
Tel: 01225 466329

Berkshire

The Inn on the Green - The Old Cricket Common,
Cookham Dean, Berkshire SL6 9NZ. Tel: 01628 482638

The Leatherne Bottel Riverside Inn & Restaurant - The
Bridleway, Goring-On-Thames, Berkshire RG8 0HS.
Tel: 01491 872667

Cambridgeshire

Crown Lodge Hotel - Downham Road, Outwell, Wisbech,
Cambridgeshire PE14 8SE. Tel: 01945 773391

▼
Melbourn Bury - Melbourn, Cambridgeshire, Nr Royston
SG8 6DE. Tel: 01763 261151

Cheshire

Brook Meadow Hotel - Heath Lane, Childer Thornton,
Cheshire CH66 7NS. Tel: 0151 339 9350

Broxton Hall Country House Hotel - Whitchurch Road,
Broxton, Chester, Cheshire CH3 9JS. Tel: 01829 782321

Frogg Manor Hotel & Restaurant - Fullers Moor, Nantwich
Road, Broxton, Chester CH3 9JH. Tel: 01829 782629

Willington Hall Hotel - Willington, Nr Tarporley, Cheshire
CW6 0NB. Tel: 01829 752321

Cornwall

Boscundle Manor - Tregrehan, St Austell,
Cornwall PL25 3RL. Tel: 01726 813557

Cormorant On The River, Hotel & Riverside Restaurant -
Golant By Fowey, Cornwall PL23 1LL. Tel: 01726 833426

The Countryman At Trink Hotel - Old Coach Road, St Ives,
Cornwall TR26 3JQ. Tel: 01736 797571

Hell Bay Hotel - Bryher, Isles Of Scilly, Cornwall TR23 0PR.
Tel: 01720 422947

Higher Faugan Country House Hotel - Chywoone Hill,
Newlyn, Cornwall TR18 5NS. Tel: 01736 362076

Jubilee Inn - Pelynt, Nr Looe, Cornwall PL13 2JZ.
Tel: 01503 220312

The Old Quay House Hotel - 28 Fore Street, Fowey,
Cornwall PL23 1AQ. Tel: 01726 833302

The Port William - Trebarwith Strand, Nr Tintagel,
Cornwall PL34 0HB. Tel: 01840 770230

Tredethy House - Helland Bridge, Bodmin,
Cornwall PL30 4QS.

Trehaven Manor Hotel - Station Road, Looe,
Cornwall PL13 1HN. Tel: 01503 262028

Trehellas House Hotel & Restaurant - Washaway, Bodmin,
Cornwall PL30 3AD. Tel: 01208 72700

Trelawne Hotel – The Hutches Restaurant - Mawnan Smith,
Nr Falmouth, Cornwall TR11 5HS. Tel: 01326 250226

Trevalsa Court Hotel - School Hill, Mevagissey, St Austell,
Cornwall PL26 6TH. Tel: 01726 842468

Cumbria

Broadoaks Country House - Bridge Lane, Troutbeck,
Windermere, Cumbria LA23 1LA. Tel: 01539 445566

Crosby Lodge Country House Hotel - High Crosby, Crosby-
On-Eden, Carlisle, Cumbria CA6 4QZ. Tel: 01228 573618

Dale Head Hall Lakeside Hotel - Thirlmere, Keswick,
Cumbria CA12 4TN. Tel: 017687 72478

Fayrer Garden House Hotel - Lyth Valley Road, Bowness-
On-Windermere, Cumbria LA23 3JP. Tel: 015394 88195

Grey Friar Lodge - Clappersgate, Ambleside,
Cumbria LA22 9NE. Tel: 015394 33158

Hipping Hall - Cowan Bridge, Kirkby Lonsdale,
Cumbria LA6 2JJ. Tel: 015242 71187

The Leathes Head - Borrowdale, Keswick,
Cumbria CA12 5UY. Tel: 017687 77247

Linthwaite House Hotel - Crook Road, Bowness-On-
Windermere, Cumbria LA23 3JA. Tel: 015394 88600

Nanny Brow Country House Hotel & Restaurant -
Clappersgate, Ambleside, Cumbria LA22 9NF.
Tel: 015394 32036

The Queen's Head Hotel - Main Street, Hawkshead,
Cumbria LA22 0NS. Tel: 015394 36271

Sawrey House Country Hotel & Restaurant - Near Sawrey,
Hawkshead, Ambleside, Cumbria LA22 0LF.
Tel: 015394 36387

Swinside Lodge Hotel - Grange Road, Newlands, Keswick,
Cumbria CA12 5UE. Tel: 017687 72948

The Tarn End House Hotel - Talkin Tarn, Brampton,
Cumbria CA8 1LS. Tel: 016977 2340

Temple Sowerby House Hotel - Temple Sowerby, Penrith,
Cumbria CA10 1RZ. Tel: 017683 61578

Underwood - The Hill, Millom, Cumbria LA18 5EZ.
Tel: 01229 771116

White Moss House - Rydal Water, Grasmere,
Cumbria LA22 9SE. Tel: 015394 35295

Derbyshire

Biggin Hall - Biggin-By-Hartington, Buxton,
Derbyshire SK17 0DH. Tel: 01298 84451

Boar's Head Hotel - Lichfield Road, Sudbury,
Derbyshire DE6 5GX. Tel: 01283 820344

Buckingham's Hotel & Restaurant With One Table - 85
Newbold Road, Chesterfield, Derbyshire S41 7PU.
Tel: 01246 201041

The Chequers Inn - Froggatt Edge, Nr Calver,
Derbyshire S30 1ZB. Tel: 01433 630231

Dannah Farm Country House - Bowman's Lane, Shottle, Nr
Belper, Derbyshire DE56 2DR. Tel: 01773 550273/550630

Littleover Lodge Hotel - 222 Rykneld Road, Littleover,
Derby, Derbyshire DE23 7AN. Tel: 01332 510161

The Maynard Arms - Main Road, Grindleford,
Derbyshire S32 2HE. Tel: 01433 630321

▼
The Peacock Inn - Rowsley, Nr. Matlock,
Derbyshire DE4 2EB. Tel: 01629 733518

The Plough Inn - Leadmill Bridge, Hathersage,
Derbyshire S30 1BA. Tel: 01433 650319

Santo's Higham Farm - Main Road, Higham,
Derbyshire DE55 6EH. Tel: 01773 833812/3/4

The Wind In The Willows - Derbyshire Level, Glossop,
Derbyshire SK13 7PT. Tel: 01457 868001

Devon

Browns Hotel, Wine Bar & Brasserie - 80 West Street,
Tavistock, Devon PL19 8AQ. Tel: 01822 618686

Combe House Hotel & Restaurant - Gittisham, Honiton,
Nr Exeter, Devon EX14 3AD. Tel: 01404 540400

Coulsworthy House - Combe Martin, Devon EX34 0PD.
Tel: 01271 882813

The Edgemoor - Haytor Road, Bovey Tracey, South Devon
TQ13 9LE. Tel: 01626 832466

Hewitt's - Villa Spaldi - North Walk, Lynton,
Devon EX35 6HJ. Tel: 01598 752293

Home Farm Hotel - Wilmington, Nr Honiton,
Devon EX14 9JR. Tel: 01404 831278

Ilsington Country House Hotel - Ilsington Village, Near
Newton Abbot, Devon TQ13 9RR. Tel: 01364 661452

Kingston House - Staverton, Totnes, Devon TQ9 6AR.
Tel: 01803 762 235

Kitley House Hotel & Restaurant - The Kitley Estate,
Yealmpton, Plymouth, Devon PL8 2NW.
Tel: 01752 881555

The Lord Haldon Country Hotel - Dunchideock, Nr Exeter,
Devon EX6 7YF. Tel: 01392 832483

The New Inn - Coleford, Crediton, Devon EX17 5BZ.
Tel: 01363 84242

Percy's Country Hotel & Restaurant - Coombeshead Estate,
Virginstow, Devon EX21 5EA. Tel: 01409 211236

Preston House & Little's Restaurant - Saunton, Braunton,
North Devon EX33 1LG. Tel: 01271 890472

MINI LISTINGS COUNTRY HOUSES

Condé Nast Johansens are delighted to recommend over 280 country houses, small hotels and inns across Great Britain.
Call 0800 269 397 or see the order forms on page 517 to order guides.

The Rising Sun - Harbourside, Lynmouth, Devon EX35 6EG.
Tel: 01598 753223

The Sea Trout Inn - Staverton, Nr Totnes, Devon TQ9 6PA.
Tel: 01803 762274

▼

Yeoldon House Hotel - Durrant Lane, Northam,
Nr Bideford EX39 2RL. Tel: 01237 474400

Acorn Inn - Evershot, Dorset DT2 0JW. Tel: 01935 83228

The Eastbury Hotel - Long Street, Sherborne,
Dorset DT9 3BY. Tel: 01935 813131

Kemps Country House Hotel & Restaurant - East Stoke,
Wareham, Dorset BH20 6AL. Tel: 01929 462563

The Manor Hotel - West Bexington, Dorchester,
Dorset DT2 9DF. Tel: 01308 897616

Yalbury Cottage Hotel - Lower Bockhampton, Dorchester,
Dorset DT2 8PZ. Tel: 01305 262382

Durham

Grove House - Hamsterley Forest, Nr Bishop Auckland,
Co Durham DL13 3NL. Tel: 01388 488203

Horsley Hall - Eastgate, Nr Stanhope, Bishop Auckland,
Co. Durham DL13 2LJ. Tel: 01388 517239

East Sussex

The Granville - 124 Kings Road, Brighton BN1 2FA.
Tel: 01273 326302

Hooke Hall - High Street, Uckfield, East Sussex TN22 1EN.
Tel: 01825 761578

The Hope Anchor Hotel - Watch Bell Street, Rye,
East Sussex TN31 7HA. Tel: 01797 222216

Essex

The Cricketers - Clavering, Nr Saffron Walden,
Essex CB11 4QT. Tel: 01799 550442

The Crown House - Great Chesterford, Saffron Walden,
Essex CB10 1NY. Tel: 01799 530515 / 530257

The Pump House Apartment - 132 Church Street, Great
Burstead, Essex CM11 2TR. Tel: 01277 656579

Gloucestershire

Bibury Court - Bibury Court, Bibury,
Gloucestershire GL7 5NT. Tel: 01285 740337

Charlton Kings Hotel - Charlton Kings, Cheltenham,
Gloucestershire GL52 6UU. Tel: 01242 231061

The Green Dragon Inn - Cockleford, Nr Cowley,
Cheltenham, Gloucester GL53 9NW. Tel: 01242 870271

The Malt House - Broad Campden,
Gloucestershire GL55 6UU. Tel: 01386 840295

The New Inn At Coln - Coln St-Aldwyns, Nr Cirencester,
Gloucestershire GL7 5AN. Tel: 01285 750651

Three Choirs Vineyards Estate - Newent,
Gloucestershire GL18 1LS. Tel: 01531 890223

The White Hart Inn - High Street, Winchcombe,
Nr Cheltenham, Gloucestershire GL54 5LJ.
Tel: 01242 602359

The Wild Duck - Drakes Island, Ewen, Cirencester,
Gloucestershire GL7 6BY. Tel: 01285 770310

Greater Manchester

The White Hart Inn - 51 Stockport Road, Lydgate,
Saddleworth, Greater Manchester OL4 4YY.
Tel: 01457 872566

Hampshire

Gordleton Mill Inn - Silver Street, Hordle, Nr Lymington,
New Forest, Hampshire SO41 6DJ. Tel: 01590 682219

Langrish House - Langrish, Nr Petersfield,
Hampshire GU32 1RN. Tel: 01730 266941

New Mill Restaurant - New Mill Road, Eversley,
Hampshire RG27 0RA. Tel: 0118 973 2277

New Park Manor - Lyndhurst Road, Brockenhurst,
New Forest, Hampshire SO42 7QH. Tel: 01590 623467

The Nurse's Cottage - Station Road, Sway, Lymington,
Hampshire SO41 6BA. Tel: 01590 683402

Thatched Cottage Hotel & Restaurant - 16 Brookley Road,
Brockenhurst, New Forest, Hampshire SO42 7RR.
Tel: 01590 623090

Westover Hall - Park Lane, Milford-On-Sea,
Hampshire SO41 0PT. Tel: 01590 643044

Whitley Ridge Country House Hotel - Beaulieu Road,
Brockenhurst, New Forest, Hampshire SO42 7QL.
Tel: 01590 622354

Herefordshire

The Feathers Hotel - High Street, Ledbury,
Herefordshire HR8 1DS. Tel: 01531 635266

Glewstone Court - Nr Ross-On-Wye,
Herefordshire HR9 6AW. Tel: 01989 770367

The Steppes - Ullingswick, Nr Hereford,
Herefordshire HR1 3JG. Tel: 01432 820424

Wilton Court Hotel - Wilton, Ross-On-Wye,
Herefordshire HR9 6AQ. Tel: +44 (0)1989 562569

Hertfordshire

Redcoats Farmhouse Hotel And Restaurant - Redcoats
Green, Near Hitchin, Herts SG4 7JR. Tel: 01438 729500

Isle Of Wight

Rylstone Manor - Rylstone Gardens, Shanklin,
Isle Of Wight PO37 6RE. Tel: 01983 862806

Kent

The Abbot's Fireside Hotel - High Street, Elham, Near
Canterbury, Kent CT4 6TD. Tel: 01303 840265

The George Hotel - Stone Street, Cranbrook,
Kent TN17 3HE. Tel: 01580 713348

Howfield Manor - Chartham Hatch, Nr Canterbury,
Kent CT4 7HQ. Tel: 01227 738294

Ringlestone Inn and Farmhouse Hotel - Twixt Harrietsham
And Wormshill, Nr Maidstone, Kent ME17 1NX.
Tel: 01622 859900

Romney Bay House - Coast Road, Littlestone,
New Romney, Kent TN28 8QY. Tel: 01797 364747

Wallett's Court - West Cliffe, St Margaret's-At-Cliffe, Dover,
Kent CT15 6EW. Tel: 01304 852424

Lancashire

The Inn At Whitewell - Forest Of Bowland, Clitheroe,
Lancashire BB7 3AT. Tel: 01200 448222

Tree Tops Country House Restaurant & Hotel - Southport
Old Road, Formby, Nr Southport, Lancashire L37 0AB.
Tel: 01704 572430

Ye Horn's Inn - Horn's Lane, Goosnargh, Nr Preston,
Lancashire PR3 2FJ. Tel: 01772 865230

Leicestershire

▼

Abbots Oak - Warren Hills Road, Near Coalville,
Leicestershire LE67 4UY. Tel: 01530 832 328

Barnsdale Lodge - The Avenue, Rutland Water, Nr Oakham,
Rutland, Leicestershire LE15 8AH. Tel: 01572 724678

The Old Manor Hotel - 11-14 Sparrow Hill, Loughborough,
Leicestershire LE11 1BT. Tel: 01509 211228

Sutton Bonington Hall - Main Street, Sutton Bonington,
Loughborough, Leicestershire LE12 5PF.
Tel: 01509 672355

Lincolnshire

The Crown Hotel - All Saints Place, Stamford,
Lincolnshire PE9 2AG. Tel: 01780 763136

The Lea Gate Inn - Leagate Road, Coningsby,
Lincolnshire LN4 4RS. Tel: 01526 342370

Washingborough Hall - Church Hill, Washingborough,
Lincoln LN4 1BE. Tel: 01522 790340

London

Oak Lodge Hotel - 80 Village Road, Bush Hill Park, Enfield,
Middlesex EN1 2EU. Tel: 020 8360 7082

Mini Listings Country Houses

Condé Nast Johansens are delighted to recommend over 280 country houses, small hotels and inns across Great Britain.
Call 0800 269 397 or see the order forms on page 517 to order guides.

Mersyside

The Beresford - 1 Beresford Road, Oxton, Wirral CH43 1XQ.
Tel: 0151 651 0004

Norfolk

The Beeches Hotel And Victorian Gardens - 2–6 Earlham Road, Norwich, Norfolk NR2 3DB. Tel: 01603 621167

Beechwood Hotel - Cromer Road, North Walsham, Norfolk NR28 0HD. Tel: 01692 403231

Broom Hall Country Hotel - Richmond Road, Saham Toney, Thetford, Norfolk IP25 7EX. Tel: 01953 882125

Brovey Lair - Carbrooke Road, Ovington, Thetford, Norfolk IP25 6SD. Tel: 01953 882706

Caldecott Hall - Fritton, Great Yarmouth, Norfolk NR31 9EY. Tel: 01493 488488

Congham Hall - Grimston, King's Lynn, Norfolk PE32 1AH. Tel: 01485 600250

Elderton Lodge Hotel & Langtry Restaurant - Gunton Park, Thorpe Market, Nr North Walsham, Norfolk NR11 8TZ. Tel: 01263 833547

Felbrigg Lodge - Aylmerton, North Norfolk NR11 8RA. Tel: 01263 837588

The Great Escape Holiday Company - Docking, Kings Lynn, Norfolk PE31 8LY. Tel: 01485 518717

J.D. Young - 2-4 Market Place, Harleston, Norfolk IP20 9AD. Tel: 01379 852822

The Manor House - Barsham Road, Great Snoring, Norfolk NR21 0HP. Tel: 01328 820597

The Norfolk Mead Hotel - Coltishall, Norwich, Norfolk NR12 7DN. Tel: 01603 737531

The Old Rectory - 103 Yarmouth Road, Norwich, Norfolk NR7 0HF. Tel: 01603 700772

Petersfield House Hotel - Lower Street, Horning, Nr Norwich, Norfolk NR12 8PF. Tel: 01692 630741

The Roman Camp Inn - Holt Road, Aylmerton, Norwich, Norfolk NR11 8QD. Tel: 01263 838291

The Stower Grange - School Road, Drayton, Norfolk NR8 6EF. Tel: 01603 860210

Vere Lodge - South Raynham, Fakenham, Norfolk NR21 7HE. Tel: 01328 838261

The Victoria At Holkham - Park Road, Holkham, Wells-Next-The-Sea, Norfolk NR23 1RG. Tel: 01328 711008

The White Horse - Brancaster Staithe, Norfolk PE31 8BW. Tel: 01485 210262

North yorkshire

▼
The Austwick Country House Hotel & Restaurant - Austwick, Via Lancaster, North Yorkshire LA2 8BY.
Tel: 015242 51224

The Blue Lion - East Witton, Nr Leyburn, North Yorkshire DL8 4SN. Tel: 01969 624273

The Boar's Head Hotel - The Ripley Castle Estate, Harrogate, North Yorkshire HG3 3AY. Tel: 01423 771888

Dunsley Hall - Dunsley, Whitby, North Yorkshire YO21 3TL. Tel: 01947 893437

Hob Green Hotel And Restaurant - Markington, Harrogate, North Yorkshire HG3 3PJ. Tel: 01423 770031

The Red Lion - By The Bridge At Burnsall, Near Skipton, North Yorkshire BD23 6BU. Tel: 01756 720204

Rookhurst Country House Hotel - West End, Gayle, Hawes, North Yorkshire DL8 3RT. Tel: 01969 667454

Stow House Hotel - Aysgarth, Leyburn, North Yorkshire DL8 3SR. Tel: 01969 663635

The White Swan - The Market Place, Pickering, North Yorkshire YO18 7AA. Tel: 01751 472288

Northamptonshire

The Falcon Hotel - Castle Ashby, Northamptonshire NN7 1LF. Tel: 01604 696200

The Windmill At Badby - Main Street, Badby, Daventry, Northamptonshire NN11 6AN. Tel: 01327 702363

Northumberland

The Blue Bell Hotel - Market Place, Belford, Northumberland NE70 7NE. Tel: 01668 213543

The Otterburn Tower - Otterburn, Northumberland NE19 1NS. Tel: 01830 520620

Waren House Hotel - Waren Mill, Bamburgh, Northumberland NE70 7EE. Tel: 01668 214581

Nottinghamshire

Cockliffe Country House Hotel - Burnt Stump Country Park, Burnt Stump Hill, Nottinghamshire NG5 8PQ. Tel: 01159 680179

The Cottage Country House Hotel - Easthorpe Street, Ruddington, Nottingham NG11 6LA. Tel: 01159 846882

Oxfordshire

Fallowfields - Kingston Bagpuize With Southmoor, Oxfordshire OX13 5BH. Tel: 01865 820416

The George Hotel - High Street, Dorchester-On-Thames, Oxfordshire OX10 7HH. Tel: 01865 340404

Holcombe Hotel - High Street, Deddington, Nr Woodstock, Oxfordshire OX15 0SL. Tel: 01869 338274

The Jersey Arms - Middleton Stoney, Oxfordshire OX25 4AD. Tel: 01869 343234

The Kings Head Inn & Restaurant - The Green, Bledington, Nr Kingham, Oxfordshire OX7 6XQ. Tel: 01608 658365

The Lamb Inn - Sheep Street, Burford, Oxfordshire OX18 4LR. Tel: 01993 823155

The Lamb Inn - Shipton-Under-Wychwood, Oxfordshire OX7 6DQ. Tel: 01993 830465

The Mill & Old Swan - Minster Lovell, Nr Burford, Oxfordshire OX8 5RN. Tel: 01993 774441

The Shaven Crown Hotel - High Street, Shipton Under Wychwood, Oxfordshire OX7 6BA. Tel: 01993 830330

Shropshire

The Hundred House Hotel - Bridgnorth Road, Norton, Nr Shifnal, Telford, Shropshire TF11 9EE. Tel: 01952 730353

Pen-Y-Dyffryn Hall Hotel - Rhydycroesau, Nr Oswestry, Shropshire SY10 7JD. Tel: 01691 653700

Soulton Hall - Nr Wem, Shropshire SY4 5RS. Tel: 01939 232786

Stretton Hall - All Stretton, Church Stretton, Shropshire SY6 6HG. Tel: 01694 723224

Somerset

Andrew's On The Weir - Porlock Weir, Porlock, Somerset TA24 8PB. Tel: 01643 863300

▼
Ashwick Country House Hotel - Dulverton, Somerset TA22 9QD. Tel: 01398 323868

Beryl - Wells, Somerset BA5 3JP. Tel: 01749 678738

Chestnut House - Hectors Stone, Lower Road, Woolavington, Bridgwater, Somerset TA7 8EQ. Tel: 01278 683658

Compton House - Townsend, Axbridge, Somerset BS26 2AJ. Tel: 01934 733944

The Crown Hotel - Exford, Exmoor National Park, Somerset TA24 7PP. Tel: 01643 831554

Farthings Hotel & Restaurant - Hatch Beauchamp, Somerset TA3 6SG. Tel: 01823 480664

Glencot House - Glencot Lane, Wookey Hole, Nr Wells, Somerset BA5 1BH. Tel: 01749 677160

Langley House - Langley Marsh, Wiveliscombe, Somerset TA4 2UF. Tel: 01984 623318

Mount Somerset Country House Hotel - Henlade, Taunton, Somerset TA3 5NB. Tel: 01823 442500

The Old Rectory - Cricket Malherbie, Ilminster, Somerset TA19 0PW. Tel: 01460 54364

Porlock Vale House - Porlock Weir, Somerset TA24 8NY. Tel: 01643 862338

The Royal Oak Inn - Winsford, Exmoor National Park, Somerset EX24 7JE. Tel: 01643 851455

The Woodborough Inn - Sandford Road, Winscombe, Somerset BS25 1HD. Tel: 01934 844167

Woolverton House - Woolverton, Nr Bath, Somerset BA3 6QS. Tel: 01373 830415

Staffordshire

Oak Tree Farm - Hints Road, Hopwas, Nr Tamworth, Staffordshire B78 3AA. Tel: 01827 56807

Ye Olde Dog & Partridge - High Street, Tutbury, Burton-On-Trent, Staffordshire DE13 9LS. Tel: 01283 813030

MINI LISTINGS COUNTRY HOUSES

Condé Nast Johansens are delighted to recommend over 280 country houses, small hotels and inns across Great Britain. Call 0800 269 397 or see the order forms on page 517 to order guides.

Suffolk

Clarice House - Horringer Court, Horringer Road, Bury St. Edmunds, Suffolk IP29 5PH. Tel: 01284 705550

The George - The Green, Cavendish, Sudbury, Suffolk CO10 8BA. Tel: 01787 280248

The Plough Inn - Brockley Green, Nr Hundon, Sudbury, Suffolk CO10 8DT. Tel: 01440 786789

The Suffolk Golf & Country Club - Fornham St Genevieve, Bury St Edmunds, Suffolk IP28 6JQ. Tel: 01284 706777

Thornham Hall & Restaurant - Thornham Magna, Nr Eye, Suffolk IP23 8HA. Tel: 01379 783314

The White Horse Inn - Hollow Hill, Withersfield, Haverhill, Suffolk CB9 7SH. Tel: 01440 706081

Surrey

Chase Lodge - 10 Park Road, Hampton Wick, Kingston-Upon-Thames, Surrey KT1 4AS. Tel: 020 8943 1862

Stanhill Court Hotel - Stan Hill Road, Charlwood, Nr Horley, Surrey RH6 0EP. Tel: 01293 862166

Tyne & Wear

Horton Grange Country House Hotel - Berwick Hill, Ponteland, Newcastle Upon Tyne NE13 6BU. Tel: 01661 860686

Warwickshire

▼
Clarendon House - Old High Street, Kenilworth, Warwickshire CV8 1LZ. Tel: 01926 857668

Glebe Farm House - Loxley, Warwickshire CV35 9JW. Tel: 01789 842501

West Sussex

Burpham Country House Hotel - Old Down, Burpham, Nr Arundel, West Sussex BN18 9RJ. Tel: 01903 882160

The Chequers At Slaugham - Slaugham, Nr Handcross, West Sussex RH17 6AQ. Tel: 01444 400239/400996

Crouchers Country Hotel & Restaurant - Birdham Road, Apuldram, Near Chichester, West Sussex PO20 7EH. Tel: 01243 784995

Forge Hotel - Chilgrove, Chichester, West Sussex PO18 9HX. Tel: 01243 535333

The Half Moon Inn - Kirdford, Near Petworth, West Sussex RH14 0LT. Tel: 01403 820223

The Mill House Hotel - Mill Lane, Ashington, West Sussex RH20 3BX. Tel: 01903 892426

The Old Tollgate Restaurant And Hotel - The Street, Bramber, Steyning, West Sussex BN44 3WE. Tel: 01903 879494

West Yorkshire

The Rock Inn Hotel - Holywell Green, Halifax, West Yorkshire HX4 9BS. Tel: 01422 379721

The Shibden Mill Inn - Shibden Mill Fold, Shibden, Halifax, West Yorkshire HX3 7UL. Tel: 01422 365840

The Weavers Shed Restaurant With Rooms - Knowl Road, Golcar, Huddersfield, West Yorkshire HD7 4AN. Tel: 01484 654284

Wiltshire

The George Inn - Longbridge Deverill, Warminster, Wiltshire BA12 7DG. Tel: 01985 840396

Hinton Grange - Nr Dyrham, Hinton, Wiltshire SN14 8HG. Tel: 0117 937 2916

The Old Manor Hotel - Trowle, Bradford-On-Avon, Wiltshire BA14 9BL. Tel: 01225 777393

Rudloe Hall - Leafly Lane, Near Box, Wiltshire SN13 0PA. Tel: 01225 810555

Stanton Manor - Stanton Saint Quintin, Nr Chippenham, Wiltshire SN14 6DQ. Tel: 01666 837552

Widbrook Grange - Trowbridge Road, Bradford-On-Avon, Nr Bath, Wiltshire BA15 1UH. Tel: 01225 864750/863173

Worcestershire

The Mill at Harvington - Anchor Lane, Harvington, Evesham, Worcestershire WR11 8PA. Tel: 01386 870688

The Mount Pleasant Hotel - Belle Vue Terrace, Malvern, Worcestershire WR14 4PZ. Tel: 01684 561837

The White Lion Hotel - High Street, Upton-Upon-Severn, Nr Malvern, Worcestershire WR8 0HJ. Tel: 01684 592551

Channel Islands

Guernsey

Bella Luce Hotel & Restaurant - La Fosse, St Martins, Guernsey GY4 6EB. Tel: 01481 238764

La Favorita Hotel - Fermain Bay, Guernsey, GY4 6SD. Tel: 01481 235666

Les Douvres Hotel & Restaurant - Rue De La Motte, St Martins, Guernsey GY4 6ER. Tel: 01481 238731

Les Rocquettes Hotel - Les Gravees, St Peter Port, Guernsey GY1 1RN. Tel: 01481 722146

The White House - Herm Island, Guernsey GY1 3HR. Tel: 01481 722159

Jersey

Eulah Country House - Mont Cochon, St. Helier, Jersey JE2 3SA. Tel: 01534 626626

Sark

La Sablonnerie - Little Sark, Sark GY9 0SD. Tel: 01481 832061

Ireland

Clare

Hyland's Burren Hotel - Ballyvaughan, Co Clare. Tel: 00 353 65 7077037

Dublin

Aberdeen Lodge - 53-55 Park Avenue, Dublin Ireland. Tel: 00 353 1 283 8155

Galway

Ross Lake House Hotel - Rosscahill, Oughterard, Co Galway, Ireland. Tel: 00 353 91 550109

Kerry

Caragh Lodge - Caragh Lake, Co Kerry. Tel: 00 353 66 9769115

Emlagh House - Dingle, Co Kerry. Tel: 00 353 66 915 2345

Gorman's Clifftop House & Restaurant - Glaise Bheag, Ballydavid, Dingle Peninsula – Tralee, Co Kerry. Tel: 00 353 66 9155162

Killarney Royal Hotel - College Street, Killarney, Co Kerry. Tel: 00 353 64 31853

Sligo

Coopershill House - Riverstown, Co Sligo. Tel: 00 353 71 65108

Tipperary

Cashel Palace Hotel - Main Street, Cashel, Co Tipperary. Tel: 00 353 62 62707

Wexford

Kilmokea Country Manor & Gardens - Kilmokea – Gt. Island, Campile, Co Wexford. Tel: 00 353 51 388109

Scotland

Aberdeenshire

Maryculter House Hotel - South Deeside Road, Maryculter, Aberdeen AB12 5GB. Tel: 01224 732124

Balgonie Country House - Braemar Place, Ballater, Royal Deeside, Aberdeenshire AB35 5NQ. Tel: 013397 55482

MINI LISTINGS COUNTRY HOUSES

Condé Nast Johansens are delighted to recommend over 280 country houses, small hotels and inns across Great Britain.
Call 0800 269 397 or see the order forms on page 517 to order guides.

Angus

Castleton House Hotel - Glamis, By Forfar, Angus DD8 1SJ. Tel: 01307 840340

Argyll & Bute

Ballachulish House - Ballachulish, Argyll PH49 4JX. Tel: 01855 811266

Barcaldine House - Barcaldine, Oban, Argyll PA37 1SG. Tel: 01631 720219

The Frog At Port Dunstaffnage - Dunstaffnage Marina, Connel, By Oban, Argyll PA37 1PX. Tel: 01631 567005

Kirkton House - Darleith Road, Cardross, Argyll & Bute G82 5EZ. Tel: 01389 841951

Loch Melfort Hotel & Restaurant - Arduaine, By Oban, Argyll PA34 4XG. Tel: 01852 200233

Royal Hotel - Tighnabruaich, Argyll PA21 2BE. Tel: 01700 811239

Western Isles Hotel - Tobermory, Isle Of Mull, Argyllshire PA75 6PR. Tel: 01688 302012

Dumfries & Galloway

Fernhill Hotel - Heugh Road, Portpatrick DG9 8TD. Tel: 01776 810220

Highland

Corriegour Lodge Hotel - Loch Lochy, By Spean Bridge, Inverness-Shire PH34 4EB. Tel: 01397 712685

Culduthel Lodge - 14 Culduthel Road, Inverness, Inverness-Shire IV2 4AG. Tel: 01463 240089

Hotel Eilean Iarmain - Sleat, Isle Of Skye IV43 8QR. Tel: 01471 833332

The Lodge On The Loch - Onich, Near Fort William, Highlands PH33 6RY. Tel: 01855 821237

Portland Arms Hotel - Lybster, Caithness KW3 6BS. Tel: 01593 721721

Perth & Kinross

Ardeonaig - South Loch Tay Side, By Killin, Perthshire FK21 8SU. Tel: 01567 820400

The Four Seasons Hotel - St Fillans, Perthshire PH6 2NF. Tel: 01764 685333

Knockendarroch House - Higher Oakfield, Pitlochry, Perthshire PH16 5HT. Tel: 01796 473473

The Lake Hotel - Port Of Menteith, Perthshire FK8 3RA. Tel: 01877 385258

Parklands Hotel & Acanthus Restaurant - St. Leonard's Bank, Perth PH2 8EB. Tel: 01738 622451

The Pend - 5 Brae Street, Dunkeld, Perthshire PH8 0BA. Tel: 01350 727586

Renfrewshire

Bowfield Hotel & Country Club - Howwood, Renfrewshire PA9 1LA. Tel: 01505 705225

South Ayrshire

Culzean Castle – The Eisenhower Apartment - Maybole, Ayrshire KA19 8LE. Tel: 01655 884455

Wales

Bridgend

The Great House - High Street, Laleston, Bridgend CF32 0HP. Tel: 01656 657644

Cardiff

Inn At The Elm Tree - St Brides Wentlooge, Nr Newport NP10 8SQ. Tel: 01633 680225

Ceredigion

Conrah Country House Hotel - Rhydgaled, Chancery, Aberystwyth, Ceredigion SY23 4DF. Tel: 01970 617941

Conwy

Castle Hotel - High Street, Conwy LL32 8DB. Tel: 01492 582 800

The Old Rectory Country House - Llanrwst Road, Llansanffraid Glan Conwy, Conwy LL28 5LF. Tel: 01492 580611

Sychnant Pass House - Sychnant Pass Road, Conwy LL32 8BJ. Tel: 01492 596868

Tan-Y-Foel - Capel Garmon, Nr Betws-Y-Coed, Conwy LL26 0RE. Tel: 01690 710507

Denbighshire

The West Arms Hotel - Llanarmon D C, Ceiriog Valley, Nr Llangollen, Denbighshire LL20 7LD. Tel: 01691 600665

Gwynedd

Bae Abermaw - Panorama Hill, Barmouth, Gwynedd LL42 1DQ. Tel: 01341 280550

▼

Bontddu Hall - Bontddu, Nr Barmouth, Gwynedd LL40 2UF. Tel: 01341 430661

Bryn Tegid Country House - Bala, Gwynedd LL23 7YG. Tel: 01678 521645

Plas Dolmelynllyn - Ganllwyd, Dolgellau, Gwynedd LL40 2HP. Tel: 01341 440273

Porth Tocyn Country House Hotel - Abersoch, Pwllheli, Gwynedd LL53 7BU. Tel: 01758 713303

Isle Of Anglesey

Ye Olde Bull's Head - Castle Street, Beaumaris, Isle Of Anglesey LL58 8AP. Tel: 01248 810329

Monmouthshire

The Bell At Skenfrith - Skenfrith, Monmouthshire NP7 8UH. Tel: 01600 750235

Parva Farmhouse And Restaurant - Tintern, Chepstow, Monmouthshire NP16 6SQ. Tel: 01291 689411

Pembrokeshire

Stone Hall Hotel & Restaurant - Welsh Hook, Haverfordwest, Pembrokeshire SA62 5NS. Tel: 01348 840212

Powys

Glangrwyney Court - Glangrwyney, Nr Crickhowell, Powys NP8 1ES. Tel: 01873 811288

Peterstone Court - Llanhamlach, Brecon, Powys LD3 7YB. Tel: 01874 665387

Swansea

Norton House Hotel And Restaurant - Norton Road, Mumbles, Swansea SA3 5TQ. Tel: 01792 404891

Vale Of Glamorgan

Egerton Grey - Porthkerry, Nr Cardiff, Vale Of Glamorgan CF62 3BZ. Tel: 01446 711666

HISTORIC HOUSES, CASTLES & GARDENS

Incorporating Museums & Galleries.

We are pleased to feature over 200 places to visit during your stay at a Condé Nast Johansens recommended hotel.

England

Bedfordshire

Cecil Higgins Art Gallery – Castle Lane, Bedford, Bedfordshire MK40 4AF. Tel: 01234 211222

John Bunyan Museum – Bunyan Meeting Free Church, Mill Street, Bedford, Bedfordshire MK40 3EU.
Tel: 01234 213722

Woburn Abbey – Woburn, Bedfordshire MK17 9WA.
Tel: 01525 290666

Berkshire

Savill Garden – Windsor Great Park, Berkshire.
Tel: 01753 847518

Taplow Court – Berry Hill, Taplow, Nr Maidenhead, Berkshire SL6 0ER. Tel: 01628 591209

Buckinghamshire

Hughenden Manor – High Wycombe, Buckinghamshire HP14 4LA. Tel: 01494 755573

Stowe Landscape Gardens – Stowe, Buckingham, Buckinghamshire MK18 5EH. Tel: 01280 818809

Waddesdon Manor – Waddesdon, Nr Aylesbury, Buckinghamshire HP18 0JH. Tel: 01296 653211

Cambridgeshire

Ely Cathedral – The Chapter House, The College, Ely, Cambridgeshire CB7 4DL. Tel: 01353 667735

King's College – Cambridge, Cambridgeshire CB2 1ST.
Tel: 01223 331212

Cheshire

Adlington Hall – Nr Macclesfield, Cheshire SK10 4LF.
Tel: 01625 820201

Dorfold Hall – Nantwich, Cheshire CW5 8LD.
Tel: 01270 625245

Dunham Massey Hall, Park & Garden – Dunham, Altrincham, Cheshire WA14 4SJ. Tel: 0161 941 1025

Ness Botanic Gardens – Ness, Neston, South Wirral, Cheshire CH64 4AY. Tel: 0151 353 0123

Norton Priory Museum & Gardens – Tudor Road, Manor Park, Cheshire WA7 1SX. Tel: 01928 569895

Tabley House Stately Home – Tabley House, Knutsford, Cheshire WA16 0HB. Tel: 01565 750151

County Durham

Raby Castle – Staindrop, Darlington, County Durham DL2 3AH. Tel: 01833 660207 / 660202

Cornwall

Jamaica Inn Museums – Jamaica Inn Courtyard, Bolventor, Launceston, Cornwall PL15 7TS. Tel: 0156 68 68 38

Cumbria

Holker Hall and Gardens – Cark-in-Cartmel, Nr Grange-over-Sands, Cumbria LA11 7PL. Tel: 01539 558328

Isel Hall – Cockermouth, Cumbria CA13 0QG.

Levens Hall & Gardens – Kendal, Cumbria LA8 0PD.
Tel: 01539 560321

Mirehouse & Keswick – Mirehouse, Keswick, Cumbria CA12 4QE. Tel: 01768 772287

Windermere Steamboat Centre – Rayrigg Road, Windermere, Cumbria LA23 1BN. Tel: 01539 445565

Wordsworth House – Main Street, Cockermouth, Cumbria CA13 9RX. Tel: 01900 824805

Derbyshire

Haddon Hall – Bakewell, Derbyshire DE45 1LA.
Tel: 01629 812855

Hardwick Hall – Doe Lea, Chesterfield, Derbyshire S44 5QJ.
Tel: 01246 850430

Melbourne Hall & Gardens – Melbourne, Derbyshire DE73 1EN. Tel: 01332 862502

Tissington Hall – Tissington, Ashbourne, Derbyshire DE6 1RA. Tel: 01335 352200

Devon

Cadhay – Ottery St Mary, Devon EX11 1QT.
Tel: 01404 812432

The Royal Horticultural Society, Garden Rosemoor – Great Torrington, North Devon EX38 8PH. Tel: 01805 624067

Dorset

Abbotsbury Sub Tropical Gardens – Bullers Way, Abbotsbury, Nr Weymouth, Dorset DT3 4LA.
Tel: 01305 871387

Chiffchaffs – Chaffeymoor, Bourton, Gillingham, Dorset SP8 5BY. Tel: 01747 840841

Compton Acres – 164 Canford Cliffs Road, Canford Cliffs, Poole, Dorset BH13 7ES. Tel: 01202 700778

Cranborne Manor Garden – Cranborne, Wimborne, Dorset BH21 5PP. Tel: 01725 517248

Deans Court Garden – Deans Court, Wimborne, Dorset BH21 1EE. Tel: 01202 886116

Mapperton – Mapperton, Beaminster, Dorset DT8 3NR.
Tel: 01308 862645

Minterne Gardens – Minterne Magna, Dorchester, Dorset DT2 7AU. Tel: 01300 341370

Sherborne Castle – New Road, Sherborne, Dorset DT9 5NR.
Tel: 01935 813182

Tolpuddle Museum – Tolpuddle, Dorset DT2 7EH.
Tel: 01305 848237

East Riding of Yorkshire

Burton Agnes Hall & Gardens – Burton Agnes, Driffield, East Riding of Yorkshire YO25 4NB. Tel: 01262 490324

East Sussex

Bentley Wildfowl & Motor Museum – Halland, Nr Lewes, East Sussex BN8 5AF. Tel: 01825 840573

Charleston – Firle, East Sussex BN8 6LL. Tel: 01323 811626

Firle Place – The Estate Office, Lewes, East Sussex BN8 6NS.
Tel: 01273 858043

Garden and Grounds of Herstmonceux Castle – Herstmonceux Castle, Hailsham, East Sussex BN27 1RN.
Tel: 01323 833816

Merriments Gardens – Hurst Green, East Sussex TN19 7RA.
Tel: 01580 860666

Pashley Manor Gardens – Ticehurst, East Sussex TN5 7HE.
Tel: 01580 200888

Wilmington Priory – Wilmington, Nr Eastbourne, East Sussex BN26 5SW. Tel: 01628 825920

Essex

Hedingham Castle – Bayley Street, Castle Hedingham, Halstead, Essex CO9 3DJ. Tel: 01787 460261

Ingatestone Hall – Hall Lane, Ingatestone, Essex CM4 9NR.
Tel: 01277 353010

The Gardens of Easton – Warwick House, Easton Lodge, Essex CM6 2BB. Tel: 01371 876979

The Sir Alfred Munnings Art Museum – Castle House, Dedham, Essex CO7 6AZ. Tel: 01206 322127

Gloucestershire

Chavenage House – Chavenage, Tetbury, Gloucestershire GL8 8XP. Tel: 01666 502329

Cheltenham Art Gallery & Museum – Clarence Street, Cheltenham, Gloucestershire GL50 3JT.
Tel: 01242 237431

Frampton Court – Frampton-on-Severn, Gloucestershire GL2 7DY. Tel: 01452 740267

Hardwicke Court – Gloucester, Gloucestershire GL2 4RS.
Tel: 01452 720212

Sezincote – Moreton-in-Marsh, Gloucestershire GL56 9AW.
Tel: 01386 700444

Greater Manchester

Heaton Hall – Heaton Park, Prestwich, Manchester, Greater Manchester M25 5SW.
Tel: 0161 773 1231/ 0161 235 8888

Ordsall Hall Museum – Ordsall Lane, Salford, Greater Manchester M5 4WU. Tel: 0161 872 0251

Salford Museums & Art Gallery – Peel Park, Crescent, Salford, Greater Manchester M5 4WU. Tel: 0161 736 2649

Wythenshawe Hall – Wythenshawe Park, Northenden, Manchester, Greater Manchester M23 0AB.
Tel: 0161 998 2331

Hampshire

Avington Park – Winchester, Hampshire SO21 1DB.
Tel: 01962 779260

Beaulieu – John Montagu Building, Beaulieu, Hampshire SO42 7ZN. Tel: 01590 612345

Broadlands – Romsey, Hampshire SO51 9ZD.
Tel: 01794 505010

Historic Houses, Castles & Gardens

Incorporating Museums & Galleries.

www.historichouses.co.uk

Gilbert White's House and The Oates Museum – Selborne, Hampshire GU34 3JH. Tel: 01420 511275

Greywell Hill House – Greywell, Hook, Hampshire RG29 1DG

Hall Farm – Bentworth, Alton, Hampshire GU34 5JU. Tel: 01420 564010

Mottisfont Abbey – Mottisfont, Nr Romsey, Hampshire SO51 0LP. Tel: 01794 340757

Pylewell Park – South Baddesley, Lymington, Hampshire SO41 5SJ. Tel: 01329 833130

The Vyne – The National Trust, Sherborne St John, Basingstoke, Hampshire RG24 9HL. Tel: 01256 881337

Uppark – South Harting, Petersfield, Hampshire GU31 5QR. Tel: 01730 825415

Herefordshire

Eastnor Castle – Eastnor, Ledbury, Herefordshire HR8 1RL. Tel: 01531 633160

Hertfordshire

Ashridge – Ringshall, Berkhamsted, Hertfordshire HP4 1NS. Tel: 01442 843491

Gorhambury – St. Albans, Hertfordshire AL3 6AH. Tel: 01727 855000

Hatfield House, Park & Gardens – Hatfield, Hertfordshire AL9 5NQ. Tel: 01707 287010

Isle of Wight

Deacons Nursery – Moor View, Godshill, Isle of Wight PO38 3HW. Tel: 01983 840750

Kent

Belmont House and Gardens – Belmont Park, Throwley, Nr Faversham, Kent ME13 0HH. Tel: 01795 890202

Cobham Hall – Cobham, Kent DA12 3BL. Tel: 01474 823371

Dickens House Museum – 2 Victoria Parade, Broadstairs, Kent CT10 1QS. Tel: 01843 863453

Finchcocks, Living Museum of Music – Goudhurst, Kent TN17 1HH. Tel: 01580 211702

Graham Clarke Up the Garden Studio – Green Lane, Boughton Monchelsea, Maidstone, Kent ME17 4LF. Tel: 01622 743938

Groombridge Place Gardens & Enchanted Forest – Groombridge, Tunbridge Wells, Kent TN3 9QG. Tel: 01892 861444

Hever Castle & Gardens – Edenbridge, Kent TN8 7NG. Tel: 01732 865224

Leeds Castle – Maidstone, Kent ME17 1PL. Tel: 01622 765400

Mount Ephraim Gardens – Hernhill, Nr Faversham, Kent ME13 9TX. Tel: 01227 751496

Penshurst Place & Gardens – Penshurst, Nr Tonbridge, Kent TN11 8DG. Tel: 01892 870307

Scotney Castle, Garden & Estate – Lamberhurst, Tunbridge Wells, Kent TN3 8JN. Tel: 01892 891081

Smallhythe Place – Smallhythe, Tenterden, Kent TN30 7NG. Tel: 01580 762334

The New College of Cobham – Cobhambury Road, Graves End, Kent DA12 3BG. Tel: 01474 814280

Lancashire

Stonyhurst College – Stonyhurst, Clitheroe, Lancashire BB7 9PZ. Tel: 01254 826345

Townhead House – Slaidburn, Via CLitheroe, Lancashire BBY 3AG

Leicestershire

Hazel Kaye's Garden & Nursery – 1700 Melton Rd, Rearsby, Leicester, Leicestershire LE7 4YR. Tel: 01664 424578

Stanford Hall – Stanford Park, Lutterworth, Leicestershire LE17 6DH. Tel: 01788 860250

Lincolnshire

Burghley House – Stamford, Lincolnshire PE9 3JY. Tel: 01780 752451

London

Burgh House – New End Square, Hampstead, London NW3 1LT. Tel: 020 7431 0144

Dulwich Picture Gallery – Gallery Road, London SE21 7AD. Tel: 020 8299 8711

Handel House Museum – 25 Brook Street, London W1K 4HB. Tel: 020 7495 1685

Imperial War Museum – Lambeth Road, London SE1 6HZ. Tel: 020 7416 5000

▼

Kensington Palace State Apartments – Kensington, London W8 4PX. Tel: 0870 751 5176

Leighton House Museum – 12 Holland Park Road, London W14 8LZ. Tel: 020 7602 3316

National Portrait Gallery – St Martin's Place, London WC2H 0HE. Tel: 020 7306 0055

Pitshanger Manor House – Walpole Park, Mattock Lane, Ealing, London W5 5EQ. Tel: 020 8567 1227

Royal Institution Michael Faraday Museum – 21 Albemarle Street, London W1S 4BS. Tel: 020 7409 2992

Sir John Soane's Museum – 13 Lincoln's Inn Fields, London WC2A 3BP. Tel: 020 7405 2107

Somerset House – Strand, London WC2R 1LA. Tel: 020 7845 4600

St. John's Gate – St John's Lane, Clerkenwell, London EC1M 4DA. Tel: 020 7324 4070

The Fan Museum – 12 Crooms Hill, Greenwich, London SE10 8ER. Tel: 020 8305 1441

The Traveller's Club – 106 Pall Mall, London SW1Y 5EP. Tel: 020 7930 8688

Tower of London – Tower Hill, London EC3N 4AB. Tel: 0870 751 5177

Middlesex

Orleans House Gallery – Riverside, Twickenham, Middlesex TW1 3DJ. Tel: 020 8892 0221

Strawberry Hill House – St. Mary's University College, Strawberry Hill, Waldegrave Road, Twickenham, Middlesex TW1 4SX. Tel: 020 8270 4114

Syon Park – London Road, Brentford, Middlesex TW8 8JF. Tel: 020 8560 0882

Norfolk

Hoveton Hall Gardens – Hoveton, Wroxham, Norfolk NR12 8RJ. Tel: 01603 782798

Walsingham Abbey Grounds – c/o The Estate Office, Little Walsingham, Norfolk NR22 6BP. Tel: 01328 820259 / 820510

Wolterton and Mannington Estate – Mannington Hall, Norwich, Norfolk NR11 7BB. Tel: 01263 584175

North Yorkshire

Castle Howard – York, North Yorkshire YO6 7DA. Tel: 01653 648333

Duncombe Park – Helmsley, York, North Yorkshire YO62 5EB. Tel: 01439 770213

Hovingham Hall – Hovingham, York, North Yorkshire YO62 4LU. Tel: 01653 628771

Ripley Castle – Ripley Castle Estate, Harrogate, North Yorkshire HG3 3AY. Tel: 01423 770152

Sion Hill Hall – Kirby Wiske, Thirsk, North Yorkshire YO7 4EU. Tel: 01845 587206

The Forbidden Corner – The Tupgill Park Estate, Coverham, Middleham, North Yorkshire DL8 4TJ. Tel: 01969 640638

The Royal Horticultural Society Garden Harlow Carr – Crag Lane, Harrogate, North Yorkshire HG3 1QB. Tel: 01423 565418

Thorp Perrow Arboretum & The Falcons of Thorp Perrow – Bedale, North Yorkshire DL8 2PR. Tel: 01677 425323

Yorkshire Garden World – Main Road, West Haddlesey, Nr Selby, North Yorkshire YO8 8QA. Tel: 01757 228279

Northamptonshire

Althorp – Northampton, Northants NN7 4HQ. Tel: 01604 770107

Cottesbrooke Hall and Gardens – Cottesbrooke, Northampton, Northamptonshire NN6 8PF. Tel: 01604 505808

Haddonstone Show Garden – The Forge House, Church Lane, East Haddon, Northamptonshire NN6 8DB. Tel: 01604 770711

Kelmarsh Hall & Gardens – Kelmarsh, Northampton, Northamptonshire NN6 9LT. Tel: 01604 686543

Northumberland

Alnwick Castle – Alnwick, Northumberland NE66 1NQ. Tel: 01665 510777/ 511100

Chillingham Castle – Chillingham, Alnwick, Northumberland NE66 5NJ. Tel: 01668 215359

Chipchase Castle – Chipchase, Wark on Tyne, Hexham, Northumberland NE48 3NT. Tel: 01434 230203

Paxton House & Country Park – Berwick-upon-Tweed, Northumberland TD15 1SZ. Tel: 01289 386291

Seaton Delaval Hall – Seaton Sluice, Whitley Bay, Northumberland NE26 4QR. Tel: 0191 237 1493 / 0786

Oxfordshire

Ditchley Park – Enstone, Chipping Norton, Oxfordshire OX7 4ER. Tel: 01608 677346

Kingston Bagpuize House – Kingston Bagpuize, Abingdon, Oxfordshire OX13 5AX. Tel: 01865 820259

Mapledurham House – Mapledurham, Nr Reading, Oxfordshire RG4 7TR. Tel: 01189 723350

River & Rowing Museum – Mill Meadows, Henley-on-Thames, Oxfordshire RG9 1BF. Tel: 01491 415600

Stonor Park – Stonor, Henley-on-Thames, Oxfordshire RG9 6HF. Tel: 01491 638587

Sulgrave Manor – Manor Road, Sulgrave, Banbury, Oxfordshire OX17 2SD. Tel: 01295 760205

Historic Houses, Castles & Gardens

Incorporating Museums & Galleries.

www.historichouses.co.uk

Upton House – Nr Banbury, Oxon OX15 6HT.
Tel: 01295 670266

Wallingford Castle Gardens – Castle Street, Wallingford,
Oxfordshire. Tel: 01491 835373

Shropshire

Hawkstone Park & Follies – Weston-under-Redcastle,
Shrewsbury, Shropshire SY4 5UY. Tel: 01939 200 611

Hodnet Hall Gardens – Hodnet, Market Drayton,
Shropshire TF9 3NN. Tel: 01630 685786

Hopton Court – Kidderminster, Shropshire DY14 0EF.
Tel: 01299 270734

Royal Air force Museum – Cosford, Shifnal,
Shropshire TF11 8UP. Tel: 01902 376200

Shipton Hall – Shipton, Much Wenlock,
Shropshire TF13 6JZ. Tel: 01746 785225

Shrewsbury Castle & Shropshire Regimental Museum –
Castle Street, Shrewsbury, Shropshire SY1 2AT.
Tel: 01743 358516

Shrewsbury Museum & Art Gallery – Barker Street,
Shrewsbury, Shropshire SY1 1QH. Tel: 01743 361196

The Dorothy Clive Garden – Willoughbridge, Market
Drayton, Shropshire TF9 4EU. Tel: 01630 647237

Weston Park – Weston-under-Lizard, Nr Shifnal,
Shropshire TF11 8LE. Tel: 01952 852100

Somerset

Barford Park – Enmore, Nr Bridgwater, Somerset TA5 1AG.
Tel: 01278 671269

Great House Farm – Wells Road, Theale, Wedmore,
Somerset BS28 4SJ. Tel: 01934 713133

Milton Lodge Gardens – Old Bristol Road, Wells,
Somerset BA5 3AQ. Tel: 01749 672168

Museum of Costume & Assembly Rooms – Bennett Street,
Bath, Somerset BA1 2QH. Tel: 01225 477789 / 477785

Orchard Wyndham – Williton, Taunton, Somerset TA4 4HH.
Tel: 01984 632309

▼
Roman Baths & Pump Room – Abbey Church Yard, Bath,
Somerset BA1 1LZ. Tel: 01225 477785

The American Museum in Britain – Claverton Manor, Bath,
Somerset BA2 7BD. Tel: 01225 460503

Staffordshire

Ford Green Hall – Ford Green Road, Smallthorne, Stoke-on-
Trent, Staffordshire ST6 1NG. Tel: 01782 233195

Sandon Hall – Sandon, Staffordshire ST18 0BZ.
Tel: 01889 508004

Whitmore Hall – Whitmore, Newcastle-under-Lyme,
Staffordshire ST5 5HW. Tel: 01782 680478

Suffolk

Ancient House – Clare, Suffolk CO10 8NY.
Tel: 01628 825920

Otley Hall – Hall Lane, Otley, Ipswich, Suffolk IP6 9PA.
Tel: 01473 890264

Shrubland Park Gardens – Shrubland Estate, Coddenham,
Ipswich, Suffolk IP6 9QQ. Tel: 01473 830221

Surrey

Clandon Park – West Clandon, Guildford, Surrey GU4 7RQ.
Tel: 01483 222482

Claremont House – Claremont Drive, Esher,
Surrey KT10 9LY. Tel: 01372 467841

Goddards – Abinger Common, Dorking, Surrey RH5 6TH.
Tel: 01628 825920

Great Fosters – Stroude Road, Egham, Surrey TW20 9UR.
Tel: 01784 433822

Hampton Court Palace – East Molesey, Surrey KT8 9AU.
Tel: 0870 751 5175

Hatchlands – East Clandon, Guildford, Surrey GU4 7RT.
Tel: 01483 222482

Loseley Park – Estate Office, Guildford, Surrey GU3 1HS.
Tel: 01483 304440

Merton Heritage Centre – The Canons, Madeira Road,
Mitcham, Surrey CR4 4HD. Tel: 020 8640 9387

Painshill Landscape Garden – Portsmouth Road, Cobham,
Surrey KT11 1JE. Tel: 01932 868113

The Royal Horticultural Society, Wisley Garden –
Nr Woking, Surrey GU23 6QB. Tel: 01483 224234

Warwickshire

Arbury Hall – Nuneaton, Warwickshire CV10 7PT.
Tel: 024 7638 2804

Ragley Hall – Alcester, Warwickshire B49 5NJ.
Tel: 01789 762090

Shakespeare Houses – The Shakespeare Centre, Henley
Street, Stratford-upon-Avon, Warwickshire CV37 6QW.
Tel: 01789 204016

West Midlands

Barber Institute of Fine Arts – The University of
Birmingham, Edgbaston, Birmingham,
West Midlands B15 2TS. Tel 0121 414 7333

Castle Bromwich Hall Gardens – Chester Road, Castle
Bromwich, Birmingham, West Midlands B36 9BT.
Tel: 0121-749 4100

The Birmingham Botanical Gardens and Glasshouses –
Westbourne Road, Edgbaston, Birmingham, West
Midlands B15 3TR. Tel: 0121 454 1860

West Sussex

Borde Hill Garden – Balcombe Road, West Sussex RH16
1XP. Tel: 01444 450326

Chichester District Museum – 29 Little London, Chichester,
West Sussex PO19 1PB. Tel: 01243 784683

Denmans Garden – Clock House, Denmans, Fontwell,
West Sussex BN18 0SU. Tel: 01243 542808

Goodwood House – Goodwood, Chichester,
West Sussex PO18 0PX. Tel: 01243 755000

High Beeches Gardens – High Beeches, Handcross,
West Sussex RH17 6HQ. Tel: 01444 400589

Leonardslee - Lakes & Gardens – Lower Beeding, Horsham,
West Sussex RH13 6PP. Tel: 01403 891212

Weald and Downland Open Air Museum – Singleton,
Chichester, West Sussex PO21 4JU. Tel: 01243 811363

West Dean Gardens – West Dean, Chichester,
West Sussex PO18 0QZ. Tel: 01243 818210

Worthing Museum & Art Gallery – Chapel Road, Worthing,
West Sussex BN11 1HP. Tel: 01903 239999

West Yorkshire

Bramham Park – Estate Office, Bramham Park, Wetherby,
West Yorkshire LS23 6ND. Tel: 01937 846000

Harewood House – The Harewood House Trust,
Moorhouse. Harewood, Leeds, West Yorkshire LS17 9LQ.
Tel: 0113 218 1010

Ledston Hall – Hall Lane, Ledstone, West Yorkshire WF10
2BB. Tel: 01423 523 423

Wiltshire

Charlton Park House – Charlton, Malmesbury,
Wiltshire SN16 9DG. Tel: 01666 824389

Hamptworth Lodge – Landford, Salisbury,
Wiltshire SP5 2EA. Tel: 01794 390215

▼
Longleat – Warminster, Wiltshire BA12 7NW.
Tel: 01985 844400

Salisbury Cathedral – Visitor Services, 33 The Close,
Salisbury, Wiltshire SP1 2EJ. Tel: 01722 555120

Sheldon Manor – Nr Chippenham, Wiltshire SN14 0RG.
Tel: 01249 653120

The Peto Garden At Iford Manor – Bradford-on-Avon,
Wiltshire BA15 2BA. Tel: 01225 863146

Worcestershire

Hagley Hall – Hagley, Worcestershire DY9 9LG.
Tel: 01562 882408

Harvington Hall – Harvington, Kidderminister,
Worcester DY10 4LR. Tel: 01562 777846

Little Malvern Court – Nr Malvern,
Worcestershire WR14 4JN. Tel: 01684 892988

Spetchley Park Gardens – Spetchley Park, Worcester,
Worcestershire WR5 1RS. Tel: 01453 810303

Ireland

Co Antrim

Benvarden Gardens – Benvarden Dervolk,
Co Antrim BT53 6NN. Tel: 028 2074 1331

Co Cork

Bantry House & Gardens – Bantry, Co Cork.
Tel: + 353 2 750 047

Co Down

North Down Heritage Centre – Town Hall, Bangor,
Co Down BT20 4BT. Tel: 028 9127 1200

Seaforde Gardens – Seaforde, Downpatrick,
Co Down BT30 8PG. Tel: 028 4481 1225

HISTORIC HOUSES, CASTLES & GARDENS

Incorporating Museums & Galleries.

www.historichouses.co.uk

Co Kildare

Japanese Gardens & St Fiachra's Garden – Tully, Kildare Town, Co Kildare. Tel: +353 45 521617

Co Wicklow

Powerscourt Gardens & Waterfall – Powerscourt Estate, Enniskerry, Co Wicklow. Tel: +353 1 204 6000

Scotland

Aberdeenshire

Craigston Castle – Turriff, Aberdeenshire AB53 5PX. Tel: 01888 551228

Angus

Glamis Castle – Glamis, by Forfar, Angus DD8 1RJ. Tel: 01307 840393

Ayrshire

Auchinleck House – Ochiltree, Ayrshire. Tel: 01628 825920

Kelburn Castle and Country Centre – Kelburn, Fairlie (Nr Largs), Ayrshire KA29 0BE. Tel: 01475 568685

▼

Inveraray Castle – Cherry Park, Inveraray, Argyll PA32 8XE. Tel: 01499 302203

Maybole Castle – Maybole, Ayrshire KA19 7BX. Tel: 01655 883765

Sorn Castle – Sorn, Mauchline, Ayrshire KA5 6HR. Tel: 0141 942 6460

Dumfries

Drumlanrig Castle, Gardens and Country Park – Nr Thornhill, Dumfries DG3 4AQ. Tel: 01848 330248

East Lothian

Lennoxlove House – Haddington, East Lothian EH41 4NZ. Tel: 01620 823720

Edinburgh

Dalmeny House – South Queensferry, Edinburgh EH30 9TQ. Tel: 0131 331 1888

Fife

Callendar House – Callendar Park, Falkirk, Fife FK1 1YR. Tel: 01324 503770

Isle of Skye

Armadale Castle, Gardens & Museum of the Isles – Armadale, Sleat, Isle of Skye IV45 8RS. Tel: 01471 844305

Perthshire

Scone Palace – Scone, Perth, Perthshire PH2 6BD. Tel: 01738 552300

Scottish Borders

Bowhill House & Country Park – Bowhill, Selkirk, Scottish Borders TD7 5ET. Tel: 01750 22204

Traquair House – Innerleithen, Peebles EH44 6PW. Tel: 01896 830323

South Lanarkshire

New Lanark World Heritage Site – New Lanark Mills, South Lanarkshire ML11 9DB. Tel: 01555 661345

West Lothian

Hopetoun House – South Queensferry, West Lothian EH30 9SL. Tel: 0131 331 2451

Newliston – Kirkliston, West Lothian EH29 9EB. Tel: 0131 333 3231

Wales

Carmarthenshire

Aberglasney Gardens – Llangathen, Carmarthenshire SA32 8QH. Tel: 01558 668998

Conway

Bodnant Garden – Tal-y-Cafn, Nr Colwyn Bay, Conway LL28 5RE. Tel: 01492 650460

Flintshire

Golden Grove – Llanasa, Nr. Holywell, Flintshire CH8 9NA. Tel: 01745 854452

Gwynedd

Gwydir Castle – Llanrwst, Gwynedd LL26 0PN. Tel: 01492 641687

Monmouthshire

Llanvihangel Court – Llanvihangel Crucorney, Abergavenny, Monmouthshire NP7 8DH. Tel: 01873 890217

Penhow Castle – Penhow, Monmouthshire NP26 3AD. Tel: 01633 400800

Usk Castle – Usk, Monmouthshire NP15 1SD. Tel: 01291 672563

Newport

Fourteen Locks Canal Centre – High Cross, Newport NP10 9GN. Tel: 01633 894802

Newport Museum and Art Gallery – John Frost Square, Newport NP20 1PA. Tel: 01633 840064

Newport Transporter Bridge Visitor Centre – Usk Way, NewPort, South Wales NP20 2JT. Tel: 01633 250322

Tredegar House – Newport NP10 8YW. Tel: 01633 815880

Pembrokeshire

Carew Castle & Tidal Mill – Carew, Nr.Tenby, Pembrokeshire SA70 8SL. Tel: 01646 651782

Powys

The Judge's Lodging – Broad Street, Presteigne, Powys LD8 2AD. Tel: 01544 260650

South Glamorgan

Museum Of Welsh Life – St Fagans, Cardiff, South Glamorgan CF5 6XB. Tel: 029 2057 3500

Continental Europe

Belgium

Kasteel Ooidonk – Ooidonkdreef 9, B9800 Deinze. Tel: 0032 9 282 35 70

France

▼

Château de Chenonceau – 37150 Chenonceaux. Tel: +33 2 47 23 90 07

Chateau Royal D'Amboise – Chateau Royal, B.P. 271, 37403 Amboise. Tel: 00 33 2 47 57 00 98

Floral Park and Chateau of Martinvast – Domaine de Beaurepaire, 50690 Martinvast. Tel: +33 2 33 87 20 80

The Netherlands

Palace Het Loo National Museum – Koninklijk Park 1, 7315 JA Apeldoorn, Holland. Tel: +31 55 577 2400

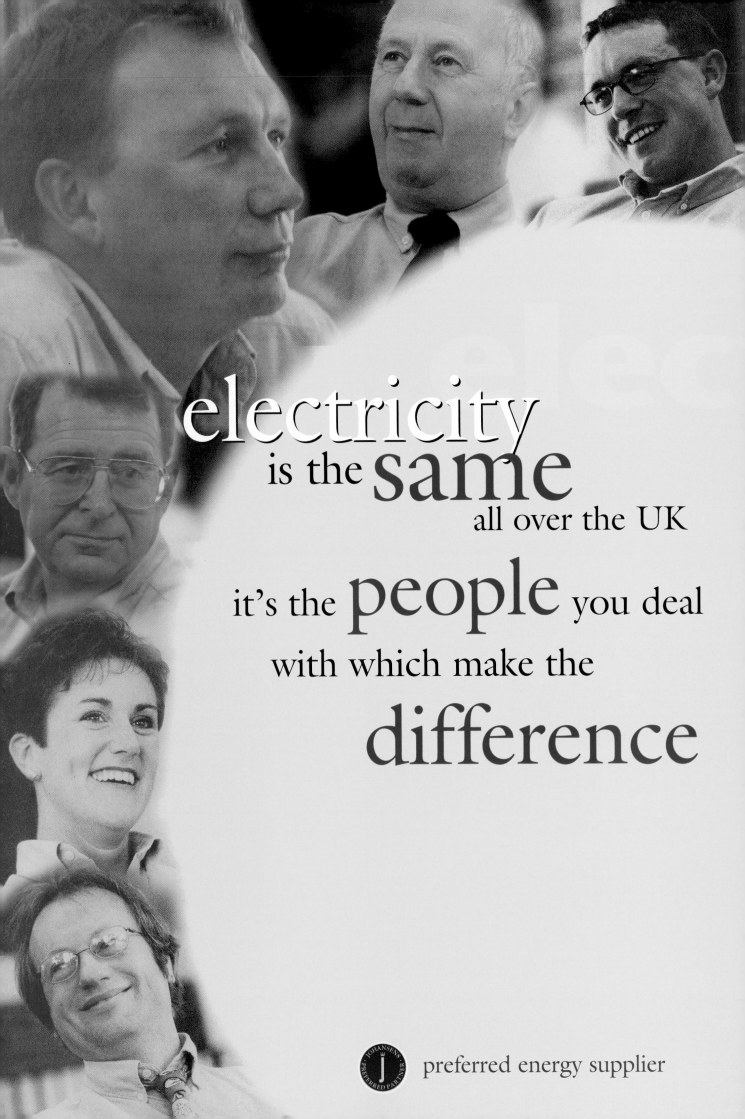

electricity is the same all over the UK

it's the people you deal with which make the difference

preferred energy supplier

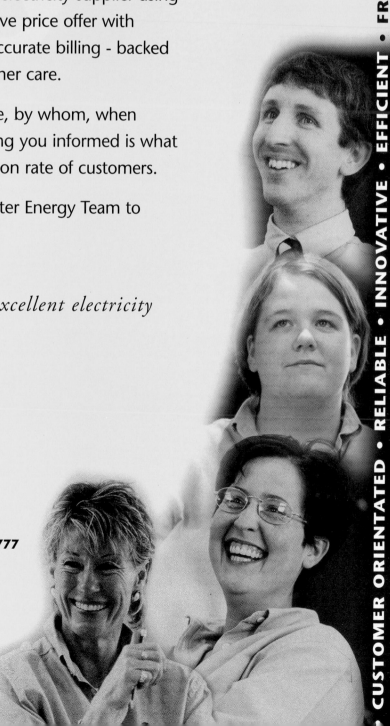

Maverick Energy specialise in the business of electricity supply.

Having been energy consultants and brokers for 7 years we know what you need, and want, in terms of customer care.

To safeguard our beliefs in how the industry could be, we've become a licensed electricity supplier using simple principles. A competitive price offer with straightforward, timely and accurate billing - backed up with solid, tangible customer care.

Doing what needs to be done, by whom, when agreed, as agreed, and keeping you informed is what gives us a 97% annual retention rate of customers.

You will struggle to find a better Energy Team to work with.

Contact us to receive an excellent electricity price for your premises.

maverick
ENERGY

27 Shamrock Way, Hythe Marina Village, Hythe, Hampshire, SO45 6DY.

T **(023) 80 841555**   F **(023) 80 841777**

Email: rachel@maverickenergy.co.uk

Website: www.maverickenergy.co.uk

CUSTOMER ORIENTATED • RELIABLE • INNOVATIVE • EFFICIENT • FRIENDLY • ENERGETIC • ACCURATE •

Condé Nast Johansens are delighted to recommend over 190 properties across North America, Mexico, Bermuda, The Caribbean, The Pacific. Call 0800 269 397 or see the order forms on page 519 to order guides.

ARIZONA - SEDONA

Canyon Villa Inn

125 Canyon Circle Drive, Sedona, Arizona 86351
Tel: 1 520 284 1226
Fax: 1 520 284 2114

ARIZONA - SEDONA

L'Auberge De Sedona

L'Auberge Lane, PO Box B, Sedona, Arizona 86339
Tel: 1 928 282 1661
Fax: 1 928 282 2885

ARIZONA - TUCSON

Tanque Verde Ranch

14301 East Speedway, Tucson, Arizona 85748
Tel: 1 520 296 6275
Fax: 1 520 721 9426

ARIZONA - TUCSON

White Stallion Ranch

9251 West Twin Peaks Road, Tucson, Arizona 85743
Tel: 1 520 297 0252
Fax: 1 520 744 2786

CALIFORNIA - EUREKA

Carter House

301 L Street, Eureka, California 95501
Tel: 1 707 444 8062
Fax: 1 707 444 8067

CALIFORNIA - FERNDALE

Gingerbread Mansion Inn

P.O.Box 40; 400 Berding Street, Ferndale, California 95536
Tel: 1 707 786 4000
Fax: 1 707 786 4381

CALIFORNIA - LA JOLLA

The Bed & Breakfast Inn At La Jolla

7753 Draper Avenue, La Jolla, California 92037
Tel: 1 858 456 2066
Fax: 1 858 456 1510

CALIFORNIA - MILL VALLEY

Mill Valley Inn

165 Throckmorton Avenue, Mill Valley, California 94941
Tel: 1 415 389 6608
Fax: 1 415 389 5051

CALIFORNIA - NEWPORT BEACH

Doryman's Inn

2102 West Ocean Front, Newport Beach, California 92663
Tel: 1 949 675 7300
Fax: 1 949 675 9300

CALIFORNIA - PALM DESERT

Shadow Mountain Resort & Club

45750 San Luis Rey, Palm Desert, California 92260
Tel: 1 760 346 6123
Fax: 1 760 346 6518

CALIFORNIA - PALM SPRINGS

Caliente Tropics Resort

411 East Palm Canyon Drive, Palm Springs, California 92264
Tel: 1 760 327 1391
Fax: 1 760 318 1883

CALIFORNIA - PALM SPRINGS

L'Horizon

1050 East Palm Canyon Drive, Palm Springs, California 92264
Tel: 1 760 323 1858
Fax: 1 760 327 2933

CALIFORNIA - PALM SPRINGS

The Willows

412 West Tahquitz Canyon Way, Palm Springs, California 92262
Tel: 1 760 320 0771
Fax: 1 760 320 0780

CALIFORNIA - SAN FRANCISCO

Nob Hill Lambourne

725 Pine Street, San Francisco, California 94108
Tel: 1 415 433 2287
Fax: 1 415 433 0975

CALIFORNIA - SAN FRANCISCO BAY AREA

Gerstle Park Inn

34 Grove Street, San Rafael, California 94901
Tel: 1 415 721 7611
Fax: 1 415 721 7600

CALIFORNIA - SANTA ANA

Woolley's Petite Suites

2721 Hotel Terrace Road, Santa Ana, California 92705
Tel: 1 714 540 1111
Fax: 1 714 662 1643

CALIFORNIA - SANTA BARBARA

Upham Hotel

1404 De La Vina Street, Santa Barbara, California 93101
Tel: 1 805 962 0058
Fax: 1 805 963 2825

CALIFORNIA - SANTA MONICA

The Georgian Hotel

1415 Ocean Avenue, Santa Monica, California 90405
Tel: 1 310 395 9945
Fax: 1 310 451 3374

CALIFORNIA - TIBURON

Waters Edge Hotel

25 Main Street, Tiburon, California 94920
Tel: 1 415 789 5999
Fax: 1 415 789 5888

COLORADO - BEAVER CREEK

The Inn at Beaver Creek

10 Elk Track Lane, Beaver Creek Resort, Colorado, 81620
Tel: 1 970 845 5990
Fax: 1 970 845 6204

MINI LISTINGS NORTH AMERICA

Condé Nast Johansens are delighted to recommend over 190 properties across North America, Mexico, Bermuda, The Caribbean, The Pacific.

Call 0800 269 397 or see the order forms on page 519 to order guides.

COLORADO - DENVER

Castle Marne

1572 Race Street, Denver, Colorado 80206
Tel: 1 303 331 0621
Fax: 1 303 331 0623

COLORADO - ESTES PARK

The Stanley Hotel

333 Wonderview Avenue, PO Box 1767, Estes Park,
Colorado. 80517
Tel: 1 970 577 4018
Fax: 1 970 586 4964

COLORADO - MANITOU SPRINGS

The Cliff House at Pikes Peak

306 Cañon Avenue, Manitou Springs, Colorado 80829
Tel: 1 719 685 3000
Fax: 1 719 685 3913

COLORADO - STEAMBOAT SPRINGS

Vista Verde Guest Ranch

PO Box 770465, Steamboat Springs, Colorado 80477
Tel: 1 970 879 3858
Fax: 1 970 879 1413

COLORADO - VAIL

Sonnenalp Resort of Vail

20 Vail Road, Vail, Colorado 81657
Tel: 1 970 476 5656
Fax: 1 970 476 1639

DELAWARE - REHOBOTH BEACH

Boardwalk Plaza Hotel

Olive Avenue & The Boardwalk, Rehoboth Beach, Delaware
19971
Tel: 1 302 227 0441
Fax: 1 302 227 0561

FLORIDA - DELRAY BEACH

The Sundy House Resort

106 South Swinton Avenue, Delray Beach, Florida 33444
Tel: 1 561 272 5678
Fax: 1 561 272 1115

FLORIDA - KEY WEST

Simonton Court Historic Inn & Cottages

320 Simonton Street, Key West, Florida 33040
Tel: 1 305 294 6386
Fax: 1 305 293 8446

FLORIDA - MIAMI BEACH

Fisher Island

1 Fisher Island Drive, Miami Beach, Florida 33109
Tel: 1 305 535 6020
Fax: 1 305 535 6003

FLORIDA - NAPLES

Hotel Escalante

290 Fifth Avenue South, Naples, Florida 34102
Tel: 1 941 659 3466
Fax: 1 941 262 8748

GEORGIA - PERRY

Henderson Village

125 South Langston Circle, Perry, Georgia 31069
Tel: 1 478 988 8696
Fax: 1 478 988 9009

GEORGIA - SAVANNAH

The Eliza Thompson House

5 West Jones Street, Savannah, Georgia 31401
Tel: 1 912 236 3620
Fax: 1 912 238 1920

GEORGIA - SAVANNAH

Granite Steps

126 East Gaston Street, Savannah, Georgia 31401
Tel: 1 912 233 5380
Fax: 1 912 236 3116

GEORGIA - SAVANNAH

The President's Quarters

225 East President Street, Savannah, Georgia 31401
Tel: 1 912 233 1600
Fax: 1 912 238 0849

ILLINOIS - CHICAGO

The Sutton Place Hotel

21 East Bellevue Place, Chicago, Illinois 60611
Tel: 1 312 266 2100
Fax: 1 312 266 2103

LOUISIANA - NAPOLEANVILLE

Madewood Plantation House

4250 Highway 308, Napoleanville,Louisiana 70390
Tel: 1 985 369 7151
Fax: 1 985 369 9848

LOUISIANA - NEW ORLEANS

Hotel Maison De Ville

727 Rue Toulouse, New Orleans, Louisiana 70130
Tel: 1 504 561 5858
Fax: 1 504 528 9939

MARYLAND - ANNAPOLIS

The Annapolis Inn

144 Prince George Street, Annapolis, Maryland 21401-1723
Tel: 1 410 295 5200
Fax: 1 410 295 5201

MARYLAND - TANEYTOWN

Antrim 1844

30 Trevanion Rd, Taneytown, Maryland 21787
Tel: 1 410 756 6812
Fax: 1 410 756 2744

MARYLAND - WASINGTON D.C.

The George Washington University Inn

824 New Hampshire Avenue, N.W. Washington D.C., District
of Columbia 20037
Tel: 1 202 337 6620
Fax: 1 202 298 7499

Condé Nast Johansens are delighted to recommend over 190 properties across North America, Mexico, Bermuda, The Caribbean, The Pacific. Call 0800 269 397 or see the order forms on page 519 to order guides.

MISSISSIPPI - BILOXI

Green Oaks
580 Beach Boulevard, Biloxi, Mississippi 39530
Tel: 1 228 436 6257
Fax: 1 228 436 6225

MISSISSIPPI - JACKSON

Fairview Inn
734 Fairview Street, Jackson, Mississippi 39202
Tel: 1 601 948 3429
Fax: 1 601 948 1203

MISSISSIPPI - NATCHEZ

Dunleith Plantation
84 Homochitto Street, Natchez, Mississippi, 39120
Tel: 1 601 446 8500
Fax: 1 601 446 8554

MISSISSIPPI - NATCHEZ

Monmouth Plantation
36 Melrose Avenue AT, John A Quitman Parkway, Natches, Mississippi 39120
Tel: 1 601 442 5852
Fax: 1 601 446 7762

MISSISSIPPI - VICKSBURG

Anchuca Historic Mansion & Inn
1010 First East Street, Vicksburg, Mississippi 39183
Tel: 1 601 661 0111
Fax: 1 601 661 0111

MISSISSIPPI - VICKSBURG

The Duff Green Mansion
1114 First East Street, Vicksburg, Mississippi 39180
Tel: 1 601 636 6968
Fax: 1 601 661 0079

MISSOURI - ST LOUIS

Chase Park Plaza Hotel
212 North Kingshighway Boulevard, St Louis, Missouri 63108
Tel: 1 314 633 3000
Fax: 1 314 633 1133

NEW ENGLAND / CONNECTICUT - IVORYTON

Copper Beech Inn
46 Main Street, Ivoryton, Connecticut 06442
Tel: 1 860 767 0330

NEW ENGLAND / CONNECTICUT - MYSTIC

The Inn at Mystic
US1 & State 27, PO Box 216, Mystic, Connecticut 06355
Tel: 1 860 536 9604
Fax: 1 860 572 1635

NEW ENGLAND / CONNECTICUT - MYSTIC

Stonecroft Country Inn
515 Pumpkin Hill Road, Ledyard, Connecticut 06339
Tel: 1 860 572 0771
Fax: 1 860 572 9161

NEW ENGLAND / CONNECTICUT - NEW PRESTON

The Boulders Inn
East Shore Road, Route 45, New Preston, Connecticut 06777
Tel: 1 860 868 0541
Fax: 1 860 868 1925

NEW ENGLAND / CONNECTICUT - OLD MYSTIC

The Old Mystic Inn
52 MAIN STREET, OLD MYSTIC, CONNECTICUT 06372-0733
Tel: 1 860 572 9422
Fax: 1 860 572 9954

NEW ENGLAND / CONNECTICUT - RIDGEFIELD

West Lane Inn & The Inn at Ridgefield
22 West Lane, Ridgefield, Connecticut 06877
Tel: 1 203 438 7323
Fax: 1 203 438 8282

NEW ENGLAND / MAINE - CAMDEN

Blackberry Inn
82 Elm Street, Camden, Maine 04843
Tel: 1 207 236 6060
Fax: 1 207 236 9032

NEW ENGLAND / MAINE - CAMDEN

Camden Maine Stay
22 High Street, Camden, Maine 04843
Tel: 1 207 236 9636
Fax: 1 207 236 0621

NEW ENGLAND / MAINE - CAMDEN

Hartstone Inn
41 Elm Street, Camden, Maine, 04843
Tel: 1 207 236 4259
Fax: 1 207 236 9575

NEW ENGLAND / MAINE - GREENVILLE

The Lodge At Moosehead Lake
Upon Lily Bay Road, Box 1167, Greenville, Maine 04441
Tel: 1 207 695 4400
Fax: 1 207 695 2281

NEW ENGLAND / MAINE - KENNEBUNKPORT

The Captain Lord Mansion
6 Pleasant Street, Kennebunkport, Maine 04046-0800
Tel: 1 207 967 3141

NEW ENGLAND / MAINE - MOOSEHEAD LAKE

Greenville Inn
PO Box 1194, Norris Street, Greenville, Maine 04441
Tel: 1 207 695 2206
Fax: 1 207 695 0335

NEW ENGLAND / MAINE - NEWCASTLE

The Newcastle Inn
60 River Road, Newcastle, Maine 04553
Tel: 1 207 563 5685
Fax: 1 207 563 6877

MINI LISTINGS NORTH AMERICA

Condé Nast Johansens are delighted to recommend over 190 properties across North America, Mexico, Bermuda, The Caribbean, The Pacific.

Call 0800 269 397 or see the order forms on page 519 to order guides.

NEW ENGLAND / MAINE - ROCKLAND

Captain Lindsey House

5 Lindsey Street, Rockland, Maine 04841
Tel: 1 207 596 7950
Fax: 1 207 596 2758

NEW ENGLAND / MASSACHUSETTS - BOSTON

A Cambridge House

2218 Massachusetts Avenue, Cambridge, Massachusetts
02140–1836
Tel: 1 617 491 6300
Fax: 1 617 868 2848

NEW ENGLAND / MASSACHUSETTS - BOSTON

The Charles Street Inn

94 Charles Street, Boston, Massachusetts 02114–4643
Tel: 1 617 314 8900
Fax: 1 617 371 0009

NEW ENGLAND / MASSACHUSETTS - BOSTON

The Lenox Hotel

710 Boylston Street, Boston, Massachusetts 02116-2699
Tel: 1 617 536 5300
Fax: 1 617 236 0351

NEW ENGLAND / MASSACHUSETTS - CAPE COD

The Captain's House Inn

369–377 Old Harbor Road, Chatham, Cape Cod,
Massachusetts 02633
Tel: 1 508 945 0127
Fax: 1 508 945 0866

NEW ENGLAND / MASSACHUSETTS - CAPE COD

Wedgewood Inn

83 Main Street, Route 6A, Yarmouth Port, Massachusetts
02675
Tel: 1 508 362 5157
Fax: 1 508 362 5851

NEW ENGLAND / MASSACHUSETTS - CAPE COD

The Whalewalk Inn

220 Bridge Road, Eastham (Cape Cod), Massachusetts 02642
Tel: 1 508 255 0617
Fax: 1 508 240 0017

NEW ENGLAND / MASSACHUSETTS - DEERFIELD

Deerfield Inn

81 Old Main Street, Deerfield, Massachusetts 01342-0305
Tel: 1 413 774 5587
Fax: 1 413 775 7221

NEW ENGLAND / MASSACHUSETTS - LENOX

Wheatleigh

Hawthorne Road, Lenox, Massachusetts 01240
Tel: 1 413 637 0610
Fax: 1 413 637 4507

NEW ENGLAND / MASSACHUSETTS - MARBLEHEAD

The Harbor Light Inn

58 Washington Street, Marblehead, Massachusetts 01945
Tel: 1 781 631 2186
Fax: 1 781 631 2216

NEW ENGLAND / MASSACHUSETTS - MARTHA'S VINEYARD

Hob Knob Inn

128 Main Street, po box 239, Edgartown, Massachusetts
02539
Tel: 1 508 627 9510
Fax: 1 508 627 4560

NEW ENGLAND / MASSACHUSETTS - MARTHA'S VINEYARD

Thorncroft Inn

460 Main Street, PO Box 1022, Vineyard Haven,
Massachusetts 02568
Tel: 1 508 693 3333
Fax: 1 508 693 5419

NEW ENGLAND / MASSACHUSETTS - MARTHA'S VINEYARD

The Victorian Inn

24 South Water Street, Edgartown, Massachusetts 02539
Tel: 1 508 627 4784

NEW ENGLAND / MASSACHUSETTS - NANTUCKET

The Pineapple Inn

10 Hussey Street, Nantucket, Massachusetts 02554
Tel: 1 508 228 9992
Fax: 1 508 325 6051

NEW ENGLAND / MASSACHUSETTS - NANTUCKET

Union Street Inn

7 Union Street, Nantucket, Massachusetts 02554
Tel: 1 508 228 9222
Fax: 1 508 325 0484

NEW ENGLAND / MASSACHUSETTS - ROCKPORT

Seacrest Manor

99 Marmion Way, Rockport, Massachusetts 01966
Tel: 1 978 546 2211

NEW ENGLAND / NEW HAMPSHIRE - CHESTERFIELD

Chesterfield Inn

Route 9, PO Box 155, Chesterfield, New Hampshire 03443-
0155
Tel: 1 603 256 3211
Fax: 1 603 256 6131

NEW ENGLAND / NEW HAMPSHIRE - HOLDERNESS

The Manor on Golden Pond

Route 3, PO Box T, Holderness, New Hampshire 03245
Tel: 1 603 968 3348
Fax: 1 603 968 2116

NEW ENGLAND / NEW HAMPSHIRE - JACKSON

The Inn at Thorn Hill

Thorn Hill Road, Jackson Village, New Hampshire 03846
Tel: 1 603 383 4242

NEW ENGLAND / RHODE ISLAND - BLOCK ISLAND

The Atlantic Inn

PO Box 1788, Block Island, Rhode Island 02807
Tel: 1 401 466 5883
Fax: 1 401 466 5678

MINI LISTINGS NORTH AMERICA

Condé Nast Johansens are delighted to recommend over 190 properties across North America, Mexico, Bermuda, The Caribbean, The Pacific. Call 0800 269 397 or see the order forms on page 519 to order guides.

NEW ENGLAND / RHODE ISLAND - NEWPORT

Cliffside Inn
2 Seaview Avenue, Newport, Rhode Island 02840
Tel: 1 401 847 1811
Fax: 1 401 848 5850

NEW ENGLAND / RHODE ISLAND - NEWPORT

The Francis Malbone House
392 Thames Street, Newport, Rhode Island 02840
Tel: 1 401 846 0392
Fax: 1 401 848 5956

NEW ENGLAND / RHODE ISLAND - NEWPORT

The Inn At Shadow Lawn
120 Miantonomi Avenue, Newport, Rhode Island 02842
Tel: 1 401 847 0902
Fax: 401 848 6529

NEW ENGLAND / RHODE ISLAND - PROVIDENCE

Historic Jacob Hill Inn
PO Box 41326, Providence, Rhode Island 02940
Tel: 1 508 336 9165
Fax: 1 508 336 0951

NEW ENGLAND / VERMONT - CHITTENDEN

Fox Creek Inn
49 Dam Road, Chittenden, Vermont 05737
Tel: 1 802 483 6213
Fax: 1 802 483 2623

NEW ENGLAND / VERMONT - CHITTENDEN

Mountain Top Inn & Resort
195 Mountain Top Road, Chittenden, Vermont 05737
Tel: 1 802 483 2311
Fax: 1 802 483 6373

NEW ENGLAND / VERMONT - LOWER WATERFORD

Rabbit Hill Inn
48 Lower Waterford Road, Lower Waterford, Vermont 05848
Tel: 1 802 748 5168
Fax: 1 802 748 8342

NEW ENGLAND / VERMONT - MANCHESTER VILLAGE

1811 House
PO Box 39, Route 7A, Manchester Village, Vermont 05254
Tel: 1 802 362 1811
Fax: 1 802 362 2443

NEW ENGLAND / VERMONT - MANCHESTER VILLAGE

The Village Country Inn
Route 7A, po box 408, Manchester Village, Vermont 05254
Tel: 1 802 362 1792
Fax: 1 802 362 7238

NEW ENGLAND / VERMONT - NEWFANE

Four Columns Inn
PO Box 278, Newfane, Vermont 05345
Tel: 1 802 365 7713

NEW ENGLAND / VERMONT - STOWE

The Mountain Road Resort At Stowe
PO Box 8, 1007 Mountain Road, Stowe, Vermont 05672
Tel: 1 802 253 4566
Fax: 1 802 253 7397

NEW ENGLAND / VERMONT - WEST TOWNSHEND

Windham Hill Inn
West Townshend, Vermont 05359
Tel: 1 802 874 4080
Fax: 1 802 874 4702

NEW ENGLAND / VERMONT - WESTON

The Inn At Weston
Scenic Route 100, Weston, Vermont 05161
Tel: 1 802 824 6789
Fax: 1 802 824 3073

NEW ENGLAND / VERMONT - WOODSTOCK

The Jackson House Inn
114-3 Senior Lane, Woodstock, Vermont 05091
Tel: 1 802 457 2065
Fax: 1 802 457 9290

NEW ENGLAND / VERMONT - WOODSTOCK

Woodstock Inn & Resort
Fourteen The Green, Woodstock, Vermont, 05091-1298
Tel: 1 802 457 1100
Fax: 1 802 457 6699

NEW MEXICO - SANTA FE

Hotel St Francis
210 Don Gaspar Avenue, Santa Fe, New Mexico 87501
Tel: 1 505 983 5700
Fax: 1 505 992 6340

NEW MEXICO - SANTA FE

Bishop's Lodge
PO Box 2367, Santa Fe, New Mexico, 87504
Tel: 1 505 983 6377
Fax: 1 505 989 8739

NEW MEXICO - TAOS

Casitas at El Monte
125 La Posta Road, PO Box 20, Taos, New Mexico 87671
Tel: 1 800 828 8267
Fax: 1 505 758 5089

NEW MEXICO - TAOS

The Inn on La Loma Plaza
315 Ranchitos Road, Taos, New Mexico 87571
Tel: 1 505 758 1717
Fax: 1 505 751 0155

NEW YORK - CAZENOVIA

The Brewster Inn
6 Ledyard Avenue, Cazenovia, New York 13035
Tel: 1 315 655 9232
Fax: 1 315 655 2130

MINI LISTINGS NORTH AMERICA

Condé Nast Johansens are delighted to recommend over 190 properties across North America, Mexico, Bermuda, The Caribbean, The Pacific.
Call 0800 269 397 or see the order forms on page 519 to order guides.

NEW YORK - EAST AURORA

Roycroft Inn

40 South Grove Street, East Aurora, New York 14052
Tel: 1 877 652 5552
Fax: 1 716 655 5345

NEW YORK - GENEVA

Geneva On The Lake

1001 Lochland Road (Route 14 South), Geneva, New York 14456
Tel: 1 315 789 7190
Fax: 1 315 789 0322

NEW YORK - ITHACA

William Henry Miller Inn

303 North Aurora Street, Ithaca, New York 14850
Tel: 1 607 256 4553
Fax: 607 256 0092

NEW YORK - NEW YORK CITY

Bryant Park Hotel

40 West 40th Street, New York, New York 10018
Tel: 1 212 642 2109
Fax: 1 212 642 2107

NEW YORK - NEW YORK CITY

The Kitano New York

66 Park Avenue New York, New York 10016
Tel: 1 212 885 7000
Fax: 1 212 885 7100

NEW YORK - NORTHERN CATSKILL MOUNTAINS

Albergo Allegria

#43 Route 296, Windham, New York 12496
Tel: 1 518 734 5560
Fax: 1 518 734 5570

NEW YORK - SARATOGA SPRINGS

Saratoga Arms

495–497 Broadway, Saratoga Springs, New York 12866
Tel: 1 518 584 1775
Fax: 1 518 581 4064

NORTH CAROLINA - ASHEVILLE

The Wright Inn & Carriage House

235 Pearson Drive, Asheville, North Carolina 28801
Tel: 1 828 251 0789
Fax: 1 828 251 0929

NORTH CAROLINA - BALD HEAD ISLAND

Theodosia's Bed & Breakfast

PO Box 3130, 2 Keelson Row, Bald Head Island, North Carolina 28461
Tel: 1 910 457 6563
Fax: 1 910 457 6055

NORTH CAROLINA - BALSAM

Balsam Mountain Inn

PO Box 40, Balsam, North Carolina 28707
Tel: 1 828 456 9498
Fax: 1 828 456 9298

NORTH CAROLINA - BEAUFORT

The Cedars Inn

305 Front Street, Beaufort, North Carolina 28516
Tel: 1 252 728 7036
Fax: 1 252 728 1685

NORTH CAROLINA - BLOWING ROCK

Chetola Resort

PO Box 17, North Main Street, Blowing Rock, North Carolina 28605
Tel: 1 828 295 5500
Fax: 1 828 295 5529

NORTH CAROLINA - BLOWING ROCK

Gideon Ridge

PO Box 1929, Blowing Rock, North Carolina 28605
Tel: 1 828 295 3644
Fax: 1 828 295 4586

NORTH CAROLINA - CASHIERS

Millstone Inn

119 Lodge Lane, Hwy 64 West, Cashiers, North Carolina 28717
Tel: 1 828 743 2737
Fax: 1 828 743 0208

NORTH CAROLINA - CHARLOTTE

Ballantyne Resort

10000 Ballantyne Commons Parkway, Charlotte, North Carolina 28277
Tel: 1 704 248 4000
Fax: 1 704 248 4005

NORTH CAROLINA - CHARLOTTE

The Park

2200 Rexford Road, Charlotte, North Carolina 28211
Tel: 1 704 364 8220
Fax: 1 704 365 4712

NORTH CAROLINA - DURHAM

Morehead Manor Bed & Breakfast

914 Vickers Avenue, Durham, North Carolina 27701
Tel: 1 919 687 4366
Fax: 1 919 687 4245

NORTH CAROLINA - EDENTON

The Lords Proprietors' Inn

300 North Broad Street, Edenton, North Carolina 27932
Tel: 1 252 482 3641
Fax: 1 252 482 2432

NORTH CAROLINA - GLENVILLE

Innisfree Victorian Inn and Garden House

PO Box 469, Glenville, North Carolina 28736
Tel: 1 828 743 2946

NORTH CAROLINA - HENDERSONVILLE

Claddagh Inn

755 North Main Street, Hendersonville, North Carolina, 28792
Tel: 1 828 697 7778

MINI LISTINGS NORTH AMERICA

Condé Nast Johansens are delighted to recommend over 190 properties across North America, Mexico, Bermuda, The Caribbean, The Pacific. Call 0800 269 397 or see the order forms on page 519 to order guides.

NORTH CAROLINA - HIGHLANDS

Inn at Half - Mile Farm
PO Box 2769, 214 Half Mile Drive, Highlands, North Carolina 28741
Tel: 1 828 526 8170
Fax: 1 828 526 2625

NORTH CAROLINA - MANTEO

The White Doe Inn & Whispering Bay
PO Box 1029, 319 Sir Walter Raleigh Street, Manteo, North Carolina 27954
Tel: 1 252 473 9851
Fax: 1 252 473 4708

NORTH CAROLINA - RALEIGH - DURHAM

The Siena Hotel
1505 E. Franklin Street, Chapel Hill, North Carolina 27514
Tel: 1 919 929 4000
Fax: 1 919 968 8527

NORTH CAROLINA - ROBBINSVILLE

Snowbird Mountain Lodge
275 Santeetlah Road, Robbinsville, North Carolina 28771
Tel: 1 828 479 3433
Fax: 1 828 479 3473

NORTH CAROLINA - TRYON

Pine Crest Inn
85 Pine Crest Lane, Tryon, North Carolina 28782
Tel: 1 828 859 9135
Fax: 1 828 859 9135

NORTH CAROLINA - WAYNESVILLE

The Swag Country Inn
2300 Swag Road, Waynesville, North Carolina 28785
Tel: 1 828 926 0430
Fax: 1 828 926 2036

NORTH CAROLINA - WILMINGTON

The Verandas
202 NUN STREET, WILMINGTON, NORTH CAROLINA 28401-5020
Tel: 1 910 251 2212
Fax: 1 910 251 8932

NORTH CAROLINA - WINSTON SALEM

Augustus T Zevely Inn
803 South Main Street, Winston-Salem, North Carolina 27101
Tel: 1 336 748 9299
Fax: 1 336 721 2211

OREGON - GRANTS PASS

Weasku Inn
5560 Rogue River Highway, Grants Pass, Oregon 97527
Tel: 1 541 471 8000
Fax: 1 541 471 7038

PENNSYLVANIA - PHILADELPHIA

Rittenhouse Square European Boutique Hotel
1715 Rittenhouse Square, Philadelphia, Pennsylvania 19103
Tel: 1 215 546 6500
Fax: 1 215 546 8787

PENNSYLVANIA - PHILIDELPHIA

The Thomas Bond House
129 South 2nd Street, Philadelphia, Pennsylvania 19106
Tel: 1 215 923 8523
Fax: 1 215 923 8504

SOUTH CAROLINA - AIKEN

Rosemary & Lookaway Inn
804 Carolina Avenue, North Augusta, South Carolina 29841
Tel: 1 803 278 6222
Fax: 1 803 278 4877

SOUTH CAROLINA - CHARLESTON

Vendue Inn
19 VENDUE RANGE, CHARLESTON, SOUTH CAROLINA 29401
Tel: 1 843 577 7970
Fax: 1 843 577 2913

SOUTH CAROLINA - PAWLEYS ISLAND

Litchfield Plantation
Kings River Road, Box 290, Pawleys Island, South Carolina 29585
Tel: 1 843 237 9121
Fax: 1 843 237 1041

SOUTH CAROLINA - TRAVELERS REST

La Bastide
10 ROAD OF VINES, TRAVELERS REST, SOUTH CAROLINA 29690
Tel: 1 864 836 8463
Fax: 1 864 836 4820

TENNESSEE - KINGSTON

Whitestone Country Inn
1200 Paint Rock Road, Kingston, Tennessee 37763
Tel: 1 865 376 0113
Fax: 1 865 376 4454

TENNESSEE - WALLAND

Blackberry Farm
1471 West Millers Cove Road, Walland, Great Smoky Mountains, Tennessee 37886
Tel: 1 865 380 2260
Fax: 1 865 681 7753

TEXAS - BOERNE

Ye Kendall Inn
128 West Blanco, Boerne, Texas 78006
Tel: 1 830 249 2138
Fax: 1 830 249 7371

TEXAS - DALLAS

Hotel Adolphus
1321 Commerce Street, Dallas, Texas 75202
Tel: 1 214 742 8200
Fax: 1 214 651 3563

TEXAS - KYLE

The Inn Above Onion Creek
4444 Highway 150 West, Kyle, Texas 78640
Tel: 1 512 268 1617
Fax: 1 512 268 1090

MINI LISTINGS NORTH AMERICA

Condé Nast Johansens are delighted to recommend over 190 properties across North America, Mexico, Bermuda, The Caribbean, The Pacific.
Call 0800 269 397 or see the order forms on page 519 to order guides.

TEXAS - SAN ANTONIO

Havana River Walk Inn
1015 Navarro, San Antonio, Texas 78205
Tel: 1 210 222 2008
Fax: 1 210 222 2717

TEXAS - TYLER

Kiepersol Estates
21508 Merlot Lane, Tyler, Texas 75703
Tel: 1 903 894 3300
Fax: 1 903 894 4140

VIRGINIA - CHARLOTTESVILLE

200 South Street Inn
200 South Street, Charlottesville, Virginia, 22902
Tel: 1 434 964 7008
Fax: 1 434 979 4403

VIRGINIA - CHARLOTTESVILLE

Clifton - The Country Inn & Estate
1296 Clifton Inn Drive, Charlottesville, Virginia 22911
Tel: 1 434 971 1800
Fax: 1 434 971 7098

VIRGINIA - CHARLOTTESVILLE

Prospect Hill Plantation Inn
po box 6909, charlottesville, VIRGINIA 22906
Tel: 1 540 967 0844
Fax: 1 540 967 0102

VIRGINIA - CULPEPER

Prince Michel Restaurant & Suites
Prince Michel de Virginia, HCR 4, Box 77, Leon, Virginia
22725
Tel: 1 540 547 9720
Fax: 1 540 547 3088

VIRGINIA - MIDDLEBURG

The Goodstone Inn & Estate
36205 Snake Hill Road, Middleburg, Virginia 20117
Tel: 1 540 687 4645
Fax: 1 540 687 6115

VIRGINIA - ORANGE

Willow Grove Inn
14079 Plantation Way, Orange, Virginia 22960
Tel: 1 540 672 5982
Fax: 1 540 672 3674

VIRGINIA - STAUNTON

Frederick House
28 North New street, Staunton, Virginia 24401
Tel: 1 540 885 4220
Fax: 1 540 885 5180

VIRGINIA - WHITE POST

L'Auberge Provençale
PO Box 190, White Post, Virginia 22663
Tel: 1 540 837 1375
Fax: 1 540 837 2004

VIRGINIA - WILLIAMSBURG

Legacy of Williamsburg Inn
930 James Towmn Road, Williamsburg, Virginia
23185–3917
Tel: 1 757 220 0524
Fax: 1 757 220 2211

WYOMING - CHEYENNE

Nagle Warren Mansion
222 East 17Th Street, Cheyenne, Wyoming 82001
Tel: 1 307 637 3333
Fax: 1 307 638 6879

MEXICO - BAJA CALIFORNIA

Casa Natalia
Blvd Mijares 4, San Jose Del Cabo, Baja California Sur 23400
Tel: 52 624 14 251 00
Fax: 52 624 14251 10

MEXICO - CANCUN

Villas Tacul
Boulevard Kukulkan, KM 5.5, Cancun, Quintana Roo, 77500
Mexico
Tel: 52 998 883 00 00
Fax: 52 998 849 70 70

MEXICO - ISLA MUJERES

La Casa De Los Sueños
Carretera Garrafon, S/N Isla Mujeres, Quintana Roo, Mexico
77400
Tel: 52 99887 70651
Fax: 52 99887 70708

MEXICO - RIVIERA MAYA

Maroma
highway 307 km 51, riviera maya, Quintana Roo, 77710
Mexico
Tel: 52 998 872 8200
Fax: 52 998 872 8220

MEXICO - ZIHUATANEJO

Hotel Villa Del Sol
Playa La Ropa S/N, PO Box 84, Zihuatanejo 40880, Mexico
Tel: 52 755 4 2239/3239
Fax: 52 7554 2758/4066

BERMUDA - DEVONSHIRE

Ariel Sands
34 South Shore Road, Devonshire, Bermuda
Tel: 1 441 236 1010
Fax: 1 441 236 0087

BERMUDA - HAMILTON

Rosedon Hotel
PO Box Hm 290, Hamilton Hmax, Bermuda
Tel: 1 441 295 1640
Fax: 1 441 295 5904

BERMUDA - PAGET

Fourways Inn
PO Box Pg 294, Paget Pg Bx, Bermuda
Tel: 1 441 236 6517
Fax: 1 441 236 5528

MINI LISTINGS NORTH AMERICA

Condé Nast Johansens are delighted to recommend over 190 properties across North America, Mexico, Bermuda, The Caribbean, The Pacific. Call 0800 269 397 or see the order forms on page 519 to order guides.

BERMUDA - PAGET

Newstead Hotel
27 Harbour Road, Paget Pg02, Bermuda
Tel: 1 441 236 6060
Fax: 1 441 236 7454

BERMUDA - SOMERSET

Cambridge Beaches
Kings Point, Somerset, MA02 Bermuda
Tel: 1 441 234 0331
Fax: 1 441 234 3352

BERMUDA - SOUTHAMPTON

The Reefs
56 South Shore Road, Southampton, SN02 Bermuda
Tel: 1 441 238 0222
Fax: 1 441 238 8372

BERMUDA - WARWICK

Surf Side Beach Club
90 South Shore Road, Warwick, Bermuda
Tel: 1 441 236 7100
Fax: 1 441 236 9765

CARIBBEAN - ANGUILLA

Frangipani Beach Club
PO Box 1378, Meads Bay, Anguilla, West Indies
Tel: 1 264 497 6442/6444
Fax: 1 264 497 6440

CARIBBEAN - ANTIGUA

Blue Waters
PO Box 256, St Johns, Antigua, West Indies
Tel: 1 268 462 0290
Fax: 1 268 462 0293

CARIBBEAN - ANTIGUA

Curtain Bluff
PO Box 288, Antigua, West Indies
Tel: 1 268 462 8400
Fax: 1 268 462 8409

CARIBBEAN - ANTIGUA

Galley Bay
Five Islands, PO Box 305, St John's, Antigua, West Indies
Tel: 1 268 462 0302
Fax: 1 268 462 4551

CARIBBEAN - ANTIGUA

The inn at English Harbour
PO Box 187, ST Johns, Antigua, West Indies
Tel: 1 268 460 1014
Fax: 1 268 460 1603

CARIBBEAN - BARBADOS

Coral Reef Club
St James, Barbados, West Indies
Tel: 1 246 422 2372
Fax: 1 246 422 1776

CARIBBEAN - BARBADOS

The Sandpiper
Holetown, St James, Barbados, West Indies
Tel: 1 246 422 2251
Fax: 1 246 422 0900

CARIBBEAN - CURAÇAO

Avila Beach Hotel
Penstraat 130, Willemstad, Curaçao, Netherlands Antilles, West Indies
Tel: 599 9 461 4377
Fax: 599 9 461 1493

CARIBBEAN - GRENADA

Spice Island Beach Resort
Grand Anse Beach, Box 6, St. George's, Grenada, West Indies
Tel: 1 473 444 4423
Fax: 1 473 444 4807

CARIBBEAN - JAMAICA

Blue Lagoon Villas
Fairy Hill, Port Antonio, Jamaica, West Indies
Tel: 1 876 993 7701
Fax: 1 876 993 8492

CARIBBEAN - JAMAICA

Grand Lido Sans Souci
PO Box 103, Ocho Rios, St Ann, Jamaica, West Indies
Tel: 1 876 994 1206
Fax: 1 876 994 1544

CARIBBEAN - JAMAICA

Half Moon Golf, Tennis & Beach Club
Montego Bay, Jamaica, West Indies
Tel: 1 876 953 2211
Fax: 1 876 953 2731

CARIBBEAN - JAMAICA

Mocking Bird Hill
PO Box 254, Port Antonio, Jamaica
Tel: 1 876 993 7134
Fax: 1 876 993 7133

CARIBBEAN - NEVIS

The Hermitage
Nevis, West Indies
Tel: 1 869 469 3477
Fax: 1 869 469 2481

CARIBBEAN - NEVIS

Montpelier Plantation Inn
Montpelier Estate, PO Box 474, Nevis, West Indies
Tel: 1 869 469 3462
Fax: 1 869 469 2932

CARIBBEAN - NEVIS

Nisbet Plantation Beach Club
St James Parish, Nevis, West Indies
Tel: +1 869 469 9325
Fax: +1 869 469 9864

Condé Nast Johansens are delighted to recommend over 190 properties across North America, Mexico, Bermuda, The Caribbean, The Pacific.
Call 0800 269 397 or see the order forms on page 519 to order guides.

CARIBBEAN - ST KITTS

The Golden Lemon
DIEPPE BAY, ST KITTS, WEST INDIES
Tel: 1 869 465 7260
Fax: 1 869 465 4019

CARIBBEAN - ST KITTS

Ottley's Plantation Inn
PO BOX 345, BASSETERRE, ST KITTS, WEST INDIES
Tel: 1 869 465 7234
Fax: 1 869 465 4760

CARIBBEAN - ST KITTS

Rawlins Plantation Inn
PO Box 340, St Kitts, West Indies
Tel: 1 869 465 6221
Fax: 1 869 465 4954

CARIBBEAN - ST LUCIA

Anse Chastanet
PO Box 7000, Soufriere, St Lucia, West Indies
Tel: 1 758 459 7000
Fax: 1 758 459 7700

CARIBBEAN - ST LUCIA

Mago Estate Hotel
PO Box 247, Soufrière, St Lucia, West Indies
Tel: 1 758 459 5880
Fax: 1 758 459 7352

CARIBBEAN - ST. VINCENT

Camelot Inn - A Boutique Hotel
PO Box 787, Kingstown, The Grenadines, St Vincent, West Indies
Tel: 1 784 456 2100
Fax: 1 784 456 2233

CARIBBEAN - ST. VINCENT

Grand View Beach Hotel
Villa Point, Box 173, St Vincent, West Indies
Tel: 1 784 458 4811
Fax: 1 784 457 4174

CARIBBEAN - ST VINCENT & THE GRENADINES

Palm Island
ST VINCENT & THE GRENADINES, WEST INDIES
Tel: 1 800 345 0271
Fax: 1 954 481 1661

CARIBBEAN - TURKS & CAICOS ISLANDS

Point Grace
PO Box 700, Providenciales, Turks and Caicos Islands, British west indies
Tel: 1 649 946 5096
Fax: 1 649 946 5097

CARIBBEAN - TURKS & CAICOS

The Sands at Grace Bay
PO BOX 681, PROVIDENCIALES, TURKS & CAICOS islands, british WEST INDIES
Tel: 1 649 946 5199
Fax: 1 649 946 5198

FIJI ISLANDS - LABASA

Nukubati Island
PO Box 1928, Labasa, Fiji Islands
Tel: 61 2 93888 196
Fax: 61 2 93888 204

FIJI ISLANDS - LAUTOKA

Blue Lagoon Cruises
183 Vitogo Parade, Lautoka, Fiji Islands
Tel: 679 661 622
Fax: 679 664 098

FIJI ISLANDS - SAVU SAVU

Namale
Savu Savu, Fili Islands
Tel: 1 858 535 6380
Fax: 1 858 535 6385

FIJI ISLANDS - SUVA

The Wakaya Club
PO Box 15424, Suva, Fiji Islands
Tel: 679 448 128
Fax: 679 448 406.

FIJI ISLANDS - TOBERUA ISLAND

Toberua Island Resort
PO Box 567, Suva, Fiji Islands
Tel: 679 347 2777
Fax: 679 347 2888

FIJI ISLANDS - VOMO ISLANDS

Vomo Island
PO BOX 5650, LAUTOKA, FIJI ISLANDS
Tel: 679 668 122/668 133
Fax: 679 668 500

FIJI ISLANDS - YASAWA ISLANDS

Turtle Island
YASAWA ISLANDS, PO BOX 9317, NADI AIRPORT, NADI, FIJI ISLANDS
Tel: 61 3 9823 8300
Fax: 61 3 9618 1199

FIJI ISLANDS - YASAWA ISLAND

Yasawa Island Resort
PO Box 10128, Nadi Airport, Nadi, Fiji Islands
Tel: 679 6 772 2266
Fax: 679 672 4456

SAMOA - APIA

Aggie Grey's Hotel
PO Box 67, Apia, Samoa
Tel: 685 228 80
Fax: 685 232 03

MINI LISTINGS EUROPE

Condé Nast Johansens are delighted to recommend over 320 properties across Europe and The Mediterranean.
Call 0800 269 397 or see the order forms on page 517 to order guides.

Andorra

PAS DE LA CASA

Font d'Argent Hotel Ski & Resort - C/ Bearn 20, 22, 24, Pas de La Casa, Andorra. Tel: +376 739 739

Austria

KÄRNTEN (PATERGASSEN)

Almdorf "Seinerzeit" - Fellacheralm, 9564 Patergassen, Austria. Tel: +43 4275 7201KÄRNTEN (KLAGENFURT)

Hotel Palais Porcia - Neuer Platz 13, 9020 Klagenfurt, Austria. Tel: +43 463 51 15 90

KÄRNTEN (VELDEN)

Seeschlössl Velden - Klagenfurter Strasse 34, 9220 Velden, Austria. Tel: +43 4274 2824

NIEDERÖSTERREICH (DÜRNSTEIN)

Hotel Schloss Dürnstein - 3601 Dürnstein, Austria. Tel: +43 2711 212

SALZBURG (BAD GASTEIN)

Hotel & Spa Haus Hirt - An Der Kaiserpromenade 14, 5640 Bad Gastein, Austria. Tel: +43 64 34 27 97

SALZBURG (BAD HOFGASTEIN)

Das Moser - Kaiser-Franz-Platz 2, 5630 Bad Hofgastein, Austria. Tel: + 43 6432 6209

SALZBURG (BAD HOFGASTEIN)

Grand Park Hotel Bad Hofgastein - Kurgartenstrasse 26, 5630 Bad Hofgastein, Austria. Tel: +43 6432 63560

▼
TIROL (IGLS)

Schlosshotel Igls - Viller Steig 2, 6080 Igls, Tirol, Austria. Tel: +43 512 37 72 17

TIROL (IGLS)

Sporthotel Igls - Hilberstrasse 17, 6080 Igls, Tirol, Austria. Tel: +43 512 37 72 41

VORARLBERG (LECH)

Sporthotel Kristiania - Omesberg 331, 6764 Lech Am Arlberg, Austria. Tel: +43 5583 25 610

VORARLBERG (ZÜRS)

Thurnhers Alpenhof - 6763 Zürs – Arlberg, Austria. Tel: +43 5583 2191

WIEN (VIENNA)

Grand Hotel Wien - Kärntner Ring 9, 1010 Vienna, Austria. Tel: +43 1 515 80 0

Belgium

ANTWERP

Firean Hotel - Karel Oomsstraat 6, 2018 Antwerp, Belgium. Tel: +32 3 237 02 60

BRUGES

Hotel Acacia - Korte Zilverstraat 3A, 8000 Bruges, Belgium. Tel: +32 50 34 44 11

BRUGES

Hotel De Tuilerieën - Dyver 7, 8000 Bruges, Belgium. Tel: +32 50 34 36 91

BRUGES

Hotel Montanus - Nieuwe Gentweg 78, 8000 Bruges, Belgium. Tel: +32 50 33 11 76

BRUGES

Hotel Prinsenhof - Ontvangersstraat 9, 8000 Bruges, Belgium. Tel: +32 50 34 26 90

DE HAAN

Romantik Manoir Carpe Diem - Prins Karellaan 12, 8420 de Haan, Belgium. Tel: +32 59 23 32 20

FLORENVILLE

Hostellerie Le Prieuré de Conques - Rue de Conques 2, 6820 Florenville, Belgium. Tel: +32 61 41 14 17

KNOKKE~HEIST

Romantik Hotel Manoir du Dragon - Albertlaan 73, 8300 Knokke~Heist, Belgium. Tel: +32 50 63 05 80

KORTRIJK

Hotel Damier - Grote Markt 41, 8500 Kortrijk, Belgium. Tel: +32 56 22 15 47

MALMÉDY

Hostellerie Trôs Marets - Route des Trôs Marets, 4960 Malmédy, Belgium. Tel: +32 80 33 79 17

MARCHE~EN~FAMENNE

Château d'Hassonville - Route d'Hassonville 105, 6900 Marche~en~Famenne, Belgium. Tel: +32 84 31 10 25

Cyprus

LIMASSOL

Le Meridien Limassol Spa & Resort - Po Box 56560, 3308 Limassol, Cyprus. Tel: +357 25 862 000

Czech Republic

PRAGUE

Hotel Hoffmeister - Pod Bruskou 7, Klárov, 11800 Prague 1, Czech Republic. Tel: +420 2 51017 111

PRAGUE

Romantik Hotel U Raka - Cerninska 10/93, 11800 Prague 1, Czech Republic.. Tel: +420 2205 111 00

PRAGUE

Sieber Hotel & Apartments - Slezská 55, 130 00 Prague 3, Czech Republic. Tel: +420 2 24 25 00 25

Denmark

NYBORG

Hotel Hesselet - Christianslundsvej 119, 5800 Nyborg, Denmark. Tel: +45 65 31 30 29

Estonia

▼
PÄRNU

Villa Ammende - Mere Pst. 7, 80012 Pärnu, Estonia. Tel: +372 44 73888

France

ALSACE~LORRAINE (COLMAR)

Hostellerie Le Maréchal - 4 Place Six Montagnes Noires, Petite Venise, 68000 Colmar, France. Tel: +33 3 89 41 60 32

ALSACE~LORRAINE (COLMAR)

Hôtel Les Têtes - 19 Rue de Têtes, 68000 Colmar, France. Tel: +33 3 89 24 43 43

ALSACE~LORRAINE (COLMAR - ROUFFACH)

Château d'Isenbourg - 68250 Rouffach, France. Tel: +33 3 89 78 58 50

ALSACE~LORRAINE (GÉRARDMER – VOSGES)

Hostellerie Les Bas Rupts - 88400 Gérardmer, Vosges, France. Tel: +33 3 29 63 09 25

ALSACE~LORRAINE (MURBACH – BUHL)

Hostellerie St Barnabé - 68530 Murbach – Buhl, France. Tel: +33 3 89 62 14 14

ALSACE~LORRAINE (OBERNAI - OTTROTT)

A L'Ami Fritz - 8 Rue des Châteaux, 67530 Ottrott, France. Tel: +33 3 88 95 80 81

ALSACE~LORRAINE (STRASBOURG – OSTWALD)

Château de L'Ile - 4 Quai Heydt, 67540 Ostwald, France. Tel: +33 3 88 66 85 00

ALSACE~LORRAINE (THIONVILLE)

L'Horizon - 50 Route du Crève~Cœur, 57100 Thionville, France. Tel: +33 3 82 88 53 65

AUVERGNE - LIMOUSIN (SAINT~FLOUR)

Hostellerie Château de Varillettes - 15100 Saint~Georges par Saint~Flour, France. Tel: +33 4 71 60 45 05

Mini Listings Europe

Condé Nast Johansens are delighted to recommend over 320 properties across Europe and The Mediterranean.
Call 0800 269 397 or see the order forms on page 517 to order guides.

BRITTANY (BILLIERS)
Domaine de Rochevilaine - Pointe de Pen Lan, 56190
Billiers, France. Tel: +33 2 97 41 61 61

BRITTANY (LA GOUESNIÈRE - SAINT~MALO)
Château de Bonaban - 35350 La Gouesnière, France.
Tel: +33 2 99 58 24 50

BRITTANY (AMBOISE)
Le Manoir Les Minimes - 34 Quai Charles Guinot, 37400
Amboise, France. Tel: +33 2 47 30 40 40

▼
BRITTANY (MOËLAN~SUR~MER)
Manoir de Kertalg - Route de Riec-Sur-Belon, 29350
Moelan~sur~Mer, France. Tel: +33 2 98 39 77 77

BRITTANY (PLOERDÜT)
Château du Launay - 56160 Ploerdüt, France.
Tel: +33 2 97 39 46 32

BRITTANY (RENNES)
LeCoq~Gadby - 156 Rue d'Antrain, 35700 Rennes,
France. Tel: +33 2 99 38 05 55

BRITTANY (SAINT MALO – PLEVEN)
Manoir du Vaumadeuc - 22130 Pleven, France.
Tel: +33 2 96 84 46 17

BRITTANY (SAINT MALO – SAINT BRIEUC)
Manoir de la Hazaie - 22400 Planguenoual, France.
Tel: +33 2 9632 7371

BRITTANY (TREBEURDEN)
Ti Al Lannec - 14 Allée de Mézo~Guen, BP 3, 22560
Trebeurden, France. Tel: +33 296 15 01 01

BURGUNDY - FRANCHE~COMTÉ (AVALLON)
Château de Vault de Lugny - 11 Rue du Château, 89200
Avallon, France. Tel: +33 3 86 34 07 86

BURGUNDY - FRANCHE~COMTÉ (AVALLON)
Hostellerie de la Poste - 13 Place Vauban, 89200 Avallon,
France. Tel: +33 3 86 34 16 16

BURGUNDY - FRANCHE~COMTÉ (BEAUNE)
Ermitage de Corton - R.N. 74, 21200 Chorey~les~Beaune,
France. Tel: +33 3 80 22 05 28

BURGUNDY - FRANCHE~COMTÉ (POLIGNY – JURA)
Hostellerie des Monts de Vaux - Les Monts de Vaux,
39800 Poligny, France. Tel: +33 3 84 37 12 50

BURGUNDY - FRANCHE~COMTÉ (VILLEFARGEAU – AUXERRE)
Le Petit Manoir des Bruyères - 5 Allée de
Charbuy~les~Bruyères, 89240 Villefargeau, France.
Tel: +33 3 86 41 32 82

BURGUNDY - FRANCHÉ~COMTÉ (VOUGEOT)
Château de Gilly - Gilly~lès~Cîteaux, 21640 Vougeot,
France. Tel: +33 3 80 62 89 98

CHAMPAGNE - ARDENNES (ÉPERNAY)
Hostellerie La Briqueterie - 4 Route de Sézanne, 51530
Vinay – Épernay, France. Tel: +33 3 26 59 99 99

CHAMPAGNE - ARDENNES (TINQUEUX – REIMS)
L'Assiette Champenoise - 40 Avenue Paul Vaillant
Couturier, 51430 Tinqueux, France.
Tel: +33 3 26 84 64 64

CÔTE D'AZUR (CAGNES~SUR~MER)
Domaine Cocagne - Colline de La Route de Vence, 30,
Chemin du Pain de Sucre, 08600 Cagnes~sur~Mer,
France. Tel: +33 4 92 13 57 77

CÔTE D'AZUR (CANNES)
Le Cavendish - 11 Boulevard Carnot, 06400 Cannes,
France. Tel: +33 4 97 06 26 00

CÔTE D'AZUR (ÈZE VILLAGE)
Château Eza - Rue de La Pise, 06360 Èze Village, France.
Tel: +33 4 93 41 12 24

CÔTE D'AZUR (LE ROYAL – CANADEL~SUR~MER)
Le Bailli de Suffren - Avenue des Américains – Goffe de
Saint~Tropez, 83820 Le Rayol – Canadel~sur~Mer,
France. Tel: +33 4 98 04 47 00

CÔTE D'AZUR (MANDELIEU – CANNES)
Ermitage du Riou - Avenue Henri Clews, 06210
Mandelieu~La~Napoule, France. Tel: + 33 4 93 49 95 56

CÔTE D'AZUR (MOUGINS)
Le Mas Candille - Boulevard Clément Rebuffel, 06250
Mougins, France. Tel: +33 4 92 28 43 43

CÔTE D'AZUR (NICE)
Hôtel La Pérouse - 11, Quai Rauba~Capeu, 06300 Nice,
France. Tel: +33 4 93 62 34 63

CÔTE D'AZUR (SAINT~TROPEZ - RAMATUELLE)
La Ferme d'Augustin - Plage de Tahiti, 83350 Ramatuelle,
Nr Saint-Tropez, France. Tel: +33 4 94 55 97 00

CÔTE D'AZUR (SAINT~PAUL~DE~VENCE)
Le Mas d'Artigny - Route de la Colle, 06570
Saint~Paul~de~Vence, France. Tel: +33 4 93 32 84 54

CÔTE D'AZUR (SERRE~CHEVALIER)
L'Auberge du Choucas - 05220 Monetier~Les~Bains,
Serre~Chevalier, Hautes~Alpes, France.
Tel: +33 4 92 24 42 73

CÔTE D'AZUR (VENCE)
Relais Cantemerle - 258 Chemin Cantemerle, 06140
Vence, France. Tel: +33 4 93 58 08 18

LOIRE VALLEY (AMBOISE)
Château de Pray - Route de Chargé, 37400 Amboise,
France. Tel: +33 2 47 57 23 67

LOIRE VALLEY (AMBOISE)
Le Choiseul - 36 Quai Charles Guinot, 37400 Amboise,
France. Tel: +33 2 47 30 45 45

LOIRE VALLEY (CHINON)
Château de Danzay - RD 749, 37420 Chinon, France.
Tel: +33 2 47 58 46 86

LOIRE VALLEY (CHISSAY~EN~TOURRAINE)
Hostellerie Château de Chissay - 41400
Chissay~en~Touraine, France. Tel: +33 2 54 32 32 01

LOIRE VALLEY (LANGEAIS)
Château de Rochecotte - Saint~Patrice, 37130 Langeais,
France. Tel: +33 2 47 96 16 16

LOIRE VALLEY (MISSILLAC)
Domaine de La Bretesche - 44780 Missillac, France.
Tel: +33 2 51 76 86 96

LOIRE VALLEY (SAUMUR-CHÊNEHUTTE~LES~TUFFEAUX)
Le Prieuré - 49350 Chênehutte~Les~Tuffeaux, France.
Tel: +33 2 41 67 90 14

LOIRE VALLEY (TOURS - LUYNES)
Domaine de Beauvois - Le Pont Clouet, Route de
Clere~les~Pins, 37230 Luynes, France.
Tel: +33 2 47 55 50 11

LOIRE VALLEY (TOURS - MONTBAZON)
Château d'Artigny - 37250 Montbazon, France.
Tel: +33 2 47 34 30 30

LOIRE VALLEY (TOURS - MONTBAZON)
Domaine de La Tortinière - Route de Ballan~Miré, 37250
Montbazon, France. Tel: +33 2 47 34 35 00

MIDI~PYRÉNÉES (CORDES~SUR~CIEL)
Le Grand Ecuyer - Haute de la Cité, 81170
Cordes~Sur~Ciel, France. Tel: +33 5 63 53 79 50

NORMANDY (BAGNOLES DE L'ORNE)
Bois Joli - 12, Avenue Philippe du Rozier, 61140 Bagnoles
de L'Orne, France. Tel: +33 2 33 37 92 77

NORMANDY (BREUIL~EN~BESSIN)
Château de Goville - 14330 Breuil~en~Bessin, France.
Tel: +33 2 31 22 19 28

NORMANDY (ETRETAT)
Le Donjon - Chemin de Saint Clair, 76790 Etretat, France.
Tel: +33 2 35 27 08 23

NORMANDY (HONFLEUR – CRICQUEBOEUF)
Manoir de la Poterie - Chemin Paul Ruel, 14113
Cricqueboeuf, France. Tel: +33 2 31 88 10 40

NORMANDY (PACY~SUR~EURE)
Hostellerie Château de Brécourt - Douains, 27120
Pacy~sur~Eure, France. Tel: +33 2 32 52 40 50

NORTH - PICARDY (ABBEVILLE – ST. RIQUIER)
Abbatis Villa Hôtel Jean De Bruges - 18, Place de L'Eglise,
80135 St. Riquier, France. Tel: +33 3 22 28 30 30

NORTH - PICARDY (BETHUNE - GOSNAY)
La Chartreuse Du Val St Esprit - 62199 Gosnay, France.
Tel: +33 3 21 62 80 00

NORTH - PICARDY (CALAIS - RECQUES~SUR~HEM)
Château de Cocove - 62890 Recques~sur~Hem, France.
Tel: +33 3 21 82 68 29

▼
NORTH - PICARDY (ELINCOURT~SAINTE~MARGUERITE)
Château de Bellinglise - 60157
Elincourt~Sainte~Marguerite, France.
Tel: +33 3 44 96 00 33

NORTH - PICARDY (ERMENONVILLE)
Hostellerie Château d'Ermenonville - 60950
Ermenonville, France. Tel: +33 3 44 54 00 26

NORTH - PICARDY (FÈRE~EN~TARDENOIS)
Château de Fère - 02130 Fère~en~Tardenois, France.
Tel: + 33 3 23 82 21 13

NORTH - PICARDY (LILLE)
Carlton Hotel - Rue de Paris, 59000 Lille, France.
Tel: +33 3 20 13 33 13

MINI LISTINGS EUROPE

Condé Nast Johansens are delighted to recommend over 320 properties across Europe and The Mediterranean.
Call 0800 269 397 or see the order forms on page 517 to order guides.

NORTH - PICARDY (VERVINS)
La Tour du Roy - 02140 Vervins, France.
Tel: +33 3 23 98 00 11

PARIS (CHAMPS~ELYSÉES)
La Trémoille - 14 Rue de La Trémoille, 75008 Paris,
France. Tel: +33 1 56 52 14 00

▼

PARIS (CHAMPS~ELYSÉES)
Hôtel Plaza Athénée - 25 Avenue Montaigne, 75008
Paris, France. Tel: +33 1 53 67 66 65

PARIS (CHAMPS~ELYSÉES)
Hôtel San Regis - 12 Rue Jean Goujon, 75008 Paris,
France. Tel: +33 1 44 95 16 16

PARIS (CHAMPS~ELYSÉES)
Résidence Alma Marceau**** - 5 Rue Jean Giraudoux,
75016 Paris, France. Tel: +33 1 53 57 67 89

PARIS (ÉTOILE – PORTE MAILLOT)
L'Hôtel Pergolèse - 3 Rue Pergolèse, 75116 Paris, France.
Tel: +33 1 53 64 04 04

PARIS (ÉTOILE – PORTE MAILLOT)
La Villa Maillot - 143 Avenue de Malakoff, 75116 Paris,
France. Tel: +33 1 53 64 52 52

PARIS (INVALIDES)
Hôtel Le Tourville - 16 Avenue de Tourville, 75007 Paris,
France. Tel: +33 1 47 05 62 62

PARIS (JARDIN DU LUXEMBOURG)
Le Sainte~Beuve - 9 Rue Sainte~Beuve, 75006 Paris,
France. Tel: +33 1 45 48 20 07

PARIS (MADELEINE)
Hôtel de L'Arcade - 9 Rue de L'Arcade, 75008 Paris,
France. Tel: +33 1 53 30 60 00

PARIS (MADELEINE)
Hôtel Le Lavoisier - 21 Rue Lavoisier, 75008 Paris, France.
Tel: +33 1 53 30 06 06

PARIS (OPÉRA – MONTMATRE)
Hôtel Lamartine - 39 Rue Lamartine, 75009 Paris, France.
Tel: +33 1 48 78 78 58

PARIS (PANTHÉON)
Hôtel des Grands Hommes - 17 Place du Panthéon,
75005 Paris, France. Tel: +33 1 46 34 19 60

PARIS (PANTHÉON)
Hôtel du Panthéon - 19 Place du Panthéon, 75005 Paris,
France. Tel: +33 1 43 54 32 95

PARIS (SAINT~GERMAIN)
ArtusHotel - 34 Rue de Buci, 75006 Paris, France.
Tel: +33 1 43 29 07 20

PARIS (SAINT~GERMAIN)
Hôtel Le Saint~Grégoire - 43 Rue de L'Abbé Grégoire,
75006 Paris, France. Tel: 33 1 45 48 23 23

PARIS (SAINT~GERMAIN)
Hôtel Pont Royal - 7 Rue de Montalembert, 75007 Paris,
France. Tel: +33 1 42 84 70 00

PARIS (SAINT~GERMAIN)
L' Hôtel - 13, Rue des Beaux Arts, 75006 Paris, France.
Tel: +33 1 44 41 99 00

PARIS REGION (CERNAY~LA~VILLE)
Hostellerie Abbaye des Vaux de Cernay - 78720
Cernay~La~Ville, France. Tel: +33 1 34 85 23 00

PARIS REGION (ST. SYMPHORIEN~LE~CHÂTEAU)
Château d'Esclimont - 28700 St. Symphorien~
Le~Château, France. Tel: +33 2 37 31 15 15

PARIS REGION (GRESSY~EN~FRANCE – CHANTILLY)
Le Manoir de Gressy - 77410 Gressy~en~France, Roissy
Cdg, Nr Paris, France. Tel: +33 1 60 26 68 00

PARIS REGION (VILLE D'AVRAY)
Les Étangs de Corot - 53 Rue de Versailles, 92410 Ville
d'Avray, France. Tel: +33 1 41 15 37 00

PARIS REGION (YERRES – ORLY)
Hostellerie Château du Maréchal de Saxe - Domaine de
La Grange, 91330 Yerres, France. Tel: +33 1 69 48 78 53

POITOU~CHARENTES (COGNAC – CHÂTEAUBERNARD)
Château de L'Yeuse - 65 Rue de Bellevue, Quartier de
echassier, 16100 Châteaubernard, France.
Tel: +33 5 45 36 82 60

POITOU~CHARENTES (POITIERS – MIGNALOUX)
Manoir de Beauvoir Golf & Hôtel - 635 Route de
Beauvoir, 86550 Mignaloux – Beauvoir, France.
Tel: +33 5 49 55 47 47

POITOU~CHARENTES (POITIERS – SAINT~MAIXENT~L'ECOLE)
Logis St. Martin - Chemin de Pissot, 79400
Saint~Maixent~L'Ecole, France. Tel: +33 549 0558 68

PROVENCE (AIX~EN~PROVENCE)
Le Pigonnet - 5 Avenue du Pigonnet, 13090
Aix~en~Provence, France. Tel: +33 4 42 59 02 90

PROVENCE (GRIGNAN)
Le Clair de la Plume - Place du Mail, 26230 Grignan,
France. Tel: +33 4 75 91 81 30

PROVENCE (GRIGNAN)
Manoir de la Roseraie - Route de Valréas, 26230 Grignan,
France. Tel: +33 4 75 46 58 15

PROVENCE (LES~BAUX~DE~PROVENCE)
Mas de l'Oulivie - 13520 Les~Baux~de~Provence,
France. Tel: +33 4 90 54 35 78

PROVENCE (LES SAINTES~MARIES~DE~LA~MER)
Mas de La Fouque - Route du Petit Rhône, 13460 Les
Saintes~Maries~de~La~Mer, France.
Tel: +33 4 90 97 81 02

PROVENCE (SAINT~RÉMY~DE~PROVENCE)
Château des Alpilles - Route Départementale 31,
Ancienne Route du Grès, 13210
Saint~Rémy~de~Provence, France.
Tel: +33 4 90 92 03 33

PROVENCE (UZÈS)
Château d'Arpaillargues - Hôtel Marie d'Agoult, 30700
Uzès, France. Tel: +33 4 66 22 14 48

RHÔNE~ALPES (CHAMBERY – COISE~SAINT~JEAN)
Château de La Tour du Puits - 73800 Coise~Saint~Jean,
France. Tel: +33 4 79 28 88 00

RHÔNE~ALPES (COURCHEVEL 1850)
Hôtel Annapurna - 73120 Courchevel (1850), France.
Tel: +33 4 79 08 04 60

RHÔNE~ALPES (COURCHEVEL 1850)
Le Kilimandjaro - Route de L'Altiport, 73121 Courchevel
1850 Cedex, France. Tel: +33 4 79 01 18 74

RHÔNE~ALPES (DIVONNE~LES~BAINS)
Château de Divonne - 01220 Divonne~les~Bains, France.
Tel: +33 4 50 20 00 32

RHÔNE~ALPES (DIVONNE~LES~BAINS)
Le Domaine de Divonne Casino, Golf & Spa Resort -
Avenue des Thermes, 01220 Divonne-les-Bains, France.
Tel: +33 4 50 40 34 34

RHÔNE~ALPES (LES GÉTS)
Chalet Hôtel La Marmotte - 61 Rue du Chéne, 74260 Les
Géts, France. Tel: + 33 4 50 75 80 33

RHÔNE~ALPES (LYON)
La Tour Rose - 22 Rue du Boeuf, 69005 Lyon, France.
Tel: +33 4 78 92 69 10

RHÔNE~ALPES (SCIEZ~SUR~LÉMAN)
Château de Coudrée - Domaine de Coudrée, Bonnatrait,
74140 Sciez~sur~Léman, France. Tel: +33 4 50 72 62 33

SOUTH WEST (BIARRITZ)
Hôtel du Palais - Avenue de L'Impératrice, 64200 Biarritz,
France. Tel: +33 5 59 41 64 00

SOUTH WEST (LE BUISSON~DE~CADOUIN)
Le Manoir de Bellerive - Route de Siorac, 24480 Le-
Buisson~de~Cadouin, France. Tel: +33 5 53 22 16 16

SOUTH WEST (SAINT~JEAN~DE~LUZ)
Hotel Lehen Tokia - Chemin Achotarreta, 64500 Ciboure,
Saint~Jean~De~Luz, France. Tel: +33 5 59 47 18 16

SOUTH WEST (SAINTE~RADEGONDE – SAINT~EMILION)
Château de Sanse - 33350 Sainte~Radegonde, France.
Tel: +33 5 57 56 41 10

WESTERN LOIRE (CHAMPIGNÉ)
Château des Briottières - 49330 Champigné, France.
Tel: +33 2 41 42 00 02

WESTERN LOIRE (NANTES – LES SORINIÉRES)
Hostellerie Abbaye de Villeneuve - 44480 Nantes – Les
Sorinières, France. Tel: +33 2 40 04 40 25

WESTERN LOIRE (NOIRMOUTIER)
Hostellerie du Général d'Elbée - Place du Château, 85330
Noirmoutier~en~L'Isle, France. Tel: +33 2 51 39 10 29

Germany

DÜSSELDORF – WASSENBERG
Hotel Burg Wassenberg **** - Auf Dem Burgberg 17,
41849 Wassenberg, Germany. Tel: +49 2432 9490

OBERWESEL – RHEIN
Burghotel auf Schönburg - 55430 Oberwesel – Rhein,
Germany. Tel: +49 67 44 93 930

▼

ROTHENBURG OB DER TAUBER
Hotel Eisenhut - Herrngasse 3-7, 91541 Rothenburg Ob
Der Tauber, Germany. Tel: +49 9861 7050

MINI LISTINGS EUROPE

Condé Nast Johansens are delighted to recommend over 320 properties across Europe and The Mediterranean.
Call 0800 269 397 or see the order forms on page 517 to order guides.

Great Britain & Ireland

ENGLAND (AMBERLEY)
Amberley Castle - Amberley, Nr Arundel, West Sussex BN18 9ND, England. Tel: +44 1798 831 992

ENGLAND (BAMBURGH)
Waren House Hotel - Waren Mill, Bamburgh, Northumberland NE70 7EE, England.
Tel: +44 1668 214581

ENGLAND (DERBY - NOTTINGHAM)
Risley Hall Country House Hotel - Derby Road, Risley, Derbyshire DE72 3SS, England. Tel: +44 115 939 9000

ENGLAND (LONDON)
Beaufort House - 45 Beaufort Gardens, Knightsbridge, London SW3 1PN, England. Tel: +44 20 7584 2600

ENGLAND (LONDON)
Draycott House Apartments - 10 Draycott Avenue, Chelsea, London SW3 3AA, England.
Tel: +44 20 7584 4659

ENGLAND (LONDON)
Kensington House Hotel - 15-16 Prince Of Wales Terrace, Kensington, London W8 5PQ, England.
Tel: +44 20 7937 2345

ENGLAND (LONDON)
Number Eleven Cadogan Gardens - 11 Cadogan Gardens, Sloane Square, Knightsbridge, London SW3 2RJ. Tel: +44 20 7730 7000

ENGLAND (LONDON)
Number Sixteen - 16 Sumner Place, London SW7 3EG, England. Tel: +44 20 7589 5232

ENGLAND (LONDON)
Pembridge Court Hotel - 34 Pembridge Gardens, London W2 4DX, England. Tel: +44 20 7229 9977

ENGLAND (LONDON)
The Academy, The Bloomsbury Town House - 21 Gower Street, London WC1E 6HG, England.
Tel: +44 20 7631 4115

ENGLAND (LONDON)
The Beaufort - 33 Beaufort Gardens, Knightsbridge, London SW3 1PP, England. Tel: +44 20 7584 5252

ENGLAND (LONDON)
The Colonnade, The Little Venice Town House - 2 Warrington Crescent, London W9 1ER, England.
Tel: +44 20 7286 1052

ENGLAND (LONDON)
The Cranley - 10–12 Bina Gardens, South Kensington, London SW5 0LA, England. Tel: +44 20 7373 0123

ENGLAND (LONDON)
The Dorchester - Park Lane, Mayfair, London W1A 2HJ, England. Tel: +44 20 7629 8888

ENGLAND (LONDON)
The Halkin - 5 Halkin Street, Belgravia, London SW1X 7DJ, England. Tel: +44 20 7333 1000

ENGLAND (LONDON)
The Leonard - 15 Seymour Street, London W1H 7JW, England. Tel: +44 20 7935 2010

ENGLAND (LONDON)
The Milestone Hotel and Apartments - 1 Kensington Court, London, W8 5DL, England. Tel: +44 20 7917 1000

ENGLAND (LONDON)
Twenty Nevern Square - 20 Nevern Square, London SW5 9PD, England. Tel: +44 20 7565 9555

ENGLAND (LYNTON)
Hewitt's - Villa Spaldi - North Walk, Lynton, Devon EX35 6HJ, England. Tel: +44 1598 752 293

ENGLAND (MELTON MOWBRAY)
Stapleford Park Hotel, Spa, Golf & Sporting Estate - Nr Melton Mowbray, Leicestershire LE14 2EF, England.
Tel: +44 1572 787 522

Greece

ATHENS
Hotel Pentelikon - 66 Diligianni Street, 14562 Athens, Greece. Tel: +30 10 62 30 650-6

CRETE
St Nicolas Bay Hotel - 72100 Agios Nikolaos, Crete, Greece. Tel: +30 2841 025041/2/3

▼
CRETE
The Peninsula at Porto Elounda de luxe Resort - 72053 Elounda, Crete, Greece. Tel: +30 84 10 41 903

PAROS
Astir of Paros - Kolymbithres, Naoussa, 84401 Paro, Greece. Tel: +30 284 51976

Italy

CAMPANIA (POSITANO)
Hotel Villa Franca - Viale Pasitea 318, 84017 Positano (SA), Italy. Tel: +39 089 875655

CAMPANIA (POSITANO)
Hotel Poseidon - Via Pasitea 148, 84017 Positano (Salerno), Italy. Tel: +39 089 811111

CAMPANIA (RAVELLO)
Hotel Villa Maria - Via S.Chiara 2, 84010 Ravello (SA), Italy. Tel: +39 089 857255

CAMPANIA (SAN. AGATA SUI DUE GOLFI)
Oasi Olimpia Relais - Via Deserto 26, San Agata sui due Golfi, 80064 Hassa Lubrense (NA), Italy.
Tel: +39 081 8080560

CAMPANIA (SORRENTO)
Grand Hotel Cocumella - Via Cocumella 7, 80065 Sant'Agnello, Sorrento, Italy. Tel: +39 081 878 2933

CAMPANIA (SORRENTO)
Grand Hotel Excelsior Vittoria - Piazza Tasso 34, 80067 Sorrento (Naples), Italy. Tel: +39 081 807 1044

EMILIA ROMAGNA (BAGNO DI ROMAGNA TERME)
Hotel Tosco Romagnolo - Piazza Dante Alighieri 2, 47021 Bagno di Romagna Terme, Italy. Tel: +39 0543 911260

EMILIA ROMAGNA (BOLOGNA)
Grand Hotel Baglioni - Via Indipendenza 8, 40121 Bologna, Italy. Tel: +39 051 225445

EMILIA ROMAGNA (BRISIGHELLA)
Relais Torre Pratesi - Via Cavina 11, 48013 Brisighella, Italy. Tel: +39 0546 84545

EMILIA ROMAGNA (FERRARA)
Ripagrande Hotel - Via Ripagrande 21, 44100 Ferrara, Italy. Tel: +39 0532 765250

EMILIA ROMAGNA (RICCIONE)
Hotel des Nations - Lungomare Costituzione 2, 47838 Riccione (Rn), Italy. Tel: +39 0541 647878

LAZIO (PALO LAZIALE – ROME)
La Posta Vecchia - Loc. Palo Laziale, 00055 Ladispoli, Rome, Italy. Tel: +39 0699 49501

LAZIO (ROME)
Hotel Aventino - Via San. Domenico 10, 00153 Rome, Italy. Tel: +39 06 5745 174

LAZIO (ROME)
Hotel Farnese - Via Alessandro Farnese 30 (Angolo Viale Giulio Cesare), 00192 Rome, Italy.
Tel: +39 06 321 25 53/4

LAZIO (ROME)
Hotel Giulio Cesare - Via degli Scipioni 287, 00192 Rome, Italy. Tel: +39 06 321 0751

LIGURIA (FINALE LIGURE)
Hotel Punta Est - Via Aurelia 1, 17024 Finale Ligure, Italy. Tel: +39 019 600611

LIGURIA (SESTRI - LEVANTE)
Hotel Vis à Vis - Via della Chiusa 28, 16039 Sestri Levante, (GE), Italy. Tel: +39 0185 42661/480801

▼
LOMBARDY (ERBUSCO - FRANCIACORTA)
L'Albereta - Via Vittorio Emanuele 11, 25030 Erbusco (Bs), Italy. Tel: +39 030 7760 550

LOMBARDY (MANTOVA)
Albergo San Lorenzo - Piazza Concordia 14, 46100 Mantova, Italy. Tel: +39 0376 220500

PIEMONTE (CUNEO)
Lovera Palace Hotel - Via Roma, 37, 12100 Cuneo, Italy. Tel: +39 0171 690 420

PIEMONTE (STRESA – LAKE MAGGIORE)
Hotel Villa Aminta - Via Sempione Nord 123, 28838 Stresa (VB), Italy. Tel: +39 0323 933 818

Condé Nast Johansens are delighted to recommend over 320 properties across Europe and The Mediterranean.
Call 0800 269 397 or see the order forms on page 517 to order guides.

PIEMONTE (TORINO)
Hotel Victoria - Via Nino Costa 4, 10123 Torino, Italy.
Tel: +39 011 56 11909

PUGLIA (SAVELLETRI DI FASANO)
Masseria San Domenico - Litoranea 379, 72010 Savelletri
di Fasano (Brindisi) Italy. Tel: +39 080 482 7990

SICILY (ETNA)
Hotel Villa Paradiso dell'Etna - Via Per Viagrande 37,
95037 San Giovanni La Punta, Italy. Tel: +39 095 7512409

SICILY (GIARDINI NAXOS)
Hellenia Yachting Hotel - Via Jannuzzo 41, 98035
Giardini Naxos (ME), Italy. Tel: +39 (0)942 51737

SICILY (TAORMINA RIVIERA – MARINA D'AGRO)
Hotel Baia Taormina - Statale Dello Ionio 39, 98030
Marina D'Agro (ME), Italy. Tel: +39 0942 756292

▼
TRENTINO - ALTO ADIGE (MADONNA DI CAMPIGLIO)
Hotel Lorenzetti - Via Dolomiti Di Brenta 119, 38084
Madonna Di Campiglio (Tn) Italy. Tel: +39 0465 44 14 04

TRENTINO - ALTO ADIGE (MARLING – MERAN)
Romantik Hotel Oberwirt - St Felixweg 2, 39020 Marling
– Meran, Italy. Tel: +39 0473 44 71 11

TRENTINO - ALTO ADIGE (MERAN)
Park Hotel Mignon - Via Grabmayr 5, 39012 Meran, Italy.
Tel: +39 0473 230353

TRENTINO – ALTO ADIGE (NOVA LEVANTE)
Posthotel Weisses Rössl - Via Carezza 30, 39056 Nova
Levante (Bz), Dolomites, Italy. Tel: +39 0471 613113

TRENTINO – ALTO ADIGE (SAN CASSIANO)
Hotel & Spa Rosa Alpina - Strada Micura de Rue 20,
39030 San Cassiano (BZ) Italy.. Tel: +39 0471 849500

TUSCANY (ASCIANO - SIENA)
CasaBianca - Loc. Casabianca , 53041 Asciano (SI), Italy.
Tel: +39 0577 704362

TUSCANY (CASTIGLION FIORENTINO)
Relais San Pietro in Polvano - Località Polvano, 52043
Castiglion Fiorentino (AR), Italy. Tel: +39 0575 650100

TUSCANY (COLLE VAL D'ELSA - SIENA)
Relais della Rovere - Via Piemonte 10, Loc. Badia, 53034
Colle Val D'Elsa (SI), Italy. Tel: +39 0577 924696

TUSCANY (ELBA ISLAND - CAPOLIVERI)
Grand Hotel Elba International - Baia della Fontanella,
Isola D'Elba, 57031 Capoliveri (LI), Italy.
Tel: +39 0565 946111

TUSCANY (FLORENCE)
Hotel J and J - Via di Mezzo 20, 50121 Florence, Italy.
Tel: +39 055 263121

TUSCANY (FLORENCE)
Villa Montartino - Via Gherardo Silvani 151, 50125
Florence, Italy. Tel: +39 055 223520

TUSCANY (LIDO DI CAMAIORE)
Hotel Villa Ariston - Viale C. Colombo 355, 55043 Lido Di
Camaiore – Lucca, Italy. Tel: +39 0584 610633

TUSCANY (MONTERIGGIONI – SIENA)
Hotel Monteriggioni - Via 1 Maggio 4, 53035
Monteriggioni, Italy. Tel: +39 0577 305009

TUSCANY (MONTERIGGIONI – STROVE)
Castel Pietraio - Strada Di Strove 33, 53035
Monteriggioni, Italy. Tel: +39 0577 300020

TUSCANY (PIEVESCOLA)
Hotel Relais La Suvera - 53030 Pievescola – Siena, Italy.
Tel: +39 0577 960300

TUSCANY (PORTO ERCOLE)
Il Pellicano - 58018 Porto Ercole (Gr), Tuscany, Italy.
Tel: +39 0564 858111

TUSCANY (PORTO SANTO STEFANO – ARGENTARIO)
Hotel Torre di Cala Piccola - Porto Santo Stefano, 58019
Argentario, Italy. Tel: +39 0564 825111

TUSCANY (PUNTA ALA)
Hotel Cala del Porto - Via Del Pozzo, 58040 Punta Ana,
Italy. Tel: +39 0564 922455

TUSCANY (RADDA IN CHIANTI)
Palazzo Leopoldo - Via Roma 33, 53017 Radda In Chianti,
Italy. Tel: +39 0577 735605

TUSCANY (SIENA)
Hotel Certosa di Maggiano - Strada Di Certosa 82, 53100
Siena, Italy. Tel: +39 0577 288180

UMBRIA (ASSISI)
Romantik Hotel Le Silve di Armenzano - 06081 Loc.
Armenzano, Assisi (PG), Italy. Tel: +39 075 801 9000

UMBRIA (COLLE SAN PAOLO - PERUGIA)
Romantik Hotel Villa di Monte Solare - Via Montali 7,
06070 Colle San Paolo - Panicale (PG), Italy.
Tel: +39 075 832376

UMBRIA (GUBBIO)
Castello di Petroia - Località Petroia, 06020 Gubbio (Pg),
Italy. Tel: +39 075 92 02 87 / 92 01 09

UMBRIA (OSCANO - PERUGIA)
Castello dell'Oscano Historical Residence - 06134
Perugia, Localita Cenerente, Italy. Tel: +39 075 584371

UMBRIA (PIAZZANO - CORTONA)
Villa di Piazzano - Località Piazzano, 06069 Tuoro Sul
Trasimeno (PG), Italy. Tel: +39 075 826226

UMBRIA (SPOLETO)
Villa Milani - Residenza d'Epoca - Loc. Colle Attivoli 4,
06049 Spoleto, Italy. Tel: +39 0743 225056

UMBRIA (TODI)
Hotel Bramante - Via Orvietana 48, 06059 Todi (PG), Italy.
Tel: +39 075 8348381/2/3

VENETIA (BASSANO DEL GRAPPA)
Hotel Ca' Sette - Via Cunizza Da Romano 4, 36061
Bassano del Grappa, Italy. Tel: +39 0424 383350

VENETIA (LIDO DI JESELO)
Park Hotel Brasilia - Via Levantina, 30017 Lido Di Jesolo,
Italy. Tel: +39 0421 380851

VENETIA (MOGLIANO VENETO)
Hotel Villa Condulmer - Via Preganziol 1, 31020
Mogliano Veneto, Italy. Tel: +39 041 5972 700

VENETIA (NEGRAR – VERONA)
Relais La Magioca - Via Moron 3, 37024 Negrar (Verona),
Italy. Tel: +39 045 600 0167

VENETIA (SARCEDO - VICENZA)
Casa Belmonte Relais - Via Belmonte 2, 36030 Sarcedo,
Italy. Tel: +39 0445 884833

VENETIA (VENICE)
Hotel Giorgione - SS. Apostoli 4587, 30131 Venice, Italy.
Tel: +39 041 522 5810

VENETIA (VENICE – LIDO)
Albergo Quattro Fontane - 30126 Lido Di Venezia,
Venice, Italy. Tel: +39 041 526 0227

Luxembourg

REMICH
Hotel Saint~Nicolas - 31 Esplanade, 5533 Remich,
Luxembourg. Tel: +352 2666 3

Monaco

MONTE~CARLO
Monte~Carlo Beach Hotel - Avenue Princesse Grace,
06190 Roquebrune – Cap~Martin, France.
Tel: +377 92 16 25 25

The Netherlands

AMSTERDAM
Ambassade Hotel - Herengracht 341, 1016 Az
Amsterdam, The Netherlands. Tel: +31 20 5550222

AMSTERDAM
Blakes - Keizersgracht 384, 1016 GB Amsterdam, The
Netherlands. Tel: +31 20 530 20 10

AMSTERDAM
Seven One Seven - Prinsengracht 717, 1017 Jw
Amsterdam, The Netherlands. Tel: +31 20 42 70 717

LATTROP
Hotel de Holtweijde - Spiekweg 7, 7635 Lattrop, The
Netherlands. Tel: +31 541 229 234

▼
MAASTRICHT
Château St Gerlach - Joseph Corneli Allée 1, 6301 KK
Valkenburg A/D Geul, Maastricht, The Netherlands.
Tel: +31 43 608 88 88

OOTMARSUM
Hotel de Wiemsel - Winhofflaan 2, 7631 Hx Ootmarsum,
The Netherlands. Tel: +31 541 292 155

Mini Listings Europe

Condé Nast Johansens are delighted to recommend over 320 properties across Europe and The Mediterranean.
Call 0800 269 397 or see the order forms on page 517 to order guides.

Norway

OPPDAL – DOVREFJELL
Kongsvold Fjeldstue - Dovrefjell, 7340 Oppdal, Norway.
Tel: +47 72 40 43 40

OSLO
Hotel Bastion - Skippergaten 7, 0152 Oslo, Norway.
Tel: +47 22 47 77 00

SOLVORN
Walaker Hotell - 6879 Solvorn, Sogn, Norway.
Tel: +47 576 82080

VOSS
Fleischers Hotel - 5700 Voss, Norway.
Tel: +47 56 52 05 00

Portugal

ALENTEJO (REDONDO)
Convento de São Paulo - Aldeia Da Serra, 7170 –120
Redondo, Portugal. Tel: +351 266 989160

ALGARVE (LAGOS)
Romantik Hotel Vivenda Miranda - Porto de Mós, 8600
Lagos, Portugal. Tel: +351 282 763222

LISBON & TAGUS VALLEY (LISBON)
Solar Do Castelo - Rua das Cozinhas 2, 1100–181 Lisbon,
Portugal. Tel: +351 218 870 909

LISBON & TAGUS VALLEY (SINTRA)
Tivoli Hotel Palácio de Seteais - Rua Barbosa de Bocage,
10, Seteais, 2710 Sintra, Portugal. Tel: +351 219 233 200

▼
MADEIRA (FUNCHAL)
Quinta da Bela Vista - Caminho do Avista Navios 4, 9000
Funchal, Madeira, Portugal. Tel: +351 291 706400

MADEIRA (FUNCHAL)
Quinta das Vistas Palacio Gardens - Caminho de Santa
Antonio 52-A, 9000-187 Funchal, Madeira, Portugal.
Tel: +351 291 750 007

MADEIRA (FUNCHAL)
Quinta do Estreito - Rua José Joaquim da Costa, Estreito
de Câmara De Lobos, 9325–034 Madeira, Portugal.
Tel: +351 291 910530

MADEIRA (FUNCHAL)
Quinta do Monte - Caminho do Monte 192, 9050-288
Funchal, Madeira, Portugal. Tel: +351 291 780 100

MADEIRA (FUNCHAL)
Quinta Perestrello - Rua do Dr. Pita 3, 9000-089 Funchal,
Madeira, Portugal. Tel: +351 291 706700

OPORTO & NORTHERN PORTUGAL (PINHÃO)
Vintage House Hotel - Lugar da Ponte, 5085-034 Pinhão,
Portugal. Tel: +351 22 371 999 / 375 4633

Spain

ANDALUCÍA (ANTEQUERA)
Hotel Antequera Golf - Sta Catalina S/N, 29200
Antequera, Spain. Tel: +34 95 27 04 531

ANDALUCÍA (ARCOS DE LA FRONTERA)
Hacienda El Santiscal - Avda. El Santiscal 129 (Lago De
Arcos), 11630 Arcos de La Frontera, Spain.
Tel: +34 956 70 83 13

ANDALUCÍA (BENAHAVIS – MARBELLA)
Amanhavis Hotel - Calle del Pilar 3, 29679 Benahavis,
Málaga, Spain. Tel: +34 952 85 60 26

ANDALUCÍA (DOÑANA NATIONAL PARK)
El Cortijo de Los Mimbrales - Ctra del Rocio -
Matalascañas, Km 30, 21750 Almonte (Huelva), Spain.
Tel: +34 959 44 22 37

ANDALUCÍA (GRANADA)
Hotel La Bobadilla - Finca La Bobadilla, Apto. 144, 18300
Loja, Granada, Spain. Tel: +34 958 32 18 61

ANDALUCÍA (JEREZ DE LA FRONTERA)
Hotel Villa Jerez - Avda. de La Cruz Roja 7, 11407 Jerez
de La Frontera, Spain. Tel: +34 956 15 31 00

ANDALUCÍA (MÁLAGA)
Hotel La Casona de la Ciudad **** - C/Marqués de
Salvatierra 5, 29400 Ronda, Málaga, Spain.
Tel: +34 952 87 95 95/96

ANDALUCÍA (MÁLAGA)
Hotel La Fuente de La Higuera - Partido de Los
Frontones, 29400 Ronda, Málaga, Spain.
Tel: +34 95 2 11 43 55

ANDALUCÍA (MÁLAGA)
La Posada del Torcal - 29230 Villanueva de La
Concepción, Málaga, Spain. Tel: +34 952 03 11 77

ANDALUCÍA (MÁLAGA)
El Molino de Santillán - Ctra. de Macharaviaya, Km 3,
29730 Rincón de La Victoria, Málaga, Spain.
Tel: +34 952 40 09 49

ANDALUCÍA (MARBELLA – ESTEPONA)
Las Dunas Beach Hotel & Spa - La Boladilla Baja, Crta. de
Cádiz Km 163.5, 29689 Marbella – Estepona (Málaga),
Spain. Tel: +34 952 79 43 45

ANDALUCÍA (MIJAS~COSTA)
Hotel Byblos Andaluz - Mijas Golf, 29650 Mijas~Costa,
Málaga, Spain. Tel: +34 952 47 30 50

ANDALUCÍA (SEVILLA)
Cortijo El Esparragal - Ctra. de Merida, KM 795, 41860
Gerena (Sevilla), Spain. Tel: +34 955 78 27 02

ANDALUCÍA (SEVILLA)
Hacienda Benazuza El Bulli Hotel - 41800 Sanlúcar La
Mayor, Seville, Spain. Tel: +34 955 70 33 44

ANDALUCÍA (SEVILLA)
Hotel Cortijo Águila Real - Ctra. Guillena–Burguillos Km
4, 41210 Guillena, Sevilla, Spain. Tel: +34 955 78 50 06

ANDALUCÍA (SEVILLA)
Hotel Hacienda La Boticaria - Ctra. Alcalá - Utrera Km.2,
41500 Alcalá de Guadaira, Sevilla, Spain.
Tel: +34 955 69 88 20

ANDALUCÍA (SEVILLA)
Palacio Marqués de la Gomera - C/ San Pedro 20, 41640
Osuna, Sevilla, Spain. Tel: +34 95 4 81 22 23

ANDALUCÍA (SEVILLA)
Palacio de San Benito - c/San Benito S/N, 41370 Cazalla
de La Sierra, Sevilla, Spain. Tel: +34 954 88 33 36

ANDALUCÍA (SOTOGRANDE)
Almenara Golf Hotel & Spa - Avenida Almenara, 11310
Sotogrande, Spain. Tel: + 34 956 58 20 00

ARAGÓN (TERUEL)
La Parada del Compte - Antigua Estación de Ferrocarril,
44597 Torre del Compte, Teruel, Spain.
Tel: +34 978 76 90 72

ASTURIAS (VILLAMAYOR)
Palacio de Cutre - La Goleta S/N Villamayor, 33583
Infiesto, Asturias, Spain. Tel: +34 985 70 80 72

BALEARIC ISLANDS (IBIZA)
Cas Gasi - Apdo. Correos 117, 07814 Santa Gertrudis,
Ibiza, Balearic Islands. Tel: +34 971 19 71 73

▼
BALEARIC ISLANDS (MALLORCA)
Ca's Xorc - Carretera de Deía, Km 56,1 07100 Sóller,
Mallorca, Balearic Islands. Tel: +34 971 63 82 80

BALEARIC ISLANDS (MALLORCA)
Can Furiós Petit Hotel - Cami Vell Binibona 11, Binibona,
07314 Caimari, Mallorca, Balearic Islands.
Tel: +34 971 51 57 51

BALEARIC ISLANDS (MALLORCA)
Hotel Monnaber Nou - Possessió Monnaber Nou, 07310
Campanet, Mallorca, Balearic Islands.
Tel: +34 971 87 71 76

BALEARIC ISLANDS (MALLORCA)
Hotel Vistamar de Valldemossa - Ctra Valldemossa,
Andratx Km. 2, 07170 Valldemossa, Mallorca, Balearic
Islands. Tel: +34 971 61 23 00

BALEARIC ISLANDS (MALLORCA)
Read's - Ca'N Moragues, 07320 Santa María, Mallorca,
Balearic Islands. Tel: +34 971 14 02 62

BALEARIC ISLANDS (MALLORCA)
Sa Posada d'Aumallia - Camino Son Prohens 1027, 07200
Felanitx, Mallorca, Balearic Islands. Tel: +34 971 58 26 57

BALEARIC ISLANDS (MALLORCA)
Scott's - Plaza de La Iglesia 12, 07350 Binissalem,
Mallorca, Balearic Islands. Tel: +34 971 87 01 00

CANARY ISLANDS (FUERTEVENTURA)
Elba Palace Golf Hotel - Urb. Fuerteventura Golf Club,
35610 Antigua, Fuerteventura. Tel: +34 928 16 39 22

CANARY ISLANDS (GRAN CANARIA)
Gran Hotel Costa Meloneras **** - C/Mar Mediterráneo
1, 35100 maspalomas, Gran Canaria, Canary Islands.
Tel: +34 928 12 81 00

Condé Nast Johansens are delighted to recommend over 320 properties across Europe and The Mediterranean.
Call 0800 269 397 or see the order forms on page 517 to order guides.

CANARY ISLANDS (LANZAROTE)
Finca de Las Salinas - C/ La Cuesta 17, 35570 Yaiza, Lanzarote, Canary Islands. Tel: +34 928 83 03 25

▼
CANARY ISLANDS (LANZAROTE)
Gran Meliá Volcán - Urb. Castillo del Aguila, Playa Blanco, Lanzarote, Canary Islands. Tel: +34 928 51 91 85

CANARY ISLANDS (TENERIFE)
Gran Hotel Bahía del Duque Resort - 38660 Adeje, Costa Adeje, Tenerife South, Canary Islands. Tel: +34 922 74 69 33/34

CANARY ISLANDS (TENERIFE)
Hotel Botánico *****GL - Avda. Richard J. Yeoward, Urb. Botánico, 38400 Puerto de La Cruz, Tenerife, Canary Islands. Tel: +34 922 38 14 00

CANARY ISLANDS (TENERIFE)
Hotel Jardín Tropical - Calle Gran Bretaña, 38670 Costa Adeje, Tenerife, Canary Islands. Tel: +34 922 74 60 00

CANTABRIA (VILLACARRIEDO)
Palacio de Soñanes - Bomo Quintanal 1, Villacarriedo, Cantabria, Spain. Tel: +34 942 59 06 00

CASTILLA~LA MANCHA (ALMAGRO)
La Casa del Rector - c/Pedro Oviedo 8, 13270 Almagro, Ciudad Real, Spain. Tel: +34 926 26 12 59

CASTILLA Y LEÓN (ÁVILA)
El Milano Real - C/ Toleo S/N, Hoyos del Espino, 05634 Ávila, Spain. Tel: +34 920 349 108

CASTILLA Y LEÓN (SALAMANCA)
Hotel Rector - Rector Esperabé 10–Apartado 399, 37008 Salamanca, Spain. Tel: +34 923 21 84 82

CASTILLA Y LEÓN (SEGOVIA)
Caserío de Lobones - Valverde del Majano, 40140 Segovia, Spain. Tel: +34 921 12 84 08

CATALUÑA (BARCELONA)
Hotel Claris - Pau Claris 150, 08009 Barcelona, Spain. Tel: +34 934 87 62 62

CATALUÑA (BARCELONA)
Hotel Colón - Avenida de La Catedral 7, 08002 Barcelona, Spain. Tel: +34 933 01 14 04

CATALUÑA (BARCELONA)
The Gallery - Rossellón 249, 08008 Barcelona, Spain. Tel: +34 934 15 99 11

CATALUÑA (COSTA BRAVA)
Hotel Rigat Park - Playa de Fenals, 17310 Lloret de Mar, Costa Brava, Spain. Tel: +34 972 36 52 00

CATALUÑA (GERONA)
Hotel Golf Peralada - C/ Rocaberti S/N, 17491 peralada, Gerona, Spain. Tel: +34 972 53 88 30

CATALUÑA (GERONA)
Mas Falgarona - Avinyonet de Puigventos, 17742 Gerona, Spain. Tel: +34 972 54 66 28

CATALUÑA (SITGES)
Hotel Estela Barcelona - Avda. Port d'Aiguadolç S/N, 08870 Sitges (Barcelona), Spain. Tel: +34 938 11 45 45

CATALUÑA (TARRAGONA)
Hotel Termes Montbrió Resort, Spa & Park - Carrer Nou 38, 43340 Montbrió del Camp (Tarragona), Spain. Tel: +34 977 81 40 00

CATALUÑA (VILADRAU - GERONA)
Xalet La Coromina - Carretera de Vic S/N, 17406 Viladrau, Spain. Tel: +34 938 84 92 64

MADRID (MADRID)
Antiguo Convento - C/ de Las Monjas, S/N Boadilla del Monte, 28660 Madrid, Spain.. Tel: + 34 91 632 22 20

MADRID (MADRID)
Hotel Villa Real - Plaza de Las Cortes 10, 28014 Madrid, Spain. Tel: +34 914 20 37 67

MURCIA (CARTAGENA - LA MANGA)
Hyatt Regency La Manga - Los Belones, 30385 Cartagena, Murcia, Spain. Tel: +34 968 33 12 34

VALENCIA (DÉNIA)
Hotel Buena Vista - Partida Tossalet 82, La Xara, 03709 Dénia, Spain. Tel: +34 965 78 79 95

VALENCIA (XÀTIVA)
Hotel Mont Sant - Subida Al Castillo, s/n Xàtiva, 46800 Valencia, Spain. Tel: +34 962 27 50 81

Sweden

BORGHOLM
Halltorps Gästgiveri - 38792 Borgholm, Sweden. Tel: +46 485 85000

HESTRA – SMÅLAND
Hestravikens Wärdshus - vik, 33027, hestra, Småland, Sweden. Tel: +46 370 33 68 00

LAGAN
Romantik Hotel Toftaholm Herrgård - Toftaholm Pa, 34014 Lagan, Sweden. Tel: +46 370 440 55

MALMO - GENARP
Häckeberga Manor - 24013 Genarp, Sweden. Tel: +46 40 48 04 40

TÄLLBERG
Romantik Hotel Åkerblads - 79370 Tällberg, Sweden. Tel: +46 247 50800

Switzerland

CHÂTEAU D'OEX
Hostellerie Bon Accueil - 1837 Château d'Oex, Switzerland. Tel: +41 26 924 6320

GSTAAD
Le Grand Chalet - Neueretstrasse, 3780 Gstaad, Switzerland. Tel: +41 33 748 7676

KANDERSTEG
Royal Park ***** Hotel - 3718 Kandersteg, Bernese Oberland, Switzerland. Tel: +41 33 675 88 88

Turkey

ANTALYA
Marina Residence & Restaurant - Mermerli Sokak No. 15, Kaleici, 07100 Antalya, Turkey. Tel: +90 242 247 5490

ANTALYA
Outdoor Centre Resort - Gift Gesmeier Mevkii, Beldibi, Antalya, Turkey. Tel: +90 242 824 9666

ANTALYA
Renaissance Antalya Resort - PO Box 654, 07004 Beldibi - Kemer, Antalya, Turkey. Tel: +90 242 824 84 31

ANTALYA
Talya Hotel - Fevzi Çakmak Caddesi No. 30, 07100 Antalya, Turkey. Tel: +90 242 248 6800

▼
ANTALYA
Tekeli Konaklari - Dizdar Hasan Sokak, Kaleici, Antalya, Turkey. Tel: +90 242 244 54 65

ANTALYA
Tuvana Residence - Tuzcular Mahallesi, Karanlik Sokak 7, 07100 Kaleiçi - Antalya,Turkey. Tel: +90 242 247 60 15

BODRUM
Divan Palmira Hotel - Kelesharim Cad 6, 48483 Türkbükü – Bodrum, Turkey. Tel: +90 252 377 5601

BODRUM
L'Ambience Hotel - Bodrum - Eski ÇeSme Meukii, Gümbet Kavsagi, 48400 Bodrum - Mugla, Turkey. Tel: +90 252 313 83 30

GÖREME – CAPPADOCIA
CCS - Cappadocia Cave Suites - Gafelli Mahallesi, unlü Sokak, 05180 Göreme – Nevsehir, Turkey. Tel: +90 384 271 2800

KALKAN
Hotel Villa Mahal - P.K. 4 Kalkan, 07960 Antalya, Turkey. Tel: +90 242 844 32 68

UGHISAR - CAPPADOCIA
Museum Hotel - Tekelli Mahallesi 1, Urghisar - Nevsehir, Turkey. Tel: +90 384 219 22 20

ÜRGÜP - CAPPADOCIA
Ürgüp Evi - Esbelli Mahallesi 54, 5400 Ürgüp-Nevsehir, Turkey. Tel: +90 384 341 3173

NORTHERN CYPRUS (GIRNE - KYRENIA)
Hotel Bellapais Gardens - Crusader Road, Bellapais, Girne, Northern Cyprus. Tel: +90 392 815 60 66

NORTHERN CYPRUS (GIRNE)
The Hideaway Club - Karaman Road, Edremit, Girne, Northen Cyprus. Tel: +90 392 822 2620

Home cinema from two speakers

The *New* Bose 3·2·1 digital home entertainment system

The critics approved: "Even though I knew the midrange and high frequency sound were emanating from only two speakers at the front of the room, it sure didn't sound that way – I know I heard swords clanking where surround speakers should have been." – Sound & Vision (US)

Bass module not shown

INDEX BY PROPERTY

INDEX BY PROPERTY

Rise
and
Shine

While you're away, get each day off to a flying start.

Because the world doesn't stop when you do. Sudden market shifts and new global business developments can change everything. But if you know you're in touch, you can relax.

Which is why the FT provides you with essential tools and business information to help keep you ahead, wherever you are.

During your stay you can get constant access to the very latest business developments and market news from Europe's leading business resource, making sure you retain your competitive edge even whilst at leisure.

Ask for the FT at your hotel's reception.

FT

London

England

A

B

C

INDEX BY LOCATION

Channel Islands

Ireland

Scotland

Wales

〰 Hotels with heated indoor swimming pool

〰 Outdoor pool

♪ Fishing on-site

⛳ Golf course on-site

INDEX BY CONSORTIUM

PERFECT HOSPITALITY BEGINS

WITH PERFECT FORM.

Classic furniture from Selva is the calling card of exclusive establishments.
By creating uniquely stylish surroundings, Selva spoils
not only your guests, but you, as well: with custom solutions,
creative ideas, and the most modern logistics. We would be happy to make
an appointment for you to visit our hotel furnishings showroom in Bolzano.

SELVA®

HOTEL STYLE
A brand of Selva Style International

In UK and Ireland: Lidija Braithwaite - LPB Agencies   16 Lenham Avenue, Saltdean   Brigton, East Sussex BN2 8AE
Tel./Fax 01273 385 255   Mobile: 0771 852 2 746   e-mail: lpbagencies@cwcom.net

Selva AG/SpA, I-39100 Bolzano (Italy), Via Luigi-Negrelli-Straße 4
Tel. 0471 240111   Fax 0471 240211   e-mail: selva@selva.com   www.selva.com

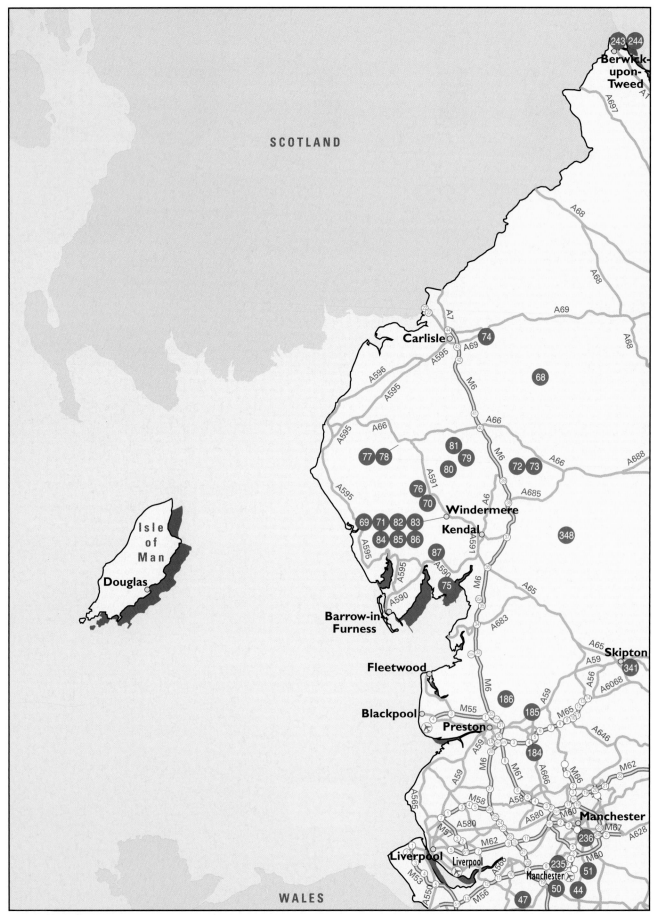

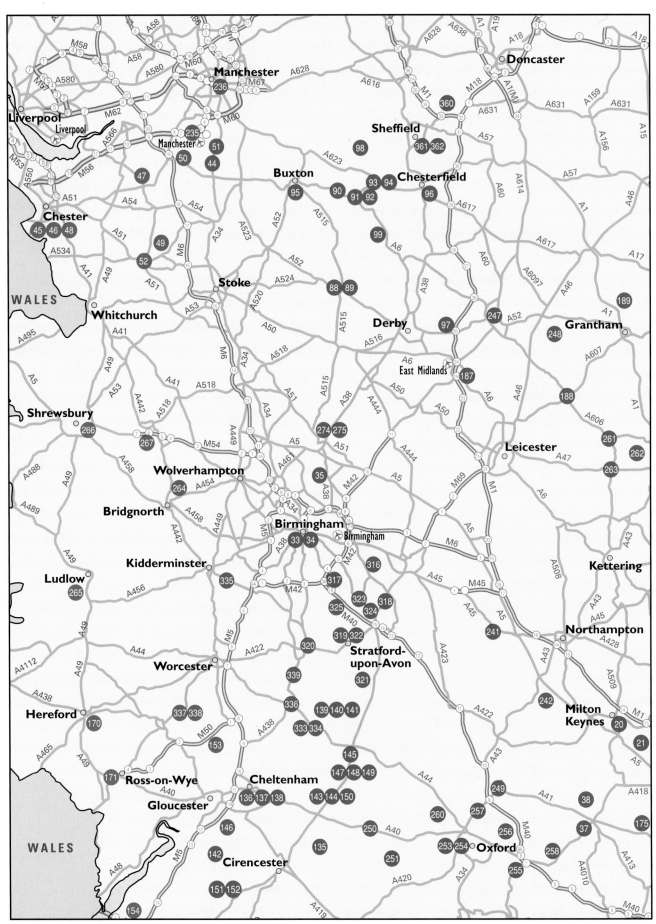

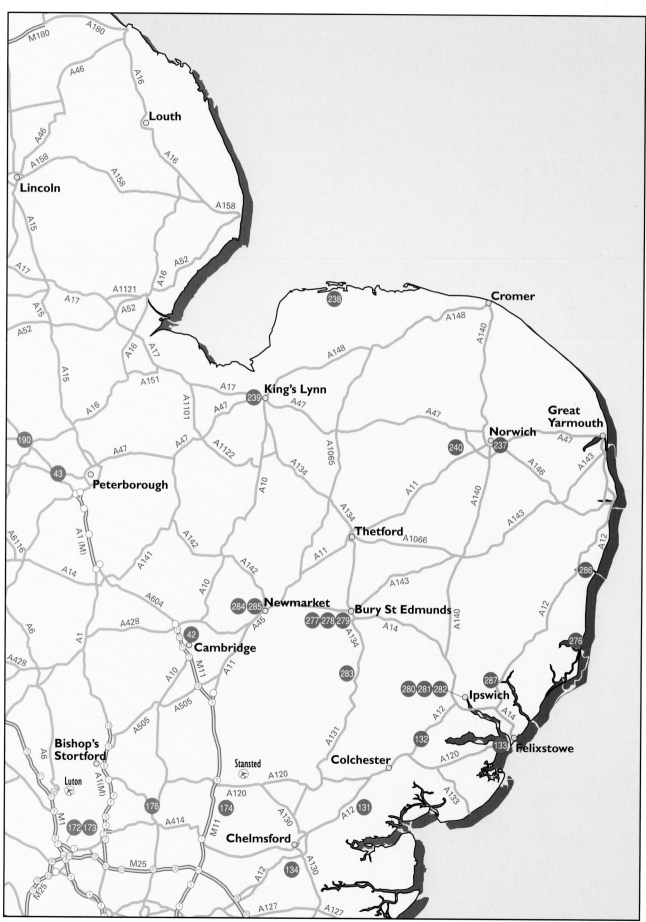

© Lovell Johns Limited, Oxford

CHANNEL ISLANDS & SOUTH WEST ENGLAND

Hotel location shown in red with page number

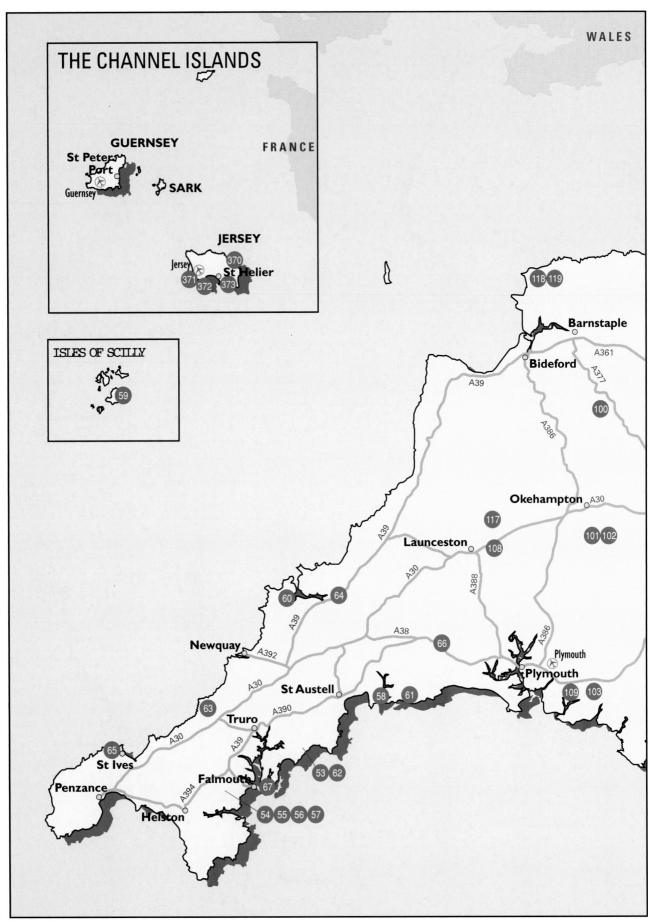

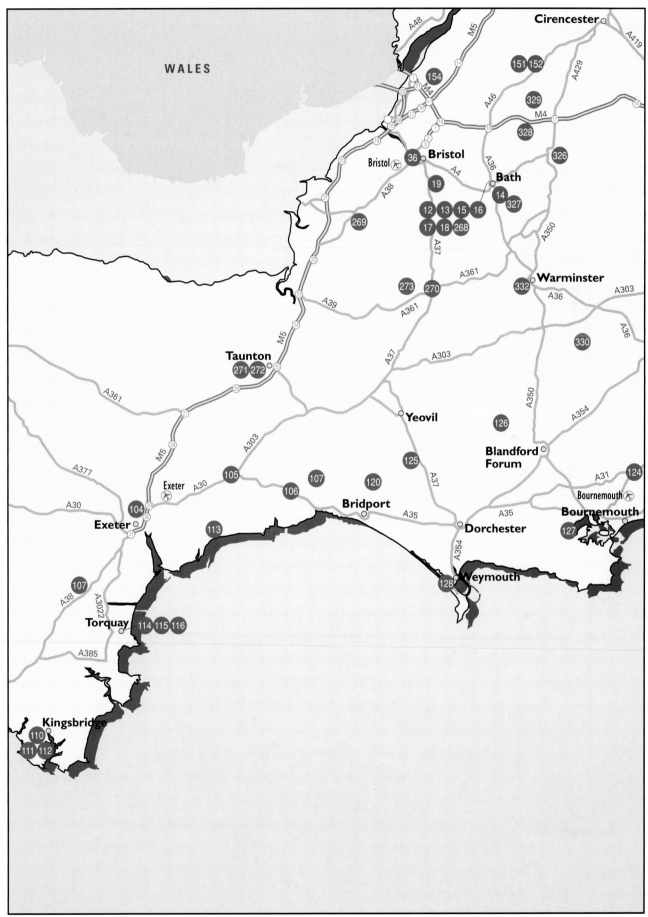

WALES

Cirencester

151 152

154

329

328

326

Bristol

36 Bristol

Bath

19

14 327

12 13 15 16

269

17 18 268

A37

Warminster

273 270

332

330

Taunton

271 272

Yeovil

126

Blandford Forum

125

Exeter

105

107

120

127

106

Bridport

Bournemouth

Bournemouth

124

Exeter

Dorchester

113

Weymouth

128

107

Torquay

114 115 116

Kingsbridge

110

111 112

© Lovell Johns Limited, Oxford

SOUTHERN ENGLAND

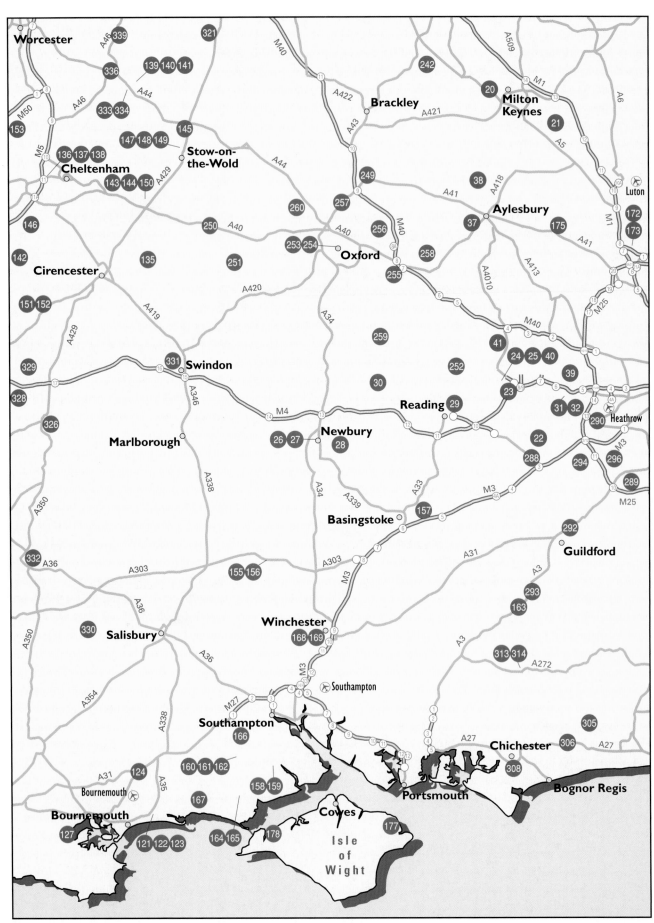

© Lovell Johns Limited, Oxford

LONDON

Hotel location shown in red with page number

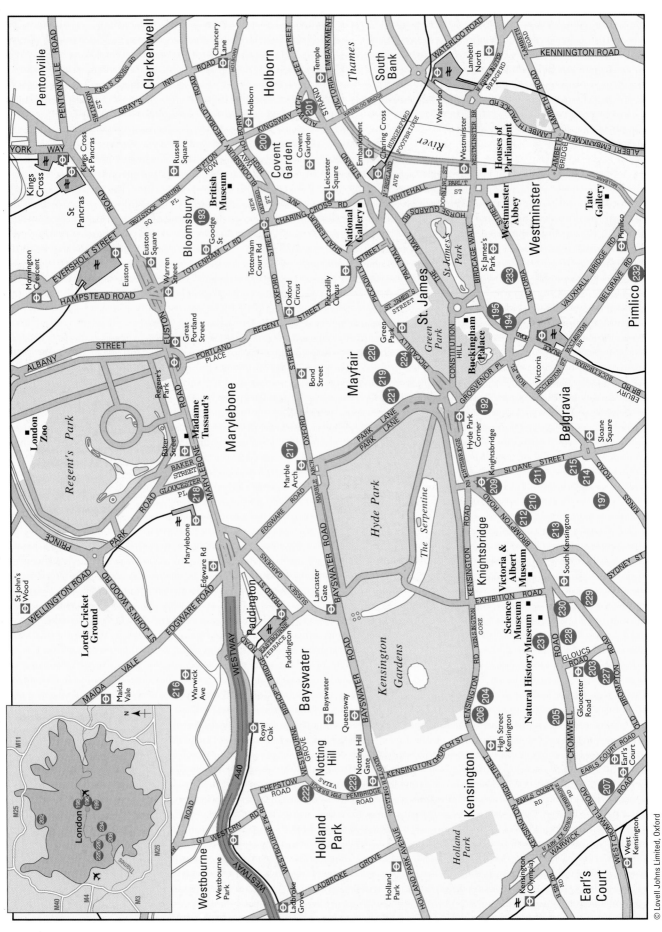

SCOTLAND

City of Derry

Coleraine

Londonderry

Larne

Belfast

Belfast

Armagh

Newry

Sligo

Ballina

Cavan

Dundalk

390

Knock International

Longford

Drogheda

389

388

Athlone

Dublin

Galway

379 381 382 Dublin

380

Dun Laoghaire

386

394

Shannon

376 Shannon

Limerick

Kilkenny

392

Tralee

387

391

Wexford

384 Killarney

Waterford

393

385 Kenmare

383

Cork

377 Cork

WALES

SCOTLAND

Hotel location shown in red with page number

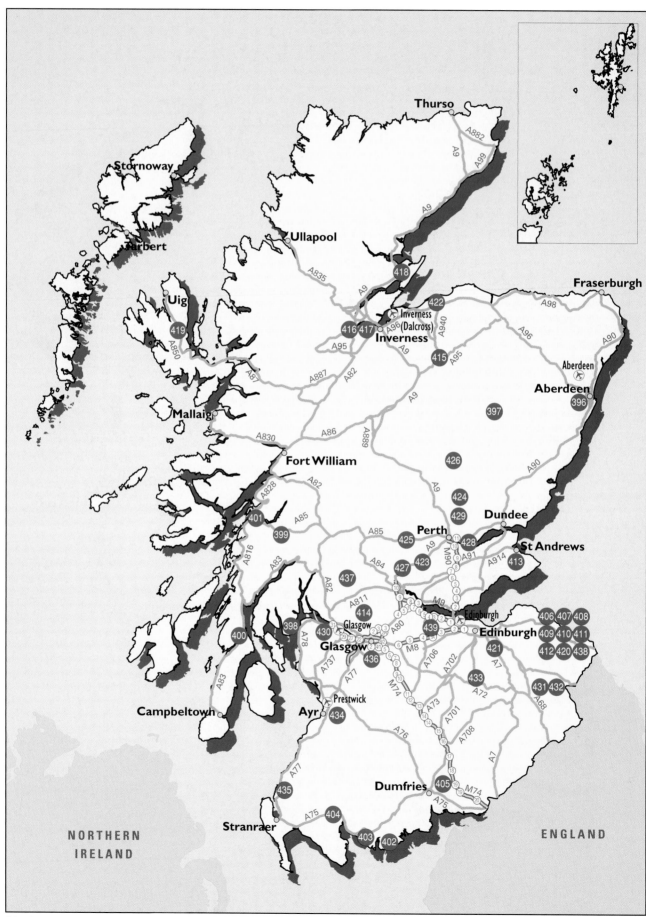

© Lovell Johns Limited, Oxford

We want to ensure that you continue to only stay in the finest hotels, those currently recommended by Condé Nast Johansens. Our team of inspectors visit thousands of properties every year with only the very best receiving Condé Nast Johansens recommendation. Each year there are many newly recommended properties whilst others are rejected for not maintaining standards.

We would like you to use only the latest guides and so are pleased to offer a contribution to the cost when you update each year. As a 2003 guide owner, when you order guides from Condé Nast Johansens 2004 range, please use the order form on page 519 and we will be pleased to reduce the total amount payable by £5.

This reduction will be in addition to any savings you will already have made by ordering two guides or more.

This offer only extends to orders for 2004 guides using an order form from a 2003 guide and must be received by us by 30th August 2003. These 2004 guide orders will be dispatched upon publication in October 2003.

To order 2004 guides simply complete the order form in the usual way, enclose a copy of this voucher and reduce your total final payment by £5 (only one voucher per order). **Please note that if you wish to order further copies of the *2003 guides* you need only return the completed order form as the £5 voucher will not apply.**

For further information call 0800 269 397 and we look forward to keeping you updated with Condé Nast Johansens latest recommended hotels

JOIN OUR FREE MAILING LIST PLUS
WIN ONE OF 20 "CHAIRMAN'S COLLECTIONS"

Join Condé Nast Johansens free mailing list and receive regular information on hotel special offers, promotions and free prize draws.

Simply complete your details below and return this form to **Condé Nast Johansens Ltd, FREEPOST (CB264), London SE27 0BR** (no stamp required)

Your name:..

Your address:...

....

....

Postcode:..

Your telephone:..

Your e-mail:..

The details provided will be used to keep you informed of future products and special offers provided by Condé Nast Johansens and other carefully selected third parties. If you do not wish to receive this information please tick this box ❑ (Your telephone number will not be used for marketing purposes)

Recommend a friend to be added to our free mailing list and qualify for entry in our free prize draw for one of 20 Condé Nast Johansens "Chairman's Collections".

PLEASE REMEMBER TO COMPLETE YOUR OWN DETAILS IN THE LEFT HAND PANEL IN ORDER TO BE INCLUDED.

Friend's name:..

Friend's address:...

....

....

Postcode:..

Friend's telephone:..

Friend's e-mail:...

The details provided will be used to keep you informed of future products and special offers provided by Condé Nast Johansens and other carefully selected third parties. If you do not wish to receive this information please tick this box ❑ (Your telephone number will not be used for marketing purposes)

Prize Draw Terms and Conditions: 1. All entries must be received by 29th August 2003. 2. Entries recommending a friend will go into a prize draw on 1st September 2003. 3. The prize is one of twenty 2004 edition "Chairman's Collections", as described on the order form in this guide. 4. The winners will be the first 20 names drawn by an independent observer. 5. The 20 winners will be notified in writing as soon as possible after 1st September 2003. 6. No cash alternative is available. 7. Entrants must be over 18. 8. Only one entry per household. 9. Employees of Condé Nast Johansens Ltd., its recommended hotels, agencies and suppliers are not eligible to participate in this promotion. 10. Condé Nast Johansens reserves the right to feature and photograph the winners for future publicity purposes. 11. No responsibility can be taken for entries lost, damaged or delayed. 12. For a list of winners please send an SAE to Condé Nast Johansens, FREEPOST (CB264), London SE27 0BR. 13. Entry into the prize draw will be deemed as an acceptance of these rules

CONDÉ NAST JOHANSENS

440 Recommendations

I wish to order

QUANTITY

copy/ies priced at £19.95 each.

Total cost

£

282 Recommendations

I wish to order

QUANTITY

copy/ies priced at £16.95 each.

Total cost

£

324 Recommendations

I wish to order

QUANTITY

copy/ies priced at £16.95 each.

Total cost

£

199 Recommendations

I wish to order

QUANTITY

copy/ies priced at £13.95 each.

Total cost

£

230 Recommendations
(published Feb 2003)

I wish to order

QUANTITY

copy/ies priced at £25.00 each.

Total cost

£

Pocket Guide

1250 Recommendations

I wish to order

QUANTITY

copy/ies priced at £7.95 each.

Total cost

£

Johansens Gold Blocked Slip Case priced at £5 each

Johansens Luxury Luggage Tag priced at £15 each

To order these items please fill in the appropriate section below

The Chairman's Collection

Order the complete collection of
Condé Nast Johansens Recommended Guides for only £75

PLUS FREE *Luxury Luggage Tag* worth £15

PLUS FREE *Slip Case* worth £5

The Chairman's Collection contains all six titles pictured above. The Recommended Venues guide will be dispatched separately on publication in February 2003.

Now please complete your order and payment details

tick

I have ordered 2 titles - **£5 off**   −£5.00

I have ordered 3 titles - **£10 off**   −£10.00

I have ordered 4 titles - **£20 off**   −£15.00

Total cost of books ordered minus discount
(excluding the Chairman's Collection)   £

Luxury Luggage Tag at **£15**
Quantity and total cost: £

Johansens Gold Blocked SLIP CASE at **£5**
Quantity and total cost: £

I wish to order the
Chairman's Collection at **£75**
Quantity and total cost: £

Packing & delivery: (all UK orders) add **£4.90**
(Outside UK) add **£6.00** per guide
or Chairman's Collection add **£25.00**   £

GRAND TOTAL   £

I have chosen my Condé Nast Johansens Guides and (please tick)

I enclose a cheque payable to Condé Nast Johansens ☐

Please debit my credit/charge card account ☐

☐ MasterCard   ☐ Visa   ☐ Switch (Issue Number)

Card Holders Name   (Mr/Mrs/Miss)

Address

Postcode

Telephone

E-mail

Card No.   Exp Date

Signature

NOW send to
Condé Nast Johansens Ltd, FREEPOST (CB264), LONDON SE27 0BR (no stamp required)
Fax orders welcome on 020 8655 7817

GUEST SURVEY REPORT

Evaluate your stay in a Condé Nast Johansens Recommendation

Dear Guest,

Following your stay in a Condé Nast Johansens recommendation, please spare a moment to complete this Guest Survey Report. This is an important source of information for Johansens, to maintain the highest standards for our recommendations and to support the work of our team of inspectors.

It is also the prime source of nominations for Condé Nast Johansens Awards for Excellence, which are made annually to those properties worldwide that represent the finest standards and best value for money in luxury, independent travel.

Thank you for your time and I hope that when choosing future accommodation Condé Nast Johansens will be your guide.

Yours faithfully,

Tim Sinclair

Sales & Marketing Director, Condé Nast Johansens

p.s. Guest Survey Reports may also be completed online at www.johansens.com

1. Your details

Your name: ....

Your address: ....

....

....

Postcode: ....

Telephone: ....

E-mail: ....

2. Hotel details

Name of hotel: ....

....

Location: ....

Date of visit: ....

3. Your rating of the hotel

Please tick one box in each category below (as applicable)

	Excellent	Good	Disappointing	Poor
Bedrooms	◯	◯	◯	◯
Public Rooms	◯	◯	◯	◯
Food/Restaurant	◯	◯	◯	◯
Service	◯	◯	◯	◯
Welcome/Friendliness	◯	◯	◯	◯
Value For Money	◯	◯	◯	◯

4. Any other comments

If you wish to make additional comments, please write separately to the Publisher, Condé Nast Johansens Ltd, Freepost CB264, Therese House, Glasshouse Yard, London EC1B 1HP

....

....

....

....

Please return completed form to **Condé Nast Johansens, FREEPOST (CB264), LONDON SE27 0BR** (no stamp required).
Alternatively send by fax to 020 8655 7817

Order **2** guides get **£5 off** · Order **3** guides get **£10 off** · Order **4** guides get **£20 off**

Order the Chairman's Collection worth £100 for just **£75**

Simply complete the form below, total the cost and then deduct the appropriate discount. State your preferred method of payment and mail to Condé Nast Johansens Ltd, FREEPOST (CB264), LONDON SE27 0BR (no stamp required). Fax orders welcome on 020 8655 7817

ALTERNATIVELY YOU CAN ORDER IMMEDIATELY ON FREEPHONE 0800 269 397, please quote ref: D007

440 Recommendations

I wish to order

QUANTITY

copy/ies priced at £19.95 each.

Total cost

£

282 Recommendations

I wish to order

QUANTITY

copy/ies priced at £16.95 each.

Total cost

£

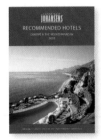

324 Recommendations

I wish to order

QUANTITY

copy/ies priced at £16.95 each.

Total cost

£

199 Recommendations

I wish to order

QUANTITY

copy/ies priced at £13.95 each.

Total cost

£

230 Recommendations
(published Feb 2003)

I wish to order

QUANTITY

copy/ies priced at £25.00 each.

Total cost

£

Pocket Guide

1250 Recommendations

I wish to order

QUANTITY

copy/ies priced at £7.95 each.

Total cost

£

Johansens Gold Blocked Slip Case priced at £5 each

Johansens Luxury Luggage Tag priced at £15 each

To order these items please fill in the appropriate section below

The Chairman's Collection

Order the complete collection of
Condé Nast Johansens Recommended Guides for only £75

PLUS FREE *Luxury Luggage Tag* worth £15

PLUS FREE *Slip Case* worth £5

The Chairman's Collection contains all six titles pictured above. The Recommended Venues guide will be dispatched separately on publication in February 2003.

Now please complete your order and payment details

tick

I have ordered 2 titles - **£5** off | −£5.00

I have ordered 3 titles - **£10** off | −£10.00

I have ordered 4 titles - **£20** off | −£15.00

Total cost of books ordered minus discount *(excluding the Chairman's Collection)* | £

Luxury Luggage Tag at **£15** Quantity and total cost: | £

Johansens Gold Blocked SLIP CASE at **£5** Quantity and total cost: | £

I wish to order the Chairman's Collection at **£75** Quantity and total cost: | £

Packing & delivery: (all UK orders) add **£4.90**
(Outside UK) add **£6.00** per guide
or Chairman's Collection add **£25.00** | £

GRAND TOTAL | £

I have chosen my Condé Nast Johansens Guides and (please tick)

I enclose a cheque payable to Condé Nast Johansens ☐

Please debit my credit/charge card account ☐

☐ MasterCard ☐ Visa ☐ Switch (Issue Number)

Card Holders Name (Mr/Mrs/Miss)

Address

Postcode

Telephone

E-mail

Card No.   Exp Date

Signature

NOW send to
Condé Nast Johansens Ltd, FREEPOST (CB264), LONDON SE27 0BR (no stamp required)
Fax orders welcome on 020 8655 7817

The details provided may be used to keep you informed of future products and special offers provided by Condé Nast Johansens and other carefully selected third parties. If you do not wish to recieve such information please tick this box ☐.
(Your phone number will only be used to ensure the fast and safe delivery of your order)

GUEST SURVEY REPORT

Evaluate your stay in a Condé Nast Johansens Recommendation

Dear Guest,

Following your stay in a Condé Nast Johansens recommendation, please spare a moment to complete this Guest Survey Report. This is an important source of information for Johansens, to maintain the highest standards for our recommendations and to support the work of our team of inspectors.

It is also the prime source of nominations for Condé Nast Johansens Awards for Excellence, which are made annually to those properties worldwide that represent the finest standards and best value for money in luxury, independent travel.

Thank you for your time and I hope that when choosing future accommodation Condé Nast Johansens will be your guide.

Yours faithfully,

Tim Sinclair

Sales & Marketing Director, Condé Nast Johansens

p.s. Guest Survey Reports may also be completed online at www.johansens.com

1. Your details

Your name: ....

Your address: ....

....

....

Postcode: ....

Telephone: ....

E-mail: ....

2. Hotel details

Name of hotel: ....

....

Location: ....

Date of visit: ....

3. Your rating of the hotel

Please tick one box in each category below (as applicable)

	Excellent	Good	Disappointing	Poor
Bedrooms	○	○	○	○
Public Rooms	○	○	○	○
Food/Restaurant	○	○	○	○
Service	○	○	○	○
Welcome/Friendliness	○	○	○	○
Value For Money	○	○	○	○

4. Any other comments

If you wish to make additional comments, please write separately to the Publisher, Condé Nast Johansens Ltd, Freepost CB264, Therese House, Glasshouse Yard, London EC1B 1HP

....

....

....

....

....

Please return completed form to **Condé Nast Johansens, FREEPOST (CB264), LONDON SE27 0BR** (no stamp required).

Alternatively send by fax to 020 8655 7817

ORDER FORM
Choose from our wide range of titles below

CONDÉ NAST JOHANSENS

Order **2** guides get **£5 off** · Order **3** guides get **£10 off** · Order **4** guides get **£20 off**
Order the Chairman's Collection worth £100 for just **£75**

Simply complete the form below, total the cost and then deduct the appropriate discount. State your preferred method of payment and mail to Condé Nast Johansens Ltd, FREEPOST (CB264), LONDON SE27 0BR (no stamp required). Fax orders welcome on 020 8655 7817

ALTERNATIVELY YOU CAN ORDER IMMEDIATELY ON FREEPHONE 0800 269 397, please quote ref: D007

440 Recommendations

I wish to order

QUANTITY

copy/ies priced at £19.95 each.
Total cost

£

282 Recommendations

I wish to order

QUANTITY

copy/ies priced at £16.95 each.
Total cost

£

324 Recommendations

I wish to order

QUANTITY

copy/ies priced at £16.95 each.
Total cost

£

199 Recommendations

I wish to order

QUANTITY

copy/ies priced at £13.95 each.
Total cost

£

230 Recommendations
(published Feb 2003)

I wish to order

QUANTITY

copy/ies priced at £25.00 each.
Total cost

£

Pocket Guide

1250 Recommendations

I wish to order

QUANTITY

copy/ies priced at £7.95 each.
Total cost

£

Johansens Gold Blocked Slip Case priced at £5 each

Johansens Luxury Luggage Tag priced at £15 each

To order these items please fill in the appropriate section below

The Chairman's Collection
Order the complete collection of
Condé Nast Johansens Recommended Guides for only **£75**
PLUS FREE Luxury Luggage Tag worth £15
PLUS FREE Slip Case worth £5
The Chairman's Collection contains all six titles pictured above. The Recommended Venues guide will be dispatched separately on publication in February 2003.

Now please complete your order and payment details

tick

	tick	
I have ordered 2 titles - **£5 off**		−£5.00
I have ordered 3 titles - **£10 off**		−£10.00
I have ordered 4 titles - **£20 off**		−£15.00

I have chosen my Condé Nast Johansens Guides and (please tick)
I enclose a cheque payable to Condé Nast Johansens ☐
Please debit my credit/charge card account ☐
☐ MasterCard   ☐ Visa   ☐ Switch (Issue Number) ⬜

Total cost of books ordered minus discount
(excluding the Chairman's Collection)   £

Luxury Luggage Tag at **£15**
Quantity and total cost: £

Johansens Gold Blocked SLIP CASE at **£5**
Quantity and total cost: £

I wish to order the
Chairman's Collection at **£75**
Quantity and total cost: £

Packing & delivery: (all UK orders) add **£4.90**
(Outside UK) add **£6.00** per guide
or Chairman's Collection add **£25.00**   £

GRAND TOTAL   £

Card Holders Name (Mr/Mrs/Miss)
Address
Postcode
Telephone
E-mail
Card No.   Exp Date
Signature

NOW send to
Condé Nast Johansens Ltd, FREEPOST (CB264), LONDON SE27 0BR (no stamp required)
Fax orders welcome on 020 8655 7817

The details provided may be used to keep you informed of future products and special offers provided by Condé Nast Johansens and other carefully selected third parties. If you do not wish to recieve such information please tick this box ☐.
(Your phone number will only be used to ensure the fast and safe delivery of your order)

GUEST SURVEY REPORT

Evaluate your stay in a Condé Nast Johansens Recommendation

Dear Guest,

Following your stay in a Condé Nast Johansens recommendation, please spare a moment to complete this Guest Survey Report. This is an important source of information for Johansens, to maintain the highest standards for our recommendations and to support the work of our team of inspectors.

It is also the prime source of nominations for Condé Nast Johansens Awards for Excellence, which are made annually to those properties worldwide that represent the finest standards and best value for money in luxury, independent travel.

Thank you for your time and I hope that when choosing future accommodation Condé Nast Johansens will be your guide.

Yours faithfully,

Tim Sinclair
Sales & Marketing Director, Condé Nast Johansens

p.s. Guest Survey Reports may also be completed online at www.johansens.com

1. Your details

Your name: ....

Your address: ....

....

....

Postcode: ....

Telephone: ....

E-mail: ....

2. Hotel details

Name of hotel: ....

....

Location: ....

Date of visit: ....

3. Your rating of the hotel

Please tick one box in each category below (as applicable)

	Excellent	Good	Disappointing	Poor
Bedrooms	○	○	○	○
Public Rooms	○	○	○	○
Food/Restaurant	○	○	○	○
Service	○	○	○	○
Welcome/Friendliness	○	○	○	○
Value For Money	○	○	○	○

4. Any other comments

If you wish to make additional comments, please write separately to the Publisher, Condé Nast Johansens Ltd, Freepost CB264, Therese House, Glasshouse Yard, London EC1B 1HP

....

....

....

....

....

....

Please return completed form to **Condé Nast Johansens, FREEPOST (CB264), LONDON SE27 0BR** (no stamp required).
Alternatively send by fax to 020 8655 7817

ORDER FORM

Choose from our wide range of titles below

CONDÉ NAST JOHANSENS

Order **2** guides get **£5 off** • Order **3** guides get **£10 off** • Order **4** guides get **£20 off**

Order the Chairman's Collection worth £100 for just **£75**

Simply complete the form below, total the cost and then deduct the appropriate discount. State your preferred method of payment and mail to Condé Nast Johansens Ltd, FREEPOST (CB264), LONDON SE27 0BR (no stamp required). Fax orders welcome on 020 8655 7817

ALTERNATIVELY YOU CAN ORDER IMMEDIATELY ON FREEPHONE 0800 269 397, please quote ref: D007

440 Recommendations

I wish to order

QUANTITY

copy/ies priced at £19.95 each.
Total cost

£

282 Recommendations

I wish to order

QUANTITY

copy/ies priced at £16.95 each.
Total cost

£

324 Recommendations

I wish to order

QUANTITY

copy/ies priced at £16.95 each.
Total cost

£

199 Recommendations

I wish to order

QUANTITY

copy/ies priced at £13.95 each.
Total cost

£

230 Recommendations (published Feb 2003)

I wish to order

QUANTITY

copy/ies priced at £25.00 each.
Total cost

£

Pocket Guide
1250 Recommendations

I wish to order

QUANTITY

copy/ies priced at £7.95 each.
Total cost

£

Johansens Gold Blocked Slip Case priced at £5

Johansens Luxury Luggage Tag priced at £15 each

To order these items please fill in the appropriate section below

The Chairman's Collection

Order the complete collection of
Condé Nast Johansens Recommended Guides for only £75

PLUS FREE *Luxury Luggage Tag* worth £15
PLUS FREE *Slip Case* worth £5

The Chairman's Collection contains all six titles pictured above. The Recommended Venues guide will be dispatched separately on publication in February 2003.

Now please complete your order and payment details

tick

I have ordered 2 titles - **£5** off   −£5.00

I have ordered 3 titles - **£10** off   −£10.00

I have ordered 4 titles - **£20** off   −£15.00

Total cost of books ordered minus discount
(excluding the Chairman's Collection)   £

Luxury Luggage Tag at **£15**
Quantity and total cost: £

Johansens Gold Blocked SLIP CASE at **£5**
Quantity and total cost: £

I wish to order the
Chairman's Collection at **£75**
Quantity and total cost: £

Packing & delivery: (all UK orders) add **£4.90**
(Outside UK) add **£6.00** per guide
or Chairman's Collection add **£25.00**   £

GRAND TOTAL   £

I have chosen my Condé Nast Johansens Guides and (please tick)

I enclose a cheque payable to Condé Nast Johansens ☐

Please debit my credit/charge card account ☐

☐ MasterCard   ☐ Visa   ☐ Switch (Issue Number)

Card Holders Name (Mr/Mrs/Miss)

Address

Postcode

Telephone

E-mail

Card No.   Exp Date

Signature

NOW send to
Condé Nast Johansens Ltd, FREEPOST (CB264), LONDON SE27 0BR (no stamp required)
Fax orders welcome on 020 8655 7817

The details provided may be used to keep you informed of future products and special offers provided by Condé Nast Johansens and other carefully selected third parties. If you do not wish to recieve such information please tick this box ☐.
(Your phone number will only be used to ensure the fast and safe delivery of your order)

GUEST SURVEY REPORT

Evaluate your stay in a Condé Nast Johansens Recommendation

Dear Guest,

Following your stay in a Condé Nast Johansens recommendation, please spare a moment to complete this Guest Survey Report. This is an important source of information for Johansens, to maintain the highest standards for our recommendations and to support the work of our team of inspectors.

It is also the prime source of nominations for Condé Nast Johansens Awards for Excellence, which are made annually to those properties worldwide that represent the finest standards and best value for money in luxury, independent travel.

Thank you for your time and I hope that when choosing future accommodation Condé Nast Johansens will be your guide.

Yours faithfully,

Tim Sinclair

Sales & Marketing Director, Condé Nast Johansens

p.s. Guest Survey Reports may also be completed online at www.johansens.com

1. Your details

Your name: ....

Your address: ....

....

....

Postcode: ....

Telephone: ....

E-mail: ....

2. Hotel details

Name of hotel: ....

....

Location: ....

Date of visit: ....

3. Your rating of the hotel

Please tick one box in each category below (as applicable)

	Excellent	Good	Disappointing	Poor
Bedrooms	○	○	○	○
Public Rooms	○	○	○	○
Food/Restaurant	○	○	○	○
Service	○	○	○	○
Welcome/Friendliness	○	○	○	○
Value For Money	○	○	○	○

4. Any other comments

If you wish to make additional comments, please write separately to the Publisher, Condé Nast Johansens Ltd, Freepost CB264, Therese House, Glasshouse Yard, London EC1B 1HP

....

....

....

....

Please return completed form to **Condé Nast Johansens, FREEPOST (CB264), LONDON SE27 0BR** (no stamp required).
Alternatively send by fax to 020 8655 7817

ORDER FORM

CONDÉ NAST JOHANSENS

Choose from our wide range of titles below

Order **2** guides get **£5 off** · Order **3** guides get **£10 off** · Order **4** guides get **£20 off**

Order the Chairman's Collection worth £100 for just **£75**

Simply complete the form below, total the cost and then deduct the appropriate discount. State your preferred method of payment and mail to Condé Nast Johansens Ltd, FREEPOST (CB264), LONDON SE27 0BR (no stamp required). Fax orders welcome on 020 8655 7817

ALTERNATIVELY YOU CAN ORDER IMMEDIATELY ON FREEPHONE 0800 269 397, please quote ref: D007

440 Recommendations

I wish to order

QUANTITY

copy/ies priced at £19.95 each.

Total cost

£

282 Recommendations

I wish to order

QUANTITY

copy/ies priced at £16.95 each.

Total cost

£

324 Recommendations

I wish to order

QUANTITY

copy/ies priced at £16.95 each.

Total cost

£

199 Recommendations

I wish to order

QUANTITY

copy/ies priced at £13.95 each.

Total cost

£

230 Recommendations
(published Feb 2003)

I wish to order

QUANTITY

copy/ies priced at £25.00 each.

Total cost

£

Pocket Guide

1250 Recommendations

I wish to order

QUANTITY

copy/ies priced at £7.95 each.

Total cost

£

Johansens Gold Blocked Slip Case priced at £5 each

Johansens Luxury Luggage Tag priced at £15 each

To order these items please fill in the appropriate section below

The Chairman's Collection

Order the complete collection of
Condé Nast Johansens Recommended Guides for only £75

PLUS FREE *Luxury Luggage Tag* worth £15

PLUS FREE *Slip Case* worth £5

The Chairman's Collection contains all six titles pictured above. The Recommended Venues guide will be dispatched separately on publication in February 2003.

Now please complete your order and payment details

	tick	
I have ordered 2 titles - **£5 off**		−£5.00
I have ordered 3 titles - **£10 off**		−£10.00
I have ordered 4 titles - **£20 off**		−£15.00
Total cost of books ordered minus discount (excluding the Chairman's Collection)		£
Luxury Luggage Tag at **£15** Quantity and total cost:		£
Johansens Gold Blocked SLIP CASE at **£5** Quantity and total cost:		£
I wish to order the Chairman's Collection at **£75** Quantity and total cost:		£
Packing & delivery: (all UK orders) add **£4.90** (Outside UK) add **£6.00** per guide or Chairman's Collection add **£25.00**		£

GRAND TOTAL £

I have chosen my Condé Nast Johansens Guides and (please tick)

I enclose a cheque payable to Condé Nast Johansens ☐

Please debit my credit/charge card account ☐

☐ MasterCard ☐ Visa ☐ Switch (Issue Number)

Card Holders Name (Mr/Mrs/Miss)

Address

Postcode

Telephone

E-mail

Card No.

Exp Date

Signature

NOW send to
Condé Nast Johansens Ltd, FREEPOST (CB264), LONDON SE27 0BR (no stamp required)
Fax orders welcome on 020 8655 7817

The details provided may be used to keep you informed of future products and special offers provided by Condé Nast Johansens and other carefully selected third parties. If you do not wish to recieve such information please tick this box ☐.
(Your phone number will only be used to ensure the fast and safe delivery of your order)

HOTEL BROCHURE REQUEST

Find out further information on the hotels of your choice

The Condé Nast Johansens Hotel Brochure Request Service has been established to give guests the opportunity to obtain more information about a recommendation, additional to that contained within the Johansens guide.

Condé Nast Johansens will pass your request to the recommendation specified who will directly send you a brochure.

Hotel name(s) and location(s) (BLOCK CAPITALS)   Page in guide

1 _____   _____

2 _____   _____

3 _____   _____

4 _____   _____

5 _____   _____

The recommendation(s) you have chosen will send their brochures directly to the address below

Your name: _____

Your address: _____

_____ Postcode: _____

Telephone: _____ E-mail: _____

The details provided may be used to keep you informed of future products and special offers provided by Condé Nast Johansens and other carefully selected third parties. If you do not wish to recieve such information please tick this box ☐.

Please return completed form to **Condé Nast Johansens, FREEPOST (CB264), LONDON SE27 0BR** (no stamp required). Alternatively send by fax to 020 8655 7817

HOTEL BROCHURE REQUEST

Find out further information on the hotels of your choice

The Condé Nast Johansens Hotel Brochure Request Service has been established to give guests the opportunity to obtain more information about a recommendation, additional to that contained within the Johansens guide.

Condé Nast Johansens will pass your request to the recommendation specified who will directly send you a brochure.

Hotel name(s) and location(s) (BLOCK CAPITALS)   Page in guide

1 _____   _____

2 _____   _____

3 _____   _____

4 _____   _____

5 _____   _____

The recommendation(s) you have chosen will send their brochures directly to the address below

Your name: _____

Your address: _____

_____ Postcode: _____

Telephone: _____ E-mail: _____

The details provided may be used to keep you informed of future products and special offers provided by Condé Nast Johansens and other carefully selected third parties. If you do not wish to recieve such information please tick this box ☐.

Please return completed form to **Condé Nast Johansens, FREEPOST (CB264), LONDON SE27 0BR** (no stamp required). Alternatively send by fax to 020 8655 7817

Order **2** guides get **£5 off** · Order **3** guides get **£10 off** · Order **4** guides get **£20 off**

Order the Chairman's Collection worth £100 for just **£75**

Simply complete the form below, total the cost and then deduct the appropriate discount. State your preferred method of payment and mail to Condé Nast Johansens Ltd, FREEPOST (CB264), LONDON SE27 0BR (no stamp required). Fax orders welcome on 020 8655 7817

ALTERNATIVELY YOU CAN ORDER IMMEDIATELY ON FREEPHONE 0800 269 397, please quote ref: D007

440 Recommendations

I wish to order

QUANTITY

copy/ies priced at £19.95 each.

Total cost

£

282 Recommendations

I wish to order

QUANTITY

copy/ies priced at £16.95 each.

Total cost

£

324 Recommendations

I wish to order

QUANTITY

copy/ies priced at £16.95 each.

Total cost

£

199 Recommendations

I wish to order

QUANTITY

copy/ies priced at £13.95 each.

Total cost

£

230 Recommendations (published Feb 2003)

I wish to order

QUANTITY

copy/ies priced at £25.00 each.

Total cost

£

Pocket Guide

1250 Recommendations

I wish to order

QUANTITY

copy/ies priced at £7.95 each.

Total cost

£

Johansens Gold Blocked Slip Case priced at £5 each

Johansens Luxury Luggage Tag priced at £15 each

To order these items please fill in the appropriate section below

The Chairman's Collection

Order the complete collection of
Condé Nast Johansens Recommended Guides for only £75

PLUS FREE Luxury Luggage Tag *worth £15*

PLUS FREE Slip Case *worth £5*

The Chairman's Collection contains all six titles pictured above. The Recommended Venues guide will be dispatched separately on publication in February 2003.

Now please complete your order and payment details

tick

I have ordered 2 titles - **£5 off**		−£5.00
I have ordered 3 titles - **£10 off**		−£10.00
I have ordered 4 titles - **£20 off**		−£15.00

I have chosen my Condé Nast Johansens Guides and (please tick)

I enclose a cheque payable to Condé Nast Johansens ☐

Please debit my credit/charge card account ☐

☐ MasterCard ☐ Visa ☐ Switch (Issue Number) ▭

Total cost of books ordered minus discount
(excluding the Chairman's Collection) £

Card Holders Name (Mr/Mrs/Miss)

Luxury Luggage Tag at **£15**
Quantity and total cost: £

Address

Johansens Gold Blocked SLIP CASE at **£5**
Quantity and total cost: £

Postcode

Telephone

I wish to order the
Chairman's Collection at **£75**
Quantity and total cost: £

E-mail

Card No.

Exp Date

Signature

Packing & delivery: (all UK orders) add **£4.90**
(Outside UK) add **£6.00** per guide
or Chairman's Collection add **£25.00** £

NOW send to
Condé Nast Johansens Ltd, FREEPOST (CB264), LONDON SE27 0BR (no stamp required)
Fax orders welcome on 020 8655 7817

GRAND TOTAL £

HOTEL BROCHURE REQUEST

Find out further information on the hotels of your choice

The Condé Nast Johansens Hotel Brochure Request Service has been established to give guests the opportunity to obtain more information about a recommendation, additional to that contained within the Johansens guide.

Condé Nast Johansens will pass your request to the recommendation specified who will directly send you a brochure.

Hotel name(s) and location(s) (BLOCK CAPITALS)   Page in guide

1 ....

2 ....

3 ....

4 ....

5 ....

The recommendation(s) you have chosen will send their brochures directly to the address below

Your name: ....

Your address: ....

.... Postcode: ....

Telephone: .... E-mail: ....

Please return completed form to **Condé Nast Johansens, FREEPOST (CB264), LONDON SE27 0BR** (no stamp required). Alternatively send by fax to 020 8655 7817

HOTEL BROCHURE REQUEST

Find out further information on the hotels of your choice

The Condé Nast Johansens Hotel Brochure Request Service has been established to give guests the opportunity to obtain more information about a recommendation, additional to that contained within the Johansens guide.

Condé Nast Johansens will pass your request to the recommendation specified who will directly send you a brochure.

Hotel name(s) and location(s) (BLOCK CAPITALS)   Page in guide

1 ....

2 ....

3 ....

4 ....

5 ....

The recommendation(s) you have chosen will send their brochures directly to the address below

Your name: ....

Your address: ....

.... Postcode: ....

Telephone: .... E-mail: ....

The details provided may be used to keep you informed of future products and special offers provided by Condé Nast Johansens and other carefully selected third parties. If you do not wish to recieve such information please tick this box ☐.

Please return completed form to **Condé Nast Johansens, FREEPOST (CB264), LONDON SE27 0BR** (no stamp required). Alternatively send by fax to 020 8655 7817